The Complete Book of
HERBS
& SPICES

DORLING KINDERSLEY
LONDON · NEW YORK · SYDNEY · MOSCOW

Contents

Part I Herbs

Part II Spices

A Dorling Kindersley Book

Editors: Carolyn Ryden, Tanya Hines, Joanna Chisholm, Nicola Nieburg

Art Editors: Sarah Scrutton, Tina Vaughan

DTP Designer: Karen Ruane

Managing Editor: Susannah Marriott

Managing Art Editor: Toni Kay

Photography: Dave King, Martin Norris

First published in Great Britian in 1997 by
Dorling Kindersley Limited
9 Henrietta Street, LondonWC2E 8PS

Visit us on the World Wide Web at
http://www.dk.com

The Complete Book of Herbs
Copyright © 1988 Dorling Kindersley Limited, London
Text and garden designs copyright © Lesley Bremness, 1988

The Complete Book of Spices
Copyright © 1990 Dorling Kindersley Limited, London
Text copyright © Jill Norman, 1990

Originally published as *The Complete Book of Herbs* and *The Complete Book of Spices*

A CIP catalogue record for this book is available from the British Library

ISBN 0-75130-494-8

Printed and bound in Slovakia by Neographia

A NOTE TO THE READER

Herbs are very powerful healing tools. If they are misused, they can be harmful. This book is not a medical reference book. The advice it contains is general, not specific and neither the author nor the publishers can be held responsible for any adverse reactions to the recipes, formulas, recommendations or instructions contained herein. Before trying any herbal formula, sample a small quantity first in case you have any adverse or allergic reaction. Do not try self-diagnosis or attempt self-treatment for serious or long term problems without consulting a qualified medical herbalist. Do not take herbal remedies if you are undergoing any other course of medical treatment without seeking professional advice.

PART 1

HERBS

LESLEY BREMNESS

Foreword

The ideal garden appeals to all the senses, to touch and smell as well as sight, so herbs play a vital role. Indeed, it is difficult to imagine a flower garden devoid of them. Add to this their venerable history, stretching right back to classical times, and it is clear that herb gardening is a rich and rewarding subject for study.

Some National Trust gardens or parts of gardens are devoted wholly to herbs, although herbs are grown in many gardens simply for their value as garden plants. Cotton lavender, sage, rue, wall germander and hyssop are useful as edgings and low hedges in formal gardens. Many border plants are also classed as medicinal and can be seen grouped with other herbaceous perennials in many Trust gardens. Other herbs are widely used as ground cover.

Naturally, herbs figure prominently in gardens reconstructed following seventeenth-century ideas. Moseley Old Hall in Staffordshire has a tiny herb garden and formal beds of wall germander. At Little Moreton Hall in Cheshire, herbs are grown in box-edged beds on either side of the knot garden and at Charlecote, near Stratford-upon-Avon, the collection of plants mentioned in the works of Shakespeare contains many herbs.

The walled garden at Felbrigg Hall, Norfolk, has been restored by the Trust with fruit trees, flower borders, vegetables and borders containing culinary herbs. At Gunby Hall in Lincolnshire, a walled garden of similar character contains a formal layout devoted entirely to plants for flowering and fragrance set in paving.

With the current popularity of herbs, it would be easy for the Trust to make herb gardens everywhere, but the Trust's principal aim is to retain each garden's individuality. Hence herb gardens are made and restored where they are traditional to the place or part of the original design of the garden. At Castle Drogo, Devon, the formal garden, like the house, was designed by Sir Edwin Lutyens and part of the scheme includes a small herb garden.

The Trust's most comprehensive herb garden is at Acorn Bank, near Penrith in Cumbria. The walled, former kitchen garden is devoted entirely to the cultivation of 200 different herbs. It includes some unusual flavouring and garnishing herbs, but specializes in those recommended for curing various ills.

Appropriately for a great Elizabethan house, Hardwick Hall in Derbyshire contains the Trust's largest herb garden. This is set on the site of the former kitchen garden and planted with many of the herbs that would have been familiar to Bess of Hardwick and her sixteenth-century household.

John Sales   Chief Gardens Adviser, the National Trust

An ornamental sundial (left) surrounded by beds of lavender in the garden at Polesden Lacey, Surrey.

A colourful border of flowering herbs (opposite) in the National Trust's herb garden at Acorn Bank in Cumbria. Designed as a highly attractive walled garden, Acorn Bank is well planted with an enormous variety of traditional medicinal herbs.

Introduction

Herbs are plants to serve and delight us, offering us an ever increasing rapport with nature. Our changing understanding of the word "herb" reflects our changing relationship with the plant kingdom. There was a time when all plants were important to humankind; they were considered the children of the Earth Mother, each marked by divinity and worthy of respect. With industrialization, the rise of science and technology, our involvement with nature diminished. This change has led to a more limited concept of the term "herb" and even today, herbs are considered by many people to be only a dozen or so seasoning plants.

An early Western attempt to classify plants was made in the fourth century by the Greek philosopher, Theophrastus, who divided the plant world into trees, shrubs and herbs, mainly by size; the herb category including a plant group similar to the large range now botanically classified as herbaceous. This broad concept of a herb was also reflected in the Book of Genesis where God caused the earth "to bring forth grass, the herb yielding seed and the fruit tree yielding fruit". Such a large range of herbs included plants which were important to people on many levels – physical, mental and spiritual. Indeed, plants have often been used as symbols of spiritual progress, as in the "tree of knowledge" and the apple in the garden of Eden, and several cultures have a concept of paradise as a garden full of beautiful and useful plants capable of affecting all aspects of their lives.

Early writings
Early plant knowledge was passed on verbally. As both the body of knowledge and populations grew it became more important to record accurately the accumulated information on herbs for safe identification and dosage. Many of the earliest writings are about herbs – the plants important to a community in ceremony, magic and medicine. Babylonian clay tablets from 3000 BC illustrate medical treatments and later they record herbal imports.

During the next 1,000 years, parallel cultures in China, Assyria, Egypt and India developed a written record of mainly medicinal herbs. The Chinese "Canon of Herbs" is credited to a legendary emperor, Shen Nung, who died in 2698 BC (although the present texts were compiled much later). This emperor, "the divine husbandman", tasted many plants on behalf of the Chinese people to discover which were poisonous. His canon includes 252 plant descriptions and notes on their effects on the human body, where they could be gathered, and how to preserve and administer them, thus setting the standard for future pharmacopoeias.

From very early on, the Chinese tried to eliminate superstition and stressed the importance of practical knowledge. This is reflected in the more sophisticated Nei Ching or "Canon of Medicine", credited to another legendary emperor, Huang Ti (died 2598 BC), although the existing texts are thought to have been compiled much later, probably around 600 BC.

The Chinese have always held a wide view of plants. Herbs were not divided into compartments as they are in many Western minds today. To the Chinese the chrysanthemum is useful, beautiful and virtuous. Chrysanthemums were first grown for their medicinal properties and were a valued ingredient of the Taoist elixir. They were believed to be full of magic juices and perhaps that reason contributed to their beauty. One story tells of the people of Nanyang, in central China, who lived to be 100 years old because their drinking water came from a stream with many chrysanthemums growing beside it. The essence of the plants was thought to seep into the water and continually revitalize the inhabitants. Today in China, chrysanthemums are featured in spectacular flower displays and used medicinally, and one form is used in soups, salads and banquet dishes.

Early Western records of herbs describe a mixture of medicinal and magical usage of plants. Egyptian writings dating from 1550 BC contain medical prescriptions and notes on the aromatic and cosmetic uses of herbs as these were important aspects in religious ceremonies. Around the same time, descriptions of herbs and magical charms were compiled in the sacred Ayurvedas of India.

The classical Greek and Roman writings made an attempt to remove superstition and eventually reached their peak in Dioscorides' De Materia Medica of 512 AD. This describes 600 healing plants and is the earliest surviving herbal with illustrations. It became the basis of herbal knowledge until the seventeenth century.

Theophrastus also wrote a treatise on perfumes and cosmetics and described the effects of different herb and flower essences. A short time later another treatise of perfumes by Apollonius described where the best crops of herbs for perfume requirements could be found; the best marjoram essence came from the Aegean island of Cos, the best cypress from Egypt and saffron reached high perfection on Rhodes.

Herbs and cookery
The use of herbs in cooking features in the first century cook book written by the Roman epicure Apicius. It shows fascinating and adventurous combinations of herb flavours. For example, glob artichokes were cooked in a mixture of fresh

fennel, coriander, mint and rue pounded together and added to pepper, lovage, honey, oil and liquamen (a strong fish-based sauce which the Romans used in place of salt).

For centuries, herbs were a staple of daily life. In England in 1699 John Evelyn wrote *Acetaria: A Discourse of Sallets*, which listed 73 salad herbs, giving details of the part of each herb used; whether seed, flower, bud, leaf, stalk or root, and how it was best prepared; raw, chopped, steamed, blanched or pickled. This broad usage continued for centuries, demonstrated by the fact that even 200 years ago, the word vegetable was not commonly used – we spoke of pot herbs (for bulk in the cooking pot), salet (salad) herbs, sweet herbs (flavourings) and simples (medicinal herbs from which "compounds" were made).

Herbs as garden plants

As communities became more secure and gardening developed for pleasure, books included the aesthetic appeal of herbs as garden plants. There was not the distinction between use and aesthetic appeal that we have now. *Herbys Necessary for a Gardyn* was compiled by Thomas Fromon around 1535 and included more than 30 species grown as much for pleasure as "for savour and beaute". Among them he included columbine, germander, stickadove (thought to be Lavender stoechas) and wallflower.

In his essay *Of Gardens*, Francis Bacon includes many herbs in his sketch of an ideal garden. His famous opening is often quoted: "God Almighty first planted a garden. And indeed, it is the purest of human pleasures. It is the greatest refreshment

to the spirits of man." He goes on to describe possible fragrant delights month by month: "The breath of flowers is far sweeter in the air, (where it comes and goes, like the warbling of music) than in the hand." He speaks of setting whole alleys of scented herbs; burnet, wild thyme and watermint "to have the pleasure when you walk or tread". He includes many garden elements of interest today: tall alleys or hedges for shade and shelter with openings to reveal distant views; a fountain or some water course in motion; knot gardens to be placed and planted so they can be viewed from a high window in the house; paths wide enough to walk comfortably on and a wild area with honeysuckle, sweetbrier, violets, strawberries and primroses.

The age of herbals

Herbals, books that provided plant descriptions and details of their medical uses, became increasingly popular in the sixteenth century. Although other botanic herbals had been written, it was fifteen centuries before any surpassed Dioscorides for botanic accuracy. In the sixteenth century, three famous herbals were printed in Germany and the third, Leonhart Fuch's *De Historia Stirpium* of 1542, has charming naturalistic illustrations of herbs drawn from direct observation instead of being copied from old woodcuts as in most previous herbals. His text, however, was based mostly on the writings of Dioscorides. The tradition of botany and medicine continued in a number of publications including

A seventeenth-century knot garden *features plants of the era, miniature box hedges and ornamental topiary.*

Gerard's Herbal (1597) by John Gerard, who grew over 1,000 species in his garden. In 1629, John Parkinson's herbal *Theatrum Botanicum* appeared, cataloguing over 3,000 species. This was followed by the most famous of all herbals, *The English Physician* (also known as *The Complete Herbal*) by Nicholas Culpeper, in 1649. Although this volume contained much useful medical knowledge, it was derided by many because Culpeper viewed the astrological aspects of plants as important. However, this had little effect on its popularity and it is still in print today.

Scholars made a valiant attempt to eliminate unscientific attitudes, but the common people held deep beliefs about the significance of plants: plants were deemed to serve humanity, each with a purpose for our benefit. The belief known as the Doctrine of Signatures, which emerged in the first century AD, suggested that some aspect of a plant's appearance, usually its leaf shape or colouring, would give a clue to its medicinal properties. This notion remained popular for fifteen centuries, and appeared in several independent cultures at different times, from the Chinese to that of the North American Indians, although Culpeper was its last important champion.

Up to the seventeenth century, herbals had contained botany and medicine but as science emerged, plants were classified, dissected and demystified and botany and medicine went their separate ways. Great strides were made in herbal knowledge using new technical skills to analyse a plant's components and to produce standardized tinctures and extracts. But in the face of glamorous science, with its skill in synthesizing drugs, herbalism declined and our involvement with nature seemed to diminish.

In 1931 an Englishwoman, Mrs M. Grieve, decided to change this situation and wrote *A Modern Herbal* which drew together scientific and traditional information. Around this time the renewed interest in herbs began, partly spurred on by the food and medical shortages of World War I. Old seasoning, salad and pot herbs were remembered and, in the trenches, garlic, thyme and moss were rediscovered to play life-saving medical roles.

The lure of herbs today

Recently, there has been a tremendous surge of interest in herbs. Research on medicinal and cosmetic uses and new ideas for decorative and scented applications are continually adding to the large body of herbal knowledge and skills. The object of this book is again to combine traditional with scientific knowledge and present the many innovative ways herbs can be used to enhance life in the home and at work. The practical approach will, I hope, encourage you to further inventiveness by providing a glimpse of the inexhaustible potential of herbs.

The renewed interest in herbs has many spurs. A revival of the culinary arts has prompted earnest efforts to grow and buy fresh herbs. The cuisine of other cultures has created an interest in unusual varieties of herbs. A wish for nutritious food, alternative medicines and a balanced ecology has further extended the boundaries. A concern about the side-effects of some modern chemicals has revived the use of herbal cosmetics, dyes and household cleaning agents. Our growing sensitivity to scents has increased our desire for and appreciation of fresh herbal fragrances in all areas of our lives.

A bright red cartwheel (*above*) *makes an attractive and practical bed for planting a range of culinary herbs.*

Herbs and stone (*right*) *blend well together in this informal herb garden.*

A lush and colourful border (*opposite*) *with old roses and giant angelica flowers amidst a range of traditional cottage garden plants.*

To many people, an interest in one aspect of herbs acts as a catalyst for other related subjects. Many begin with an interest in cooking, perhaps fuelled by holidays abroad, and this may lead on to the study of the nutritious and health-enhancing properties of herbs, and their medicinal qualities. Others may be interested in growing herbs and, having created a herb garden, may find unexpected further pleasure in the individual herbs, their fresh scents and many uses.

In my own experience, I began with a great keenness for organic gardening but the prairie-puritan in my background permitted me to devote my energies only to vegetables. When I discovered herbs were useful and beautiful, I allowed a small door in my mind to open and found an enormous world of interesting plants waiting.

If pressed for the reason for my new-found enthusiasm, I would say how delicious herbs were and that they could transform an ordinary dish into a culinary delight, or I would explain how handy they were with a growing family for treating colds, coughs and other minor ailments, but in truth these were the extra benefits. The real pleasure for me was just being with the herbs.

They are such pretty plants with their soft and subtle colours, and have such an enthusiastic vitality because they are mainly the same, original, wild species and have not been hybridized. This makes them very easy to grow and generally trouble-free – indeed they often promote the health of neighbouring plants. They also give the whole garden and the gardener a pleasing sense of useful abundance.

Weeding became an unexpected delight; the fragrance, texture and shapes would lead my mind to thoughts of ancient rituals and ceremonies, the healing herb women of so many cultures, the exchange of secret messages through a cryptic posy of herbs; separate colourful threads would emerge linking the past with the present.

My range of herbs grew and I soon started to discover the many uses of these plants for myself. Herbal cosmetics were a real treasure – I could use the best quality ingredients and make them for a fraction of shop costs. Visitors would exchange stories about the craft use of herbs, about dye plants and herbal cleaning agents – the versatility and application of herbs seemed almost endless, and more and more areas of my existence seemed to be permeated by herbs.

As my original training was in art, I found myself considering how the aesthetics of herbs affected my life. They are certainly visually appealing, both in the garden and as fresh and simple decorations indoors. Through scent, I remembered the writers in history who have spoken of the ability of "sweet perfumes" to lift the spirits, now confirmed by research. And then there is their appeal to touch – the velvety leaves of marsh mallow must be amongst the most sensuous plants in existence – and to taste. What could be more rewarding when tidying a neglected corner of the herb garden, than to discover a wild strawberry waiting to be picked, or enhancing a simple dish with a handful of fresh picked parsley and chives.

As my collection has grown into a herb garden, it has become an important retreat, a place that somehow has the ability to still the mind and encourage problem solving. In a sense, I feel that the Earth Mother has returned to centre stage. For me, these plants have regained their ancient significance as partners to be treated with reverence and gratitude, and the meaning of the word "herb" is expanding to its widest potential.

A tranquil corner of the author's garden (left) with *colourful highlights provided by scarlet blooms of bergamot, white musk mallow and purple spires of viper's bugloss.*

An overall view of the author's herb garden (opposite) *shows a selection of medicinal, culinary and dye herbs planted in mixed beds.*

HERBS
IN THE
GARDEN

Herbs offer a rewarding combination of beauty
and usefulness, and for those who have never felt
the urge to grow plants, this benevolent and
generous range is the perfect introduction to
gardening. A small amount of effort is soon
rewarded by aromatic silver and green foliage,
scented decorative flowers, savoury
leaves and spicy seeds.
Herbs can be tucked into existing flower borders,
vegetable beds or decorative pots. As adaptable
plants, many will grow happily on a balcony or
patio, or even indoors. When more space
is available, a separate area set aside for herbs
often becomes a special place for peace
and enchantment. This may take the form of a
traditional herb garden, neatly divided into beds
and paths, or it may be more free-form and flowing.
Herb garden styles and layouts are as varied as
the people who cultivate and enjoy herbs. They
can be as small or as large as space permits.
The following pages describe how to set about
designing a herb garden, and provide detailed
plans for planting schemes in a variety of
settings. There is also a wide range of inspiring
ideas for theme herb gardens, designed to
reflect personal interests.

*A spacious path, flanked by well-stocked borders, leads to a stone
sundial in this informal herb garden.*

Planning a herb garden

Before embarking on your design, consider how much time and effort you are willing to put into your herb garden and how much maintenance any proposed scheme is likely to require. Don't be too ambitious or it will become a chore rather than a pleasure. If you are new to gardening, start with a small area or a few large containers and a limited number of herbs. As your enthusiasm grows, you can expand your herb garden and its contents.

SELECTING YOUR SITE

The ideal site is quiet and sunny with a protective surround. These conditions suit most herbs and will help to make a peaceful retreat. Such ready-made idyllic sites are few and far between but they are not difficult to create.

Aim for an area where at least three-quarters of the space is in the sun for most of the day. As many aromatic herbs are Mediterranean in origin, a slope that faces the sun for five to six hours each day is ideal as it will offer good drainage as well as extra solar energy. Spend time in the proposed site, noting the sun's passage over it, where shadows fall, which corners are sheltered from wind and the areas where water collects. If any part of the plot is waterlogged, it is worth making rubble-filled trenches, laying drainage pipes or making raised beds (see p. 261) before starting any further work, to avoid future frustration and loss of plants. Consider wind protection, particularly for evergreen herbs such as rosemary and sweet bay in the spring, and around a proposed seat or bench. A traditional hedge or wall (a frequent asset in small city gardens), or a screen supporting climbing plants, creates a feeling of seclusion, confines the perfumes of aromatic plants and reduces wind buffeting. It can also reduce outside noise and mask undesirable views.

Apart from the physical aspects of a site, think about its location in terms of how you plan to use it. Will herbs be close to your kitchen door for convenient picking? Will their scents drift indoors? Or do you want to create a herb garden retreat, removed from household activities?

DESIGNING YOUR GARDEN

Having selected your site, decide on the style of garden you want; whether it is to be a formal scheme following geometric patterns or an informal collection or grouping that dictates its own shape. The style of your home and neighbourhood may give you a preference for formality or informality, or you may decide to try a combination of the two. Look at the pictures of other herb gardens in magazines and books and try to visit any in your area. Formal herb gardens are based on well-defined patterns and geometric shapes, with the beds and paths designed to give a sense of order and balance as well as access. Traditionally, the planting schemes were relatively sparse with the emphasis on individual species. Today, many gardeners prefer to contrast the exuberant natural growth of herbs with the tidy formality of traditional designs.

In informal gardens, plants are massed together in a profusion of colour and different species, with the herbs often intermingled with flowers and vegetables. The effect is natural and romantic. However, such seemingly disorganized growth requires some planning so neighbouring plants complement rather than clash, and have sufficient sunlight. Paths must still provide access so some structure is necessary to make the overall design work and to allow for maintenance.

DRAWING UP A PLAN

Once you have selected your site, measure its sides and prepare to draw up the area on squared grid paper, making each square represent a convenient measurement such as 6 inches or 10 centimetres. Start the measurements from a base line which is either parallel to your house or at right angles to it. Draw in the measured outline of your site in clear bold lines and mark in the main fixtures which will remain: fences, buildings, trees, etc. Be as accurate as possible and note any changes of level which may require steps or raised beds.

Now you are ready to try out some design schemes with tracing paper laid over the site plan. Establish the overall feel of a design before filling in any detail and be prepared to discard page after page. Everyone has a natural sense of beauty and shape, often buried by looking too much at detail, but eventually you will know when a design feels right. Then you can start to mark in paths, beds and other details. If you wish to make a modern, free-flowing design, start with bold sweeping lines. People often have a tendency to draw small tight curves, but when translated into three dimensions, all lines are exaggerated. Hold up the design to a mirror to check its balance.

If you are designing a formal scheme, make a loose grid of lines on the plan based on the surroundings. Extend the lines of the house, doors, windows, garage, walls, and other boundaries so you have a selection of lines to choose your main pathways from. Each path should then line up with an existing structure, integrating your design.

Paths

For convenient access, herbs should never be more than 2 ft 6 in (75 cm) from a path, so beds should be no more than 4–5 ft (1.2–1.5 m) wide unless you insert stepping stones. Paths are also crucial to design for the colour and patterns they can bring as well as the way they can define shape (see below and pp. 260–1). In all garden plans, avoid putting a path straight through the space. It suggests rushing ahead, whereas a herb garden should be a place where you linger. Have a path change direction, or break its flow by altering the pattern of its fabric or adding a piece of sculpture or a tall herb.

FILLING IN THE DETAILS

Your design should now be an interesting pattern of lines. This is the time to extend your conception into three dimensions. Imagine you are sculpting

paths and layers through a large cube of greenery. Consider adding different levels and further interest to the design. Three parallel lines on a plan need not necessarily mean a path and a border, they could represent three steps, a change of pattern in the path, or an edging herb.

Decide what form of enclosure to have (see pp. 255–9), bearing in mind any views you may wish either to hide or to emphasize. Place a chair where you propose to have a seat and stick canes into the ground at different heights to consider the effect various enclosures may have.

GARDEN DESIGNS

The illustrations below show some of the ways in which a rectangular or square space can be divided to make a formal arrangement of beds and linking paths. Other

traditional designs are a simple ladder shape with square beds between narrow brick paths or wooden planks, and stepping stones arranged in a chequerboard pattern.

Brick circle
Bricks arranged in a circular path enclose two intersecting paths which cross at the centre.

Brick diamond
Bricks arranged in a herringbone pattern add extra interest and flow to this design.

Square within a square
Tiles arranged as diamonds and laid in concrete give a simple design an ornate effect.

Diagonal paths
A mixture of paving materials emphasizing lines to create a knot garden effect.

Interlocking diamonds
A diamond ribbon of santolina entwines with one of dwarf box. Where a hedge meets a brick path, the pattern is continued with a line of pebbles.

Oblongs and right angles
A long central bed is enclosed by bricks which have been laid out in a herringbone pattern to add extra interest to the design.

Diamonds and squares
A brick path divides square beds and creates a central diamond shape. The beds are edged with curry plants and box to emphasize their shape.

Wheel beds
Cartwheels are a practical and effective way to divide beds into separate planting areas. Here, a gravel path surrounds and links each wheel.

WORKING OUT A PLANTING SCHEME

Once you have planned the garden's physical layout, plot out where you might position the plants you want to grow in terms of their requirements and usage: culinary plants by the kitchen door, aromatic plants under the windows, further beds of dye, historical or medicinal plants, depending on your interests. Check the respective requirements of individual plants, and plot out their positions, bearing in mind aspects like contrasting leaf size and colour, complementary plant shapes and heights. As a guide, one plant per square foot or ten per square metre allows plenty of space for perennials to grow.

Position annuals so you don't have to disturb perennials when planting or removing them. Use tall plants as focal points in central beds or as screens. Where you have the space, group several plants of the same species together to increase their effect. Use grid paper to plot out their eventual ground size as well as their colours and height. Often plants are drawn as tiny circles when in fact they are exuberant growers. Close planting may look effective but soon leads to overcrowding. Fortunately, most herbs are easy to transplant.

MARKING OUT THE SITE

Once the soil has been prepared for planting as described on p. 251, transfer your design to the ground. Mark out the boundaries of the plot with stakes, then start to mark out the beds and paths. You can use a large cardboard box as a set square to help indicate right angles in the soil for geometric designs. As a guide for angles of 45°, mark the two diagonals on the square end of a box with coloured tape. To draw out circles, make a compass using a cane as a central stake and a marker which reaches the ground on a taut piece of string. To mark out small repeated shapes, use a card template and trace around it. Delineate areas with string and pegs or a sprinkling of lime.

The author's herb garden *is a mixture of formal and informal styles. It has paved areas, lawn, knot garden beds, species beds and informal, cottage-style borders. Its design is flexible so it can expand as new interests demand.*

A small all-purpose herb garden

As most herbs require very little space, you can grow a surprising variety in a relatively small area. Many herbs have more than one use so you can satisfy a wide range of interests with comparatively few plants. Of those shown in this garden: fennel, rosemary, sage, and thyme are culinary, medicinal, cosmetic and aromatic; lavender, bergamot and balm can be used to make scented gifts and comforting teas; tansy can be used to keep away flies, and marsh mallow makes a soothing ingredient for skin creams. In addition to offering many uses, these herbs are delightful flowering plants that will attract butterflies, bees and birds to your garden.

This design makes the most of a small space with its sweeping, curved path around the bed of low-growing culinary herbs, the backdrop of majestic plants such as angelica, sweet Joe Pye and marsh mallows, the ornamental bowl of water to attract birds, and the wooden bench surrounded by sweet-scented plants. Even in such a confined space, it is worth making room for a seat so you can relax in your garden.

Plant key

1 Honeysuckle *Lonicera periclymenum* Fragrant pale yellow flowers
2 Angelica *Angelica archangelica* Provides stature
3 Tansy *Tanacetum vulgare* Adds height and pungent foliage
4 Marsh mallow *Althaea officinalis* Adds height, velvet foliage and pale pink flowers
5 Sweet Joe Pye *Eupatorium purpureum* Majestic with large pink flower heads
6 Bronze fennel *Foeniculum vulgare* Highly decorative
7 Lungwort *Pulmonaria officinalis* Provides attractive green spotted leaves
8 Purple sage *Salvia officinalis* 'Purpurascens' Attractive purple leaves have strong flavour
9 Foxgloves *Digitalis purpurea* Statuesque and colourful
10 Variegated lemon balm *Melissa officinalis* 'Variegata' Fresh citrus scent
11 Chives *Allium schoenoprasum* Edible and attractive
12 Calendula *Calendula officinalis* Cheery orange flowers
13 Lavender *Lavandula angustifolia* 'Hidcote' Dwarf

form with silver leaves and dark purple flowers
14 Bergamot *Monarda didyma* Striking, decorative flowers and scented leaves
15 Lawn chamomile *Chamaemelum nobile* Makes a thick, sweet-smelling path border when clipped
16 Parsley *Petroselinum crispum* An essential culinary herb with dense green foliage
17 Salad burnet *Poterium sanguisorba* Add young leaves to salads and drinks
18 Golden marjoram *Origanum vulgare* 'Aureum' Aromatic golden leaves
19 Rosemary *Rosmarinus officinalis* 'Severn sea' Blue flowers appear in early spring
20 Thyme *Thymus praecox* 'Coccineus' Creeping thyme
21 Sweet woodruff *Galium odoratum* Plant under tall herbs

Features
Terracotta container of water to reflect the sky and attract small birds
Gravel path with larger pebbles along the inside curve to accentuate its shape
Wooden bench surrounded by aromatic plants

GARDEN PLAN

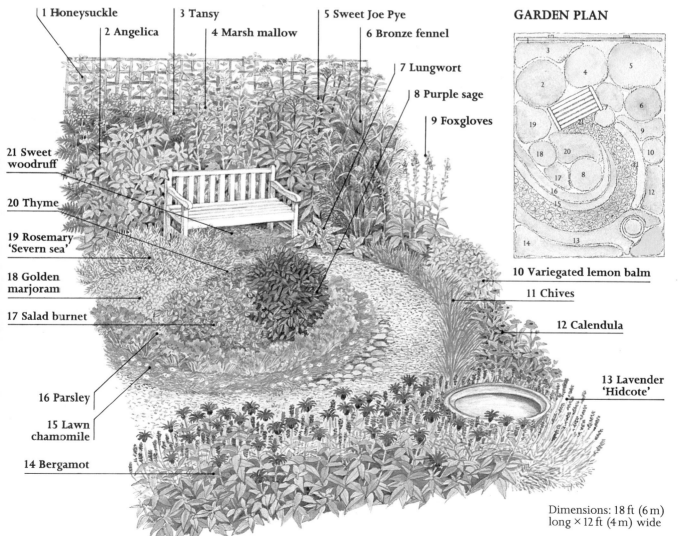

1 Honeysuckle
2 Angelica
3 Tansy
4 Marsh mallow
5 Sweet Joe Pye
6 Bronze fennel
7 Lungwort
8 Purple sage
9 Foxgloves
21 Sweet woodruff
20 Thyme
19 Rosemary 'Severn sea'
18 Golden marjoram
17 Salad burnet
16 Parsley
15 Lawn chamomile
14 Bergamot
10 Variegated lemon balm
11 Chives
12 Calendula
13 Lavender 'Hidcote'

Dimensions: 18 ft (6 m) long × 12 ft (4 m) wide

19

A large all-purpose herb garden

Having a generous-sized plot in which to make a herb garden offers enormous scope for the creative gardener. With such space, you can have separate areas which reflect your various interests and can expand with them. Corners or beds may be planted along different themes; for example, Shakespearean herbs in one corner (see p. 35) and Anglo-Saxon amulet herbs (betony, vervain, peony, plantain, yarrow and rose) in another.

Space for a wide range of plants provides the opportunity to grow collections of species: a whole bed of thymes, one of sages, one of rosemary and another of marjorams. A large garden also gives scope for growing herbal trees.

This design is based on our family herb garden with its informal border containing dye herbs, cosmetic herbs and tall culinary herbs on either side of the entrance, a scented arbour, china sinks planted with collections of alpine varieties, and many decorative, flowering herbs.

The beds are divided into groupings of medicinal herbs, salad plants, species collections (which form a patchwork of colour in summer), aromatic shrubs and miniature knot beds, each planted with different coloured santolinas in interweaving patterns. The layout of the lawn and brick paths allows access to all plants and defines the overall shape of the garden.

GARDEN PLAN

The planting key opposite lists details of the garden plants

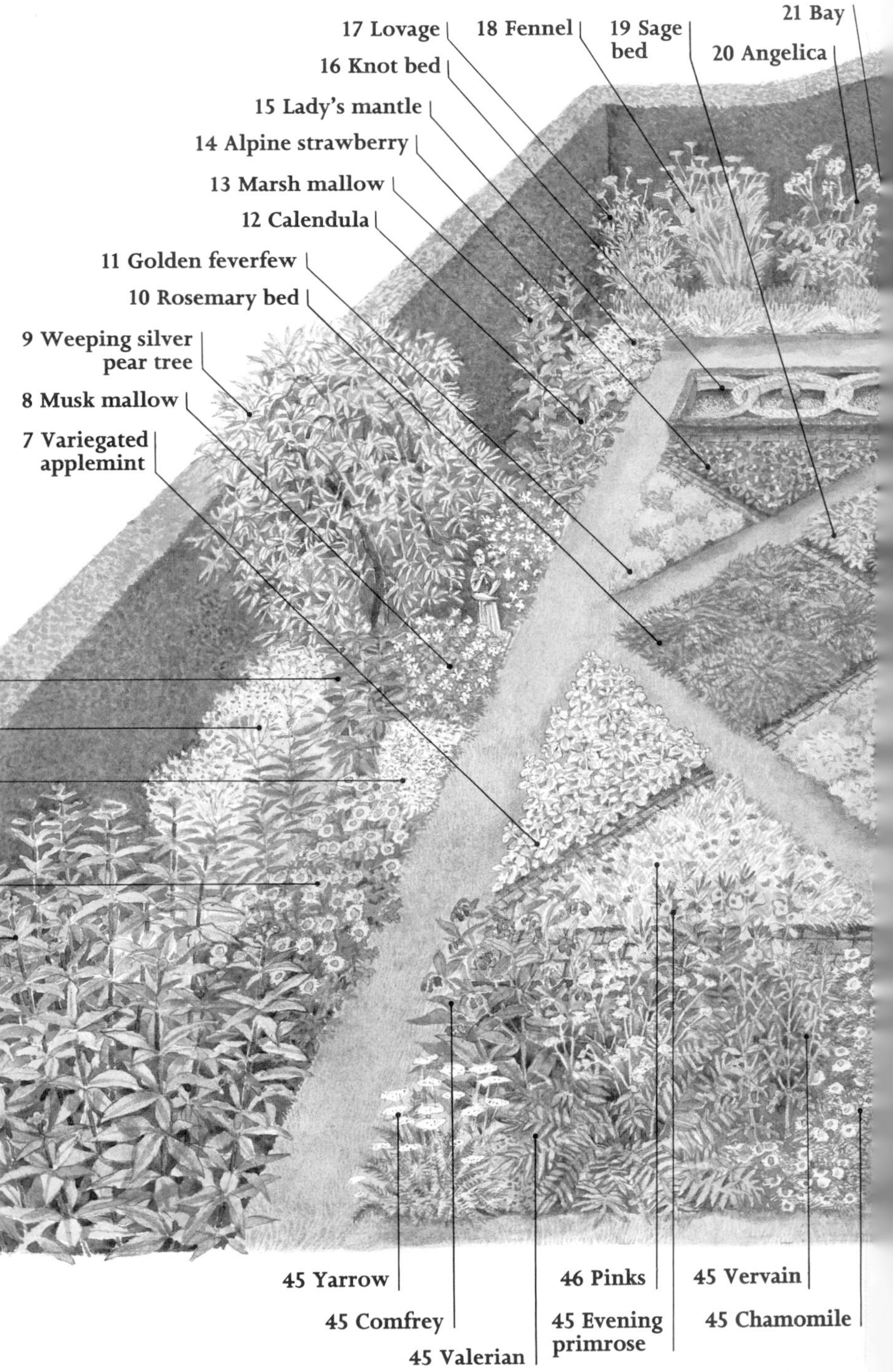

17 Lovage
18 Fennel
19 Sage bed
21 Bay
20 Angelica
16 Knot bed
15 Lady's mantle
14 Alpine strawberry
13 Marsh mallow
12 Calendula
11 Golden feverfew
10 Rosemary bed
9 Weeping silver pear tree
8 Musk mallow
7 Variegated applemint

6 Soapwort
5 Woad
4 Lady's bedstraw
3 Yew hedge
2 Dyer's chamomile
1 Sweet Joe Pye

45 Yarrow
46 Pinks
45 Vervain
45 Comfrey
45 Evening primrose
45 Chamomile
45 Valerian

Dimensions: 50 ft (15 m) long
× 30 ft (9 m) wide

Plant key

1 Sweet Joe Pye *Eupatorium purpureum* Majestic plant with pink-tinged flowers and sturdy purple stems
2 Dyer's chamomile *Anthemis tinctoria* Yields a yellow dye
3 Yew hedge *Taxus baccata* Provides shelter and an evergreen backdrop
4 Lady's bedstraw *Galium verum* Produces masses of tiny yellow flowers
5 Woad *Isatis tinctoria* Yields a rich blue dye
6 Soapwort *Saponaria officinalis* For cleansing fragile fabrics

7 Variegated applemint *Mentha suaveolens* 'Variegata' Attractive leaves and scent
8 Musk mallow *Malva moschata* Produces white or pale pink flowers; faintly scented
9 Weeping silver pear tree *Pyrus salicifolia* 'Pendula' Attractive, silver-leaved pendulous branches
10 Rosemary *Rosmarinus officinalis* Collection of species and varieties
11 Golden feverfew *Tanacetum parthenium* 'Aureum' Aromatic with daisy flowers
12 Calendula *Calendula officinalis* Bright orange flowers which

have cosmetic and culinary uses
13 Marsh mallow *Althaea officinalis* Skin-softening herb
14 Alpine strawberry *Fragaria vesca* Provides edible fruits
15 Lady's mantle *Alchemilla vulgaris* Large round leaves for cosmetic use
16 Knot beds with overlapping lines of **santolinas** (see No. 43) surrounded by a **box hedge** *Buxus sempervirens* 'Suffruticosa'
17 Lovage *Levisticum officinale* A decorative plant with strong savoury flavour
18 Fennel *Foeniculum vulgare* A handsome, feathery plant

19 Sage *Salvia* species bed
20 Angelica *Angelica archangelica* Grows to monumental height
21 Bay *Laurus nobilis* Trained to form a ball of foliage
22 Lawn chamomile *Chamaemelum nobile* 'Treneague' A sweet-scented welcome mat
23 Lavenders *Lavandula* species Select for colour and height
24 Curry plant *Helichrysum angustifolium* Spicy, silver foliage
25 Bronze fennel *Foeniculum vulgare* Rich, bronze leaves
26 Elecampane *Inula helenium* Statuesque with yellow flowers and enormous leaves
27 Sorrel *Rumex acetosa* Lush foliage and spires of flowers
28 Welsh onion *Allium fistulosum* Provides winter leaves for flavouring
29 Bugle *Ajuga reptans* Pretty blue flowers
30 Orris *Iris florentina* Striking plant with scented root
31 Thymes *Thymus* species A bed of colourful thymes
32 Akebia *Akebia quinata* Scented climber trained to form an arbour
33 Sweet woodruff *Galium odoratum* Plant where its sweet scent can be appreciated
34 Bergamot *Monarda didyma* Aromatic and attractive
35 Madonna lily *Lilium candidum* Exotic blooms
36 Sweet cicely *Myrrhis odorata* Edible fresh seeds
37 Lemon balm *Melissa officinalis* Strong lemon scent
38 Foxgloves *Digitalis purpurea* Spires of flowers add colour to the back of the border
39 Medicinal rhubarb *Rheum officinale* Large, ornate leaves
40 Alpine herbs in sink
41 Catmint *Nepeta mussinii* Decorative purple flowers
42 Salad herbs bed with **purple basil** *Ocimum basilicum* 'Dark Opal', **coriander** *Coriandrum sativum*, **parsley** *Petroselinum crispum*, **chives** *Allium schoenoprasum*, **purslane** *Portulaca oleracea*
43 Green and silver-leafed santolinas *Santolina virens, S. chamaecyparissus* and *S.c.* 'Lemon Queen'
44 Marjorams *Origanum* species Marjoram collection
45 Medicinal herbs: chamomile *Matricaria recutita*, **vervain** *Verbena officinalis*, **evening primrose** *Oenothera biennis*, **valerian** *Valeriana officinalis*, **comfrey** *Symphytum officinale*, **yarrow** *Achillea millefolium*
46 Pinks *Dianthus* cultivars

Features
Garden bench sheltered by the planted arbour
Brick paths and **lawn paths** criss-cross the garden
A stone statue of Pan

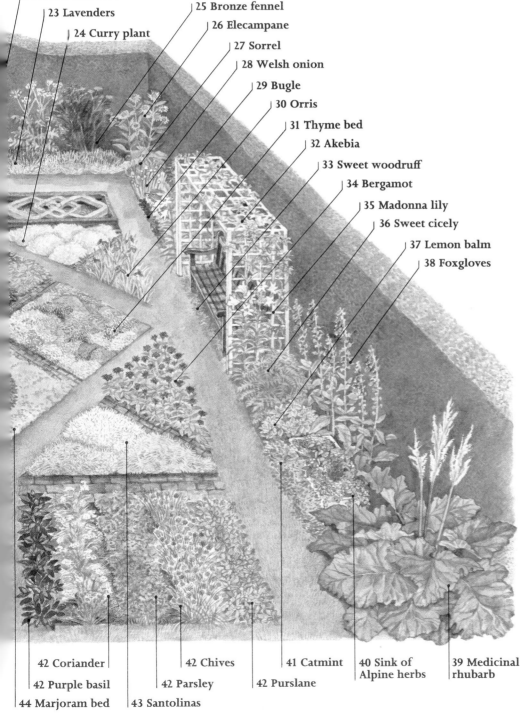

22 Lawn chamomile
23 Lavenders
24 Curry plant
25 Bronze fennel
26 Elecampane
27 Sorrel
28 Welsh onion
29 Bugle
30 Orris
31 Thyme bed
32 Akebia
33 Sweet woodruff
34 Bergamot
35 Madonna lily
36 Sweet cicely
37 Lemon balm
38 Foxgloves

42 Coriander
42 Purple basil
44 Marjoram bed
43 Santolinas
42 Chives
42 Parsley
41 Catmint
42 Purslane
40 Sink of Alpine herbs
39 Medicinal rhubarb

Patios and balconies

As cities continue to grow, space becomes more limited and, increasingly, people live in high-rise dwellings far removed from the earth and its soothing greenery. Those with a balcony or patio have the opportunity to create a private outdoor space in which to daydream and cultivate a selection of aromatic herbs.

To make the best use of such limited space, it is important to plant in all three dimensions, as shown in the scheme below. Use troughs, barrels, sinks and pots on the floor; tiers of pots or shelves up the walls; hanging baskets, and trellis or some other form of screening with plants trained over to add height, shade and shelter. Make the most of the space you have by planting creeping thymes

between bricks and pavers, or in cracks in walls, and by arranging containers in groups that complement each other. Over large areas of wall, fix interlocking clay pots so you can plant a vertical garden. This type of scheme is useful and attractive when filled with small culinary and trailing herbs, particularly if you include some bright, flowering varieties such as the wild strawberries, nasturtiums and chives featured here.

In sheltered areas that get sun only some of the day, take advantage of those herbs that thrive in part shade: angelica, bergamot, bugle, chervil, comfrey, feverfew, foxglove, lungwort, mints, parsley, sweet cicely and sweet violets. Try bay, bistort, clary sage, lady's mantle, lovage, marsh

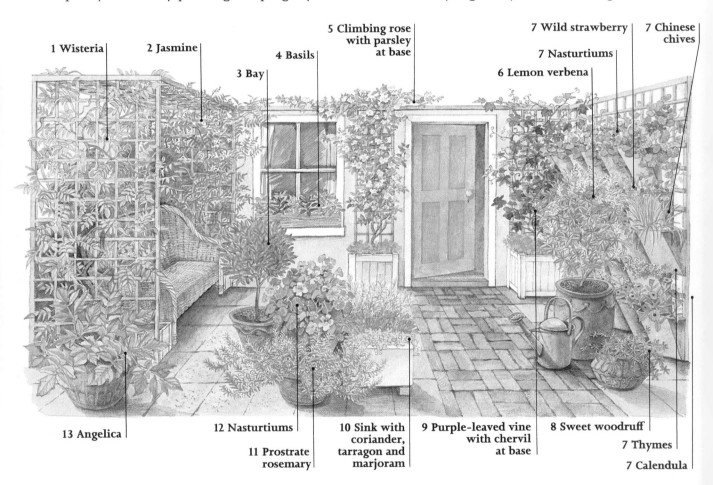

1 Wisteria
2 Jasmine
3 Bay
4 Basils
5 Climbing rose with parsley at base
6 Lemon verbena
7 Wild strawberry
7 Nasturtiums
7 Chinese chives
13 Angelica
12 Nasturtiums
11 Prostrate rosemary
10 Sink with coriander, tarragon and marjoram
9 Purple-leaved vine with chervil at base
8 Sweet woodruff
7 Thymes
7 Calendula

Plant key

1 Wisteria *Wisteria sinensis* Fragrant lilac flowers appear in spring
2 Jasmine *Jasminum officinale x stephanense* Vigorous climber with fragrant pink flowers
3 Bay *Laurus nobilis* trimmed to form a neat tree
4 Basil *Ocimum basilicum* A selection of basils including dark opal and the smaller-leafed bush basil. These are grown in pots on the window-sill for easy access and to make their transition indoors easier

5 Versailles box planted with climbing **rose** *Rosa* 'Mme Alfred Carrière' with **parsley** *Petroselinum crispum* at the base
6 A tall pot of fragrant **lemon verbena** *Aloysia triphylla*
7 Wall of ceramic pot units planted with (top row) **nasturtiums** *Tropaeolum majus*; (2nd row) **wild strawberry** *Fragaria vesca*; (3rd row) **Chinese chives** *Allium tuberosum*, salad herbs such as **orach** *Atriplex hortensis*, and **purslane** *Portulaca oleracea*; (4th row) **thymes** *Thymus* species; (bottom row)

Calendula *Calendula officinalis* and **mints** *Mentha* species
8 A pot of fragrant **sweet woodruff** *Galium odoratum*
9 Versailles box planted with flavoursome **chervil** *Anthriscus cerefolium* and a purple-leaved **vine** *Vitis vinifera* 'Purpurea' which may produce grapes on a sheltered, sunny patio
10 Culinary herbs Old porcelain sink positioned conveniently near the door and planted with favourite culinary herbs: **coriander** *Coriandrum sativum*, **tarragon**

Artemisia dracunculus and **marjoram** *Origanum onites*
11 Prostrate rosemary *Rosmarinus officinalis* 'Prostratus' An attractive, trailing form to grow in pots
12 Nasturtium *Tropaeolum majus* Attractive, bright and edible flowers and leaves spill over container's edges
13 Angelica *Angelica archangelica* Potentially tall plant anchored in a large pot which its roots can spread in

mallow, rue, salad burnet, sorrel, tansy and yarrow as well. To help them along, white tiles or white walls will magnify the available light.

If you have a roof garden or high-level balcony, consider structural safety and shelter. If it is windy, some form of screening should come high on your list of planning considerations. Everything will need careful anchoring, including the soil, which should be topped with gravel chippings to prevent it blowing away. Soft-leaved herbs such as lemon balm or angelica will become tattered in high winds, whereas narrow-leaved evergreens such as rosemary and lavender are more suited to such a location, although their appearance may become irregular and gnarled if winds are strong.

Careful placing of plant-filled pots can soften the harsh angles of walled yards and balconies. Rearrange containers frequently either to vary the aesthetic effect or simply so that you maximize the amount of sunlight they enjoy.

For container-grown herbs, life is often a cycle of feast and famine. They experience thorough wetness when watered, but in hot sun when the soil dries out, their roots have nowhere to extend to in their search for extra moisture. The sun may blaze down for several hours, then disappear behind a building, bringing a sharp drop in temperature. Bear all these factors in mind (see p. 264) when selecting herbs and positioning containers on your patio or balcony.

Clusters of tiny, creeping herbs (*above*) *add colour and softness to a brick-paved area.*

A stately stone urn (*left*) *planted with lemon-scented pelargoniums makes a showpiece in this patio garden.*

An attractive collection of patio pots (*below*) *filled with parsley, nasturtiums, sage, rosemary, flowering and scented pelargoniums and thyme, indicate an orderly gardener with civilized priorities.*

An indoor herb garden

Herbs grown indoors add a fresh fragrance to interiors and because they're near to hand, it encourages you to make maximum use of their leaves. For their part, the herbs gain a longer growing season and protection from severe weather conditions.

"Green fingers" are a result of interested observation and being sensitive to your plants' needs. Basically, herbs require a sunny or light area, water and air humidity, and freedom from draughts and extremes of temperature. Most herbs fare better and look more attractive in groups. Watering is easier and the plants respond well to the mini climate which grouping creates.

A windowsill is the most convenient location, especially if you can make full use of the light,

incorporating shelves or pots on the surrounding walls. The indoor garden illustrated below is designed all around the light source with a hanging basket at the top, climbing herbs and potted herbs on shelves at the sides and a trough full of potted herbs at the base.

Consider growing herbs to enhance different rooms: a clipped bay or sweet myrtle in a sunny entrance hall; peppermint in the moist air of a bathroom; healing aloe vera next to the medicine chest; scented geraniums, pineapple sage and lemon verbena to scent a living room; soothing lavender in the bedroom; hanging baskets planted with prostrate sage and trailing catmint in a stair-well and a grid system on which to bracket pots of culinary herbs on a sunny kitchen wall.

A window garden
Herbs grouped together around a window enjoy maximum light and improved humidity. Turn pots when necessary to prevent uneven growth.

1 Hanging basket with prostrate sage and creeping pennyroyal

16 Nasturtium

2 Golden hop

3 Borage

4 Sorrel

5 Sweet basil

6 Tarragon

7 Lungwort

8 Golden marjoram

9 Parsley

15 Bay

14 Rosemary

13 Chives

12 Salad burnet

11 Golden creeping lemon thyme

10 Spearmint

Plant key

1 Hanging basket with **prostrate sage** *Salvia officinalis* 'Prostratus' which has blue flowers in early summer, and **creeping pennyroyal** *Mentha pulegium*, which has lilac flowers in midsummer

2 Golden hop *Humulus lupulus* 'Aureus' trained to grow around the window frame. Female plants produce flowers in late summer

3 Borage *Borago officinalis* Use its flowers to garnish food and drinks

4 Sorrel *Rumex acetosa* Lush leaves can be used as spinach

5 Sweet basil *Ocimum basilicum* An excellent indoor plant. Pinch off flowers to encourage leaf production

6 Tarragon *Artemisia dracunculus* Aromatic leaves

7 Lungwort *Pulmonaria officinalis* Pink/blue flowers in spring

8 Golden marjoram *Origanum vulgare* 'Aureum' Attractive leaves with good flavour

9 Parsley *Petroselinum crispum* Grow two plants so you always have a good supply

10 Spearmint *Mentha spicata* Refreshing flavour for teas and garnishes. Pinch off flowers for better leaf production

11 Golden creeping lemon thyme *Thymus x citriodorus* 'Aureus' Aromatic and colourful foliage

12 Salad burnet *Poterium sanguisorba* Use in salads

13 Chives *Allium schoenoprasum* Cut off the attractive flowers for better leaf production

14 Rosemary *Rosmarinus officinalis* Blue flowers appear in late spring

15 Bay *Laurus nobilis* Trimmed into a ball

16 Nasturtium *Tropaeolum majus* Trained on a wire around the window

Theme gardens

Much of the allure of herbs is in their many practical and historical associations. Stories, myths and legends featuring herbs abound. The more you find out about herbs, the more you are encouraged to investigate further. This increase in knowledge enhances the pleasure of planning and having a herb garden, and can be used as the basis for making a thematic herb garden.

To plan a theme garden, select plants according to your interests. You may wish to grow solely culinary herbs, or cosmetic, dye or medicinal herbs. If you enjoy discovering how people lived in other ages, you could plant a Roman cook's garden (see p. 34) or a Tudor "My lady's garden" featuring cosmetic and aromatic herbs laid out in a formal scheme.

As the following pages show, you can plant a bed or a whole garden of herbs according to their usage, or you can create a garden based on another culture's style and interests, such as the Chinese and Persian designs shown later in this chapter.

Herbs are excellent plants to grow in community gardens but are often overlooked in favour of more ornamental plants. A school garden could be planned around a period of local history; a church garden could select herbs mentioned in the Bible or particularly associated with the Virgin Mary. In such gardens, clear labelling is important and paths should be wide, comfortable and safe. Some ideas are illustrated on the following pages.

A country kitchen garden (above) planted with herbs and vegetables which are both attractive and useful.

A garden of Chinese medicinal herbs (below) with a statue of Li Shizhen, a Chinese doctor who wrote a practical compendium of medical plants in 1578 after 27 years of travelling through China collecting and testing remedies. His work lists 1,173 plants and 11,000 recipes and has been translated into Japanese, English, Latin, French and German.

An aromatic herb garden

A garden specially created for its qualities of scent is a continuing delight, both for the gardener and for those who visit it. The aromatic herb garden is a place for perfumed plants of all kinds and sizes – from roses and scented climbers with herbal properties to tiny creeping herbs. Softly scented herbaceous plants can be planted beside some of the more fragrant varieties of culinary favourites, such as sages, rosemarys, mints and thymes listed in the key below.

A fragrant corner can be created in almost any garden, including a balcony, provided you consider three main elements. First, plan for herbs on several levels: at your feet, at hand and nose height and above your head (use trellises, arbours and hanging baskets). Second, consider some form of enclosure to still the wind, confine the perfume and create a feeling of pleasurable seclusion. Third,

have a garden seat on which you can linger and enjoy this special place while watching the many bees, butterflies and birds that will visit it.

The design opposite has all of these ingredients: aromatic plants at different levels, from underfoot to overhead, an enclosure created by the sweetbrier hedge and trellis, and a relaxing garden bench designed with its armrests and seat as planting areas for creeping thymes, chamomile, sweet myrtle and lemon verbena. As you approach the seat, your feet will release aromas from the creeping herbs planted in the path.

The plan is based on a series of semi-circles, most of which are planted symmetrically, with the same herbs appearing on either side. The formal, circular shape of the overall scheme marks out the area and increases the feeling of stepping into a peaceful, private garden.

GARDEN PLAN

Plant key

1 Sweetbrier rose *Rosa eglanteria* A climbing rose with sweet pink blooms and apple-scented leaves
2 Climbing rose *Rosa* 'Mme Alfred Carrière' Beautiful, scented blush pink blooms
3 Parsley *Petroselinum crispum* Offers fresh green leaves for nibbling. Benefits from shade of taller plants
4 Early Dutch honeysuckle *Lonicera periclymenum* 'Belgica' Early flowering and sweetly scented, especially in the evenings
5 Sweet woodruff *Galium odoratum* White star-like flowers and aromatic leaves when dried
6 Lemon verbena *Aloysia triphylla* Lemon scented foliage and pink flowers
7 Eau de cologne mint *Mentha piperita* 'Citrata' Attractive and aromatic
8 Akebia *Akebia quinata* Semi-evergreen with fragrant red-purple flowers
9 White jasmine *Jasminum officinale* Sweet-scented flowers
10 Sweet violet *Viola odorata* Early spring flowers
11 Lawn chamomile *Chamaemelum nobile* 'Treneague' Bright green leaves with a delicious apple scent
12 Golden hop *Humulus lupulus* 'Aureus' Attractive gold foliage
13 Green, gold and silver creeping thymes *Thymus praecox* 'Coccineus', *T.p.* 'Doone valley', *T.p.* 'Silver Lemon Queen' All have attractive leaf-colourings and flowers

14 Sweet myrtle *Myrtus communis* 'Tarentina' Spicy orange scent
15 Climbing rose *Rosa* 'New Dawn' Continuous, scented blooms
16 Madonna lily *Lilium candidum* Honey-scented, waxy white flowers
17 Clary sage *Salvia sclarea* Pungent large leaves
18 Rosemary *Rosmarinus officinalis* 'Miss Jessup's Upright' Pale blue flowers appear in spring
19 Clove pink *Dianthus plumarius* Sweet-scented, pretty flowers and silver-blue leaves

20 Catmint *Nepeta mussinii* Pungent leaves and pretty mauve flowers
21 Corsican mint *Mentha requienii* Tiny peppermint-scented leaves form a refreshing square mat to walk on
22 Pine-scented thyme *Thymus caespititius* (*T. azoricus*) Fresh scent and tiny pink flowers planted as a fragrant square mat
23 Creeping lemon thyme *Thymus praecox* 'Citriodorus' Lemon-scented; pink flowering mat to walk on
24 Caraway-scented thyme *Thymus herba-barona* Deep rose-purple flowers

25 Lavender *Lavandula angustifolia* 'Hidcote' Deep purple flowers, strong scent and attractive silver leaves
26 Bergamot *Monarda didyma* Rich red flowers and eau de cologne scent
27 Musk mallow *Malva moschata* Faintly musk-scented with small pink and white flowers
28 Variegated lemon balm *Melissa officinalis* 'Variegata' Gold-splashed, lemon-scented leaves
29 Sweet rocket *Hesperis matronalis* Sweet scented, purple and white flowers. Their fragrance becomes much stronger in the evening, once the sun has gone down
30 Soapwort *Saponaria officinalis* Soft pink summer flowers scent the air with a raspberry fragrance

Features
Wooden slatted seat set on a brick base (see p. 262). This is backed by a semi-circular cavity wall, which forms a planter for a collection of thymes. The seat is planted with chamomile and beside it are herbs which need handling to coax out their scent
Brick path constructed with old floor bricks or paviers (see p. 261). The path is designed with planting areas for creeping aromatic herbs
Trellis planted with sweet-scented climbing plants to form a fragrant windbreak
Ornamental urn filled with water for floating scented flower heads on

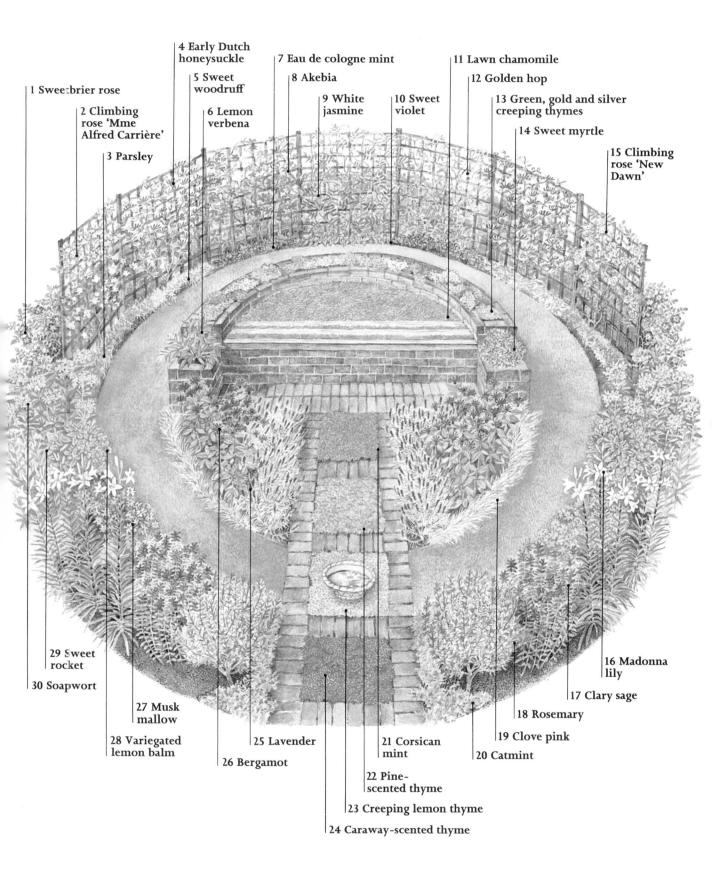

1 Sweetbrier rose

2 Climbing rose 'Mme Alfred Carrière'

3 Parsley

4 Early Dutch honeysuckle

5 Sweet woodruff

6 Lemon verbena

7 Eau de cologne mint

8 Akebia

9 White jasmine

10 Sweet violet

11 Lawn chamomile

12 Golden hop

13 Green, gold and silver creeping thymes

14 Sweet myrtle

15 Climbing rose 'New Dawn'

16 Madonna lily

17 Clary sage

18 Rosemary

19 Clove pink

20 Catmint

21 Corsican mint

22 Pine-scented thyme

23 Creeping lemon thyme

24 Caraway-scented thyme

25 Lavender

26 Bergamot

27 Musk mallow

28 Variegated lemon balm

29 Sweet rocket

30 Soapwort

Overall diameter 24 ft (8 m)

A children's herb garden

Growing herbs is both a learning experience and a great deal of fun. There is the excitement of planting seeds and seeing if they sprout; the appearance of leaves, flowers and visiting insects; and finally the harvesting and using of different plant parts. All these aspects offer children the opportunity to see how useful plants can be.

As most herbs are easy to grow, select plants that children can enjoy in different ways. For pre-school children, prepare a small, sunny plot and help them to sow mustard and cress seed. They will have the fun of watching them germinate and then be able to pick and eat the leaves.

The garden below contains plants with highly aromatic leaves to crush and smell; plants with edible leaves and seeds; flowers that will attract bees and butterflies, and plants with striking seed heads which are fun to play with. As children become older they will want to extend the range to suit their own interests.

Sensible advice for planning a children's garden is to keep it simple, but when I consulted my offspring, all four wanted a maze. We arrived at the compromise below, which is ideal for chasing games with its linked, curved paths radiating out from a central point.

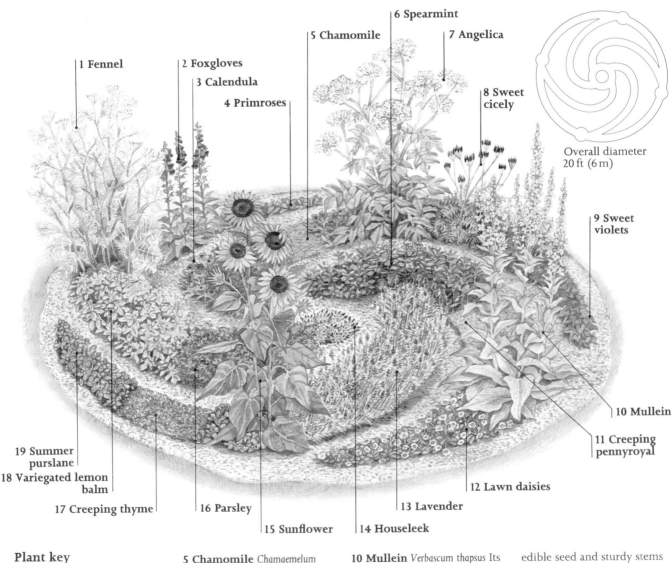

KEYLINE

Overall diameter 20 ft (6 m)

1 Fennel
2 Foxgloves
3 Calendula
4 Primroses
5 Chamomile
6 Spearmint
7 Angelica
8 Sweet cicely
9 Sweet violets
10 Mullein
11 Creeping pennyroyal
12 Lawn daisies
13 Lavender
14 Houseleek
15 Sunflower
16 Parsley
17 Creeping thyme
18 Variegated lemon balm
19 Summer purslane

Plant key

1 Fennel *Foeniculum vulgare* Edible leaves and seeds

2 Foxglove *Digitalis purpurea* Interesting flowers which attract bees. Ensure your child is responsible enough not to eat any of the plant

3 Calendula *Calendula officinalis* Colourful flowers with edible petals for budding cooks

4 Primroses *Primula vulgaris* Produces early flowers

5 Chamomile *Chamaemelum nobile* Carpeting herb with flowers for a soothing bedtime drink

6 Spearmint *Mentha spicata* Minty leaves to nibble

7 Angelica *Angelica archangelica* Offers soothing leaves for car journeys

8 Sweet cicely *Myrrhis odorata* Edible green seeds

9 Sweet violets *Viola odorata* Scented flowers for candying

10 Mullein *Verbascum thapsus* Its stalks make good rods

11 Creeping pennyroyal *Mentha pulegium* Mint-flavoured leaves; can be walked on

12 Lawn daisy *Bellis perennis* Flowers for daisy chains

13 Lavender *Lavandula angustifolia* Offers fragrant flowers

14 Houseleek *Sempervivum tectorum* Soothes cuts and stings

15 Sunflower *Helianthus annuus* A delight to watch growing;

edible seed and sturdy stems for building sticks

16 Parsley *Petroselinum c. spum* Edible leaves and currency for bribing the cook

17 Creeping thyme *Thymus praecox* Sweet-scented and able to withstand children's straying footsteps

18 Lemon balm *Melissa officinali* 'Variegata' Refreshing leaves

19 Summer purslane *Portulaca oleracea* Instant snack food

A moonlight garden

As a rule, gardens are planned for their appeal in daylight hours. However, many plants take on a quite magical appearance when viewed by the light of the moon.

Our eyes see differently by moonlight; most colours vanish, blue becomes white, and white and light grey appear almost fluorescent. A garden or border planted for viewing by moonlight should contain plants of these colours. For further impact, add white stones, statues and other garden features that will reflect the moon's light.

The photograph below was taken in my garden by the light of a full moon in May. Traditionally, this is considered a special night during the season of growth and renewal. I went out to sit on the

wooden bench in my herb garden and waited for my eyes to adjust to the dark. At first the moon was hidden by clouds, then it slowly appeared and the garden was transformed. I recognized a froth of white dots as forget-me-nots, a silver curved line as a hedge of curry plant, the luminous fronds of a weeping silver pear tree, and an iridescent canopy of cherry blossom. Artemisias, lavenders, silver thymes and lamiums stood out with their silver leaves, as did the white flowers of daisies, sweet cicely, chervil, caraway, comfrey and sage.

All the silvery tones were intensified by the moon's light. The scent of unseen wild wall-flowers and narcissi drifted across the garden to complete the enchanted moment.

A moonlight garden

Viewed by the light of a full moon, a garden full of herbs takes on a magical quality.

Plant key

1 Cherry tree *Prunus avium* Covered in fragrant, pale pink blossom
2 Weeping silver pear tree *Pyrus salicifolia* Graceful hanging silvery branches
3 Sweet rocket *Hesperis matronalis* Sweetly scented white flowers
4 Forget-me-nots *Myosotis sylvatica* A mass of pale blue and white flowers

5 Thymes *Thymus* species Different thymes planted in a bed to fill it with colour
6 Sweet cicely *Myrrhis odorata* Masses of flat white flower heads
7 Rosemary *Rosmarinus officinalis* A bush with pale blue flowers glowing in the moonlight
8 Evening primrose *Oenothera biennis* Tall stem outlined by the light

Feature

A stone urn containing water and floating cherry blossom
A stone statue of Pan

KEYLINE

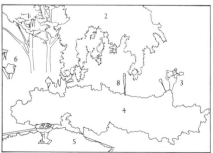

Culinary herb gardens

Although some herbs can be bought dried with their aroma intact (bay, sage, rosemary and thyme) and more shops now sell fresh cut herbs in season, growing your own is the only sure way to taste the tangy first flavours of chervil, basil, lovage and other less common culinary herbs that are being rediscovered.

A pot of the two most useful garnishing herbs – parsley and chives – will serve you well near to the kitchen door, but immediate access is not so necessary for most culinary herbs. A walk into the herb garden adds to the pleasure of cooking and the sight of other fresh herbs can inspire you to try new combinations.

Most of the culinary herbs are sun-lovers and appreciate good drainage plus wind protection. Two other considerations are a hard-surfaced, all-weather path from which you can conveniently reach the plants, and some form of exterior light or a torch kept near the kitchen door for late forages.

When deciding which herbs to grow, consider how much you are likely to use them. One plant of each of the evergreen herbs and the large perennials is enough for most households. If you are interested in salad herbs and vegetables, you will need more than one of each plant and should allow a patch at least 1 foot (30 cm) square or a row about 4 foot (1.2 m) long.

An orderly garden layout makes for convenient picking. The cartwheel and star designs shown here are both attractive and practical. The scheme for a potager (right) is more ambitious.

TWO SIMPLE PLANS
Both these designs allow for expansion as interests develop. Bricks separate the beds to provide access and delineate blocks of herbs.

Cartwheel *Start by planting the inner wheel, adding on outer circles as needed.*

Star *A hexagon forms the inner core and is transformed into a star by the six outer points.*

A potager
This plan adapts the traditional French idea of a potager, where herbs, vegetables and fruit are grown together to make a space-saving and decorative garden. It includes a choice selection of vegetables, salad plants and herbs, and fruit trees trained around arches to form a walkway. Separate beds make crop rotation possible and each bed is edged in traditional dwarf box.

12 Apple tree

11 Ruby chard

10 Sorrel

9 Florence fennel

8 French beans

7 Mangetout

6 French tarragon

5 Calendula

4 Parsley

3 Chives

2 Purple basil

1 Compact marjoram

25 Dwarf box

24 Shrubby thymes

Dimensions 15 ft (5 m) square

Plant key

1 Compact marjoram
Origanum vulgare 'Compactum'
Dwarf variety with well-
flavoured leaves
2 Purple basil *Ocimum basilicum*
'Dark opal' Deep purple leaves
and a slightly spicier flavour
than the standard sweet basil
3 Chives *Allium schoenoprasum*
Flavoursome leaves and pretty
purple flowers, also edible
4 Parsley *Petroselinum crispum*
Bright green leaves, essential
for any kitchen garden
5 Calendula *Calendula officinalis*
Add colour to any garden and
attractive as a garnish
6 French tarragon *Artemisia
dracunculus* For delicate and
distinctive flavour

7 Mangetout (Snow peas)
Pisum sativum var. *macrocarpon*
Produce delicately flavoured
pods for eating whole
8 French beans *Phaseolus vulgaris*
Provide bright orange flowers
as well as edible pods
9 Florence fennel *Foeniculum
vulgare dulce* Cultivate for the
sweet swollen stems
10 Sorrel *Rumex acetosa* Lush
leaves and red-green flowers
11 Ruby chard *Beta vulgaris*
'Rhubarb beet' Bright red
stalks and leaves
12 Two pear trees *Pyrus
communis* and two **apple trees**
Malus domestica Trained
(espaliered) over a system of
arches to make a covered
walkway

13 Globe artichokes *Cynara
scolymus* Magnificent thistle-
like flowers and delicious
vegetable heads
14 Red cabbage *Brassica oleracea*
'Ruby Red' Quick-growing
and attractive, edible leaves
15 Leeks *Allium porrum* Easy to
grow, valuable winter
vegetable
16 Chinese leaves *Brassica
pekinensis* Good in salads and as
a vegetable
17 Sage *Salvia officinalis* Attracts
bees and has many uses in and
out of the kitchen
18 Dill *Anethum graveolens* Good
for flavouring
19 Coriander *Coriandrum
sativum* Grow for its leaves
and seeds

20 Chervil *Anthriscus cerefolium*
Delicious culinary herb
21 Salad rocket *Eruca vesicaria*
Spicy leaves to add to salads
22 Lettuce *Lactuca sativa* 'Lollo'
Attractive red-tipped leaves
23 Purple chicory *Cichorium
intybus* Attractive red leaves
24 Thymes *Thymus vulgaris, T. x
citriodorus, T. herba-barona* A
selection of shrubby thymes
grown for their different
flavours
25 Dwarf box *Buxus sempervirens*
'Suffruticosa' A 6 in (15 cm)
hedge surrounds each bed

Feature
Brick path constructed with
weatherproofed paviers
provides access to all the beds

12 Pear tree

13 Globe artichokes

14 Red cabbage

15 Leeks

16 Chinese leaves

17 Sage

18 Dill

GARDEN PLAN

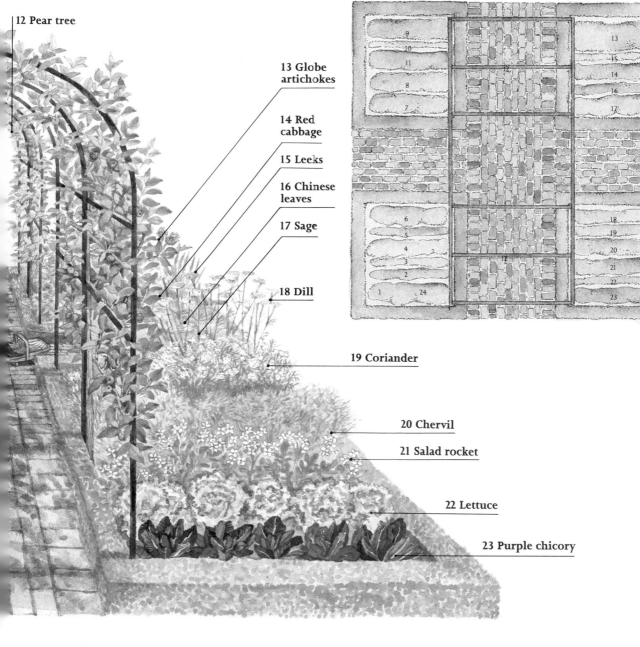

19 Coriander

20 Chervil

21 Salad rocket

22 Lettuce

23 Purple chicory

A Chinese herb garden

The Chinese have long been experts in the art of gardening in small courtyards. They create privacy, serenity and an air of mystery by dividing their space into still smaller areas with bamboo screens, moon-gates (circular entrances in walls) and skilled use of texture, light and shade.

Although the concept of a domestic herb garden does not exist in China, medicinal herbs have been highly valued for over 4,000 years and are grown in botanic gardens. In Kunming, the city of eternal spring, botanists make regular trips to the Yunnan mountains to collect herbs for display in a national garden with rocks, water and shady pergolas.

The garden below is based on a small courtyard near the theatre pavilion of the Summer Palace,

Beijing. Planting is kept very simple, with each bed devoted to showing only one species, yet it is planned so there is something of interest in each season. Here we have bamboo, known as one of the "three friends of winter", peonies for spring blooms, roses and poppies for summer and chrysanthemums for autumn. All have medicinal properties. I have made a small concession to Western ideas by underplanting with delicious Chinese culinary herbs.

The curved top to the surrounding wall gives extra lightness and the white surface provides a backdrop for the graceful shadows of the bamboo. The moon-gate frames the view and provides a distinct entrance.

1 Wisteria   2 Sacred bamboo   4 Apricot tree   6 White peony   7 Black bamboo
3 Roses   5 Saffron

14 Opium poppy   13 Coriander   12 Chinese mustard   11 Lotus blossom   10 Chinese chives   9 Ginseng   8 Tea chrysanthemum

Plant key

1 Wisteria Wisteria floribunda Fragrant flowers in early summer; galls used medicinally
2 Sacred bamboo Nandina domestica Used medicinally
3 Roses Rosa chinensis 'Old Blush China' Continuous clusters of pale pink roses; hips used as a digestive tonic

4 Apricot tree Prunus armeniaca Blossom appears in spring; seeds used in longevity pills
5 Saffron Crocus sativus Rich purple flowers in autumn
6 Peony Paeonia lactiflora Magnificent white blooms; roots used medicinally
7 Black bamboo Phyllostachys nigra Roots used medicinally

8 Tea chrysanthemum Chrysanthemum morifolium White, yellow or pink flowers used medicinally
9 Ginseng Panax ginseng Takes 3–7 years to mature. Pink flowers late summer. Root used as a tonic and elixir
10 Chinese chives Allium tuberosum Mild garlic flavour

11 Lotus blossom Nelumbo nucifera Floating in a glazed pot; beautiful aroma and flowers
12 Chinese mustard Brassica chinensis Flavoursome leaves
13 Coriander Coriandrum sativum Aromatic seeds
14 Opium poppy Papaver somniferum Luscious blooms from midsummer

A paradise garden

An enclosed pleasure garden, a paradise garden contains axial water channels, aromatic trees, fruits, fragrant herbs and colourful flowers. Developed in Egypt 4,000 years ago as a formal oasis, it reached its perfection under the Persians and the Moghuls in India. The style of geometric paths and rectangular beds was repeated in the monastic gardens of Europe.

This design follows the Persian tradition, with shallow pools lined with deep blue tiles, and decorative paving tiles. The central feature is an open pavilion, lavishly decorated with mosaic tiles in the traditional style, to give the effect of a sparkling jewelled retreat. Bright, flowering herbs add to this tapestry of colour.

Although the season for flowers is short in very hot climates, the aromatic evergreen trees and herbs, perpetual flowering roses, ornamental tiles and blue water channels provide colour, shade and pleasure all year round.

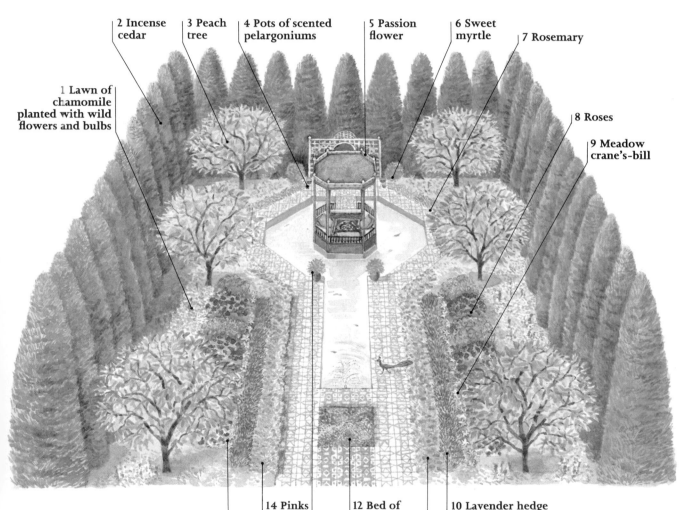

- **2 Incense cedar**
- **3 Peach tree**
- **4 Pots of scented pelargoniums**
- **5 Passion flower**
- **6 Sweet myrtle**
- **7 Rosemary**
- **1 Lawn of chamomile planted with wild flowers and bulbs**
- **8 Roses**
- **9 Meadow crane's-bill**
- **14 Pinks**
- **12 Bed of thymes**
- **10 Lavender hedge**
- **11 Calendula**
- **15 Golden-rayed lilies**
- **13 Pots of lemon verbena**

Plant key

1 Lawn of chamomile *Chamaemelum nobile* An apple-scented lawn planted meadow fashion with colourful flowers and bulbs
2 Incense cedar *Calocedrus decurrens* A hedge of tall trees provides shelter and creates welcome shade
3 Peach trees *Prunus persica* Provide blossom and refreshing fruit
4 Pots of scented pelargoniums *Pelargonium graveolens* and other species

interplanted with lemongrass. Pots positioned so plants release their aroma when brushed against
5 Passion flower *Passiflora caerulea* Striking flowers
6 Sweet myrtle *Myrtus communis* 'Tarentina' A low fragrant bush
7 Rosemary *Rosmarinus officinalis* 'Prostratus' A border of low-growing rosemary
8 Roses *Rosa foetida* with bright red flowers and *Rosa damascena* with deep pink flowers, planted in alternating colours

9 Meadow crane's-bill *Geranium pratense* Planted by the roses to enhance their colour
10 Lavender hedge *Lavandula dentata* Clipped to form a low hedge of fragrant flowers
11 Calendula *Calendula officinalis* A bed of bright orange marigold flowers
12 Thymes *Thymus* species A bed of mixed thymes
13 Pots of lemon verbena *Aloysia triphylla* Provide leaves with refreshing scent
14 Pinks *Dianthus* cultivars A border of fragrant clove pinks

15 Golden-rayed lilies *Lilium auratum* Lavish, scented flowers with distinctive markings on each petal

Features
Path covered in ornate paving tiles for extra colour
Water channel lined with rich blue tiles to enhance the apparent depth of the water
Pavilion provides shade and colour as well as a retreat

Theme garden ideas

The more you involve yourself with herbs, the more ways you will find for selecting and displaying these plants. Practical uses apart, theme gardens that place herbs in a historical context are always interesting to plan, as the significant role played by herbs in ancient cultures and more recent history makes fascinating research.

Archaeologists believe that certain plants were used to season food over 50,000 years ago. Certainly, by the Neolithic period over 9,000 years ago, people had discovered how to extract oil from flax, olives, sesame seeds and the castor plant. For those interested in the continuity of plant use through the ages, a herb garden based on a particular era can be immensely rewarding, especially if you plan it in a style to match the period. Here are some ideas to start you off.

A ROMAN COOK'S HERB GARDEN
A translation from a recipe book written by the Roman epicure, Apicius, in the first century AD gives an insight into the fascinating combinations of herbs used in Roman cuisine. For example, a recipe for a sauce includes a mixture of cumin, celery seed, thyme, savory, mint and pine kernels.

A Roman-style herb garden would suit a sunny courtyard filled with terracotta pots, formal raised beds, a vine-clad pergola and a suitable statue.

Some of the herbs used in Roman cooking are:
alecost, anise, basil, bay, capers, caraway, catmint, celery seed, coriander, cumin, dill, elecampane, garlic, hyssop, mustard, myrtle, oregano, parsley, pennyroyal, pepper, rue, safflower, saffron, salad rocket, savory, Welsh onion and wormwood.

A MONASTIC HERB GARDEN FOR LIQUEURS
In their commitment to self-sufficiency, monks produced a range of spirit-based drinks flavoured by a sweetened infusion or a distillation of herbs. In the past, these liqueurs, called variously balms, cremes and elixirs, were used as medicines, tonics and love potions. Their digestive properties make liqueurs popular after-dinner drinks today.

The monks' recipes have always been guarded vigorously: Benedictine, first produced in 1510, is one of the most secret along with Chartreuse, created in 1607. However, any of the following herbs can add good flavour to spirits:
angelica, anise, balm, caraway, coriander, elecampane, fennel, hyssop, mint, speedwell, sweet cicely, sweet flag root, sweet woodruff, tansy, thyme, violets and wormwood.

A MEDICINAL HERB GARDEN
Hundreds of plants have been used medicinally in different cultures throughout history. Some are now considered highly poisonous, while new research is confirming the powerful healing properties of others. Apart from their many and ancient applications, medicinal herbs are frequently extremely decorative, striking plants, which add enormous interest to a garden regardless of whether you use them yourself.

A traditional idea is to plant the herbs out in beds according to the ailments they treat, as in the infirmary gardens of medieval monasteries. You could have a bed of herbs for coughs, colds and sore throats; a bed for herbs to help insomnia; a bed for herbs that aid digestion; and one for tonic herbs. When you have a choice of herbs, you can quickly see which are ready for picking. Consult the chapter about herbal medicine (pp. 238–250) before attempting any remedies, or just grow the herbs for show. Include a seat as sitting out in a herb garden is an excellent convalescent activity.

A bed of medicinal herbs forms an attractive corner.

AN ASTROLOGICAL HERB GARDEN
Throughout history, the rhythms of nature have intrigued mankind to the degree that various observers have developed different systems of classification according to the movements of the moon and the stars. In his herbal of 1645, Culpeper attributed each herb to a ruling heavenly body and considered it effective to treat people and diseases of the same zodiacal sign. A suitable plan for an astrological garden would have two interlocking triangles arranged to make a six-pointed star enclosed in a circle. The three points of any triangle could link signs of the same element.

HERBS AND STAR SIGNS
Aquarius elderberry, fumitory, mullein
Pisces lungwort, meadowsweet, rosehip
Aries cowslip, garlic, hops, mustard, rosemary
Taurus coltsfoot, lovage, mints, thyme
Gemini caraway, dill, lavender, parsley, vervain
Cancer agrimony, balm, daisies, hyssop, jasmine
Leo bay, borage, chamomile, marigold, poppy, rue
Virgo fennel, savory, southernwood, valerian
Libra pennyroyal, primrose, violets, yarrow
Scorpio basil, tarragon, wormwood
Sagittarius feverfew, houseleek, mallow, sage
Capricorn comfrey, sorrel, Solomon's seal

NORTH AMERICAN INDIAN HERBS

Research indicates that the Indian tribes of North America have used over 600 native plants in food, medications and decorations. Plants used by the Northern Cree of my native Alberta include sweet gale (to dye porcupine quills), horsetail (to polish arrow heads), bearberry (leaves were smoked and berries were used in necklaces and rattles), lupin (leaves used in incense), wild mint (used to flavour dried meat and take the scent of humans from animal traps), sphagnum moss (made disposable nappies) and wild rose (flowers and fruits used in food and medications). These would all be suitable plants for a woodland or wild flower garden area.

LITERARY HERB GARDENS

The Bible and the works of Chaucer and Shakespeare are rich in references to herbs. Shakespeare in particular wrote with knowledgeable delight of over 80 herbs and wild flowers. Clearly he was familiar with their usage and their symbolic associations. A design for a Shakespeare garden should follow the formal Elizabethan style, with clipped knots of evergreen shrubs and a fairy bower planted with fragrant, pretty herbs. The following plants are all mentioned in at least one of Shakespeare's plays and provide an interesting and colourful selection:

balm, bay, borage, box, clover, columbine, cowslip, daffodil, daisies, fumitory, harebell, lady's smock, larkspur, lavender, mustard, myrtle, narcissus, ox-eye daisies, oxslips, pansy, pinks, poppies, primrose, musk rose and sweetbrier roses, rosemary, rue, salad burnet, strawberry, thyme, violet, winter savory, woodbine, wormwood and yarrow.

A circular bed featuring an ornamental font surrounded by an aromatic hedge in the Shakespeare section of Washington Cathedral's herb garden.

A WITCH'S HERB GARDEN

Witchcraft is a subject that fascinates many people, and fortunately we live in an age when we can look with light-hearted curiosity at the uses made of some of the more potent and poisonous plants in the past. The fact that up to six million women have been murdered in witch hunts through the ages is a brutal scar in the history of man and the Church's struggle to maintain power.

Just as there were thought to be good and bad witches, the herbs they used were also considered as offensive and defensive. The nine Anglo-Saxon sacred herbs (chamomile, chervil, crab apple, fennel, mugwort, nettle, plantain, sainfoin, watercress) were believed to repel evil attacks. Angelica was considered the sovereign remedy against enchantments and potions. Clovers, whether three-leafed or four-leafed, were thought to have protective powers, even to the degree of releasing people from military service. Dill, garlic, houseleek and mugwort were used to protect people from spells, the devil and lightning.

A GARDEN FOR HONEY BEES

For maximum nectar production and pollination, a herb garden for bees should be in full sun and have herbs planted in groups of five or more. Erect a trellis, or some form of windbreak, if the site is not sheltered or bees will be buffeted by the wind. A hedge of holly and ivy acts as an effective windbreak and supplies nectar flowers in both spring and autumn. Clovers, lime and fruit trees, oil-seed rape, sainfoin, mustard, charlock, willow herb and dandelion are the most important nectar plants for bees. Select herbs that will provide nectar and pollen for the longest period. The following plants would supply nectar almost all year round and are listed in order of flowering:

winter aconite, crocus, lamiums, forget-me-not, rosemary, catmint, Jacob's ladder, borage, melilot, summer and winter savory, thymes, viper's bugloss, catnip, alliums, chamomile, alkanet, anise, hyssop, chicory, flax, sage, smallage, fennel, poppies, safflower, teasel, valerian, verbena, woad, basil, calendula, horehound, musk mallow, marjorams, verbascum, golden rod, mints, sunflower.

Although a bee skep is a traditional ornament in a herb garden, it is unrealistic to keep working hives within the garden boundary: bees ignore plants within a radius of approximately 50 ft (15 m) from the hive as this area may be contaminated by the bees' own cleansing flights.

A MEDITATION GARDEN

The next herb garden I would like to make is one designed for contemplation. Any private herb garden is a suitable place, but I wish to design one that will focus the mind on specific ideas. It would take the form of an eight-pointed star or an eight-sided figure with its entrance forming one side. Each of the remaining seven sections would encapsulate a different idea: a day of the week; a colour of the spectrum and perhaps a type of fragrance. The central area would be covered to make a dry sanctuary.

HERBAL
INDEX

Inspired by the herbals of John Gerard and
Nicholas Culpeper, published over 300 years ago,
the following pages form a contemporary guide
to over 100 of today's most useful, interesting
and easy-to-grow herbs.
Herbs are listed alphabetically by their botanical
names. Any that have been reclassified recently
include the alternative (in brackets). The family
name is supplied in italic after the common name.
Each herb has been photographed and
described in detail to facilitate identification.
When a number of species or varieties exists, a
selection illustrates the range available.
Details are provided of each herb's lifespan,
height and growing conditions. Botanical terms
have been kept to a minimum throughout; those
that are used are explained in the glossary on p. 279.
There is also a wealth of historical and practical
information about each herb: methods of
cultivation, harvesting and preserving, and
suggestions for usage. To follow up these ideas
consult the later chapters and the index.
Four feature sections show and describe plants
less often considered as herbs. These are backed
up by A Catalogue of Herbs on pp. 271–78.
Note: Read pp. 238–250 before making any
medicinal preparations. If you are uncertain of a
plant, do not use it. Never take anything in excess,
and consult a qualified practitioner
whenever you have any doubts.

A colourful selection of herbs including mints, marjorams and thymes.

Achillea millefolium

Yarrow/Milfoil Compositae

This unassuming plant conceals great powers. One small leaf will
speed decomposition of a wheelbarrow full of raw compost;
yarrow's root secretions will activate the disease resistance of nearby
plants; and it intensifies the medicinal actions of other herbs.
Yarrow is also a potent healer. The name *Achillea* may stem from the
battle of Troy, when Achilles healed many of his warriors after
being instructed in yarrow's ability to staunch blood flow.

Long considered sacred, yarrow stems were used by the Druids to
divine seasonal weather in Europe, while in China yarrow stems
were used to foretell the future with the assistance of the I *Ching* (the
Book of Changes or Yarrow Stalk Oracle).

Seed
Small, grey-brown, flat and
tear-shaped.

Dried leaves
These exude a mild sage-like
flavour for use as a medicinal
and cosmetic tea.

Flower
Small, dull white, sometimes pink,
flattish clusters with pungent
scent appear from
summer to
autumn.

Dried stems
50 straight stems
of even length are
"thrown" by
masters of the I
Ching before
consulting this
oriental ancient
guide to the
future.

Stem
Hollow, ridged,
branching near
top, and green.

Leaf
Narrow, aromatic,
feathery, deeply cut and
dark greyish-green; rich in
vitamins and minerals.

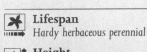

Lifespan
Hardy herbaceous perennial

Height
1–3 ft (30 cm–1 m)

CULTIVATION
Site Sunny. Tolerates light shade.
Soil Moderately rich and moist.
Propagating Sow or divide invasive
roots in spring or autumn.
Growing Thin or transplant to 12 in
(30 cm) apart. Deadhead for second
blooming. Yarrow is not suitable for
growing indoors.
Harvesting Gather leaves and
flowers in late summer.
Preserving Dry leaves and flowers.

USES
Decorative
● *Flower* Display dried heads.

Culinary
● *Leaf* Finely chop slightly bitter,
peppery young leaves into salads
and soft cheese dips. Use to garnish.

Household
● *Whole plant* Helps nearby plants to
resist disease and deepens their
fragrance and flavour. Infuse
to make a copper fertilizer.
● *Leaf* Speed decomposition by
adding one small finely chopped
fresh leaf to each wheelbarrow-load
of compost.

Cosmetic
● *Flower* Infuse fresh flowers for a
facial steam and tonic lotion. Use
the infusion as a basis for a face pack
for greasy skin or in a relaxing bath.
● *Leaf* Press fresh leaves onto a
shaving cut.

Medicinal
● *Leaf* Chew fresh leaf to aid
toothache. Infuse as a tea for
digestive problems, and to regulate
menstrual flow, induce perspiration,
cleanse the system and cure a cold.
Make a decoction for wounds,
chapped skin and rashes. Use as a
mouthwash for inflamed gums.

Note: *Extended use of yarrow leaves may
make the skin sensitive to light.*

Alchemilla vulgaris

Lady's mantle/Dewcup Rosaceae

From "little magical one", the Arab *alkemelych* (alchemy), comes *Alchemilla*, so-called because of this herb's healing reputation and the dew that collects in each enfolding leaf. The crystal drops of dew have long inspired poets and alchemists and were part of many mystic potions. So powerful a herb was acquired by the Christian Church, which named it "Our Lady's mantle". Its protective role was reflected in its nickname, "a woman's best friend", as it may regulate periods, ease the menopause and clear inflammations of the female organs. One German herbalist claims prolonged use of lady's mantle tea could cut gynaecological operations by one-third. *A. vulgaris* is an aggregate name for about 21 subspecies which seem to have similar medicinal properties.

Dried leaves
These make a cosmetic astringent and staunch bleeding.

Lifespan Hardy herbaceous perennial

Height 6–20 in (15–50 cm)

Flower
Loose clusters of small greenish-yellow flowers appear in summer.

A. alpina
Alpine lady's mantle
Small, yellow-green clusters borne in late summer and silver-edged leaves with white, silky undersides. Ht: 6 in (15 cm).

Leaf
Soft, blue-green and almost circular with seven to 11 rounded, toothed lobes joined by deep folds.

Stem
Hairy, slightly flattened, ridged, branching and green; usually bends outwards as flowers develop.

Young plant
A mass of fibrous roots develop into a short, dark rhizome; leaf stalks emerge directly from base.

CULTIVATION
Site Full sun or partial shade.
Soil Rich, moist, alkaline loam.
Propagating Sow or divide lady's mantle in spring or autumn.
Growing Thin or transplant to 2 ft (60 cm) apart. Small plants can be grown indoors.
Harvesting Select large leaves as needed. They are best during flowering period.
Preserving Dry leaves.

USES
Decorative
● *Whole plant* Attractive in hanging baskets.
● *Flowers and leaves* Add to posies.

Culinary
● *Leaf* Tear young leaves, with their mildly bitter taste, into small pieces and toss in herb salads.

Household
● *Leaf* Boil for a green wool dye.

Cosmetic
● *Leaf* Infuse dried leaves as an astringent and as a facial steam for acne. Apply infusion in a cold compress for inflamed eyes and as a tonic to reduce large pores and acne. Use in creams to soften dry rough skin. To lighten freckles, rinse with juice extracted from leaves.

Medicinal
● *Whole plant (Green parts only)* Infused as a tea to drink during pregnancy and for 10 days after giving birth to help womb contract, and to regulate monthly cycle. After the age of 40, drink infusion for 10 days each month to relieve menopausal discomfort. Also used as a mouth rinse after tooth extraction and for diarrhoea.
● *Leaf* Decoct for a compress for healing wounds and reducing inflammation. *A. alpina* has same constituents; may be more powerful.

39

Allium species
Alliums Liliaceae

One of the most popular and widespread culinary flavourings is the onion family. The value of these alliums is reflected in the Latin *unio*, "one large pearl", and the Chinese name "jewel among vegetables". Alliums also have marvellous health-giving properties. The stronger the smell, the more effective their healing powers. Pyramid builders and Roman soldiers on long marches were fed on a daily ration of garlic, whose power even extended to protection from black magic, as vampire films continue to remind us. Today, garlic is a major flavouring in many cuisines.

Chives were recorded 4,000 years ago in China and appreciated there by the traveller Marco Polo. He reported their culinary virtues to the West, where they rapidly became indispensable. Chinese chives have a garlic flavour, and the Chinese grow several forms: one for its leaves; one, 'Tenderpole', for its long-stemmed flower buds – good stir fried or as a garnish; and one to blanch (using clay pots or straw "tents" to produce yellow, sweetly flavoured bundles). These blanched chives are featured in a popular meal available on trains and street stalls in China: little finger-length pieces are served with rice and slivers of pork, often in prepacked containers with chopsticks.

Another important allium species in China and Japan is the Welsh onion (Welsh meaning "foreign"), which provides a continuous supply of bunching onions and leaves throughout the year.

A. tuberosum
Chinese chives
White, starry, sweet-scented flowers late summer, flat green leaves, mild garlic flavour and tuberous root.

A. fistulosum
Welsh onion
White flowers in summer and strong-flavoured evergreen leaves.

Seed
Black, faceted and tear-shaped, fractionally larger than a chive seed.

Seed
Black, faceted and tear-shaped, $\frac{1}{8}$ in (3 mm) long, with mild onion flavour.

Dried leaves
Require low temperature drying to retain colour; best suited to cooked recipes.

Leaves
Variable grass (leaf) sizes depend on plant's age, soil fertility and seed source.

A. schoenoprasum
Chives
Cylindrical leaves and a mild onion flavour. Globular mauve flowers midsummer.

Lifespan
Hardy perennials

Height
8 in–3 ft (20 cm–1 m)

A. cepa
Everlasting onion
"Ever-ready"
perennial producing
sharp-flavoured
"spring" onions.
Rarely flowers.

A.c. var. proliferum
**Tree onion/
Egyptian onion**
Small pickling
onions grow on stem
tips. May need
staking. Ht: 3 ft
(1 m).

A. sativum
Garlic
White flowers and
flat solid leaves with
culinary bulb.

*A.
scordoprasum*
**Rocambole/
Giant garlic**
Mild garlic-
flavoured bulb.
Mauve flowers
develop edible
aerial bulbs.

Garlic cloves
Highly flavoured
segments of a bulb.

A bed of flowering chives.

CULTIVATION

Site Sunny; tolerates partial shade.
Soil Rich, moist and well drained; tolerates poorer soil.
Propagating Take offsets or divide bulb in autumn or spring; plant garlic cloves 1½ in (4 cm) deep; sow seed in spring (not available for everlasting and tree onion).
Growing Transplant or thin to 9 in (23 cm) apart; garlic to 6 in (15 cm) apart. Water in dry spells and enrich soil annually (or monthly, when cutting chives). Remove flowers for better flavour. Divide and replant clumps every 3–4 years. Pot up in autumn for indoor supply. Can be grown indoors.
Harvesting (Chives) Cut leaves, leaving 2 in (5 cm) for regrowth. Pick flowers as they open. (Garlic) Dig bulbs in late summer; handle gently to avoid bruising.
Preserving Refrigerate chive leaves in a sealed plastic bag to retain crispness for 7 days, or freeze (in ice cubes, for convenience) or dry them. Dry flowers and bulbs. Make garlic oil, and garlic and chive vinegars.

USES

Decorative
● *Whole plant* (Tree onion) Cultivate as a novelty plant.

Culinary
● *Flower* (Chives) Sprinkle florets on salads.
● *Leaf* (Chives) Eat in salads, sandwiches and soups and as a garnish. Make butter or cream cheese (allow 1 hour for flavour to infuse). To reconstitute dried chives, moisten with salad dressing or lemon juice.
● *Bulb* (Garlic) Use sparingly; rub clove around salad bowl or fondue dish to improve flavours. Chew parsley or cardamom seed to counteract garlic breath. (Tree, everlasting and Welsh onion) Pickle in wine vinegar.

Household
● *Whole plant* (Chives) Grow as deterrent for aphids, apple scab and mildew. (Garlic) Plant under peach trees to control leafcurl and near roses to enhance scent.
● *Leaf* (Chives) Infuse as a spray for aphids, apple scab and mildew. (Garlic) Spray potato blight with a freshly made infusion.

Medicinal
● *Whole plant* All alliums contain some iron and vitamins and are a mild antibiotic. (Chives) Sprinkle on food to stimulate appetite and promote digestion. Take as a mild laxative. (Garlic) Use as an antibiotic, to cleanse blood, reduce blood pressure and clear catarrh; take as protection against common colds, worms, dysentery and typhoid.

Aloe vera (A. barbadensis)

Aloe vera Liliaceae

One of Cleopatra's secret beauty ingredients was reputed to be aloe vera, and it is still chosen by contemporary cosmetic firms for face and hand creams, suntan lotions and shampoos. Aloe vera has also attracted the interest of many governments for its ability to heal radiation burns, and the US government is said to be stockpiling the herb for use in the event of a nuclear disaster. It is the fresh sap from this remarkable herb that can heal skin and soothe burns; old sap, however, deteriorates rapidly when isolated.

A beautiful violet dye is produced from aloe plants native to the island of Socotra in the Indian Ocean, and it was thought to be the desire for this product that motivated Alexander the Great to conquer this island in the fourth century BC. Some 1,400 years later, Muslim traders reported that the island was still the only source of the herb, although it is now known to grow in Africa, China, India and Central America. There are about 350 aloe species.

Leaf
Long, very fleshy, tapering, pointed, pale green blades, often with spiny teeth along margins.

Split leaves
Inside each leaf is a clear gelatinous sap, which has an immediate soothing effect on burns and forms a clear protective seal, allowing healing to take place rapidly.

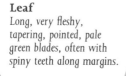

Plant base
Stemless base, which eventually produces a flowering stem, with spikes of narrow, trumpet-shaped, yellow or orange flowers, and offshoots for propagation.

Root
Strong, light brown and fibrous.

 Lifespan
Tender evergreen perennial

 Height
12 in (30 cm)

CULTIVATION

Site Full sun or light shade in frost-free location.
Soil Gritty and well drained.
Propagating Sow in spring at 70 °F (21 °C). Remove offshoots in summer; then dry for 2 days before planting in 2 parts compost to 1 part sharp sand.
Growing Maintain 41 °F (5 °C) minimum. Aloe vera is an excellent indoor plant.
Harvesting Cut leaves as needed. Best from plants at least 2 years old.
Preserving No method known at present, although a product called Aloe Vera gel is available. This contains 99.9 percent aloe vera and is sold in a dark glass bottle with instructions to keep refrigerated.

USES

Decorative
● *Whole plant* (*A. variegata*) Use as an ornamental pot plant.

Household
● *Leaf* Socotrine aloes is prepared from *Aloe perryi* on the island of Socotra and gives a rich violet dye.

Cosmetic
● *Leaf* Use the leaf sap to make a soothing and healing moisturizing cream, especially good for dry skin. Mix into shampoos to help dry or itchy scalp. Add to suntan lotions for its cooling and healing effect.

Medicinal
● *Leaf* Crush sap from fresh leaves or slice them and apply as a poultice for chapped skin, dermatitis, eczema, and burns. For small burns, break off a leaf segment and apply its sap to the burn. For large burns, split and open out a leaf; place sap against damaged skin and lightly bandage in place. Renew as necessary.

Note: *Always seek medical attention for serious burns.*

Aloysia triphylla (Lippia citriodora)

Lemon verbena *Verbenaceae*

Lemon verbena's immediate attraction lies in its leaves, which have a clean, sharp, lemony fragrance that gives unexpected pleasure with each contact. Despite such an appeal, there is remarkably little history and legend attached to this plant, which is a native of South America. Lemon verbena was, however, brought to Europe in the seventeenth century by the Spanish, who grew it for its perfume oil. Although it is not hardy, a straw-covered pruned plant with deep roots should survive some frost. New growth can appear very late, so never discard a plant until late summer.

Seed
Small, dark brown and tear-shaped.

Dried leaves
Retain their strong fresh lemon scent for 2–3 years; excellent in potpourri and sachets.

Lifespan
Half-hardy shrub

Height
2–4 ft (60cm–1.2 m) in temperate climates; to 15 ft (4.5 m) in hot climates.

Flower
Tiny, white and pale purple, loose clusters borne at top of stem in late summer.

Young plant

Leaf
Long, pointed, rough-textured with prominent central vein and strong lemony scent; arranged on stem in threes.

Stem
Ridged, round and green; red and woody in second season.

CULTIVATION
Site Full sun. Needs shelter in almost frost-free position.
Soil Light, well drained and alkaline. Poor soil produces stronger plants able to survive cold winters.
Propagating Sow in spring. Take softwood cuttings in late spring.
Growing Thin or transplant to 3 ft (1 m) apart. Prune drooping branches to encourage new growth. Grow lemon verbena indoors in winter, though it may drop its leaves. Prune and spray with warm water in spring to revive plant.
Harvesting Pick leaves anytime: best when flowers begin to bloom.
Preserving Dry leaves. Use fresh leaves to flavour oil and vinegar.

USES
Culinary
● **Leaf** Infuse as herb tea. Finely chop young leaves for drinks, fruit puddings, confectionery, apple jelly, cakes and homemade ice cream. Infuse in finger bowls.

Cosmetic
● **Leaf** Macerate in almond oil for a massage; for interesting blends, add lavender or rosemary. Use this oil in homemade lotions and creams. To reduce puffiness around eyes, make an infusion and allow to cool. Soak cotton wool in the infusion and place over eyes for 15 minutes. Infuse and add to a bath. Make floral vinegar to soften and freshen skin.

Aromatic
● **Leaf** Use in potpourri, linen sachets, sofa sacks and herb pillows and to scent ink and paper. Infuse in melted candle wax at 180 °F (82 °C) for 45 minutes to scent candles. Use its essential oil in perfumes and to sprinkle over potpourri.

Medicinal
● **Leaf** Infuse as a mildly sedative tea to soothe bronchial and nasal congestion, to reduce indigestion, flatulence, stomach cramps, nausea and palpitations.

Note: Long-term use of large amounts of leaf may cause stomach irritations.

Althaea officinalis

Marsh mallow Malvaceae

This is indeed the original source of the confectionery of this name. Marsh mallow's powdered root contains a mucilage that thickens in water and was heated with sugar to create a soothing sweet paste. However, today's spongy cubes share only sugar in common with the original recipe.

Marsh mallow is one of over 1,000 species in the *Malvaceae* family, all of which contain a healing mucilage, and its genus name, *Althaea*, is from the Greek *altho*, to cure. Introduced from China, marsh mallows were eaten by the Egyptians and Syrians, and mentioned by Pythagoras, Plato and Virgil. The plant was enjoyed by the Romans in barley soup and in a stuffing for suckling pig, while classical herbalists praised its gentle laxative properties.

Seed
Light brown and disc-shaped, slotted upright in a ring called a "cheese".

Flower
Pink or white blooms, 1½ in (4 cm) across, with purple stamens, borne in late summer to early autumn.

Dried leaves
These contain mucilage and can be infused and drunk for internal inflammation or used externally as an eye compress.

Leaf
Large, velvety, toothed, tear-shaped and grey-green, containing mucilage.

Lifespan
Hardy herbaceous perennial

Height
6 ft (2 m)

Stem
Velvety, round and light green.

Dried root
Contains a highly valued thickening and softening mucilage.

Root
Thick, long, yellow-brown and tapering, with white fibrous flesh. To release mucilage, steep second- or subsequent-year roots in cold water for 8 hours.

CULTIVATION
Site Full sun.
Soil Moist, moderate fertility.
Propagating Sow in spring. Divide base or try stem cuttings in spring.
Growing Thin or transplant to 1 ft (30 cm) apart; in second season, thin again to 2 ft (60 cm) apart. Not suitable for growing indoors.
Harvesting Collect seeds when ripe. Pick leaves as required and dig up roots in autumn.
Preserving Dry seeds and leaves. Scrape and dry roots or make into syrup (see p. 242).

USES
Decorative
● **Leaf** Add to posies.

Culinary
● **Seed** Eat fresh "cheeses" alone or sprinkled like nuts onto salads.
● **Flower** Toss on salads.
● **Leaf** Mix young leaves into salads. Add to oil and vinegar. Steam and serve as a vegetable.
● **Root** Boil to soften, then fry.

Cosmetic
● **Leaf and root** Boil leaves or use the liquid from steeped root, warmed or cold, as a soothing mucilage for dry hands, sunburn and dry hair, and in facial steams, masks and lotions. Make into an eye compress to soften skin around eyes.

Medicinal
● **Root** Infuse as a tea for coughs, diarrhoea and insomnia. Add to ointment for burns. Put in a poultice for inflammations. Used in Persia to reduce inflammation in teething babies and to stimulate growth of late teeth. Boil root, skim off the starchy by-product on the water surface and use as a gentle soap for problem skins, including psoriasis. Marsh mallow root powder has been used as a binding agent in pill manufacture.

Anethum graveolens

Dill Umbelliferae

"Woe unto you, scribes and Pharisees, hypocrites! for ye pay tithe of mint and dill and cumin, and have omitted the weightier matters of the law" (*Matthew* 23 v. 23). This biblical reference shows that herbs had a high and sufficiently stable value to be used as tax payment. Well before that, the ancient Egyptians had recorded dill as a soothing medicine, and the Greeks knew "dill stayeth the hickets" (hiccups). During the Middle Ages, it was one of St John's Eve herbs to be prized as protection against witchcraft. Magicians used dill in their spells, while lesser mortals infused it in wine to enhance passion. Early settlers took dill to North America, where it became known as "meetin' seed", because children were given dill seed to chew during long sermons.

Seed
Aromatic, flattish, oval, with brown, ribbed centre and buff wings; contains silicic acid, calcium, phosphorus and other valuable mineral salts.

Dried leaves
These retain only a little flavour so use generously when cooking and add at the last minute.

Flower
Tiny, highly aromatic, yellow blooms, arranged in flat clusters 8 in (20 cm) across, appear in midsummer.

Leaf
Aromatic, feathery, thread-like and blue-green.

Stem
Hollow, ridged, branching and blue-green; usually one main stem per plant.

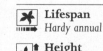

Lifespan
Hardy annual

Height
2–5 ft (60 cm–1.5 m)

CULTIVATION

Site Full sun. Protect from wind.
Soil Rich and well drained.
Propagating Sow in situ from spring until midsummer. Do not plant near fennel, as they cross-pollinate and flavours muddle. Self-seeds. Seeds viable for 3–10 years.
Growing Thin to 9–12 in (23–30 cm) apart. Can be grown indoors.
Harvesting Gather leaves when young. Pick flowering tops just as fruits begin to form. To collect seed, after flowering head turns brown, hang the whole plant over a cloth.
Preserving Dry or freeze leaves. Dry ripe seed. Make dill vinegar with flowering heads or seed.

USES

Culinary
● *Seed* Use whole or ground in soups, fish dishes, pickles, cabbage, apple pies, dill butter, cakes and breads (see p. 164). Serve seed as a digestive at the end of a rich meal.
● *Flowering top* Add one flower head per jar to pickled gherkins, cucumbers and cauliflowers (see p. 188) for a flavour stronger than dill leaves but fresher than seeds.
● *Leaf* Add finely chopped to soups, potato salads, cream cheese, eggs, salmon and grilled meats, and use as a garnish. Boil with new potatoes.

Cosmetic
● *Seed* Crush and infuse as a nail-strengthening bath. Chew to sweeten breath.

Medicinal
● *Seed* Use in a salt-free diet as it is rich in mineral salts. Make dill water for indigestion, flatulence, hiccups, stomach cramps, insomnia and colic: infuse $\frac{1}{2}$ oz (13 g) bruised seeds in 1 cup (225 ml) boiling water. Strain. Take 1 tbsp (15 ml) per adult or 1 tsp (5 ml) for babies. Repeat as needed. Infuse as a tea to stimulate milk of nursing mothers.

Angelica archangelica

Angelica Umbelliferae

An ancient and highly aromatic plant, angelica is praised in the folklore of northern European countries as a panacea for all ills. Its name is thought to derive from the fact that, in the old calendar, it usually came into bloom around the feast day of the Archangel Michael, the Great Defender, who appeared in a vision to explain its protective powers against evil.

Angelica is a moisture-loving native of damp meadows and river banks. Its large leaves have a tropical appearance and can give the garden a lush atmosphere.

Seed
Buff, $\frac{1}{4}$in (6 mm) long, produced in profusion, ripening late summer of third year.

Dried leaves
These are indispensable for herb teas.

Crystallized stem
Choose fresh, young, green stems of pencil thickness for crystallizing.

Leaf
Large, glossy, divided and bright green.

Dried root
Angelica root has the longest lasting aroma of any part of the plant.

Stem
Thick, hollow and ridged.

Lifespan
Three-year hardy herbaceous "biennial" (extendable to four years if emerging flower spikes are removed)

Height
3–8 ft (1–2.5 m)

Root
Thick, ridged, aromatic taproot, usually with two or three major side roots.

CULTIVATION
Site Light shade. Benefits from a mulch when in full sun.
Soil Deep and moist.
Propagating Allow plants to self-seed or sow fresh in early autumn. Take care when buying angelica seed; it loses most of its viability within three months.
Growing Seedlings should be transplanted in spring before the taproot becomes established. Leave a square yard/metre between plants.
Harvesting Cut stems before midsummer for crystallizing. Harvest leaves before flowering. Collect ripe seed in late summer. Dig up root in autumn of first year.
Preserving Dry leaves and root. Crystallize stems.

USES
Decorative
● *Flower* Display dried seed heads for a striking winter decoration.
● *Leaf* Long-stemmed leaves look attractive in a vase.

Culinary
● *Seed* Mix with stems and use to flavour drinks including gin, vermouth and Chartreuse.
● *Leaf* Stew with acidic fruits to reduce sugar requirement. Serve fresh chopped leaves mixed with mint and mayonnaise (see p. 182).
● *Stem* Crystallize for decoration.

Cosmetic
● *Leaf* Use for a relaxing bath.

Aromatic
● *Seed* Burn in a chafing pan to perfume a room.
● *Leaf* Use in potpourri.
● *Root* In spring, make an incision at the crown to yield an aromatic gum. Use as a fixative in potpourri.

Medicinal
● *Leaf* Make tea from fresh or dried leaves as a tonic for colds and to reduce flatulence. Crushed leaves freshen the air in a car and help prevent travel sickness.

Anthriscus cerefolium

Chervil *Umbelliferae*

In the past, the modest chervil has often been overlooked. It now enjoys increasing popularity as people discover its special delicate parsley-like flavour with a hint of myrrh. It is one of the traditional *fines herbes*, indispensable in French cuisine, and is a fresh green asset to any meal.

A graceful clump of chervil plants will retain more flavour in its feathery foliage if grown in light shade. Viewed in a herb garden by moonlight, the clusters of tiny white flowers are like fairy dust, during spring and late summer.

Flower
Tiny white clusters borne from late summer, or in late spring from overwintered seedlings.

Seed
Dark, narrow, $\frac{1}{4}$ in (6 mm) long, enclosed five in a case until ripe.

Dried leaves
Drying chervil reduces its flavour; if possible, aim for a continuous fresh supply.

Stem
Slender, hollow, slightly ridged and branching.

Lifespan
Hardy annual

Height
10–15 in (25–38 cm)

Leaf
Lacy, fern-like and light green, with a pale magenta blush in late summer.

CULTIVATION

Site Light shade in summer (ideally plant under a deciduous plant so autumn seedlings can enjoy full winter sun). In hot conditions, it quickly runs to seed.

Soil Light and well drained.

Propagating Ripe seed germinates quickly and can be used six to eight weeks after gathering. For a regular supply, sow monthly except in winter. Scatter on soil, press in lightly. Left to self-seed, chervil provides one early and one late summer crop.

Growing Thin seedlings to 6–9 in (15–23 cm) apart; do not transplant. Although chervil is hardy, some cloche protection is needed to ensure leaves in winter. Chervil makes a good indoor plant, given light shade and humidity.

Harvesting Gather leaves before flowering, once the plant reaches a height of 4 in (10 cm).

Preserving Freeze or dry leaves. Also good added to vinegar.

USES

Culinary

● **Leaf** Use generously in salads, soups, sauces, vegetables, chicken, white fish and egg dishes. Add chervil freshly chopped near the end of cooking to avoid flavour loss. In small quantities, it enhances the flavour of other herbs.

● **Stem** Chop and use raw in salads. Cook in soups and casseroles.

Cosmetic

● **Leaf** Use in an infusion or face mask to cleanse skin, maintain suppleness and discourage wrinkles.

Medicinal

● **Leaf** Eat raw for additional vitamin C, carotene, iron and magnesium. Infuse in tea to stimulate digestion and alleviate circulation disorders, liver complaints and chronic catarrh. Chervil is traditionally taken for its restorative qualities after Lent on Maundy Thursday.

Apium graveolens

Smallage/Wild celery Umbelliferae

Smallage was used to crown the victors of the Greek Nemean games, held in honour of Zeus. The son of the Nemean king was subsequently killed by a snake concealed in smallage, and so it was then carried as a funeral wreath. The Greeks also used this herb medicinally, and the Romans exploited its culinary properties: stems were puréed with pepper, lovage, oregano, onion and wine; leaves were used with dates and pine kernels as a stuffing for suckling pig. Much later, in the nineteenth century, the American Shakers grew smallage for their nostrums and other medicinal compounds.

Flower
Small, greenish-cream clusters produced in late summer of second year.

Seed
Tiny, brown, oval and aromatic.

Dried leaves
These have a slightly stronger aromatic flavour than cultivated celery and are useful in soups, stocks, stuffings and stews.

Leaf
Fan of aromatic, loosely toothed, shiny light green leaflets, forming upright rosette in first year; darker green on rising stem in second season.

✳ Lifespan
Hardy biennial

✳ Height
1–3 ft (30 cm–1 m)

Stem
Faceted, ridged, branching and green; flowering stem grows in second season.

CULTIVATION
Site Sunny with midday shade. Shelter from strong winds.
Soil Rich, moist and well drained.
Propagating Sow under heat in early spring or outdoors in late spring. Germination is slow.
Growing Transplant or thin to 16 in (40 cm) apart. Smallage is not suitable for growing indoors.
Harvesting Pick leaves in late summer or as needed. Collect seeds when ripe.
Preserving Dry seed. Dry or freeze leaves or infuse in vinegar.

USES
Culinary
● *Seed* Grind as an ingredient of celery salt. Add to soups, curries, casseroles and pickles. Use as a salt-substitute in a salt-free diet.
● *Leaf* Chop small amounts into salads, cream cheese, poultry stuffings, and use as a garnish. Add a handful of finely chopped leaves to milk for poaching fish and shellfish. Stir into thick vegetable soups and stews during last 3 minutes of cooking to retain flavour and nutritive value.

Medicinal
● *Seed* Decoct as a sedative to calm nerves, promote restfulness, ease flatulence and some kidney disorders.
● *Leaf* Rich in vitamins, mineral salts and other active ingredients of nutritive value. Smallage is reported to contain a hormone which has an effect similar to insulin, and is considered a useful seasoning for diabetics. Infuse as a tonic and appetizer and to ease indigestion and colic.
● *Leaf and stem* Extract juice and drink as a urine stimulant.

Armoracia rusticana

Horseradish Cruciferae

Originally, horseradish was cultivated chiefly as a medicinal herb. Now it is considered a flavouring herb. In the late sixteenth century, its culinary use was developed by the Germans and Danes in a fish sauce. Around 1640, this usage spread westwards to Britain, where horseradish sauce has since become strongly associated with roast beef. Its sharp pungency frequently has a dramatic effect and has been known to clear sinuses in one breath – the volatile flavouring oil is released by grating the root. The oil evaporates rapidly, so horseradish is not successful in cooked dishes.

Leaf
Large, elliptical, pointed, scallop-edged and bright green, with pungent aroma when bruised.

Dried leaves
These yield a yellow dye with a chrome mordant; may be used to dress skin wounds.

Stem
Thick, deeply ridged and round.

Root
Long, invasive and yellow with hot, pungent-tasting, white flesh. Fresh root contains calcium, sodium, magnesium and vitamin C, and has antibiotic qualities that are useful for preserving food and protecting the intestinal tract.

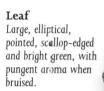

Lifespan
Hardy perennial

Height
2–3 ft (60 cm–1 m)

CULTIVATION
Site Open sunny position.
Soil Light, well-dug, rich and moist soil preferred.
Propagating Sow seed, divide roots or take root cuttings (thongs) in spring. Choose roots $\frac{1}{2}$ in (13 mm) thick. Cut into pieces 6 in (15 cm) long, and plant vertically, at a depth of 2 in (5 cm).
Growing Thin or transplant to 12 in (30 cm) apart. Do not grow indoors.
Harvesting Dig up roots as needed or in autumn. Pick young leaves.
Preserving Store roots in sand; or wash, grate or slice and dry; or immerse whole washed roots in white wine vinegar. Dry leaves.

USES
Culinary
● *Leaf* Add young leaves to salads.
● *Root* Make horseradish sauce to accompany roast beef, smoked or oily fish. Grate into coleslaw, dips, pickled beetroot, cream cheese, mayonnaise and avocado fillings.

Household
● *Whole plant* Grow near potatoes for more disease-resistant tubers.
● *Root* Infuse, dilute four times and spray apple trees against brown rot.
● *Leaf* Chop finely into dog food to dispel worms and improve body tone. Boil for a deep yellow dye.

Cosmetic
● *Root* Slice and infuse in milk for a lotion to improve skin clarity. Express juice, mix with white vinegar and use to lighten freckles.

Medicinal
● *Root* Include grated root in diet to stimulate digestion, eliminate mucus and waste fluids. Take as a syrup for bronchitis and coughs. Grate into a poultice and apply to chilblains, stiff muscles, sciatica and rheumatism.

Note: *Avoid continuous large doses when pregnant or suffering from kidney problems.*

Artemisia species

Artemisias Compositae

Artemisia was the sister and wife of the Greek/Persian King Mausolus and ruled after his death in 353 BC. In his honour she built a magnificent tomb called the Mausoleum, which was one of the Seven Wonders of the World. She was also a famous botanist and medical researcher, and this genus of 200, mostly aromatic plants was named in her honour.

The medicinal values of artemisias were discovered by people living in semi-arid and temperate regions where the plants are found. In the ancient Greek text of Dioscorides, wormwood is mentioned for its internal worm-expelling property. Indians from New Mexico to British Columbia use similar varieties to treat bronchitis and colds. The Chinese still use a leaf of wormwood rolled up in the nostril to stop nosebleeds. Many artemisias are also visually appealing. Their silver leaves are stunning when reflected in moonlight, and they also enhance any dried herb arrangement.

Mugwort, though less aromatic and attractive than other artemisias, features in the magical lore of Europe, Asia and China. In the pre-Christian "Lay of the Nine Herbs", the first incantation for protection is to mugwort, the "mother of herbs":

> Have in mind, Mugwort, what you made known,
> What you laid down, at the great denouncing.
> Una your name is, oldest of herbs,
> Of might against thirty, and against three,
> Of might against venom and the onflying,
> Of might against the vile She
> who fares through the land.

Leaf
Aromatic, deeply indented and grey-green, covered with fine silky hairs.

Seed
Tiny, taupe colour, tear-shaped; contained in slightly flattened, grey, cylindrical fruit.

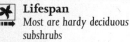

Dried leaves
These retain their aroma. Both leaves and flowering tops have medicinal and household uses.

Stem
Aromatic, downy, ridged and grey-green.

Leaf
Aromatic, thread-like, grey-green and semi-evergreen.

Dried leaves
Use as a sweet-scented insect repellent and in potpourri.

**A. abrotanum
Southernwood/
Old Man**
The sweetest perennial artemisia with its hint of lemon – evocative of childhood gardens.

Stem
Slightly ridged and green when young; smooth, woody and tan when mature.

Leaf
Indented and mid-green, with dense, cottony silver underside.

Stem
Slightly hairy, ridged, reddish and herbaceous.

**A. vulgaris
Mugwort**

✳ **Lifespan**	Most are hardy deciduous subshrubs
✳ **Height**	2–4 ft (60 cm–1.2 m)

**A. absinthium
Wormwood**
The most bitter herb except rue. 'Lambrooke Silver' has more silvery leaves; 'Faith Ravens' has leaves that are more divided.

OTHER SPECIES

A. pontica
Roman wormwood
Spreading rootstalk and strongly aromatic, feathery silver foliage. Used to flavour vermouth.

A. lanata
(A. pedemontana)
Tufted, 4 in (10 cm) high, mat-forming evergreen clumps with silky, finely cut, silver leaves.

A. arborescens
Tree artemisia
Half hardy, with finely cut, tufted, semi-evergreen silky foliage. Ht: 3½ ft (1.05 m).

A. campestris sp. borealis
(A. canadensis)
Delicate, silver, filament-like, semi-evergreen leaves with weak scent.

A. ludoviciana
'Silver King'
Silver king artemisia
Herbaceous; spreading rootstalk and willow-like, very silvery leaves.

A. lactiflora
White mugwort
Herbaceous form with plumes of fragrant cream flowers in late summer and deeply cut mid-green leaves, 6 in (15 cm) long. Ht: 5 ft (1.5 m).

A bed of tall, silver-green wormwood.

CULTIVATION

Site Full sun.
Soil Light, dry, well drained. However, *A. lactiflora* requires moist soil and will tolerate some shade.
Propagating Sow when available. Take semi-hardwood cuttings in late summer.
Growing Thin or transplant shrubby artemisias to 18 in–3 ft (45 cm–1 m) apart. Do not plant wormwood next to fennel, sage, caraway, anise and possibly other culinary and medicinal herbs as rain washes a growth-inhibiting toxin out of the leaves that affects nearby plants. For winter protection, prune all forms except southernwood in autumn. Prune southernwood in summer. Artemisias are not suitable for indoor culture.
Harvesting Pick flowering tops and leaves in mid- to late summer for medicinal use.
Preserving Dry leaves and flowering tops.

USES

Decorative
● **Leaf** (Southernwood) Plant for a neat hedge. (Wormwood) Grow for a fast temporary hedge. Pick all silver forms for bouquets, wreaths and tussie-mussies.

Culinary
● **Leaf** (Mugwort) Use in stuffings for roast goose.

Household
● **Leaf** Powder or infuse to make a moth repellent. Deter onion and carrot fly with branches laid between onion and carrot rows. When walked on, wormwood's pungent aroma masks carrot scent. Infuse to make a strong domestic disinfectant; mix a weaker infusion for an effective insecticide on older plants. Grow southernwood or wormwood near hen houses for protection against lice; near cabbages to deter cabbage butterfly, and near fruit trees to deter fruit tree moth. Hang leaves in a granary to dispel beetles.
● **Stem** Boil for a yellow dye.

Medicinal
● **Leaf** (Southernwood) Infuse as a tea for a tonic. (Mugwort) Dried leaves (moxa) are made into small cones for use in moxibustion (the Chinese practice of leaves smouldering on the skin to give deep penetrating heat) to soothe rheumatism. Use aromatic species for a disinfectant and antiseptic.

Artemisia dracunculus

Tarragon Compositae

To be connected with dragons is an honour worthy of this important culinary herb, its name tarragon deriving from the French *estragon* and the Latin *dracunculus*, a little dragon. The dragon connection may have come from tarragon's fiery tang or from its serpent-like roots. "Dragon" herbs were believed to cure the bites of venomous creatures, but tarragon's primary use today is culinary. It will also sweeten the breath, act as a soporific, and, if chewed before taking medicine, dull the taste, according to a thirteenth-century Arabian botanist, Ibnal Baithar. Two varieties of tarragon are available: French, which has the refined flavour indispensable to classic French cuisine but needs winter protection when growing; and Russian, which survives both colder and hotter climates but has a coarser flavour. French tarragon should be divided and replanted every third year to avoid deterioration, whereas the flavour of Russian tarragon improves the longer it grows in one place.

CULTIVATION

Site Sunny and sheltered.
Soil Rich, light and dry.
Propagating Divide roots in spring. Take stem cuttings in summer. (Russian tarragon) Sow in spring.
Growing Thin or transplant to 12–18 in (30–45 cm) apart. Cut back in autumn. Protect in winter with straw or similar mulch. Tarragon is suitable for growing indoors.
Harvesting Pick leaves anytime, but in late summer for main crop. If cutting branches, sever maximum of two-thirds of branch to allow for regrowth, unless it is the end of the growing season.
Preserving Freeze leaves or dry quickly at 80 °F (27 °C). Infuse leaves in oil or vinegar.

USES

Culinary

● *Leaf* Use sparingly for a warm, subtle, highly desirable flavour, which diffuses quickly through other ingredients (see p. 165). Tarragon is an important part of *fines herbes*, together with chervil and parsley. Use it to make tarragon vinegar and vinegar blends, for Béarnaise, tartar and hollandaise sauces. Add shredded leaf to avocado fillings, mayonnaise for fish dishes, salad dressings, light soups, tomatoes, omelettes and scrambled eggs. Make a herb butter for vegetables, steaks, chops and grilled fish. Rub tarragon onto roast chicken or mix with chicken stuffing. Add to preserves, pickles and mustards. Freeze in ice cubes for interesting flavour in cold drinks. (Russian tarragon) Used by Persians on grilled meat.

Medicinal

● *Leaf* Tarragon leaves are rich in iodine, mineral salts, vitamins A and C. Infuse as an appetite stimulant, digestive and general tonic. In the past, it was used against scurvy.
● *Root* Used to cure toothache.

Flower
May develop little, ball-shaped, greenish-white flowers. Only Russian tarragon sets seed in temperate climates.

Dried leaves
These retain a little flavour if carefully dried, but often hay-like overtones develop.

A. dracunculoides
Russian tarragon
Bitter flavour, lacking aniseed subtleties and aroma. Narrower and paler leaves than French tarragon. Ht: 5 ft (1.5 m).

A. dracunculus
French tarragon

Stem
Ridged, round, branching and light green, becoming brown and brittle near base.

Leaf
Glossy, long, narrow and green, with oil glands on the underside which release a bitter-sweet, warm, peppery scent with an anise undertone.

Lifespan
Hardy to a few degrees of frost; perennial

Height
2–3 ft (60 cm–1 m)

Root
Light brown, brittle, fleshy, spreading rhizome with hair-like roots.

Borago officinalis

Borage Boraginaceae

The common thread running through historical descriptions of borage is its ability to make men and women glad and merry, to comfort the heart, dispel melancholy and give courage. The Celtic name *borrach* meant courage and the Welsh name *Llawenlys* translates as herb of gladness. According to Dioscorides and Pliny, borage was the famed *nepenthe* of Homer, a herb wine that brought absolute forgetfulness.

The flowers are a beautiful pure blue often chosen by Old Masters to paint the Madonna's robe. Flowers were embroidered on fine medieval tapestries and on scarves for tournament jousters. They were included in the page borders of herbals and Books of Hours. For courage, they were floated in the stirrup-cups given to Crusaders at their departure. The noble qualities of borage may derive from its high content of calcium, potassium and mineral salts, and research suggests borage works on the adrenal gland, where courage begins.

Seed
Largish, brown-black, tri-sided and lozenge-shaped; often viable for up to eight years.

Flower
Sky blue (sometimes pink, rarely white), five-petalled stars with prominent black stamen tips nod downward in clusters at the tip of the stem.

Leaf
Dark grey-green, oval-pointed, textured, covered with prickly white hairs. Cucumber-scented juice when crushed.

Stem
Sturdy, hollow, round, branching, with prickly white hairs. Cucumber-scented juice.

Flower heads
Pick off by grasping the black stamen tips and gently separating the flower from its green back.

 Lifespan
Hardy annual

Height
1–2 ft 6 in (30–75 cm)

CULTIVATION

Site Open sunny position.
Soil Light and dry, well drained.
Propagating Seed on site or singly in pots in spring for summer flowers; autumn for spring flowers. Self-sows freely on light soils.
Growing Set 12 in (30 cm) apart. Plant among roses or summer prune to keep tidy. Possible to grow small plants indoors.
Harvesting Pick flowers and leaves.
Preserving Dry flowers; freeze in ice cubes; crystallize.

USES

Decorative
● **Flower** String together as a necklace. Add to summer arrangements.

Culinary
● **Flower** Sprinkle in salads and as a garnish; crystallize for cake decorations.
● **Young leaf** Add to cold drinks (claret cup, Pimms No.1) for their cucumber flavour and cooling effect. Chop finely in salads, yogurt, soft cheese, pickles and sandwiches. Cook as spinach or with spinach. Add to ravioli stuffing.

Household
● **Flower** Attracts bees to gardens.
● **Whole plant** Plant near strawberries as they stimulate each other's growth. May control tomato worm if planted near tomatoes. When burnt, the nitrate of potash content will emit sparks and slight explosive sounds, like fireworks.

Cosmetic
● **Leaf** Add to a face pack for dry skin. Mix with barley and bran in a bath bag to cleanse and soften skin.

Medicinal
● **Leaf** Use in a salt-free diet as rich in mineral salts. A poultice soothes inflammation and bruises.
● **Seed** Early research suggests the presence of gamma-linoleic acid (see evening primrose, p. 102).

53

Herbs for flowers and foliage

Over the last 200 years many herbs dropped out of common usage, particularly the medicinal plants, but they continued to be grown in gardens. Perhaps this was for nostalgic reasons or traditional associations but more likely it was because they are pretty garden plants that are easy to care for. Eventually their herbal connections were forgotten and now many people are surprised to discover what useful attributes some of their favourite flowers have. It is fortunate that the cultivation of these herbs continued, as occasionally a new discovery is made and a once forgotten herb is suddenly in demand. Feverfew is one such case. After research into migraines publicized its success in reducing pain, a few gardeners were able to offer seedlings for widescale cultivation.

Myosotis sylvatica
Forget-me-not (below)
A pretty plant for the front of a border with masses of tiny blue flowers. (See p. 58.)

Vinca major
'Variegata'
Variegated periwinkle (left)
Useful ground cover with white, pink or traditional blue flowers. Used medicinally. (See p. 59.)

Cheiranthus cheiri
Wild wallflower (below)
Sweet-scented flowers can be added to potpourri. Once used medicinally for its action on muscles.

Convallaria majalis
Lily-of-the-valley (right)
The fragrant, poisonous flowers are used in pot-pourri. (See p. 57.)

Buxus sempervirens **'Suffruticosa'**
Dwarf box (left)
The ideal edging plant. Once used medicinally. (See p. 273.)

Ajuga reptans
Bugle (below)
Makes good ground cover with purple and cream variegated leaf forms available. (See p. 56.)

Bellis perennis
Lawn daisy (below left)
Can be used in salads. (See p. 275.)

Hedera helix
Ivy (right)
There are many attractive leaf forms
available. The ancient Greeks
thought ivy prevented
intoxication; it is now
used cosmetically.

Aquilegia vulgaris
Columbine (right)
The essence of a
cottage garden. Its
flowers, leaves, seeds
and root were once
used medicinally.
(See p. 56.)

Lamium maculatum
Dead nettle (below)
Attractive ground cover with white,
pink, peach or mauve flower
forms and variegated
or silver leaves.
(See p. 58.)

Cardamine pratensis
Lady's smock (below)
Also called cuckoo-
flower because it
flowers when the
cuckoo returns.
Flower supplies food
for butterflies.
(See p. 57.)

Pulmonaria officinalis
Lungwort (below)
The decorative spotted
leaves were once thought
to resemble lungs and so
were used for lung ailments.
(See p. 59.)

Herbs for flowers and foliage

Ajuga reptans
Bugle   <small>Labiatae</small>

A low-growing, creeping perennial, cultivated
mainly for its decorative foliage. The oval leaves
are dark-green with a purplish tinge, although
both multi-coloured and variegated forms are
available. It bears blue tubular flowers on short
spikes from late spring throughout the summer.
Some forms produce pink or even white flowers.
Bugle is an excellent ground-cover plant, growing
to a height of 4–6 in (10–15 cm). It needs partial
shade, making it suitable for planting under taller
flowering shrubs, near hedging or a trellis.

CULTIVATION
Sow seed in moist, fertile soil in autumn or spring.
Propagate by dividing runners and planting out in
autumn or spring at 1 ft (30 cm) intervals, to allow
space for spreading.

USES
A reliable garden plant because of its eager growth and
pretty flowers and foliage. In the past, bugle was a very
popular herbal remedy. Among its many applications,
it was made into an ointment for bruises, and a lotion
of bugle, honey and alum was recommended for
mouth sores. An infusion of dried leaves and boiling
water is thought to lower blood pressure and stop
internal bleeding. It is also believed to have a mildly
narcotic effect.

Aquilegia vulgaris
Columbine   <small>Ranunculaceae</small>

This dainty and elegant border perennial has been
a garden favourite for over 300 years. It grows to a
height of 2–3 ft (60 cm–1 m) with thin, erect
flower stems topped by a loose head of drooping,
funnel-shaped flowers in late spring and early
summer. The old-fashioned columbine produces
blue, pink, or white flowers, but cultivated forms
are available in a variety of eye-catching colours.
Each of the flower's five petals has a prominent
spur, resembling an eagle's talon. Hence the plant's
botanical name *aquilegia* from the Latin word *aquila*,
meaning "eagle". In spring the grey-green, ferny
leaves are tinged with pink. While columbine
tolerates a sunny, open area of the garden it is
happiest in partial shade.

CULTIVATION
Sow seeds at 1 ft (30 cm) intervals in spring, in the
flowering site, or divide clumps in autumn or spring.
Soil should be fertile and fairly alkaline. Water well in
dry weather, and cut the stems down after flowering.

USES
Today the columbine owes its place in the herb garden
solely to its beauty and grace. Once made into an astringent lotion, it is now known to be slightly poisonous
and so is no longer used.

Cardamine pratensis
Lady's smock *Cruciferae*

Once commonly found growing wild in moist meadowland, lady's smock is seen less frequently now that fewer meadows are left undrained. The slender flower stalks can grow to 16 in (40 cm) high and have dark-green oval leaves, which resemble the leaves of bittercress, to which it is related. It bears flowers of such a pale pink or lilac that they appear white at first glance. A double-flowered form is available which has a longer flowering period. It is also known as the cuckoo-flower because it flowers at the same time of the year as the cuckoo is heard. Plant lady's smock in the shade of a tree, a wall or a fence where the ground is damp.

CULTIVATION
Sow seeds in early autumn in moist soil, and water in well. Propagate by placing a leaf, taken from the base of the stem, on moist compost, where it will soon grow roots. Divide clump in spring or autumn.

USES
Lady's smock will grow vigorously in a damp, shady part of the garden. In the eighteenth century it was recommended for scurvy, and has since been found to contain vitamin C. It also has expectorant properties, making it a useful ingredient in cough remedies. The leaves taste rather like watercress and make a welcome addition to a springtime salad.

Convallaria majalis
Lily-of-the-valley *Liliaceae*

A hardy perennial that grows from creeping, horizontal rhizomes, or underground stems, lily of the valley is an important plant in the herb garden as much for its characteristic sweet scent as for the beauty of its small, white, bell-shaped flowers which appear in late spring. The flowers are borne on a slender, arched stem about 6–8 in (15–20 cm) high between a pair of large, lance-shaped, mid-green leaves. Lily-of-the-valley grows well in moist soil in the dappled shade of deciduous trees.

CULTIVATION
Divide clumps in early autumn, then plant 6 in (15 cm) apart in well-drained soil with plenty of compost added. Place the clumps so that the point where the leaves emerge from the rhizomes is just below the surface of the soil.

USES
A plant that spreads quickly in the right conditions, its leaves provide dense ground cover until winter. The flowers have traditionally formed part of a bridal bouquet. An infusion made from the whole plant can act as a diuretic as well as slowing the pace of the heart. It is said to be a safer though weaker cardiac tonic than foxglove but it should only be used under medical supervision.

Herbs for flowers and foliage

Lamium maculatum and Lamiastrum species

Dead nettle *Labiatae*

So-named because of its strong resemblance to the stinging nettle, the dead nettle is totally unrelated and its leaves have no sting. It can be distinguished from the stinging nettle, even before its clusters of tubular white, yellow, pink or purple flowers appear, by its squarer, hollow stem. The leaves are heart-shaped at the base, and those of the purple dead nettle have a purple tinge, with an irregular white stripe in some species. Because it first flowers around the day dedicated in the old calendar to the Archangel Michael, 8 May, the dead nettle is also commonly called archangel. It is an important nectar plant for bees, particularly the white dead nettle which, in some areas, can be found in flower in midwinter.

CULTIVATION
Dead nettles grow well in most soils. Sow seeds for white and purple species in spring, for yellow species in autumn, and barely cover with soil. Or divide yellow dead nettle plants in early spring. White and purple species prefer full sun, although the yellow dead nettle will tolerate deep shade. Avoid planting in herbaceous borders, where it may spread too vigorously. Cut after flowering for good leaf cover.

USES
An adaptable plant, which provides long-flowering ground cover for wild areas of the garden. It has long been thought to have astringent properties. A decoction of the flowers was sometimes prescribed as a blood purifier. Bruised leaves applied to the skin were said to staunch bleeding, while dried leaves were made into a tea to encourage perspiration. The leaves have occasionally been used in soups or eaten as vegetables in parts of France and Sweden.

Myosotis sylvatica

Forget-me-not *Boraginaceae*

An edging or rock-garden plant, the forget-me-not provides a dense carpet of blue, fragrant flowers mid- to late spring. It has oblong, tapering mid-green leaves below open sprays of small salver-shaped flowers. Easy to grow, the forget-me-not thrives in the shade of other springtime flowers such as tulips or wallflowers. *Myosotis sylvatica*, a short-lived perennial, can grow to a height of 12 in (30 cm), so makes a striking display in a bed of its own and is attractive viewed by moonlight.

CULTIVATION
Sow seeds in late spring. Plant out 6 in (10 cm) apart in autumn in any well-drained soil. Do not allow the soil to dry out.

USES
An asset to any springtime border, with its vivid blue flowers and delicate fragrance. *Myosotis* is used in a homeopathic remedy for respiratory problems, particularly in Europe, where it is sometimes made into a syrup for pulmonary disorders. The juice of the forget-me-not was believed to harden steel. In flower language, a man who gave a woman a bunch of roses entwined with forget-me-nots and lemongrass was offering her words of love.

Pulmonaria officinalis
Lungwort   Boraginaceae

Lungwort is a hardy herbaceous perennial, often cultivated for its ornamental white-spotted oval leaves. Growing to a height of about 12 in (30 cm), it bears clusters of funnel-shaped flowers in mid- to late spring. As they open, the flowers change from pink to purplish-blue. An old cottage-garden favourite, commonly known as Jerusalem cowslip, lungwort thrives in the shade of trees and shrubs.

CULTIVATION
Seed can be sown outdoors in any soil in spring, but better plants are produced by dividing and replanting roots in a shady position in late autumn or winter. Water frequently in dry weather, and cut the stems back in autumn.

USES
The leaves of this rapidly spreading plant provide ideal ground cover for shady parts of the garden. Its name derives from the fact that its leaves resemble lungs and lungwort has long been thought to be effective in pulmonary disorders. Chesty coughs, wheezing and shortness of breath may all benefit from an infusion of the dried leaves. It is also sometimes prescribed by herbalists for diarrhoea.

Vinca major
Greater periwinkle   Apocynaceae

An evergreen, spreading perennial, the greater periwinkle's large, glossy, egg-shaped leaves occur in pairs on the stem. From midspring to early summer it bears purplish-blue, tubular flowers, each with five petals that open out flat. Sometimes more flowers appear in early autumn. The plant extends itself by long trailing and rooting stems, making it invasive if planted in a border. The botanical name *vinca* comes from the Latin *vincire*, meaning "to bind", and these roots make it an excellent choice for sloping ground, where they serve to bind the soil.

CULTIVATION
Periwinkles will grow in any ordinary, well-drained soil. Take stem sections 6 in (15 cm) long and plant in partial shade in early autumn or early spring. Or divide and replant anytime over the autumn or winter.

USES
Most attractive year-round ground cover for partially shaded areas of the garden, with the bonus of perhaps two flowerings a year. An old name for the periwinkle was sorcerer's violet, when it was an important constituent of charms and love philtres, and was believed to have the power to exorcize evil spirits. Wrapped around the affected part of the body, the periwinkle was also believed to cure cramps. Its astringent and tonic properties were thought to staunch haemorrhaging, and an ointment of bruised leaves and lard was used for treating inflammatory skin conditions. However, today herbalists use the greater periwinkle mainly in the treatment of diabetes. It is related to the plant known as rose periwinkle, which is being used in the treatment of leukaemia.

Brassica species

Mustard Cruciferae

Known since prehistoric times, mustard's uses have always been manifold: the writer Pliny, in the first century AD, listed 40 remedies with mustard as chief ingredient. The Romans also named this herb: from *mustus*, the new wine they mixed with the seed, and *ardens* for fiery. They served mustard with every imaginable dish. Its leaves are so fast growing that it was said you could grow the salad for dinner while the meat was roasting. Belief in its aphrodisiac powers ensured mustard's inclusion in love potions. Black mustard seed has the strongest flavour, brown is easier to harvest, and white mustard seed is the most preservative.

Flower
Yellow, four-petalled blooms, in small clusters, borne in midsummer; contain mild mustard flavour.

Seed (Brown mustard)
Small, mid- to dark brown, bitter-tasting spheres in upright, smooth pods. Flavour is released only when ground and mixed with a liquid. Brown mustard is less pungent than black mustard.

Seed (White mustard)
Light cream spherical seeds, which taste bitter, in horizontal, hairy pods. Slightly hairy, light green leaves. Ht: 12–18 in (30–45 cm).

CULTIVATION

Site Sunny. Benefits from light shade in summer to prevent bolting.
Soil Fertile and well drained.
Propagating Sow in spring for seed crop, or every 3 weeks throughout year for salad greens.
Growing Thin to 6 in (15 cm) for seed crop. It is not necessary to thin salad crops. Can be grown indoors.
Harvesting Gather flowers as they open. Pick seed pods before they open in late summer. Cut salad leaves 8–10 days after sowing. Pick single leaves on older plants.
Preserving Dry seed in pods or infuse in vinegar. Dry leaves.

USES

Culinary
● *Seed* (Black or brown mustard) Make into mustard sauce: add ground seed or powder to cold water to activate enzymes; leave paste for 10 minutes before use. (White mustard) Use in pickles, as a strong preservative, and in mayonnaise as an emulsifier.
● *Flower* Sprinkle on sandwiches. Toss into salads.
● *Leaf* Mix young leaves into salads.

Household
● *Seed* To clean odorous cooking pots: put in a few bruised seeds, swish with water and rinse well.

Cosmetic
● *Seed* Rub pulverised seed onto hands as a deodorizer; rinse off after 2 minutes.

Medicinal
● *Seed* Take 1 tbsp (15 ml) crushed in warm water to induce vomiting. Use powdered to make a poultice to draw blood to skin or lungs, and to relieve pain and inflammation in rheumatism, arthritis, congested lungs and chilblains. Add to a foot bath to warm and deodorize feet and relieve colds.

Note: *Mustard seed can irritate tender skins.*

Stem
Smooth, round, hard, branching and mid-green.

B. juncea
Brown mustard
Ht: 2–4 ft
(60 cm–1.2 m)

 Lifespan
Hardy annual

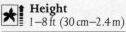 **Height**
1–8 ft (30 cm–2.4 m)

Leaf
Oval, pointed and dark green with mid-green undersides and pungent flavour. Lower leaves are toothed.

Calendula officinalis

Calendula/Marigold Compositae

One of the most versatile herbs, calendula is popular as a cheerful cottage garden flower; for its use in cosmetic and culinary recipes; as a dye plant and for its many healing properties.

As this hardy annual seems to be in flower continuously, it attracted a botanic name which reflects the belief that it was always in bloom on the first day of each month (Latin: *calends*). The regular supply of petals and young leaves contributed to its frequent use. Ancient Egyptians valued it as a rejuvenating herb. Hindus used it to decorate temple altars and Persians and Greeks garnished and flavoured food with its golden petals. In Europe it has long been used to flavour soups and stews, and to colour butter and cheese.

It is a soothing antiseptic and an excellent skin healer, especially for cracked skin and chapped lips. In the American Civil War, doctors on the battlefield employed the leaves to treat open wounds.

CULTIVATION
Site Sunny position.
Soil Fine loam but tolerates most soils, except waterlogged.
Propagating Sow seed in spring in situ or singly in pots.
Growing Plant 12–18 in (30–45 cm) apart. Deadhead for continuous flowers.
Harvesting Pick flowers when open, leaves when young.
Preserving Dry petals at low temperature to preserve colour, or macerate in oil.

USES
Decorative
● *Flower* Dry petals to add colour to potpourri.

Culinary
● *Flower* Use petals lavishly to give saffron colour and a light tangy flavour (not saffron flavour) to rice, fish and meat soups, soft cheese, yogurt, butter, omelettes, milk dishes, cakes and sweet breads. Add 1 tsp (5 ml) petals to fish and venison. Garnish meat platters, pâté, fruit salad.
● *Leaf* Sprinkle in salads and stews.

Household
● *Flower* Boil for a pale yellow dye.

Cosmetic
● *Flower* Add petals to creams and baths for cleansing, healing and softening the skin.

Medicinal
● *Flower* Soothing, healing and antiseptic. Use in ointments for leg ulcers, varicose veins, bed sores and bruises. Take in an infusion to aid digestion and promote bile production in the liver (helpful for alcoholics). Make into a healing mouthwash for gums after tooth extraction. Calendula oil is extracted from the petals by maceration. It is healing and rejuvenating, used in many skin preparations and in aromatherapy. In particular, soothes inflammations, chilblains, cracked nipples from breastfeeding (and it's non-toxic for baby).

Flower
2–3 in (4–7 cm) across, golden yellow-orange petals sometimes fluted, radiating from a pronounced centre.

Seed
Beige, $\frac{1}{4}$ in (5 mm) long, shaped like a curved apostrophe with a knobbly backbone.

Petals
Bright orange petals have the highest concentration of active ingredients.

Dried petals
These keep their colour well and have many uses.

Leaf
Mid-green, hairy base leaves are paddle-shaped, stem leaves are lance-shaped.

Stem
Green, succulent, angular, branching; covered with fine hairs.

Lifespan
Hardy annual

Height
12–20 in (30–50 cm)

Carum carvi

Caraway Umbelliferae

Definitely a herb with a pedigree, caraway has been found in the remains of Stone Age meals, Egyptian tombs, and ancient caravan stops along the Silk Road. The Arabic word for the seed, *karawya*, gives us the present name, and Isaiah speaks of its culture in the Bible. In Shakespeare's *Henry IV*, Falstaff is offered a "pippin (apple) and dish of caraways", this being a traditional finish to an Elizabethan feast. Caraway has always been popular in Germany, and when Queen Victoria married Prince Albert, Britain renewed its interest in his favourite seed.

Such an ancient herb is not without its magical properties. Caraway gave protection from witches and was believed to be able to prevent departures, so it was used in love potions.

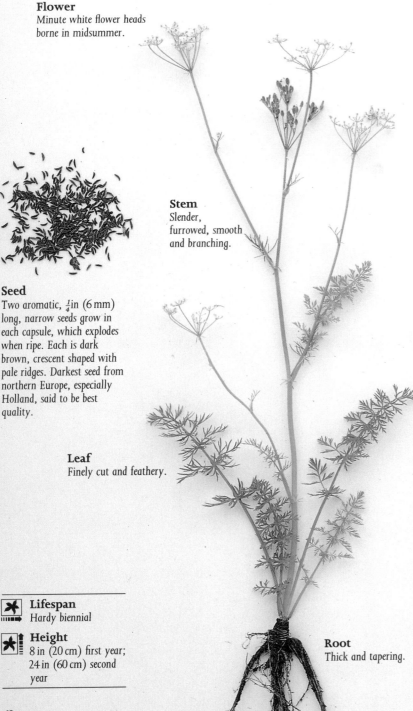

Flower
Minute white flower heads borne in midsummer.

Seed
Two aromatic, $\frac{1}{4}$in (6 mm) long, narrow seeds grow in each capsule, which explodes when ripe. Each is dark brown, crescent shaped with pale ridges. Darkest seed from northern Europe, especially Holland, said to be best quality.

Stem
Slender, furrowed, smooth and branching.

Leaf
Finely cut and feathery.

Root
Thick and tapering.

Lifespan
Hardy biennial

Height
8 in (20 cm) first year; 24 in (60 cm) second year

CULTIVATION

Site Full sun.
Soil Rich loam.
Propagating Sow outside in late spring or early autumn, in shallow drills in permanent position.
Growing Thin to 8 in (20 cm) apart, when large enough to handle. Caraway can be grown indoors in a sunny position.
Harvesting Gather leaves when young. Pick seed heads in late summer or when seeds are brown. Dig up roots in second autumn.
Preserving Hang seed heads upside down over an open container.

USES

Culinary
● *Seed* Sprinkle over rich meats, pork, goose and Hungarian beef stew to aid digestion. Add to cabbage water to reduce cooking smells. Use to flavour soups, breads, cakes, biscuits, apple pie, baked apples and cheese. Serve in a dish of mixed seeds at the end of an Indian meal. Encrust with white sugar to make caraway comfits. Its essential oil is used in liqueurs such as *Kümmel*, and in confectionery.
● *Leaf* Chop young leaves into salads and soups.
● *Roots* Cook as a root vegetable.

Household
● *Seed* Pigeon fanciers claim that tame pigeons will never stray if there is baked caraway dough in their cote.

Cosmetic
● *Seed* Use essential oil in mouthwashes and colognes.

Medicinal
● *Seed* Chew raw or infused seed to aid digestion, promote appetite, sweeten the breath and relieve flatulence. Safe for children.

Cedronella canariensis (C. triphylla)

Balm of Gilead *Labiatae*

The name of this herb conjures up biblical images of aromatic resins and healing oils. The true balm of Gilead is a rare desert shrub, *Commiphora opobalsamum*, a gift from the Queen of Sheba to Solomon. The tree is guarded and export prohibited. To share this name, and possibly scent, is the lure of *Cedronella canariensis*, which has a strange "masculine" fragrance – the kind of musky scent that gives depth to perfumes. The tree *Populus balsamifera* is also called balm of Gilead. This has leaf buds which exude a rich balsamic scent and have been used medicinally to treat coughs and sore throats.

Dried leaves
Add to spicy or "woody" potpourri mixtures for their musky scent.

Flower
Two-lipped, pink clusters, from late summer to early autumn.

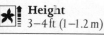
Lifespan
Half-hardy semi-evergreen shrub

Height
3–4 ft (1–1.2 m)

Stem
Prickly, square, ridged, mid-green, occasionally red-tinged at leaf joints, becoming woody in second season.

Leaf
Three-lobed, toothed, pointed and mid-green with paler underside and aromatic musky lemon-campnor scent.

CULTIVATION
Site Full sun.
Soil Well-drained, medium loam.
Propagating Sow in spring (and note that seedlings resemble nettles). Take stem cuttings in early autumn.
Growing Thin or transplant to 18 in (45 cm) apart. Balm of Gilead makes an excellent conservatory plant, but a 9–10 in (23–25 cm) pot is needed for it to reach its full size.
Harvesting Pick leaves just before flowers open or in autumn before pruning. (*Populus balsamifera*) Gather buds (see p. 274).
Preserving Dry leaves. (*Populus balsamifera*) Dry buds.

USES
Decorative
● *Whole plant* Makes an elegant greenhouse plant with its long-lasting pink flowers.

Aromatic
● *Leaf* Infuse or macerate in alcohol with other perfume ingredients to add a musky scent. Use dried leaves in spicy or "woody" potpourris. (*Populus balsamifera*) Boil buds in water to extract their covering, which contains a rich balsamic resin. Use whole buds in potpourri.

Medicinal
● *Leaf* (*Populus balsamifera*) Buds are considered to be a stimulant and tonic, antiseptic and expectorant. When used internally, they are said to treat bronchitis, coughs and laryngitis and, when used externally in creams, may relieve arthritic pain, cuts and bruises. The buds contain the aspirin substance, salicin, which is useful for minor aches and pains.
● *Stem* (*Commiphora opobalsamum*) The resin, which is seldom available in a pure state, was in the past credited with near-miraculous powers.

Chamaemelum nobile (Anthemis nobilis)

Perennial chamomile Compositae

The Egyptians dedicated chamomile to the sun and worshipped it above all other herbs for its healing properties, while Greek physicians prescribed it for fevers and female disorders. Among the Nine Sacred Herbs of the *Lacnunga*, an ancient Anglo-Saxon manuscript, chamomile is the "Maythen". Moreover, chamomile has inspired a proverb about energy in adversity, "like a chamomile bed, the more it is trodden the more it will spread".

Chamomile is also valued for its sweet apple-scented leaves. In a popular gardening book of 1638, William Lawson wrote of the "large walks, broad and long, like the Temple groves in Thessaly, raised with gravel and sand, having seats and banks of Camomile – all this delights the mind and brings health to the body". The relaxing aroma was also inhaled as snuff or smoked to relieve asthma and cure insomnia. At beauty salons, chamomile tea is often served to relax facial muscles.

A bed of perennial chamomile in flower.

Seed
Beige, narrow and tiny.

Dried flower
Yellow centre contains the active ingredients.

Dried leaves
These retain their apple scent and are used in potpourri and herb pillows.

Flower
Scented, solid, conical, golden-yellow centre with white petals, to 1 in (25 mm) across; appears in summer and autumn.

C.n. var. flore-pleno Double-flowered chamomile
Apple-scented leaves and double cream flowers.

Leaf
Apple-scented, finely cut and bright green.

C.n. 'Treneague'
Non-flowering, mat-forming clone, with apple-scented leaves. Ht: 2 in (5 cm).

Stem
Lax, ridged, round and light green.

***Matricaria recutita* German chamomile**
Annual. Tall stems, scented white flowers, with hollow, conical, yellow centres, ribbed seeds. Ht: 2 ft (60 cm).

Root
Creeping rootstock spreads plant, creating desirable carpeting surface.

***Anthemis tinctoria* Dyer's chamomile**
Golden flowers, yielding yellow-brown dye, borne all summer. Ht: 2½ ft (75 cm).

Lifespan
Hardy evergreen perennial

Height
8 in (20 cm) in full sun; 12 in (30 cm) in light shade

CULTIVATION
Site Full sun.
Soil Light and well drained.
Propagating (All except 'Treneague') Sow in spring. (Perennials) Divide in spring or autumn. Take 3 in (8 cm) cuttings from side shoots in summer.
Growing For a chamomile lawn or seat, plant 4–6 in (10–15 cm) apart. (*M. recutita*) Plant 9 in (23 cm) apart. (*A. tinctoria*) Plant 18 in (45 cm) apart.
Harvesting Gather leaves anytime. Pick flowers when fully open.
Preserving Dry flowers and leaves.

USES
Household
● *Whole plant* Grow this "physician" plant near a failing plant to revive it. Infuse and spray on seedlings to prevent "damping off" and on compost to activate decomposition.
● *Flower* (*A. tinctoria*) Boil for a strong yellow-brown dye (see p. 199).

Cosmetic
● *Flower* (*C. nobile, M. recutita*) Infuse as a facial steam and as a hand soak to soften and whiten skin. Make an eye bath or tea bag compress to reduce inflammation and eliminate fatigue shadows. Add infusion for a reviving bath. Boil flowers for 20 minutes, and use regularly as a rinse to lighten and condition fair hair.

Aromatic
● *Flower and leaf* Use in potpourri and herb pillows.

Medicinal
● *Flower* (*C. nobile, M. recutita*) Infuse flowers as a tea for a general tonic and sedative (good for restless children and nightmares). Apply a compress to treat wounds and eczema. Use in a bath to relieve sun- or wind-burnt skin.

Chenopodium bonus-henricus

Good King Henry *Chenopodiaceae*

Good King Henry has been a popular herb from Neolithic times until the last century. Its curious name is not taken from the English king, Henry VIII, with his many wives, but rather comes from Germany, where it distinguishes the plant from the poisonous mercury, which is known as "bad Henry".

Both Good King Henry and fat hen (*C. album*) have nutritious leaves. The seeds of fat hen, which are rich in fat and albumen, were a food supplement for primitive man, and fat hen was found in the stomach of preserved Iron Age Tollund Man. American wormseed (*C. ambrosioides*) is sometimes used to expel worms, but only under strict medical supervision as large doses are poisonous. It is also known in China as "fragrant tiger bones".

Flower
Tiny greenish-yellow flowers borne in early summer on 2 in (5 cm) spikes where leaf joins stem.

Seed
Tan coloured, rough, round and knobbly.

Leaf
Arrow-shaped and dark green with white mealy undersides.

Variegated leaves
Such forms occasionally appear among seedlings.

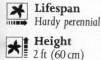

Lifespan
Hardy perennial

Height
2 ft (60 cm)

Stem
Tall, slender, ridged and green.

CULTIVATION
Site Prefers full sun but will tolerate light shade.
Soil Rich loam, deeply dug and well drained.
Propagating Sow in spring; cover seed with $\frac{1}{4}$ in (6 mm) of soil. Divide roots in autumn.
Growing Thin or transplant seedlings to 1 ft (30 cm) apart. Water in dry weather; fertilize during summer. Unsatisfactory indoors.
Harvesting Allow plants 1 year to develop, then gather leaves as required and pick flowering spikes as they begin to open.
Preserving Freeze only when an ingredient in a cooked dish.

USES
Culinary
● *Seed* (Fat hen) Grind into flour and make into gruel.
● *Flower* Steam spikes and toss in butter like broccoli.
● *Leaf* Eat young leaves raw in salads, cooked in casseroles, stuffings and soups, and puréed in savoury pies.
● *Shoot* On rich soil, cut shoots of pencil thickness and 5 in (13 cm) tall; boil, peel and eat as asparagus.

Household
● *Whole plant* Use to fatten poultry.
● *Seed* Used commercially in the manufacture of shagreen – an artificially granulated untanned leather, often dyed green.

Medicinal
● *Leaf* Eat raw or cooked as a source of iron, vitamins and minerals. A poultice and ointment cleanses and heals skin sores.
● *Root* Used in a veterinary cough remedy for sheep.

Chrysanthemum balsamita (Tanacetum balsamita)

Alecost/Costmary Compositae

According to Gerard, the sixteenth-century herbalist, alecost was "cherished for its sweete flowers and leaves". Its balsamic leaves and flowering tops were also important in brewing to help clear and preserve ale and to impart an astringent minty bitterness. Alecost was taken by settlers to America, where the Puritans carried a leaf in their bibles as a fragrant bookmark and to allay appetites during long sermons, giving alecost the nickname "bible leaf". The word "cost" derives from *kostos*, the Greek for a spicy oriental herb, so alecost means a spicy herb for ale, and costmary is Mary's (or women's) spicy herb, as it was used to ease childbirth.

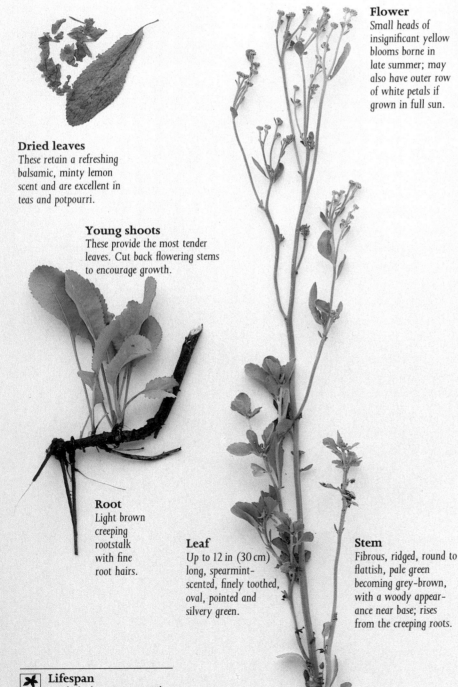

Flower
Small heads of insignificant yellow blooms borne in late summer; may also have outer row of white petals if grown in full sun.

Dried leaves
These retain a refreshing balsamic, minty lemon scent and are excellent in teas and potpourri.

Young shoots
These provide the most tender leaves. Cut back flowering stems to encourage growth.

Root
Light brown creeping rootstalk with fine root hairs.

Leaf
Up to 12 in (30 cm) long, spearmint-scented, finely toothed, oval, pointed and silvery green.

Stem
Fibrous, ridged, round to flattish, pale green becoming grey-brown, with a woody appearance near base; rises from the creeping roots.

Lifespan
Hardy herbaceous perennial

Height
2–3 ft 6 in (60 cm–1.05 m)

CULTIVATION
Site Prefers full sun.
Soil Rich, dryish and well drained.
Propagating Divide roots in spring or autumn. Seed is not viable in cool climates.
Growing Transplant to 2 ft (60 cm) apart. Small alecost plants can be grown indoors.
Harvesting Pick leaves anytime or for most aroma, as flowers open.
Preserving Dry leaves.

USES
Culinary
● *Leaf* Use in only small amounts as it has a sharp tang. Add finely chopped leaves to carrot soup, salads, game, poultry stuffing and fruit cakes. Try with melted butter on peas and new potatoes. Use to clear, flavour and preserve beer.

Household
● *Leaf* Add to linen bags to repel insects. Infuse to make a "sweet water" and use in the final rinse of linen to impart fragrance. Popular medieval strewing herb for its insect-repelling properties and lasting scent. (*Balsamita vulgaris* 'Tomentosum' or Camphor plant) Use as an insect repellent for fabrics and place in rooms for a stronger camphor scent.

Cosmetic
● *Leaf* Infuse as a scented rinse water for hair or skin.

Aromatic
● *Leaf* Use in potpourri and herb bags to intensify other herb scents.

Medicinal
● *Leaf* Infuse as a tonic tea for colds, catarrh, upset stomachs and cramps, and to ease childbirth. Lay crushed leaf on bee stings to relieve the pain. Add to a salve for burns and stings.

Chrysanthemum cinerariifolium (Pyrethrum cinerariifolium)

Pyrethrum Compositae

Although to some the name pyrethrum includes all the single-flowered chrysanthemums, it is in fact only the flowers of C. cinerariifolium that contain a natural insecticide, also called pyrethrum. Because it is non-toxic to mammals and non-accumulative, pyrethrum is also used to kill pests living on the skin of man and animals. Another advantage is suggested by the traveller Chang Yee: "It is a strange coincidence that the leaves can be used for wiping the fingers after eating crabs, to wipe away the smell. Crabs, chrysanthemums, wine and the moon are the four autumn joys of our scholars, artists and poets." Garland chrysanthemum or "chop suey greens" (C. coronarium) is popular in oriental cuisine, and C. indicum is a valued tonic and part of the Taoist elixir of immortality.

Flower
Single "daisy" heads, with long white fluted petals and flat yellow centres, appear in midsummer. They have a pungent aroma when crushed.

Seed
Beige, narrow, ribbed "fruit", blunt one end, containing a single seed.

Stem
Slender, ribbed, branching and grey-green, each bearing a single terminal flower.

Leaf
Finely divided and grey-green with silver edge created by white down on underside; has a pungent aroma similar to tansy.

Flower head
The flower is used in powdered form to make contact insecticides. The active ingredients are pyrethrin and cinerin.

Lifespan
Hardy herbaceous perennial

Height
30 in (75 cm)

CULTIVATION
Site Sunny and open.
Soil Alkaline and well drained.
Propagating Sow in late spring to summer. Divide roots in spring.
Growing Thin or transplant to 6–12 in (15–30 cm) apart. Do not grow as an indoor plant.
Harvesting Gather open flowers.
Preserving Dry. Store away from light to preserve insecticide.

USES
Decorative
● **Flower** Cut for a long-lasting flower arrangement.

Culinary
● **Leaf** (C. coronarium) Sow seed thickly and cut leaves young, like cress. Use raw in salads or stir fried.
● **Flower** (C. coronarium) This is the edible yellow chrysanthemum of Chinese recipes. Add to oriental dishes. (C. leucanthemum) Toss white petals into salads.

Household
● **Flower** Sprinkle dried powdered flowers to deter all common insect pests: bedbugs, cockroaches, flies, mosquitoes, aphids, spider mites and ants. (Note, it also kills helpful insects and fish.) Wear gloves when processing flowers as prolonged contact may cause allergies. Dust or make a paste with water to repel fleas and lice.
   The active ingredients in the powder are not water soluble. To make a spray, steep 4 oz (110 g) of pyrethrum powder in a gill (150 ml) of methylated spirit, then dilute with 12 gallons (55 litres) of water, or buy a proprietary liquid pyrethrum and follow manufacturer's instructions. Spray insecticide on herbs at dusk, so plants and bees will be safe by morning. (Solution decomposes rapidly, especially in bright sunlight.)

Note: *When the active ingredient pyrethrin or cinerin is extracted, it is toxic to humans and animals.*

Cichorium intybus

Chicory/Succory Compositae

According to folk tales, the flowers of chicory are a beautiful clear blue because they are the transformed eyes of a lass weeping for her lover's ship, which never returned. These blue flowers can be changed to bright red by the acid of ants: place a flower in an ant hill and watch the colour show.

Chicory is often grown in floral clocks for the regular opening of its flowers and their closing five hours later. These opening times relate to latitude, but the leaves always align with north. Gardeners interested in metaphysics credit this plant with life-giving forces.

Dried petals
Attractive in potpourri.

Flower
Clear blue, fluted petals; two or three borne at each leaf joint midsummer to midautumn.

Chicons
These are blanched heads produced by forcing roots in warmth and darkness.

Stem
Hollow, furrowed, green with small hairs; bitter milky juice inside.

✳ **Lifespan**
Hardy perennial

✳ **Height**
3–5 ft (1–1.5 m)

Leaf
Mid-green with hairy underside; coarsely toothed at the base; smaller arrow-shaped leaves further up the stem.

Root
Long taproot, occasionally branching; bitter milky fluid inside.

CULTIVATION
Site Sunny and open.
Soil Light, preferably alkaline soil. Dig deeply for good roots.
Propagating Sow in early summer, selecting Witloof variety for chicons and Magdeburg or Brunswick varieties for "coffee" roots.
Growing Thin or transplant to 18 in (45 cm) apart. Chicory is not suitable for growing indoors. To grow chicons, dig up roots in autumn, cut leaves to 1 in (25 mm) and trim 1 in (25 mm) off root. Bury well in sandy compost and water. Exclude light and move into a cellar or garage. Chicons are ready to eat in 3–4 weeks.
Harvesting Gather leaves when young. Dig up roots in first autumn and chicons in winter.
Preserving Dry root and leaves.

USES
Culinary
● *Flower* Use in salads; pickle buds.
● *Leaf* Seedlings can be cut and eaten fresh.
● *Root* When young, boil and serve with a sauce. Use as a coffee substitute: dig up thick, cultivated roots, wash, slice, dry in gentle heat; roast and grind.
● *Chicon* Toss in salads; braise in butter as a vegetable dish.

Household
● *Whole plant* Grow for fodder and in nutritious pasture mixtures.
● *Leaf* Boil for a blue dye.

Medicinal
● *Leaf* May be used for jaundice and spleen problems, as rich in calcium, copper and iron. A poultice soothes inflammation.
● *Root* Infuse dried root to make a tonic, mild laxative and diuretic. A decoction may alleviate gallstones, kidney stones and inflammation of the liver or urinary tract.

Coriandrum sativum

Coriander Umbelliferae

Cultivated as a medicinal and culinary herb for at least 3,000 years, coriander is mentioned in Sanskrit texts, on Egyptian papyri, in *Tales of the Arabian Nights* and in the Bible, where manna is compared with coriander seed. Coriander was brought to northern Europe by the Romans, who, combining it with cumin and vinegar, rubbed it into meat as a preservative. The Chinese once believed it conferred immortality, and in the Middle Ages it was put into love potions as an aphrodisiac. All coriander parts have a pungent aroma; one Peruvian tribe is so fond of the leaf that they exude its scent. That of the mildly narcotic seed changes considerably when it ripens to a sweet spicy flavour, which is best after a few months. Coriander's use in exotic cuisines has rekindled its popularity today.

Seed
Small, round and beige, with a light brown, ribbed spherical seed case; aromatic.

Flower
Loose, flat, white or pale pinkish-mauve heads borne from early to midsummer.

Upper leaf
Finely cut, thread-like and bright green, with a strange pungent scent.

Lower leaf
Finely scalloped and broad, with same strange scent as upper leaves, but tasting like an aromatic parsley.

Stem
Round, branching and pale green, finely grooved.

Lifespan
Hardy annual

Height
2 ft (60 cm)

CULTIVATION
Site Full sun.
Soil Rich and light.
Propagating Sow in autumn, to over-winter in mild climates, or early spring in final position, away from fennel, which seems to suffer in its presence.
Growing Thin to 8 in (20 cm) apart. Coriander can be grown indoors but its scent is unpleasant.
Harvesting Pick young leaves anytime. Collect seeds when brown but before they drop. Dig up roots in autumn.
Preserving Dry seeds, store whole or infuse to make a coriander vinegar. Freeze leaves, or place their stems in water and cover with a plastic bag to retain their freshness.

USES
Culinary
● *Seed* Use in tomato chutney, ratatouille, frankfurters and curries; also in apple pies, cakes, biscuits, and marmalade. Add whole seeds to soups, sauces and vegetable dishes.
● *Leaf* Add fresh lower leaves to curries, stews, salads, sauces and use as a garnish (see also p. 164).
● *Stem* Cook with beans and soups.
● *Root* Cook fresh root as a vegetable. Add to curries.

Household
● *Whole plant* Sow close to aniseed to speed up the latter's germination and growth.

Aromatic
● *Seed* Use in potpourri.

Medicinal
● *Seed* Chew or infuse as a tea for an apéritif, digestive tonic and mild sedative. Add essential oil to ointments for painful rheumatic joints and muscles. Used to flavour various medicines.

Dianthus species

Clove pink *Caryophyllaceae*

This herb was a flower of divinity to the Greeks, who dedicated it to the "sky father" and called it *dianthus*, meaning flower of flowers. To the Romans, it was *flos Jovis*, Jove's flower. In the making of coronets and garlands, in which both these cultures delighted, pinks were given place of honour. These flowers of love were also floated in the drinks of engaged couples, and in medieval art they indicated betrothal. Pinks have long been used to flavour dainty dishes with their spicy fragrance: flowers were crystallized, and petals were used in soups, sauces, syrups, cordials and wine. In 1699, John Evelyn suggested that the petals could be mingled with other salad ingredients but had "a more palatable relish infused in vinegar".

D. 'Inchmery' has double flowers.

CULTIVATION

Site Open sunny position.
Soil Well drained and alkaline.
Propagating Sow seed or take stem cuttings in spring. Divide roots or layer in late summer.
Growing Thin or transplant to 1 ft (30 cm) apart. Can grow indoors.
Harvesting Pick open flowers.
Preserving Air dry flowers or put in silica gel. Infuse in almond oil for sweet oil or in wine vinegar for floral vinegar. Crystallize petals.

USES

Decorative
● **Flower** Pretty and long-lasting.

Culinary
● **Flower** Remove bitter white heel. Add petals to salads, fruit pies and sandwiches. Use to flavour sugar, jam, vinegar and wine. To make a syrup: pour 1 fl oz (25 ml) boiling water on 1 oz (25 g) fresh petals, steep for 12 hours. Strain, add 8 oz (225 g) sugar, stir and bottle.

Household
● **Flower** Provides nectar for bees.

Aromatic
● **Flower** Use dried in potpourri.

Medicinal
● **Flower** Infuse petals in wine as a nerve tonic.

Note on species
D. caryophyllus, an Elizabethan gillyflower, is 2 ft (60 cm) high with erect stems and rose-purple flowers which have the richest, spicy sweet scent. The parent of carnations, it is doubtful if the true species is now available commercially.
D. plumarius, cottage pink, is the parent of most "old-fashioned pinks". The Allwoodii pinks are a cross between *D. caryophyllus* and *D. plumarius*. All clove-scented varieties can be used herbally.

Seed
Small, dark brown, flattish and round.

Flower
Single or double, white, pink or purple flowers, with very sweet, clove-like perfume, borne in summer.

D. carthusianorum
Bright pink clusters above low mound of grass-like, ridged, green leaves. Ht: 18 in (45 cm).

D. plumarius 'Doris'
One of the Allwoodii scented pinks. Pale salmon-pink flowers. Ht: 6–12 in (15–30 cm).

D. deltoides
Maiden pink
Small carmine flowers over mats of dark green foliage. Ht: 8 in (20 cm).

Dried flowers
These can be used in potpourri, and in cooking, when petals should be separated and the bitter white heel removed.

Leaf
Long, narrow and blue-green.

Stem
Smooth, round, blue-green, thickening at leaf joints.

Lifespan
Short-lived perennial; will survive frosts if soil is well drained

Height
1–3 ft (30 cm–1 m)

Eupatorium purpurea

Sweet Joe Pye *Compositae*

A glorious feature of the herb garden in late summer, the vigorous purple stems of sweet Joe Pye display clouds of rose-pink flowers. This herb was named after a North American Indian called Joe Pye, who cured a grateful New Englander of typhus. The Indian used this plant to induce profuse sweating, which broke the fever. Its Latin name Eupatorium is derived from Eupator, a first-century BC king of Persia, famed for his herbal skills. Other species, E. cannabinum and E. perfoliatum, are similar in appearance and have medicinal properties.

Flower
Tubes of rose-pink overlapping petals appear in clusters in late summer.

Seed
Brown, narrow, pointed, tufted, $\frac{1}{8}$ in (3 mm) long.

Root
Thick and purplish-brown, with cream flesh and smaller roots. Dried root is used medicinally.

Leaf
Up to 1 ft (30 cm) long, lance-shaped and green, in whorls; when bruised, emits a faint scent of apple peel.

Stem
Aromatic, thick, round and purple, with vertical line markings towards base.

 Lifespan
Hardy herbaceous perennial

 Height
3–9 ft (1–2.7 m)

CULTIVATION
Site Partial shade or sun.
Soil Any rich, alkaline soil. (E. cannabinum) Prefers marshy soil.
Propagating Sow fresh seed in autumn. Divide in spring or autumn.
Growing Thin or transplant to 3 ft (1 m) apart. Sweet Joe Pye is not suitable for indoor cultivation.
Harvesting Pick leaves anytime. Dig up roots in autumn; remove small side roots. Collect seed heads when petals have dropped.
Preserving Dry leaves, roots and seed heads.

USES
Decorative
● *Whole plant* Makes a magnificent specimen in herb garden borders. The sturdy erect stems withstand storms well.

Household
● *Seed* Crush unripe and ripe seed heads and boil for a pink-red dye.
● *Leaf* (E. cannabinum) Dried leaves were said by Culpeper to drive away wasps and flies if burned in a room.

Medicinal
● *Flowering top and leaf* (E. cannabinum) When dried, these were used as a tonic for biliousness and as a laxative, but this is now felt by some to be too toxic. (It is not related to the cannabis plant.)
● *Root* Use dried root in small doses as a tincture or infusion to induce perspiration, relieve gout and rheumatism, and promote the flow of urine (specifically to help remove stones in the bladder caused by excess uric acid – hence one of its nicknames, "gravel root"). Infusion may be used as an astringent tonic and stimulant.

Filipendula ulmaria (Spirea ulmaria)

Meadowsweet Rosaceae

Meadowsweet was the favourite strewing herb of Queen Elizabeth I, and the herbalist Gerard believed it excelled all other strewing herbs because its leaves delighted the senses without causing headaches. Meadowsweet was so frequently in demand for strewing at church weddings and for making into bridal garlands that it was given another name "bridewort". Other qualities unknown to us once made this plant – together with mistletoe, watermint and vervain – most sacred to the Druids. There is also a gold variegated leaf form, and *F. vulgaris*, which grows to 18 in (45 cm) but has larger flowers.

Flower
Cream-coloured clusters of tiny blossoms with sweet almond fragrance throughout summer.

Seed
Light brown and crescent-shaped, $\frac{1}{8}$ in (3 mm) long.

Dried flowers
Sweet almond fragrance improves with age; used for tea and potpourri.

Dried leaves
Smell of hay with a hint of wintergreen.

Lifespan
Hardy perennial

Height
2–4 ft (60 cm–1.2 m)

Leaf
Wrinkled, deeply indented and dark green with grey-green undersides; exudes pleasant wintergreen fragrance.

Root
Pinkish-red, sweetly aromatic and creeping.

Stem
Hollow, furrowed, branching and reddish.

CULTIVATION

Site Sun or partial shade.
Soil Moist, fertile and alkaline.
Propagating Sow in spring; divide meadowsweet in autumn.
Growing Thin or transplant to 12 in (30 cm) apart. Not suitable for growing indoors.
Harvesting Gather young leaves before flowers appear, and pick flowers when new.
Preserving Dry leaves and flowers.

USES

Decorative
● **Flower** Use in bouquets.

Culinary
● **Flower** Flavours herb beers, mead and wines. Gives slight almond flavour to jams and stewed fruit.
● **Leaf** Add to soup for an interesting flavour. Use in meadowsweet beer: boil 2 oz (50 g) each of meadowsweet, betony, raspberry leaves and agrimony, in 2 gallons (9 litres) of water for 15 minutes. Strain and add 2 lb (900 g) white sugar, stirring to dissolve. Bottle when nearly cool.

Household
● **Flowering top** Use to scent linen. Boil for a greenish-yellow dye.
● **Leaf and stem** Boil for a blue dye.
● **Roots** Boil for a black dye.

Cosmetic
● **Flower** Soak in rain water for an astringent, tonic, complexion water.

Aromatic
● **Flower** Dry for potpourri.
● **Leaf** Gather for strewing and adding to potpourri.

Medicinal
● **Flower buds** First discovered source of salicylic acid in 1838, from which aspirin was later synthesized.
● **Flower** Drink as a tea to help rid body of excess fluid and to alleviate heartburn, for feverish colds and mild diarrhoea. Can also be used as a mild sedative and painkiller.

Foeniculum vulgare

Fennel *Umbelliferae*

Fennel is one of our oldest cultivated plants and was much valued by the Romans. "So gladiators fierce and rude; mingled it with their daily food. And he who battled and subdued; a wreath of fennel wore" (Henry Wadsworth Longfellow). In an age of banquets, Roman warriors took fennel to keep in good health, while Roman ladies ate it to prevent obesity. Every part of the plant, from the seed to the root, is edible. It was one of the nine herbs held sacred by the Anglo-Saxons for its power against evil. With healing properties also to its credit, Charlemagne declared in 812 AD that fennel was essential in every imperial garden.

Flower
Small, aromatic, flat, yellow clusters borne in midsummer.

Seed
Curved, ribbed, aromatic, narrow and greenish-brown.

Leaf
Aromatic, finely cut, lime-green, turning dark green by autumn.

Bronze form
Pink, copper and bronze leaves, with richest colouring in spring.

Stem
Round, lined, shiny dark blue-green; succulent when new, hollowing with age.

F.v. var. dulce
Florence fennel/ Finnocchio
Grow as an annual for its succulent bulbous rootstalk, which is eaten raw or cooked. Ht: 2½–3 ft (75 cm–1 m).

Lifespan
Hardy herbaceous perennial

Height
7 ft (2.1 m)

CULTIVATION
Site Full sun (to ripen seed).
Soil Well-drained loam. Avoid clay.
Propagating Sow in late spring to early summer. (Self-seeds when established.) Divide in autumn.
Growing Thin or transplant to 20 in (50 cm) apart. Do not grow near dill, as seeds will cross-pollinate, or coriander, as it reduces fennel's seed production. Remove seed heads if not required to give better leaf production. Fennel is not suitable for growing indoors.
Harvesting Pick young stems and leaves as required. Collect ripe seed. Dig up "bulbs" in autumn.
Preserving Freeze leaves or infuse in oil or vinegar. Dry seed.

USES
Decorative
● *Whole plant* Attractive in borders.

Culinary
● *Seed* Use in sauces, fish dishes, and bread; sprout for winter salads.
● *Leaf* Finely chop over salads and cooked vegetables. Add to soups and to stuffings for oily fish.
● *Stem* Add young stems to salads.
● *Bulb* (Florence fennel) Slice or grate raw into sandwiches or salads. Cook as a root vegetable.

Cosmetic
● *Seed* Decoct as an eye bath or as a compress to reduce inflammation. Chew to sweeten breath.
● *Seed and leaf* Use in facial steams and baths for deep cleansing.

Medicinal
● *Seed* Infuse as a tea to aid digestion and constipation. Chew to allay hunger and ease indigestion. Recent research indicates fennel reduces the toxic effects of alcohol on the body.

Note: *Do not take excessive doses.*

Fragaria vesca

Wild strawberry Rosaceae

"Doubtless God Almighty could have made a better berry but doubtless God never did." Dr Butler's praise sums up most people's feelings about strawberries. Growing in cool, secret woodlands, strawberries are often associated with fairy folk, and in Bavaria, a basket of fruit is sometimes tied between a cow's horns to please the elves so that they bless the cow with abundant milk. Woodland strawberries were recommended by Sir Hugh Platt in his *Garden of Eden* (1653), as most likely to prosper in gardens. While discussing plants that scent the air, Francis Bacon noted that "the strawberry leaves dying ... yield a most excellent cordial smell".

Strawberries are one of the fruits dedicated to the Virgin Mary, and, astrologically, to the planet Venus. In Lapland, they are mixed with reindeer milk and blueberries to make a Christmas pudding. Their one unhappy association is with the fateful handkerchief that Shakespeare's Othello gave Desdemona, which was embroidered with strawberries.

Seed
Tiny, mid-brown, shiny and tear-shaped.

Dried leaves
Dry thoroughly as wilting process creates a toxin that disappears on drying; contain tannin, vitamin C and a lemon-scented essential oil.

Flower
White petals and yellow centre appear from early spring until first frosts.

Leaf
Deeply veined, toothed, three-lobed and bright green with white felted underside; rich in vitamin C.

Stem
Hairy, ridged, round and green to reddish.

Fruit
Pips, containing seeds, are scattered over each fleshy, red fruit (the tasty strawberry) throughout summer and autumn.

Lifespan
Hardy evergreen

Height
10 in (25 cm); good ground cover

Root
Short, woody rootstalk with numerous rootlets. Rooting stems (runners) are produced from stem area.

CULTIVATION
Site Cool, sun or shade, sheltered.
Soil Alkaline, moist, well drained.
Propagating Sow in spring at a temperature of 65 °F (18 °C). In spring, sever the daughter plants produced on runners and transplant to 12 in (30 cm) apart.
Growing Apply a potash fertilizer as fruits begin to form. Can be grown indoors.
Harvesting Pick fruit as ripe. Collect leaves as required. Dig up roots in autumn.
Preserving Freeze or bottle fruit. Dry leaves.

USES
Culinary
● **Leaf** Infuse with other herb teas to add "bite". Use bruised leaves to flavour meat stock.
● **Fruit** Eat fresh with cream. Use for jam, cakes, pies and syrups or to flavour liqueurs and cordials.

Cosmetic
● **Leaf** Decoct as an astringent for oily skin.
● **Fruit** Rub on teeth to remove tartar and reduce stains; leave juice on teeth for 5 minutes, then clean using warm water with a pinch of bicarbonate of soda. Apply cut strawberry to washed face to ease slight sunburn. Mash or extract juice and add to face packs to whiten skin and lighten freckles.

Aromatic
● **Leaf** Use dried in potpourri.

Medicinal
● **Leaf** Infuse as a tea for anaemia, nervousness, diarrhoea, other gastro-intestinal and urinary disorders and as a tonic for kidneys.
● **Root** Decoct as a tonic and diuretic.
● **Fruit** Eat as an iron supplement, mild laxative and for rheumatic gout. Drink to cool fevers.

Note: *Strawberries can cause an allergic reaction in some people.*

Galium odoratum (Asperula odorata)

Sweet woodruff Rubiaceae

This pretty little woodland plant will, when added to a wine-cup, "make a man merrie", wrote Gerard. Sweet-smelling garlands of woodruff were hung in churches, strewn on domestic floors, sprinkled into potpourri and linen and stuffed into mattresses, spreading its cordiality around the household. The coumarin in the leaves develops its sweet hay scent only when the plant is dried, so sweet woodruff is invaluable from the appearance of its first flowers for the traditional German May Bowl punch, through to Christmas, when it is used in herb pillows.

Lifespan
Hardy perennial

Height
12 in (30 cm); good ground cover

Flower
Brilliant white, loose clusters of star-shaped flowers appear in late spring.

Dried leaves
Smell like new-mown hay and act as a fixative in potpourri.

Leaf
The shiny green circular spokes of the leaves give the plant its "ruff" name.

Stem
Slender, squarish and smooth.

Root
Small, red-brown creeping rootstalk with hair-like roots.

CULTIVATION

Site Semi-shade, particularly good under trees. Leaf colour fades in bright sun.
Soil Prefers moist, porous loam but will survive on less rich soil.
Propagating Sow seeds when ripe in late summer in moist shaded soil. Propagation, however, is easiest by dividing the creeping rootstock after flowering is finished.
Growing Transplant in spring, 6–9 in (15–23 cm) apart. Sweet woodruff is not suitable for growing indoors.
Harvesting Pick leaves and flowering stems.
Preserving Store leaves whole to preserve scent.

USES

Decorative
● *Flowering stem* Use in garlands.

Culinary
● *Leaf* Make "an exhilarating drink to lift the spirits and create a carefree atmosphere": dry a small handful of fresh woodruff leaves in a warm cupboard for 3 hours. Remove stems and put leaves in a large bowl. Pour over juice of one lemon and half a bottle of hock or Rhine wine to cover the leaves. Put in a warm place for 3–4 hours. Add 4–6 tbsp (60–90 ml) sugar and one-and-a-half bottles of hock. Chill. Just before serving, add a bottle of sparkling white wine or champagne. For a stronger drink, add a measure of brandy. Float wild strawberries on the top.

Household
● *Leaf* Put dried leaves under carpets and amongst linen to deter moths and other insects.

Aromatic
● *Leaf* Add dried leaves to potpourri and herb pillows.

Medicinal
● *Leaf* Bruise fresh leaves and apply to wounds. Infuse dried leaves to make a refreshing and relaxing tea, which can relieve stomach pains.

Helianthus annuus

Sunflower Compositae

This remarkable flower, which was cultivated by American Indians some 3,000 years ago, is dedicated to Helios, the Greek sun god. In the fifteenth century, Aztec sun priestesses were crowned with sunflowers, carried them in their hands and wore gold jewellery with sunflower motifs. Sunflowers were introduced into Europe by Spanish explorers in the sixteenth century. Large-scale cultivation began in Russia, where the seeds are sold on street corners and offered in large bowls at railway restaurants.

All parts of sunflower are usable. The pith, for example, is one of the lightest substances known and is used in scientific laboratories. The Chinese have used it as moxa in acupuncture, and in the making of delicate silks and coarse ropes, having cultivated sunflowers for thousands of years. The plant's ability to absorb water from soil has been utilized in the reclamation of marshy land in the Netherlands.

Flower
Yellow petals surround a purple-brown central disc, borne from late summer until frosts.

Seed (shell)
Oval, flattish, thin covering, $\frac{1}{2}$ in (13 mm) long, with grey, white and brown stripes.

Seed (kernel)
Light grey, flattish and oval inside shell; rich in vitamins B1, B2, niacin, iron, phosphorus, potassium, sulphur, vegetable fats and proteins.

Leaf
Large, rough, toothed, heart-shaped and mid-green with three prominent veins.

Seed head
Edible seeds form stunning geometric concentric patterns.

 Lifespan
Tender annual

Height
3–10 ft (1–3 m)

Stem
Thick, hairy, light green and high in potash. Pith is valued for its cellular lightness. Dried stems are very hard and make excellent fuel.

CULTIVATION
Site Full sun.
Soil Any well-drained loam.
Propagating Sow seeds in their shells in spring. Avoid planting near potatoes as growth becomes stunted.
Growing Thin or transplant to 12–18 in (30–45 cm) apart. Not suitable for growing indoors.
Harvesting Pick leaves and flower buds as required. Cut flower heads when they droop. Hang until seeds fall. Gather stems in autumn.
Preserving Dry leaves and seed.

USES
Decorative
● *Whole plant* Grow as a colourful windbreak or focal point.

Culinary
● *Seed* Shell and eat kernel raw, or roast: brown 1 oz (25 g) seed with shells in $\frac{1}{2}$ tsp (2.5 ml) oil, drain and toss in salt. Add sprouted seeds to salads and sandwiches, when $\frac{1}{4}$ in (6 mm) long, before they become bitter. Cook with sunflower oil.
● *Flower* Eat raw buds in salad, or steam and serve like globe artichokes.

Household
● *Whole plant* Grow as a moisture-absorbent plant near a house to deter rising damp and drain ground.
● *Seed* Feed whole seed to chickens to increase egg laying.
● *Flower* Boil for a yellow dye.
● *Leaf* Can be smoked, dried.
● *Stem* Use fibrous pith for textiles and paper-making. Burn and scatter ashes as potash fertilizer.

Cosmetic
● *Seed* Pressed oil contains vitamin F and other substances that benefit the skin.

Medicinal
● *Seed* Eat a handful or take 15 oil drops three times a day, or boil seed for 20 minutes and take as a tea to relieve coughs, dysentery, and inflammation of the kidneys.

Helichrysum angustifolium

Curry plant Compositae

This plant from southern Europe is a relatively new addition to herbal lists. Curry plant's initial attraction lies in the intense silver of its evergreen leaves, which make it and its dwarf form, *H.a.* var. *nana*, a good choice for formal edgings and knot gardens. However, it is the sweet curry scent of its leaves which is so unusual and has caused its recent rise in popularity, especially among adventurous cooks. Visitors to my garden who accidentally brush against curry plant often look around for a picnic group to track down the source of the spicy aroma.

The genus *Helichrysum* also includes *H. bracteatum*, whose everlasting flowers, though scentless, are often added to potpourri and dried arrangements for their decorativeness.

Dried flowers
These everlasting flowers retain their colour well for potpourri and flower arrangements.

Dried leaves
These add a mild curry flavour to soups and casseroles.

Flower
Tiny, mustard-yellow clusters, with sweet mild curry scent, borne in late summer.

Leaf
Narrow, needle-like and silvery-grey with sweetish curry scent.

Stem
Downy, round and white becoming green then woody in second season.

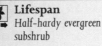

Lifespan
Half-hardy evergreen subshrub

Height
18 in (45 cm)

CULTIVATION
Site Full sun.
Soil Rich and well drained.
Propagating Take stem cuttings in spring or autumn.
Growing Plant 12 in (30 cm) apart. Prune lightly in early autumn or spring. In areas with light frost, curry plants may die back temporarily. Protect leaves with 5 in (12 cm) sleeve of straw set between chicken wire. In areas where temperature drops below 22 °F (-5 °C), bring curry plants indoors for winter protection.
Harvesting Pick leaves anytime. Gather flowers as they open.
Preserving Dry leaves and flowers.

USES
Decorative
● *Whole plant* Provides decorative silver edging in formal beds and knot gardens. (*H.a.* var. *nana*) This half-hardy dwarf form, 8 in (20 cm) high, makes a pretty edging and knot garden plant and is attractive in sink gardens.
● *Flower* (*H. bracteatum*) Dry petals to add colour to potpourri, and whole flowers for arrangements, garlands and wreaths.
● *Leaf* Add sprigs to tussie-mussies, garlands and wreaths.

Culinary
● *Leaf* Add a sprig to soups, stews, steamed vegetables, rice dishes and pickles for a mild curry flavour. Remove sprig before serving.

Hesperis matronalis

Sweet rocket Cruciferae

This pretty cottage flower has maintained its position in the herb garden because of its sweet-scented flowers as well as its medicinal properties. A native of Italy, it can be found growing wild in much of Europe and northern America as a garden escapee.

Its massed flowers, a glorious sight in midsummer, are sometimes called dame's violet or vesper-flower, since its perfume is strongest in the evening. The young leaves are occasionally eaten as a salad herb, but they are more bitter than salad rocket (see p. 135).

Flower
Sweetly fragrant, purple, mauve and white flowers appear in midsummer.

Seed
Brown, narrow and pointed, $\frac{1}{8}$ in (3 mm) long.

Stem
Slender and carries flowers in second year.

Leaf
Spear-shaped and dark green.

Lifespan
Hardy biennial. Sometimes behaves as a perennial, sending out new shoots from old roots

Height
3 ft (1 m)

CULTIVATION
Site Full sun or light shade.
Soil Prefers rich loam in beds or light woodland.
Propagating Sow outdoors in late spring.
Growing Thin seedlings or transplant in autumn to 18 in (45 cm) apart. Sweet rocket is too tall to grow indoors.
Harvesting Gather leaves when young for eating but at flowering time for medicinal properties. Collect flowers as they open.
Preserving Dry leaves and flowers.

USES
Decorative
● *Flower* Pick for a pretty, sweet-scented summer bouquet.

Culinary
● *Flower* Toss in salads. Use as a decoration for desserts.
● *Leaf* Add chopped young leaves sparingly to salads.

Aromatic
● *Flower* Add dried flowers to potpourri for their pastel colour and sweet scent.

Medicinal
● *Leaf* Dried leaves were once popular for preventing and curing scurvy. A strong dose may cause vomiting.

Humulus lupulus

Hops *Cannabaceae*

In the first century AD, the Roman writer Pliny described hops as a popular garden plant and vegetable: in spring, young shoots were sold on markets, to be eaten like asparagus. By the eighth century, this plant was used in brewing throughout most of Europe for its clearing, flavouring and preserving qualities. However, in Britain, brewers continued to rely on traditional herbs such as ground ivy and alecost until the sixteenth century, under the curious belief that hops engendered melancholy. Even in 1670, John Evelyn explained that "hops . . . preserve the drink indeed, but repay the pleasure in tormenting diseases and a shorter life".

Leaf
Large, roughly textured, toothed, heart-shaped and mid-green, with three or five lobes.

Dried flowers
Use ripe, unpollinated female flowers to clear, preserve and flavour ale with a bitter taste; can also be used medicinally and around the house.

Dried leaves
Boil for a brown dye. Sometimes added to hop pillows for bulk but they do not contain the same medicinal properties as hop flowers.

Stem
Tough, prickly haired, faceted, green tinged with red.

H.l. 'Aureus'
Soft golden leaves, best grown in full sun. Dried flowers and leaves are believed to have the same properties as the species.

Flower
Yellowish-green, cone-like female blooms borne in late summer, ripen into larger globes of pale papery bracts containing powdery glands, which have many uses. Male flowers appear on separate plants.

Lifespan
Hardy deciduous climber

Height
23 ft (7 m)

CULTIVATION

Site Sunny open position.
Soil Fertile and deeply dug.
Propagating Reproduce female plants only. Divide roots and separate rooted stems and suckers in spring. Take cuttings in early summer. Avoid sowing, as plant gender is unknown for 2–3 years.
Growing Grow 3 ft (1 m) apart against support. Hops can be grown indoors but they seldom flower.
Harvesting Pick young side-shoots in spring. Gather young leaves as required. Pick ripe flowers in early autumn. Collect stems in late autumn.
Preserving Dry leaves and stems. Dry and use female flowers within a few months, otherwise the flavour will become unpleasant.

USES

Decorative
● *Whole plant* (H.l. 'Aureus') Makes a leafy screen or focal point trained on a tripod or frame.
● *Flowers* Attractive in dried arrangements and garlands.

Culinary
● *Flower* Use dried ripe female flowers to flavour, clear and preserve beer. Parboil male flowers and toss into salads.
● *Leaf* Blanch young leaves to remove bitterness. Add to soups.
● *Shoot* Steam young side shoots and serve like asparagus.

Household
● *Leaf* Boil for a brown dye.
● *Stem* Weave into baskets and other wickerwork. Used to make durable cloth and paper.

Cosmetic
● *Flower* Infuse and add to a relaxing bath.

Medicinal
● *Flower* Sprinkle with alcohol and add to pillows to induce sleep. Infuse as a mild sedative tea for digestive problems and as an anti-septic. Add flowers to any other tea and drink as a digestive aid and appetite stimulant.

Flowering herbs

As with the early flowering herbs on p. 54, the herbal properties of these plants had been largely forgotten but they continued to be grown as attractive garden plants. Now many of these lesser known herbs are being rediscovered, particularly for their medicinal properties: agrimony, for example, is used to treat sore throats, childhood diarrhoea and cystitis. With the renewed interest in herbal decorations and potpourri, the scented flowers of mock orange and honeysuckle are doubly valued; with a return to herbal cosmetics, lupin seeds are added to face masks and scrubs. All the plants shown below have interesting uses, past and present, and all of them add decorative colour, shapes and fragrance to the garden.

Malva moschata
Musk mallow (left)
Masses of white or pink flowers appear all summer. Pretty cut leaf has a faintly musky fragrance. (See p. 84.)

Sedum rosea
Roseroot (right)
Has succulent leaves and produces clusters of yellow flowers. (See p. 85.)

Galega officinalis
Goat's rue (below)
A legume grown for its delicate pink, white or lilac flowers. Used medicinally. (See p. 276.)

Delphinium elatum
Delphinium (below)
A tall plant for borders. Pretty blue flowers for arrangements and potpourri.

Scutellaria lateriflora
Skullcap (below)
Stems of unusual blue-mauve flowers. (See p. 278.)

Digitalis x mertonensis
Foxglove (right)
One of the several attractive forms of foxglove. (See p. 82.)

Teucrium chamaedrys
Wall germander (left)
Compact evergreen leaves make good ground cover. (See p. 85.)

Echium vulgare
Viper's bugloss (above)
This herb is related to borage, and similarly its flowers are used as a garnish. (See p. 275.)

Paeonia officinalis
Peony (right)
Luscious blooms of
fragrant petals for
potpourri. (See p. 84.)

Lonicera caprifolium
Honeysuckle (above)
Early and late flowering
forms are available. (See p. 83.)

Jasminum
beesianum
Jasmine
(right)
Many forms
are available.
Use the fragrant
flowers in potpourri.

Nigella damascena
Love-in-a-mist (right)
Decorative
flowers and
seed heads.

Geranium
pratense
Meadow crane's-bill (above)
Interesting self-propagator;
ripe seed is catapulted
several feet away. Add
flowers to salads.

Agrimonia
eupatoria
Agrimony
(left)
Spires of tiny
yellow flowers.
Leaves used
medicinally.
(See p. 82.)

Philadelphus 'Virginal'
Mock orange (left)
Richly scented flowers
dry well for potpourri.

Lilium candidum
Madonna lily
(right)
Produces exotic and
fragrant flowers.
(See p. 83.)

Lupinus polyphyllus
Lupin (left)
The seed has cosmetic
uses; flowers give colour
to potpourri. (See p. 277.)

81

Flowering herbs

Agrimonia eupatoria

Agrimony *Rosaceae*

Digitalis purpurea

Foxglove *Scrophulariaceae*

A graceful perennial suitable for a sunny border, agrimony is sometimes known as church steeples because of its thin, tapering spikes of small, star-shaped yellow flowers. The mid-green leaves have serrated edges and grow in alternate large and small pairs. The flowers, which are borne throughout the summer, have an apricot scent, particularly attractive to bees and other insects. The flower spike can reach over 2 ft (60 cm) high.

CULTIVATION
Sow seed in late winter or spring or, for better results, in late summer or early autumn in well-drained soil.

USES
In Anglo-Saxon times agrimony was virtually regarded as a heal-all with almost magical powers. Its name comes from the Greek word *agremone*, used to describe plants that healed eye disorders. It contains tannin, which as well as being recommended for dressing leather is good for skin eruptions, and it yields a yellow dye. Today it is made into an apricot-scented herb tea, and an infusion of agrimony is often prescribed for gastro-intestinal complaints, coughs, cystitis and as a gargle for sore throats. It may be used in an eye bath to add sparkle to tired eyes.

In some conditions the foxglove is a perennial, but it is usually best treated as a biennial. Tall spikes, 3–5 ft (1–1.5 m) long, bear tubular, bell-like flowers throughout the summer. The flowers of the common *Digitalis purpurea* are purple or reddish, but hybrids are available in a variety of colours. The large, downy, mid-green leaves have slightly indented edges. Those of the common foxglove are oval, while D. × *mertonensis* (p. 80) has lance-shaped leaves and more luxuriant, showy flowers. Happy in full sun or partial shade, the foxglove makes a colourful and dramatic background to smaller border plants.

CULTIVATION
Sow seed in spring or early summer the year before the plant is to flower. The foxglove prefers well-drained, acid soil. Water well in dry weather and remove the central spike after flowering to increase the size of flowers on the side-shoots.

USES
For over 200 years D. *purpurea* has provided the main drug for treating heart failure. It is also a powerful diuretic. Although a synthetic form of the drug has been developed, the plant is still grown commercially for the drug industry.

Note: *Foxgloves are poisonous and should not be eaten or used domestically.*

Lilium candidum
Madonna lily Liliaceae

A favourite plant even as far back as ancient Greek and Roman times, the madonna lily, with its pure white flowers, was dedicated to the Virgin Mary in the early days of Christianity. The 3 in (8 cm), trumpet-shaped flowers, borne in midsummer, have a sweet, penetrating fragrance. The erect flower stem grows to a height of 4–5 ft (1–1.5 m), with pale-green, lance-shaped leaves growing from it. After the stem dies down in autumn, it produces a rosette of basal leaves. Once established in a site where it is happy, preferably on a sunny sheltered slope, the madonna lily will flourish if left relatively undisturbed.

CULTIVATION
Plant bulbs in early autumn in well-drained, alkaline soil. Unlike many lilies, the madonna lily roots only from the base of its bulb, which needs to be covered in no more than 2 in (5 cm) of soil. Do not allow to dry out. It can be difficult to establish.

USES
Plant along a garden path or within sight of a favourite bench to appreciate the madonna lily's striking, exotic-looking flowers and strong perfume. The flowers were once thought to be anti-epileptic and, steeped in spirit, provided a soothing lotion for bruises. The bulbs, collected in late summer, contain a rich mucilage which is used in cosmetics and added to an ointment for treating corns and burns. In some Eastern countries the bulbs are eaten cooked.

Lonicera caprifolium
Honeysuckle Caprifoliaceae

Also known as woodbine, the honeysuckle is a perennial twining climber which, given suitable support, can reach a height of 20 ft (6 m). Like the more common *Lonicera periclymenum*, L. *caprifolium* (above) can be found growing wild. It is distinguishable by its light-green oval leaves which sometimes merge across the stem rather than growing in pairs one on either side. The pink-tinged, creamy-white flowers, basically tubular with diverging lips, are borne in close pairs from midsummer to early autumn. Poisonous small orange berries appear after the flowers. The berries were once fed to chickens, and the Latin name *caprifolium*, meaning "goat's leaf", reflects the belief that honeysuckle leaves are a favourite food of goats.

CULTIVATION
Take cuttings from non-flowering shoots in summer and root in cuttings compost. Plant out during the autumn or winter, preferably in light shade.

USES
Extremely tolerant, honeysuckle will flourish vigorously in the most unpromising sites. In leaf for most of the year, it can be used to cover an unsightly wall or provide a rich summer-evening fragrance in an arbour. Perfume can be obtained from the flowers, which add scent and interesting shapes to potpourri. They are also useful, as an infusion or syrup, for treating coughs, catarrh and asthma. The plant has diuretic and laxative properties and also contains salicylic acid, from which aspirin is produced. Large doses cause vomiting.

Flowering herbs

Malva moschata
Musk mallow Malvaceae

A pretty, bushy border perennial, the musk mallow grows to a height of about 2 ft (60 cm). Spikes of large, single pink or white flowers are borne in abundance on its thick, erect stems from midsummer to early autumn. Even when the plant is not in flower, ample decoration is provided by its mid-green leaves, kidney-shaped near the base and divided on the stem. The leaves emit a musky aroma in warm weather or when gently pressed.

CULTIVATION
Sow seed in early autumn or spring, or plant rooted cuttings during autumn or winter, preferably in well-drained, fertile soil. Musk mallow needs staking in moist soil. It likes full sun but will also tolerate semi-shade. Cut down the stems in autumn.

USES
With similar properties to the common mallow (M. *sylvestris*), its larger flowers and subtle fragrance make the musk mallow the better choice in the herb garden. The leaves can be boiled and eaten as a vegetable. Both the leaves and the roots were once made into ointments and soothing syrups for coughs.

Paeonia officinalis
Peony Paeoniaceae

The sumptuous beauty of the peony makes it well worth the initial care needed to establish it in the herb garden. Several large bowls of petals, up to 5 in (12 cm) across, are borne by each flower stalk in late spring and early summer. Growing to a height of 2 ft (60 cm), the common peony was once available with only single, purplish-red flowers, but now double white or pink varieties are also to be found. The deeply indented leaves are mid-green. It thrives in an open sunny site, although early-morning sun is best avoided.

CULTIVATION
Single varieties can be grown from seed sown in autumn. The planting site should be dug deep and enriched with compost. Plant with the base of the stem no more than 1 in (2.5 cm) deep in early autumn. It will take at least three years to become properly established. Water frequently in dry weather and stake the stems. Deadhead the spent flowers and cut down in autumn.

USES
Many ancient superstitions are connected with the peony. It was thought to be a divine plant that would drive away evil spirits and keep nightmares at bay. The seeds were once used as a spice in cookery. Herbalists prescribed an infusion of the powdered root for the liver and associated complaints. It was also thought to relieve spasms and convulsions and was given to women immediately after childbirth.

Sedum rosea
Roseroot Crassulaceae

A perennial alpine or rock plant with egg-shaped, silvery-green, succulent leaves grouped closely around its thick stem. The star-shaped yellow flower heads attract bees and butterflies. When dry, the thick roots give off the scent of roses. Some sedums are used successfully to cover a dry wall, but roseroot, which can reach a height of 1 ft (30 cm), is better suited to a sunny border.

CULTIVATION
Propagate by taking stem cuttings in late summer and inserting them in compost, or divide the roots in spring and plant in full sun in a well-drained, gritty soil. Remove dead flower heads in spring.

USES
A tough, reliable plant, its flowers provide a splash of summer colour. Mentioned in herbals as early as the sixteenth century, the root of the plant was used to make a "poor man's rosewater". Roseroot is little used today except in Greenland, where the leaves are eaten in salads all year round.

Teucrium chamaedrys
Wall germander Labiatae

This small, bushy perennial, with its spreading, creeping root, bears tubular, purplish-pink flowers on short terminal spikes from midsummer to early autumn. The shiny evergreen leaves are indented and rather similar to oak leaves. Indeed the word *chamaedrys* means "ground oak". When rubbed, the leaves smell pleasantly spicy. Suitable for a rock garden, it also establishes itself well in the crevices of a dry wall, and is often found growing wild in old ruined buildings. It reaches a height of 4–8 in (10–20 cm) and prefers well-drained soil in a sunny position.

CULTIVATION
For decorative wall-covering, sow seeds outdoors in seed trays in early summer and cover lightly with soil. Plant seedlings in the wall. For a rock garden, divide the roots in autumn. Take cuttings in late spring.

USES
Wall germander is a traditional knot garden plant. The whole herb was collected in midsummer and dried. A decoction of germander was a famous remedy for gout and other pains in the limbs, such as rheumatism. Thought to be a diuretic and stimulating tonic, germander was also recommended for coughs and asthma. It was a popular strewing herb.

Hyssopus officinalis

Hyssop Labiatae

The Greek *hyssopos* may derive from the Hebrew *ezob*, or holy herb, because it was used for purifying temples and the ritual cleansing of lepers: "Purge me with hyssop, and I shall be clean" (*Psalm* 51 v.7). The biblical plant may not in fact have been common hyssop but rather a form of oregano or savory. However, research now favours common hyssop once again, with the discovery that the mould that produces penicillin grows on its leaf. This could have acted as antibiotic protection when lepers were bathed in hyssop.

A wine called *hyssopites*, made from hyssop, was mentioned by the Roman writer Pliny in the first century AD. This may have influenced the Benedictine monks who, in the tenth century, brought the herb into central Europe to flavour their liqueurs.

Seed
Brown, flattish, tear-shaped, $\frac{1}{8}$ in (3 mm) long; may have a white tip.

Dried leaves
Used in tiny quantities in cooking; also medicinally and cosmetically.

Purple form

Flower
Rich blue, lipped clusters, in leaf axils up one side of the stems, borne in late summer; loved by bees and butterflies.

White form
Occasionally found in seed of blue-flowered common hyssop.

Stem
Square, branching and green, turning woody in second year.

Leaf
Narrow, $\frac{1}{4}$–1 in (6–25 mm) long, aromatic, slightly hairy, pointed and dark green.

Pink form

H.o. 'Aristatus' Rock hyssop
Compact, with deep blue-purple flowers borne in late summer and narrow, aromatic leaves.

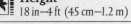

Lifespan
Hardy semi-evergreen subshrub

Height
18 in–4 ft (45 cm–1.2 m)

CULTIVATION
Site Full sun.
Soil Light, well drained, alkaline.
Propagating Divide roots in spring. Take stem cuttings from spring to autumn. (Species) Sow in spring.
Growing Transplant or thin to 2 ft (60 cm) apart, or to 1 ft (30 cm) apart, for hedging. Cut back to 8 in (20 cm) in mild-winter areas after flowering; otherwise in spring. Hyssop can be grown indoors.
Harvesting Pick flowers and young flowering tops as flowering begins. Gather leaves anytime.
Preserving Dry young leaves and flowering tops.

USES
Decorative
● *Whole plant* Grow for hedging and knots, and in borders.

Culinary
● *Flower* Toss in salads.
● *Leaf* Use small amounts. Aids digestion of fatty fish and meat. Add to game (rub on skin), rabbit pie, kidney and lamb stews, rich pâté, vegetable soup and pulses. Serve with cranberries in fruit salads. Sprinkle $\frac{1}{4}$ tsp (1 ml) under the crust of peach and apricot pies.

Household
● *Whole plant* Grow near cabbages to lure away cabbage-white butterflies. Plant near vines to increase yield.

Aromatic
● *Flower and leaf* Add to potpourri.

Medicinal
● *Flowering top* Infuse as a tea for throat and lung complaints, bronchial catarrh, and poor digestion and appetite. Use essential oil in aromatherapy for bruises.
● *Leaf* Put leaves in a poultice to heal wounds and bruises.

Note: *Do not take hyssop when pregnant.*

Inula helenium

Elecampane *Compositae*

Helen of Troy was believed to be gathering elecampane when she was abducted by Paris, and its botanic name has captured this association. Its root contains a sweet starchy substance called inulin, which is responsible for elecampane's popularity as a crystallized sweet. According to the Roman writer Pliny, the Empress Julia Augusta "let no day pass without eating some of the roots candied, to help the digestion and cause mirth". In the Middle Ages, apothecaries sold the candied root in flat, pink, sugary cakes, which were sucked to alleviate asthma and indigestion and to sweeten the breath. In ancient China large-leafed plants were grown under scholars' windows so they could listen to different sounds of rain. Elecampane can be used for a similar effect in temperate climates.

Seed
Mid-brown, torpedo-shaped, $\frac{3}{16}$ in (4 mm) long, with short tufts of hair at one end, in velvety, dark brown seed heads.

Dried petals
Dry the shaggy, daisy-like, yellow flowers and use the petals in potpourri for colour.

Leaf
Up to 18 in (45 cm) long, pointed, coarsely toothed and green, with downy grey underside.

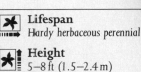

Lifespan
Hardy herbaceous perennial

Height
5–8 ft (1.5–2.4 m)

Stem
Thick, hairy, ridged, round and green, filled with white spongy pith.

Dried root
This smells of violets and is used medicinally.

Root
Thick, dark brown, tuberous and aromatic with creamy, edible flesh smelling of bananas.

CULTIVATION

Site Prefers sun.
Soil Moist and fertile.
Propagating Sow in spring or divide plant in spring or autumn.
Growing Thin or transplant to 3–4 ft (1–1.2 m) apart. Elecampane may require staking; it can become untidy. Prune in late summer. It is not suitable for indoor cultivation.
Harvesting Dig up second- or third-year roots in autumn.
Preserving Slice and dry root.

USES

Decorative
● *Whole plant* Striking garden plant.
● *Seed* Use velvety seed heads for winter arrangements.

Culinary
● **Root** Eat dried pieces or cook as a root vegetable. Be prepared for its sharp bitter flavour. Crystallize as a sweet. It was a popular ingredient in Roman times, used to stimulate the appetite and to counteract the effects of rich food. Also used more recently to flavour absinthe.

Household
● **Root** Burn over embers to scent a room. Stephen Blake, in his *Complete Gardener's Practice* of 1664, suggested a more unusual use: "To be revenged on a person who steals your tulips, sprinkle dry powdered elecampane root on clove gillyflowers, give to the party who will delight to smell it and when they draw the powder into their nostrils they will fall sneezing until tears run down their thighs."

Cosmetic
● **Root** Apply a decoction to acne.

Medicinal
● **Root** Decoct as a general tonic, as an expectorant to ease bronchitis and coughs, and as a digestive. Infuse in wine or port for a cordial. Crystallize and eat to relieve indigestion, asthma and coughs.

Lavandula angustifolia (L. officinalis or L. spica)

Lavender Labiatae

Tranquillity and purity are inherent in the unique fragrance of lavender, as reflected by the seventeenth-century angling author Izaak Walton, "I long to be in a house where the sheets smell of lavender." Its fresh clean scent was the favourite bathwater additive of the Greeks and Romans, and its name derives from the Latin *lavare* "to wash".

A popular strewing herb both for its insect-repellent properties and its long-lasting fragrance, lavender was also distilled for liberal use in masking household smells and stinking streets. Stories that the glovers of Grasse, who used lavender oil to scent their fashionable leather, were remarkably free of plague, encouraged other people to carry lavender to ward off the pestilence.

Lavender has long been used medicinally. The herbalist Gerard, for example, prescribed it to bathe the temples of those with a "light migram or swimming of the braine". One Sir James Smith also told of an alcoholic tincture created "for those who wished to indulge in a dram under the appearance of elegant medicine".

Its healing powers are now mainly obtained from the essential oil. This is distilled from shining oil glands embedded among the tiny star-shaped hairs which cover the flowers, leaves and stems. The best quality oil is extracted from *L. angustifolia* and *L. stoechas*. *L. latifolia* yields "spike" oil, used to perfume cheaper goods, while *L. intermedia* yields "lavendin", a medium-quality oil.

Seed
Four smooth, dark brown nutlets in each fruit.

Dried flowers
These produce a sweet, clean, long-lasting scent.

Flower
Small, highly scented, lavender-blue flowers borne in spikes 2–6 in (5–15 cm) long in summer.

L. angustifolia 'Loddon Pink'
A pale pink-flowered lavender that is attractive mixed with other varieties.

L.a. 'Hidcote'
Compact with dark purple flowers and small silver leaves. Slow growing.

L.a. 'Nana Alba'
White flower spikes, 1½–2 in (4–5 cm) long, with compact silver-grey foliage. Ht: 12 in (30 cm).

Stem
Square and green, becoming woody in second season.

L.a. 'Twickle Purple'
Compact with long, soft, purple spikes and broad, grey-green leaves.

L.a. 'Vera' Dutch lavender
Purple flowers with leaves that are more slender, silver and compact than the species.

L.a. 'Folgate'
Compact with rich purple-blue flowers and narrow, grey-green leaves.

L.a. 'Munstead'
Early variety with lavender flowers and greenish leaves. Ht: 12–18 in (30–45 cm).

Leaf
Narrow, fragrant and grey-green, ¾ in–2 in (2–5 cm) long.

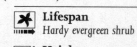

Lifespan
Hardy evergreen shrub

Height
18 in–3 ft (45 cm–1 m)

OTHER SPECIES

L.stoechas var. pedunculata
Half-hardy, magenta-pink flowers with purple bracts above and grey-green leaves.

L. lanata
Half-hardy, bright purple flowers and white woolly leaves with balsamic-lavender scent.

L.l. 'Sawyer's hybrid'
Hardy, new form with silver leaves, large flower spikes and stronger constitution than the species.

**L. stoechas
French lavender**
Half-hardy, purple flowers with purple bracts above and grey-green leaves.

L. dentata
Half-hardy, fragrant lavender flowers in winter and finely toothed, green leaves.

English lavender in flower.

CULTIVATION

Site Sunny and open, to discourage fungus disease.
Soil Well drained, sandy with lime content.
Propagating Take 4–8 in (10–20 cm) stem cuttings in autumn or spring, or divide or layer plant. (Species only) Sow from fresh seed in late summer and autumn.
Growing Thin or transplant to 18 in–2 ft (45–60 cm) apart, or 12 in (30 cm) apart for hedges. Remove faded flower stems; prune hedges and straggly plants in late autumn or spring. (L.a. 'Grappenhall') Plant 4 ft (1.2 m) apart.
Harvesting Gather flowering stems just as flowers open. Pick leaves anytime.
Preserving Dry flowering stems by laying on open trays or hanging in small bunches.

USES

Decorative
● **Whole plant** Good for hedging.
● **Flower** Hang dried in bunches on its own or with other tiny flowers. Add sprigs to wreaths and nosegays.

Culinary
● **Flower** Use to flavour jams and to make lavender vinegar (see p. 188). Mix small amounts with savoury herbs for fragrant stews. Crystallize flowers.
● **Leaf** Bitter; used in southern European cooking.

Household
● **Flower** Put dried flowers in sachets and bundles to scent drawers and to protect linen from moths. Rub fresh flowers on skin, or pin on clothes, to discourage flies.
● **Stem** Use dried as incense or scented firelighters.

Cosmetic
● **Flower** Make tonic water for delicate and sensitive skins to speed cell replacement and for an antiseptic against acne. Add to soap. Use oil in massage for muscular aches, fluid retention and cellulite.

Aromatic
● **Flower** Use in potpourri, herb pillows, linen sachets. Add a few drops of essential oil to final rinse water for scented linen or hair.

Medicinal
● **Flower** Infuse as a tea to soothe headaches, calm nerves, ease flatulence, fainting, dizziness and halitosis. Use neat essential oil as an antiseptic, mild sedative and painkiller, particularly on insect bites, stings and small (cooled) burns. Add six drops to bathwater to calm irritable children, and place one drop on the temple for headache relief. Blend for use as a massage oil in aromatherapy for throat infections, skin sores, inflammation, rheumatic aches, anxiety, insomnia and depression.

Laurus nobilis

Bay/Sweet bay/Laurel Lauraceae

The bay tree was sacred to Apollo, the Greek god of prophecy, poetry and healing. His prophecies were communicated through his priestess at Delphi, who, among other rituals, ate a bay leaf before expounding her oracle. As bay leaves are slightly narcotic in large doses, they may have induced her trance.

Apollo's temple at Delphi had its roof made entirely of bay leaves for protection against disease, witchcraft and lightning. Bay-leaf garlands were subsequently adopted as architectural mouldings. A wreath of bay leaves became the mark of excellence for poets and athletes and, to the Romans, bay was a symbol of wisdom and glory. The Latin *laurus* means "laurel" and *nobilis* "renowned"; *laureate* means "crowned with laurels", hence poet laureate and baccalaureate.

Bay was also dedicated to Apollo's son, Aesculapius, the Greek god of medicine, and it has been used against disease, especially plague, for many centuries.

Dried leaves
Use within a few days of drying to capture optimum flavour. Old dried leaves lack pungency.

Leaf
Fragrant, leathery, pointed, oval, glossy dark green, with olive-green underside and bitter flavour.

L.n. 'Aurea'
Golden bay
Golden leaves; a slightly hardier variety than the species when both are small plants.

L.n. 'Angustifolia'
Willow leaf bay
This narrow-leaved variety was promoted as less susceptible to wind damage – an aim not achieved.

Stem
Solid, round, rich purple-brown, becoming woody and grey.

L. nobilis

Lifespan
Evergreen tree. When mature, roots are hardy but leaves die in freezing winds

Height
23 ft (7 m)

CULTIVATION

Site Full sun. Protect from wind.
Soil Rich, moist and well drained.
Propagating Take 4 in (10 cm) stem cuttings or layer in late summer. Plant cuttings in heated propagator with high humidity.
Growing Transplant to 4 ft (1.2 m) apart, in frost-free area for first 2 years. Bay can be container-grown but bring indoors should the temperature drop below 5 °F (−15 °C).
Harvesting Pick leaves anytime.
Preserving Dry leaves. Use to flavour vinegar.

USES

Decorative
● *Whole plant* Clip for topiary.
● *Leaf* Make into wreaths.

Culinary
● *Leaf* Include in bouquet garni for stews, soups and sauces. Add to marinades, stock, potato soup, stuffing, pâté, curry, game and poached fish liquid. Remove leaf before serving. Boil in milk to flavour custards and rice pudding. Use as a garnish. Place in rice storage jar to flavour rice.

Household
● *Whole plant* Used as a strewing herb by highest-ranking officials.
● *Leaf* Place in flour bin and around dried figs as a weevil deterrent.

Cosmetic
● *Leaf* Add decoction to bathwater to relieve aching limbs.

Aromatic
● *Branch* Hang to fresh'en air.
● *Leaf* Crumble into potpourri.

Medicinal
● *Leaf* Infuse as a digestive aid and to stimulate the appetite. Massage blended essential oil around sprains and into rheumatic joints.

Note: *All laurels except sweet bay are poisonous.*

Levisticum officinale (Ligusticum levisticum)

Lovage *Umbelliferae*

Lovage is a handsome plant with a powerful flavour and numerous uses, both traditional and modern. Its leaves used to be laid in shoes to revive the weary traveller, and at inns it was served in a popular cordial, which was flavoured with tansy and a variety of yarrow known as *Achillea ligustica*, as well as lovage. A modern form is made by steeping fresh lovage seed in brandy, sweetening it with sugar and then drinking it to settle an upset stomach.

Lovage leaves add a strong savoury flavour to dishes, so use cautiously at first.

Seed
Brown, ridged, crescent shaped, oblong-sectioned and aromatic; about ¼ in (6 mm) long.

Dried leaves
These contain a strong flavour of yeast and celery; excellent infused as broth or for seasoning.

Dried root
These retain their aroma and are used medicinally.

Flower
Tiny, pale greenish-yellow clusters appear from mid- to late summer.

Leaf
Large, aromatic, toothed, deeply divided and glossy dark green on long stems; those leaves near top are smaller and stalkless.

Stem
Hollow, ridged, round, branching near top and greenish-red.

Lifespan
Hardy herbaceous perennial

Height
7 ft (2.1 m)

Root
Thick, grey-brown, aromatic and branching with white flesh.

CULTIVATION
Site Full sun or partial shade.
Soil Rich, moist and well drained.
Propagating Sow fresh ripe seed in late summer. (Lovage self-seeds readily.) Take root cuttings with buds in spring or autumn.
Growing Thin or transplant to 2 ft (60 cm) apart. Tie straw around stems 2–3 weeks before harvesting for blanched tender vegetable. Not suitable for growing indoors.
Harvesting Pick leaves as needed, but retain young central leaves. Gather young blanched stems in spring. Dig second- and third-season roots before flowers open each year. Gather seed when ripe.
Preserving Freeze or dry leaves. Dry seeds and roots.

USES
Decorative
● *Leaf and stem* Arrange fresh leaves and stems in a clear tall vase.

Culinary
● *Seed* Add to liqueurs and cordials. Crush in bread and pastries. Sprinkle on salads, rice or mashed potatoes.
● *Leaf* Make lovage soup (see p. 166). Add fresh or dried leaves to stock, stews and cheese, and fresh young leaves to salads. Rub leaf on chicken and around salad bowl. Drink tea for its savoury taste.
● *Stem and leaf stalk* Steam and serve with white sauce. Chop into stews and soup. Crystallize young stems. Eat raw shoots, 4 in (10 cm) long, dressed with oil and vinegar.
● *Root* Peel; then cook or pickle.

Medicinal
● *Seed, leaf and root* Infuse any of these to reduce water retention, assist in removal of waste products, act as a deodorizer, and aid rheumatism. This infusion should not be taken during pregnancy or by those with kidney problems.

Marrubium vulgare

Horehound Labiatae

For thousands of years, horehound has been much valued as a cough remedy. Egyptian priests honoured its medicinal properties and called it "seed of Horus", "bulls' blood" and "eye of the star". The Greek physician Hippocrates and other physicians down the ages have also held this herb in high esteem as a cure for many ills. It was also thought to break magical spells.

Horehound's botanical name comes from the Hebrew *marrob*, which translates as bitter juice. Its common name is derived from the Old English term for downy plant, *har hune*.

Seed
Shiny, dark brown, tear-shaped, $\frac{1}{12}$ in (2 mm) long.

	Lifespan
	Hardy perennial
	Height
	18 in (45 cm)

Flower
Small, white clusters borne from midsummer to early autumn from second year.

Dried leaves
Use as a medicinal infusion for chest, nasal and sinus congestion.

Stem
Downy, square, branching and white.

Leaf
Wrinkled, heart-shaped and green, with white woolly covering most pronounced towards tip; fruit-scented but bitter flavour; contains vitamin C.

CULTIVATION

Site Full sun. Protect from winds.
Soil Dryish and alkaline.
Propagating Divide horehound in midspring. Sow in late spring. Take stem cuttings in late summer.
Growing Thin or transplant to 1 ft (30 cm) apart. Protect from excessive winter wet. Prune in spring. Horehound can be cultivated indoors.
Harvesting Pick leaves and flowering tops at flowering time or as needed.
Preserving Dry leaves and flowering tops or make into syrup.

USES

Decorative
● *Flowers* Use dried in flower arrangements.

Household
● *Flower* Attracts bees to gardens.
● *Leaf* Infuse as a spray for cankerworm in trees. Infuse in fresh milk and set in a dish as a fly killer.

Medicinal
● *Leaf* At the first sign of a cold: finely chop nine small horehound leaves, mix with 1 tbsp (15 ml) honey and eat slowly to ease sore throat or cough. Repeat several times if necessary. Suck horehound cough sweets as an expectorant. To make cough sweets: put 4 oz (100 g) fresh horehound leaves, $\frac{1}{2}$ tsp (2.5 g) crushed aniseed and 3 crushed cardamom seeds in 1 pint (570 ml) water and simmer for 20 minutes. Strain through a filter. Over a low heat, dissolve 12 oz (350 g) white sugar and 12 oz (350 g) moist brown sugar in the liquid. Then boil over medium heat until the syrup hardens when drops are put in cold water. Pour into an oiled tray. Score when partially cooled. Store in waxed paper. Drink a cold infusion to ease digestion and heartburn, and to destroy intestinal worms.

Melilotus officinalis

Melilot/Sweet clover *Leguminosae*

The name melilot derives from *meli* meaning honey, and *lotos* meaning fodder or clover, hence its other name, sweet clover. A native of Europe, Asia and North America, it was once a popular strewing herb and fodder crop, until replaced by common clover, and was also a source of many successful medical remedies.

M. *alba* with white flowers originates from the Mediterranean and also decorates the highways of northern Alberta. There it is called Canadian sweet clover, and it is a valued honey plant. Near Gruyère, the Swiss pick a local blue form (M. *caerulea*) to flavour their cheese.

Flower
Yellow, honey-scented, pea-like flowers throughout summer and autumn.

Seed
Small, brown, egg-shaped fruit-pod, wrinkled and one-seeded.

Dried flowers
Provide colour and a little scent for potpourri; use in eye lotion.

Dried leaves
Drying process develops coumarin — a long-lasting scent of new mown hay — in the leaves.

Stem
Hollow, ridged, round, branching and green — occasionally red.

Lifespan
Hardy biennial. Behaves as an annual if sown in early spring

Height
M. officinalis 2–4 ft (60 cm–1.2 m)
M. alba 7 ft (2.1 m)

Leaf
Unevenly toothed and mid-green, with lighter underside. Faintly aromatic, leaves arranged in threes.

CULTIVATION
Site Sun; tolerates light shade.
Soil Well drained.
Propagating Sow in spring or late summer. Self-seeds in light soils.
Growing Thin or transplant to 18 in (45 cm) apart. Not suitable indoors.
Harvesting Gather leaves and flowers anytime.
Preserving Dry leaves and flowers.

USES
Culinary
● *Leaf* Use dried leaves in a "cordial" and add small amounts to sausages, pork marinades and rabbit stuffings. Gives an original flavour to beer and cheese. Used in the Swiss green cheese Schabzieger and in Gruyère.

Household
● *Flower* Attracts bees to gardens.
● *Leaf* Scatter dried leaves among clothes to deter moths.

Cosmetic
● *Flower* Add to bathwater for a comforting bath. According to *The Fairfax Stillroom* (1651), to make a "Bath for Melancholy": take 3 handfuls each of mallows, pellitory-of-the-wall; one handful each of chamomile flowers and melilot flowers, and 1 oz (25 g) of celery seed. Boil in 9 gallons (41 litres) of water until reduced to 3 gallons (14 litres) then add a quart (1.15 litres) of new milk and "go into it blood warm or something warmer".

Aromatic
● *Leaf* Add to potpourri.

Medicinal
● *Whole plant* Used dried as a mild antiseptic, in salves and to reduce the likelihood of thrombosis. Infuse for indigestion and headaches.
● *Flower* Use as a diluted infusion in a lotion or eyewash.
● *Leaf* Apply fresh leaves as a poultice for aching joints and cuts.

Mentha species

Mints Labiatae

In Greek mythology, Minthe was a nymph beloved by Pluto, who transformed her into this scented herb after his jealous wife took drastic action. Mint has been highly esteemed ever since, its value being epitomized by biblical references to the Pharisees collecting tithes in mint, dill and cumin. The Hebrews laid it on synagogue floors, and this idea was repeated centuries later in Italian churches, where the herb is called *Erba Santa Maria*.

Mint as a symbol of hospitality is mentioned by the Roman poet Ovid, who wrote of two peasants, Baucis and Philemon, who scoured their serving board with mint before feeding guests. Gerard enlarged on this theme in 1597, "they use it to strew in places of recreation, pleasure and repose,

where feasts and banquets are made". The Romans also flavoured wines and sauces with mint. However, when women who drank wine were threatened with death, secret drinkers would mask their breath by chewing a paste of mint and honey. In Japan, the refreshing, restorative scent of mint was so highly prized that the Japanese wore pomanders of its leaves.

Many mint varieties had been introduced into Europe by the ninth century. A monk writing during this time said that there were so many he would rather count the sparks of Vulcan's furnace. With more than 600 varieties, which continue to hybridize, the best way to select a good plant is by nose rather than by name.

Seed
Dark brown, roughly spherical and small.

Leaf
Oval, pointed, aromatic, green and wrinkled from deep veins.

Stem
Square, green and branching in the upper part.

**M. requienii
Corsican mint**
Tiny, peppermint-scented, bright green leaves and miniature flowers. Ht: 1 in (25 mm).

Dried leaves
These retain their flavour well for teas, cooking and medicinal uses.

**M. spicata 'Moroccan'
Moroccan spearmint**
Closely set, toothed, bright green leaves with clean spearmint flavour. Ht: 2 ft (60 cm).

**M.s. 'Variegata'
Variegated applemint**
Cream-edged leaves with mild apple-mint flavour. Lasts longer into winter than other mints. Ht: 16 in (40 cm).

**M. x gentilis 'Variegata'
Ginger mint**
Smooth gold-splashed leaf with a hint of spiciness. Prune to renew golden growth. Ht: 16 in (40 cm).

**M. raripila rubra
Red raripila spearmint**
Pointed, dark green leaves, with sweet spearmint flavour, purple stems and flowers borne in late summer. Ht: 2 ft (60 cm).

**M. suaveolens
Applemint**
Hairy, apple-scented, bright green leaves. Ht: 2 ft (60 cm).

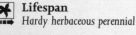

✳ **Lifespan**
Hardy herbaceous perennial

✳ **Height**
1 in–3 ft (25 mm–1 m); smaller species make good ground cover

**M. spicata 'Crispii'
Curly mint**
Crinkled, deep green leaves, with savoury apple scent. Ht: 16 in (40 cm).

OTHER SPECIES AND VARIETIES

*Exact naming is difficult as mints interbreed
so readily.*

**M. pul. 'Upright'
Upright pennyroyal**
Smooth, bright green
leaves, with strong
peppermint scent.
Ht: 12 in (30 cm).

**M. pulegium
Creeping
pennyroyal**
Bright green,
peppermint-
scented leaves, lax
stems, which root
where they contact earth.
Ht: 6 in (15 cm).

**M. x aquatica
'Citrata'
Lemon mint**
Smooth, lemon-
scented, mid-
green leaves.
Ht: 16 in (40 cm)

**M. x villosa
'Alopecuroides'
Bowles' mint**
Large, round, hairy,
apple/spearmint-scented,
mid-green leaves, pink
flowers. Ht: 3 ft (1 m).

**M. x p. 'Crispa'
Crinkle-leaved
black peppermint**
Vibrant green leaves with
strong peppermint scent,
purple stems. Ht: 2½ ft (75 cm).

**M. piperita
'Citrata'
Eau de cologne
mint**
Smooth,
bergamot-
scented,
purple-tinged,
dark green leaves,
purple stems.
Ht: 18 in (45 cm).

*The mauve flowers of **M. spicata** appear in mid- to late summer.*

CULTIVATION

Site Partial shade or sun.
Soil Moist, well-drained, alkaline soil, rich in nutrients.
Propagating Take root or stem cuttings, or divide mint, in spring and autumn. In summer, root stem cuttings in water. (Pennyroyal) Sow in spring.
Growing Thin or transplant, to 12 in (30 cm) apart, into large pots or polythene bags to restrain invasive roots. Remove all flowering stems to avoid cross-pollination between species. If rust appears, dig up plant and burn. Mints can be grown indoors.
Harvesting Pick leaves just before flowering.
Preserving Dry, freeze or infuse leaves in oil or vinegar.

USES

Decorative
● *Leaf* Use in herb posies and invalid bouquets.

Culinary
● *Leaf* Infuse either individual or blended mints as a refreshing tea. (Spearmint and peppermint) Use for mint sauce, vinegar, syrups and with chocolate in rich desserts (see p. 165). Crystallize as a sweet for decoration. (Spearmint and applemint) Add fresh leaves to new potatoes, peas, fruit salads, drinks and punches. (Pennyroyal) Use sparingly in soups and stuffings.

Household
● *Whole plant* (Spearmint and peppermint) Grow near roses to deter aphids.
● *Leaf* Scatter fresh or dried leaves around food to deter mice. (Spearmints) Rub on a new beehive to attract bees. Use leaf oil to overpower tobacco smells. (Pennyroyal) Strew in cupboards and beds to deter ants and fleas.

Cosmetic
● *Leaf* (Spearmint) Decoct strongly to heal chapped hands. Add to bathwater for an invigorating bath. (Eau de cologne) Makes a refreshing bath.

Aromatic
● *Leaf* Use in potpourri and herb bags.

Medicinal
● *Leaf* (Spearmints) Inhale drops of essential oil, or sprinkle on a handkerchief, for relief from heavy colds. (Peppermints) Infuse as a tea to help digestion, colds and influenza. Sip cold tea for hiccups and flatulence. (Spearmint and peppermint) Macerate leaves in oil; then massage affected areas for migraines, facial neuralgia and rheumatic and muscular aches, especially in winter.

Note: *Do not take pennyroyal in large doses when pregnant or suffering from kidney problems.*

Melissa officinalis

Lemon balm *Labiatae*

Sacred to the temple of Diana, and used medicinally by the Greeks some 2,000 years ago, lemon balm was called "heart's delight" in southern Europe and the "elixir of life" by the Swiss physician, Paracelsus. He believed the herb could completely revive a man, and this view was endorsed by the *London Dispensary*, in 1696: "Balm, given every morning, will renew youth, strengthen the brain and relieve languishing nature." Lemon balm was reputed to be among the regular morning teas imbibed in the thirteenth century by Llewelyn, Prince of Glamorgan, who lived to 108 years, while John Hussey, of Sydenham, England, lived to be 116 after 50 years of breakfasting on lemon balm tea with honey. Its virtue of dispelling melancholy has been praised by herbal writers for centuries, and it is still used today in aromatherapy to counter depression.

Seed
Shiny dark brown with white tip, tear-shaped, $\frac{1}{16}$ in (1 mm) long.

Dried leaves
Drying lemon balm reduces its scent and medicinal properties.

M.o. var. *variegata*
Variegated lemon balm
Gold-splashed, lemon-scented leaves. Grow in light shade, as hot sun scorches leaves, creating pale spots. Ht: 1 ft (30 cm).

Flower
Small, two-lipped, pale yellow blooms in clusters, maturing through white to pale blue, borne from summer to autumn.

Lifespan
Hardy herbaceous perennial

Height
3 ft (1 m)

Stem
Hairy, square, branching and light green, with occasional purple markings.

Leaf
Lemon-scented, hairy, strongly veined, toothed, oval and light green. Leaves turn yellow and harsh-scented when grown in full sun and dry soil.

CULTIVATION

Site Full sun with midday shade.
Soil Grows in any moist soil.
Propagating Sow in spring, slow to germinate. Divide plant or take stem cuttings in spring or autumn.
Growing Thin or transplant to 2 ft (60 cm) apart. Small plants can be grown indoors.
Harvesting Pick leaves anytime, but handle gently to avoid bruising. Their flavour is best when flowers begin to open.
Preserving Dry leaves. Add fresh leaves to vinegar.

USES

Decorative
● *Leaf* Use in invalid posies.

Culinary
● *Leaf* Finely chop fresh leaves into salads, white sauces for fish, mayonnaise, sauerkraut, pickled herrings, poultry and pork. Add to fruit salads, jellies, custards, fruit drinks and wine cups. Infuse fresh leaves for melissa tea or float in Indian tea. Add to blended vinegars: try lemon balm with tarragon.

Household
● *Leaf* Plant around beehives and orchards to attract pollinating bees. Rub on beehives before introducing a new swarm. Add juice to furniture polish. Once a strewing herb.

Cosmetic
● *Leaf* Infuse as a facial steam and as a rinse for greasy hair. Add to bathwater. It is an essential ingredient in Carmelite water.

Aromatic
● *Leaf* Use in potpourri and pillows.

Medicinal
● *Leaf* Place fresh leaves directly onto insect bites and sores, or apply in a poultice. Infuse as a tea for relief from chronic bronchial catarrh, feverish colds, headaches, and to calm and uplift tension.

Monarda didyma

Bergamot/Bee balm Labiatae

This North American native became a popular garden and tisane plant in Europe after settlers sent back seed. The name *Monarda* honours the Spanish medical botanist Dr Nicholas Monardes of Seville, who wrote his herbal on the flora of America in 1569. He probably called this herb bergamot because its leaf scent resembles that of the small, bitter, Italian bergamot orange, *Citrus bergamia*, which produces the oil used in aromatherapy, perfumes and cosmetics. The Oswego Indians infused bergamot as a drink, and it became a popular tea substitute in New England after the Boston Tea Party, in 1773. Several Indian tribes used wild bergamot for colds and bronchial complaints, and, as it contains the powerful antiseptic thymol, it is worthy of further research.

Dried flowers
These retain their colour well. Add to potpourri and teas.

Dried leaves
Dry carefully and use for potpourri and teas.

M.d. 'Blue Stocking'
Purple-blue flowers. Leaves are slightly less aromatic than the species.

Flower
Shaggy heads are a tight cluster of tubular, scarlet blooms borne in late summer.

M. fistulosa
Wild bergamot
Lavender flowers (shown in bud).

Leaf
Toothed, oval, pointed, dark green with reddish veining, exuding eau de cologne scent strongest in young leaves.

M.d. 'Croftway Pink'
Soft pink flowers.

Stem
Hairy, hard, ridged, square, branching and tinged red at leaf joints.

✴ Lifespan
Hardy herbaceous perennial

✴ Height
2–3 ft (60 cm–1 m)

CULTIVATION
Site Sun, or part shade in hot climate. Add a mulch in spring.
Soil Rich, light and moist.
Propagating Divide or take root cuttings in spring, stem cuttings in summer. (Species) Sow in spring.
Growing Thin or transplant to 18 in (45 cm) apart. Divide every 3 years, discarding dead centre. Bergamot is not suitable for growing indoors.
Harvesting Collect leaves in spring or in summer when flowers form. Pick flowers when open.
Preserving Dry leaves and flowers.

USES
Decorative
● **Flower** Use fresh and dried in flower arrangements.

Culinary
● **Flower** Scatter in salads.
● **Leaf** Infuse, or simmer for 10 minutes in an enamel saucepan for greater flavour, as a tea. Put fresh leaf into China tea for an Earl Grey flavour, into wine cups and into lemonade. Add sparingly to salads, stuffings, pork. Use for jams, jellies and bergamot milk: pour 1 cup (225 ml) of boiling milk over 1 tbsp (15 ml) dried or 3 tbsp (45 ml) shredded leaves, steep for 5–7 minutes, strain and serve.

Household
● **Flower** Attracts bumble bees (honey bees are unable to reach nectar unless holes have been made by other insects).

Cosmetic
● **Flowering top** (Wild bergamot) Boiled by Omaha and Ponca Indians to make a hair oil.

Aromatic
● **Flower and leaf** Use in potpourri.

Medicinal
● **Leaf** Infuse as a tea to relieve nausea, flatulence, menstrual pain and insomnia. Try steam inhalation for bronchial catarrh and sore throats.

Myrrhis odorata

Sweet cicely/Myrrh *Umbelliferae*

The attractive fern-like leaves of sweet cicely are among the first to appear in spring and the last to depart in autumn. The soft green leaves have a myrrh-like scent with overtones of moss and woodland and a hint of aniseed, the botanic name of this plant being from the Greek word for perfume.

An extra bonus of sweet cicely is the cluster of large, upstanding green seeds or, more properly, fruits, which appear in early summer. They have a delicious nutty flavour and characteristic scent and, besides being excellent when eaten raw, they also provide an aromatic furniture polish.

A similar North American plant, *Osmorhiza longistylis*, flowers in early summer and has a sweet, aniseed-flavoured root.

Unripe seed
Green, ridged, ¾ in (19 mm) long appear late spring. Eat raw.

Dried leaves
These retain a little scent; occasionally used medicinally, also to decorate paper and candles.

Flower
Small white flowers appear in late spring. One of the earliest nectarous flowers for bees.

Ripe seed
Dark brown, glossy, ridged, ¾ in (19 mm) long.

Leaf
Up to 18 in (45 cm) long, downy beneath, green above. White markings may appear as season progresses.

Stem
Hollow, furrowed, downy surface; branching.

Root
Thick brown taproot, occasionally branching, with white, aromatic flesh.

 Lifespan
Hardy herbaceous perennial

Height
3 ft (1 m)

CULTIVATION
Site Light shade. Tolerates sun.
Soil Rich in humus.
Propagating Sow outdoors in autumn; seed requires several months of cold winter temperatures before germination.
Growing Transplant 2 ft (60 cm) apart in spring.
Harvesting Pick young leaves any time. Collect unripe seed when green; ripe seed when dark brown. Dig up roots in autumn.
Preserving Dry or pickle unripe seed. Clean and peel root, then infuse in wine or brandy.

USES
Culinary
● *Seed* Toss unripe seeds, which have a sweet flavour and nutty texture, into fruit salads. Chop into ice cream. Use ripe seed whole in cooked dishes such as apple pie; otherwise use crushed. Used to flavour Chartreuse liqueur.
● *Leaf* Chop finely and stir into salad dressing and omelettes. Add to soups, stews and to boiling water when cooking cabbage. Cook with tart fruits (rhubarb, gooseberries, currants) to reduce acidity, thereby decreasing amount of sugar required. Add to cream for a sweeter and less fatty taste.
● *Root* Chop, peel and serve raw with salad dressing. Cook as a root vegetable and serve with butter, or cool and chop into salads.

Household
● *Seed* Crush as a furniture polish.

Medicinal
● *Whole plant* Considered to be a "wholesome" tonic (especially the root in brandy), mild antiseptic and digestive aid.
● *Leaf* A valuable "sweetener", especially for diabetics.
● *Root* When infused, enigmatically listed in old herbals as a valuable tonic for girls aged 15 to 18. Boiled root was prescribed to strengthen the elderly.

Myrtus communis

Myrtle Myrtaceae

In Greek legend, Myrrha was a favourite priestess of Venus, who transformed her into this fragrant evergreen to preserve her from too ardent a suitor. Venus wore a myrtle wreath when Paris awarded her the Golden Apple for beauty, and this herb was planted around all temples dedicated to her. Representing Venus and love, myrtle is often woven into bridal wreaths, and the Romans displayed it lavishly at feasts, weddings and celebrations. An Arabian story tells of Adam, banished from paradise, bringing a sprig of myrtle from the bower where he declared his love to Eve, and Shakespeare planned that Venus and Adonis should meet under myrtle shade. In 1640, the apothecary John Parkinson wrote, "we nourish Myrtles with great care for their beautiful aspect, sweet scent and rarity."

Bud
Remove bitter green part and sprinkle rest of bud on fruit salads.

Dried flowers
Add to potpourri.

Dried leaves
Use these long-lasting aromatic leaves for potpourri, sweet bags and herb pillows.

Lifespan
Half-hardy evergreen shrub

Height
8–10 ft (2.4–3 m)

Stem
Aromatic, ridged, round and reddish, becoming beige and woody in second year.

Flower
Sweetly scented, pure white blooms, with golden stamens, appear from midsummer to autumn.

Leaf
Shiny, leathery, and dark green with a central crease and a sweet, spicy, orange fragrance.

M.c. 'Tarentina' is a compact form.

CULTIVATION

Site Full sun. Protect from wind.
Soil Any well-drained soil or potting compost.
Propagating Take stem cuttings in mid- or late summer.
Growing Transplant to large pots. Grow indoors or outside. Needs a minimum temperature of 41 °F (5 °C).
Harvesting Pick buds, flowers and ripe berries as available. Pick leaves when myrtle is in flower for sweetest scent, or as needed.
Preserving Dry buds, flowers and berries. Dry leaves or infuse in oil (for cosmetic use) or in vinegar.

USES

Decorative
● **Branch** Use in wreaths.

Culinary
● **Branch** Lay young branches under roast pork for last 10 minutes of cooking, or on barbecues when grilling lamb.
● **Flower** Remove green part and add to fruit salads. Use powdered buds as a spice.
● **Leaf** Stuff inside roast pork after cooking for a delicate flavour.
● **Berry** Grind and use as a spice for a mild juniper-berry flavour.

Household
● **Branch** Antiseptic strewing herb. Add a decoction to furniture polish.

Cosmetic
● **Flower and leaf** Pulverize and add to ointment for blemishes. Distil or infuse as a sweet water.
● **Berry** Decoct as a dark hair rinse.

Aromatic
● **Flower and leaf** Add to potpourri.

Medicinal
● **Leaf** Infuse for a powerful antiseptic and astringent; as a tea for psoriasis and sinusitis; and as a douche for vaginal discharge. Apply in a compress to bruises and haemorrhoids.

Nepeta cataria

Catnip/Catmint Labiatae

The name *Nepeta* may derive from the Roman town Nepeti, where catnip was cultivated when it was more highly valued than today. It had a reputation as a seasoning and medicinal herb, and in less favourable times the mildly hallucinogenic dried leaves were smoked to relieve the pressures of life.

Set in a border, catnip can be a pretty plant, with its whorls of lavender or white flowers attracting the bees, if it is not damaged by cats. These animals will lie in the centre of the plant, rubbing the leaves in a state of sheer bliss, thus giving catnip its common name. The smaller catmint, N. mussinii, receives less attention from cats, and its compact form, which produces masses of lavender-blue flowers, is traditionally planted in front of lavender and roses.

A bed of flowering catmint.

Seed
Small, rich brown, oval, flattish, with a white fleck on one end. Seeds are viable for 5 years.

Dried leaves
Develop a sharp balsam-like taste; use for tea and medicinal infusions.

Stem
Tall, hairy, ridged, square and branching; has pungent scent.

N. mussinii Catmint
An attractive edging plant with mildly fragrant 6 in (15 cm) spikes of lavender-blue flowers from late spring to early autumn. Ht: 12–18 in (30–45 cm).

Leaf
Coarsely toothed, heart-shaped and grey-green with downy underside. Leaves grow in pairs opposite each other and have a penetrating mint-like scent that is loved by cats.

Lifespan
Hardy herbaceous perennial

Height
18 in–3 ft (45 cm–1 m)

CULTIVATION
Site Sun or light shade.
Soil Well drained.
Propagating Sow or divide whole plant in spring. Take softwood cuttings in late spring.
Growing Thin or transplant to 12 in (30 cm) apart. Cut back in autumn. The scent released by any bruised leaf or root will attract cats, who then molest the plant, so plants grown from seed in situ are less likely to be damaged than transplanted plants, which may need protection. N. mussinii grows indoors.
Harvesting Gather leaves when young and flowering tops.
Preserving Dry whole plant.

USES
Decorative
● *Whole plant* (N. mussinii) Makes a good garden edging plant.

Culinary
● *Leaf* Rub on meat to flavour. Drunk as tea before China tea was introduced to the West.
● *Shoot* Use in salads, when young.

Household
● *Whole plant* Attracts bees.
● *Leaf* Dry and stuff into cloth "mice" as toys for cats. Catnip scent repels rats. Plant near vegetables to deter flea beetles.

Medicinal
● *Leaf and flowering top* Contain vitamin C. Infuse to relieve colds and fevers (as catnip induces sleep and perspiration but does not increase body temperature); for restlessness and colic in children, for headaches and upset stomachs, as a mild sedative. Apply infusion externally to soothe scalp irritations. Mash leaves and flowering tops for a poultice for external bruises.

Ocimum basilicum

Basil *Labiatae*

This important culinary herb, with its warm spicy flavour, sends cooks into poetic raptures. A native of India, basil is held in reverence as a plant imbued with divine essence, and therefore the Indians chose this herb upon which to swear their oaths in court. Basil was found growing around Christ's tomb after the resurrection, so some Greek Orthodox churches use it to prepare the holy water, and pots of basil are set below church altars.

There are many varieties of basil, including bush basil, which is a South American native. In Haiti, it belongs to the pagan love goddess Erzulie, as a powerful protector, and in rural Mexico it is sometimes carried in pockets to magnetize money and to return a lover's roving eye.

A selection of pot-grown basils.

Seed
Dark brown, faceted, tear-shaped, $\frac{1}{16}$ in (1 mm) long.

Dried leaves
Pulverize to release the clove scent and use in potpourri and scented beads.

O.b. 'Purpurascens' Dark opal basil
Crinkled, purple leaves with good medium flavour, pale pink flowers.

Flower
Small, scented, whitish blooms, in circular clusters of six, appear in late summer.

O.b. 'Citriodorum' Lemon basil
Lemony scented, green leaves, white flowers. Ht: 12 in (30 cm).

Leaf
Large, toothed, oval, pointed and bright green, with a warm yet fresh, strong, clove-like scent.

O.b. 'Minimum' Bush, or Greek, basil
Compact. Tiny green leaves with good medium flavour. Hardiest variety in poor conditions. Ht: 8 in (20 cm).

Stem
Hairy, finely ridged, square, branching and light green to reddish at base.

Lifespan
Tender annual

Height
18 in (45 cm)

CULTIVATION

Site Warm sun. Protect from wind, frost and scorching, midday sun.
Soil Well drained and moist.
Propagating Sow thinly in heated location. After danger of frost has passed, sow in pots or in position.
Growing Avoid overwatering seedlings as they are prone to "damping off". Thin to 8 in (20 cm); avoid transplanting. Always water at midday, not in the evening. Syringe leaves in hot weather. Basil is excellent pot-grown indoors.
Harvesting Pick leaves when young. Gather tops as flowers open.
Preserving Freeze leaves (first paint both sides with olive oil) or dry them. Store whole leaves in olive oil with salt or dry-pack them with salt. Infuse leaves in oil or vinegar.

USES

Culinary
● *Leaf* Pound with oil or tear with fingers rather than chop. Add at last minute to cooked dishes. Sprinkle over salads and sliced tomatoes. Basil's rich pungent flavour complements garlic. Used in pesto sauce and many Mediterranean dishes, and to flavour blended vinegars. See p. 164 for further ideas.

Household
● *Whole plant* Place pots on windowsills to deter flies.

Cosmetic
● *Flowering top and leaf* Add a fresh infusion for an invigorating bath.

Medicinal
● *Leaf* Steep a few leaves in wine for several hours as a tonic. Infuse as a tea to aid digestion. Basil has many uses in aromatherapy. Put a drop of essential oil on a sleeve and inhale to allay mental fatigue.

Oenothera biennis

Evening primrose *Onagraceae*

A plant for a moonlit garden: the clear yellow flowers of evening primrose unclasp their hooked cover at twilight and open their blossom to the moon, welcoming the night with their delicate sweet fragrance and mysterious emissions of phosphorescent light. As the season progresses, the flowers often stay open all day as well.

Though probably grown in nineteenth-century monastery gardens, the evening primrose was overlooked by the Austrian monk, Gregor Mendel, when choosing plants for his famous experiments into inheritance. However, it is now grown by geneticists to demonstrate the principles of heredity. Medical research is also currently exploring ways in which the seeds, which contain the rare gamma-linoleic acid, may alleviate premenstrual tension, menopausal discomfort, psoriasis, reduce thrombosis and control multiple sclerosis and other degenerative diseases. The increasing uses of evening primrose seed may well signal a time when whole fields billow with these glorious yellow flowers.

Lifespan
Hardy biennial

Height
3–6 ft (1–2 m)

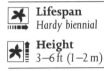

Seed
Beige, round, oily; contains gamma-linoleic acid and unknown anti-coagulant compounds of interest to medical researchers.

Flower
Fragrant clear yellow flowers, 3 in (8 cm) across, open from early summer to midautumn.

Root
Thick and conical, with yellow outside and white inside.

Stem
Sturdy, rough, hairy and reddish.

Leaf
Long, oval, pointed and mid-green, arranged in rosettes the first year; along the stem in the second.

CULTIVATION

Site Sunny and open.
Soil Well drained.
Propagating Sow spring to early summer. Self-seeds in light soil.
Growing Transplant to 12 in (30 cm) apart by autumn. Not suitable indoors.
Harvesting Collect seed when ripe. Gather leaves and stem "bark" when flowering stems have grown. Dig up roots in second year.
Preserving Dry seeds and leaves.

USES

Decorative
● *Whole plant* Long flowering season. Excellent in any garden.

Culinary
● *Leaf and stem* Once a popular food with North American Indians.
● *Root* Boil root, which tastes like sweet parsnip. Pickle and toss in salads or use as an apéritif.

Cosmetic
● *Leaf and stem* Infuse to make an astringent facial steam. Add to a hand cream as a softening agent.

Medicinal
● *Seed* Take evening primrose oil capsules for premenstrual tension, menopausal discomfort and psoriasis. Gamma-linoleic acid lowers levels of cholesterol and blood pressure. Seems to reduce the risk of thrombosis, and to relieve symptoms of multiple sclerosis and other degenerative diseases.
● *Leaf and stem* Infuse peeled "bark" and leaves to soothe cough spasms.

Research continues into treatments for rheumatoid arthritis, benign breast tumours, hyperactivity, schizophrenia, alcoholism, anorexia nervosa, Parkinson's disease, and certain forms of infertility.

Onopordum acanthium

Cotton thistle Compositae

Readers of A. A. Milne's *Winnie the Pooh* will know how fond donkeys are of thistles, and the botanic name of this herb derives from the Greek *onos*, meaning "an ass", and *perdon*, meaning "I disperse wind". This perhaps provides a clue as to why the character Eeyore led such a solitary and sorrowful existence.

O. *acanthium* is thought to be the true Scotch thistle, the emblem of Scotland. This symbol was firmly fixed by 1503, when the poet Dunbar wrote "The Thrissill and the Rose" on the union of the Scottish James IV and the English Princess Margaret. The Order of the Thistle, which ordained Scottish knighthoods, was instituted by King James V in 1540.

Seed
Dark brown, oval, faceted, ¼ in (6 mm) long.

Dried leaves
These were once used medicinally. Down used to be collected for stuffing pillows.

Flower
Magenta-purple, tufted blooms, 2 in (5 cm) across, borne in second summer.

First year plant
Clusters of silvery leaves appear in first season; tall flowering stems then grow in second season.

Stem
Spiny, winged stem of triangular section; covered with fine silvery down.

Root
Dark brown taproot, with beige side roots and white astringent flesh.

Leaf
Long, narrow, toothed with prickles, green with white down.

Lifespan
Hardy biennial

Height
9 ft (2.7 m)

CULTIVATION
Site Full sun or light shade.
Soil Tolerates any soil, but requires rich loam to reach maximum height.
Propagating Sow in late spring in situ or in pots to be transplanted in autumn. May self-seed in warm climates. Cotton thistle can be started in early spring under glass.
Growing Thin or transplant to 2½ ft (75 cm) apart. Not suitable for indoor growth.
Harvesting Pick flowers, leaves and stems as required. Collect seed and dig up roots in autumn of the plant's second season.
Preserving Dry leaves.

USES
Decorative
● *Whole plant* Makes a striking garden feature.
● *Flower* Popular in decorations.

Culinary
● *Seed* In the past, Cotton thistle seeds were used to produce an oil for cooking and lamps.
● *Flower* Prepare and cook large disc containing the florets in the same way as globe artichokes: remove petals and tough outer bracts and boil or steam until tender.
● *Stem* Blanch and peel young stems. Eat raw with oil and vinegar, or steam and serve like asparagus.

Medicinal
● *Leaf* Juice was said to relieve cancer and skin ulcers. Gerard's *Herbal* of 1597 declared it a remedy for "those with their bodies drawn backwards" (crick in the neck) based on the authority of the Roman writer Pliny.
● *Root* Decoction may diminish mucous discharges.

Origanum species

Marjorams & Oregano *Labiatae*

The Greeks have given us the legends and the name of this ancient culinary herb: *oros ganos*, joy-of-the-mountain. Those who have visited Greece, where oregano (wild marjoram) covers the hillsides and scents the summer air, would probably endorse the name. The sweet spicy scent of sweet marjoram was reputedly created by Aphrodite as a symbol of happiness. Bridal couples were crowned with garlands of marjoram, and plants were placed on tombs to give peace to departed spirits. Aristotle reported that tortoises who swallowed a snake would immediately eat oregano to prevent death so it was taken as an antidote to poisoning. The Greeks enjoyed its scent after a bath, when marjoram oil was massaged into their foreheads and hair. Earlier still, in ancient Egypt, oregano's power to heal, disinfect and preserve was well known and has been treasured ever since.

Sweet marjoram was introduced into Europe in the Middle Ages and was in demand by ladies "to put in nosegays, sweet bags and sweet washing waters". Its leaves were also rubbed over heavy oak furniture and floors to give a fragrant polish. In thundery weather, dairymaids would place marjoram by pails of fresh milk in the curious belief that this plant would preserve its sweetness. This task might well have been followed by marjoram tea – advised by the herbalist, Gerard, for those who "are given to overmuch sighing".

Seed
Dark brown, tear-shaped and tiny.

Dried leaves
These retain their flavour well and can be used in cooking.

Leaf
Oval, pointed; mid- to dark-green.

Stem
Erect to lax, hairy, round and green mottled with red.

Roots
Horizontal stems root wherever they touch the soil.

**O. majorana
Sweet/Knotted marjoram**
Half-hardy, sweet spicy-flavoured pale green leaves and white or purplish flowers producing seed clusters like "knots".

**O. vulgare
Oregano**
Slightly sprawling habit, dark green peppery-flavoured leaves (containing the powerful antiseptic thymol), white or pink flowers. Ht: 2 ft (60 cm).

**O. onites
Pot/French marjoram**
Mid-green savoury-flavoured leaves and white or pink flowers.

Lifespan
Hardy herbaceous or shrubby perennial

Height
6 in–2 ft (15–60 cm)

OTHER SPECIES AND VARIETIES

O.v. 'Variegata' Gold variegated marjoram
Mild savoury-flavoured green leaves, splashed with gold in full sun, pale pink to white flowers.

O.o. 'Crinkle Leaf'
Curled, savoury-flavoured, golden leaves that scorch in full sun, seldom flowers. Compact form.

O.v. 'Compact pink flowered'
Pungent, savoury-flavoured, dark green leaves. Compact, dark pink flower heads.

O. heracleoticum Winter marjoram
Half-hardy. Sweet spicy aromatic leaves, pink flowers. Ht: 9 in (23 cm).

O.v. 'Aureum' Golden marjoram
Mild, savoury-flavoured golden leaves that scorch in full sun.

A bed of marjorams in flower.

CULTIVATION

Site Full sun. (Gold leaf forms) Need midday shade.
Soil Well drained, dryish, alkaline, nutrient rich. Unlike most other herbs from the same family, marjorams have a stronger flavour when grown in rich soil.
Propagating Sow in spring (germination can be slow). (Hardy perennials) Divide in spring or autumn. Take root or stem cuttings from late spring to midsummer.
Growing Thin or transplant to 12–18 in (30–45 cm) apart. Cut back marjorams by two-thirds before they die down for winter. If site is not too windy, leave seed heads for bird food. Marjorams can be grown indoors.
Harvesting Pick young leaves anytime. If leaves are to be used for preserving, gather just before flowers open.
Preserving Freeze or dry leaves. Macerate in oil or vinegar. Dry flowering tops.

USES

Culinary
● **Leaf** (Sweet marjoram) Infuse as an aromatic tea. Chop finely for salads and butter sauces for fish. Add to meat dishes in last few minutes of cooking. (Pot marjoram, oregano) Blend with chili and garlic. Add to pizza, tomatoes, egg and cheese dishes. Stuff fresh haddock with marjoram and breadcrumbs. Rub into roasting meat. Often included in bouquet garni (see also p. 165).
● **Stem** Give food a faint marjoram flavour by laying stems on barbecue embers.

Household
● **Flower** Grow to attract bees and butterflies.
● **Leaf** (Sweet marjoram) Add pulverized leaves or a strong decoction to furniture polish (see p. 195).

Cosmetic
● **Leaf** (Oregano) Infuse for a relaxing bath. Infuse strongly as a hair conditioner.

Aromatic
● **Leaf** (Sweet marjoram) Use in potpourri and pillows.

Medicinal
● **Flowering top** (Sweet marjoram) Infuse as a tea for colds, headaches, simple gastro-intestinal and nervous disorders. Add a decoction or essential oil to bathwater, ointments or compress for relief from rheumatic pains and tension. Sprinkle a few drops of essential oil on a pillow to promote sleep. (Oregano) Infuse as a tea for coughs, stomach and gallbladder disorders, nervous headaches and irritability, general exhaustion and menstrual pains. Drink as a sedative to prevent sea-sickness. Apply externally as an antiseptic poultice for swellings, rheumatism and stiff necks.
● **Leaf** (Oregano) Chew, or rub on a drop of essential oil for temporary relief of toothache.

Papaver species

Poppies Papaveraceae

Around 3000 BC, the Sumerians revered poppies as cult plants. The species gives us flowers described as the handmaidens of cornfields, voluptuous garden plants, an oil, edible seed and opium.

The laboratory analysis of the opium poppy is historically the transition from the magical and religious use of plants to scientific use. It also highlights the dangers of reducing plants to their chemical components. The opium poppy gives us morphine and codeine, our most important painkillers, and also heroin, which is addictive and results in much human misery. Its growth is strictly controlled in many countries.

Seed
Minute blue-grey and kidney shaped (called maw seed). Indian or white flower seed is cream and smaller; flavours are similar.

Flower
White, pink, purple or dull red flowers appear in late summer. There is also a double form (below).

P. somniferum
Opium poppy

Ornamental double-form poppy.

Seed head
Bulbous, flat-capped, hairless capsule, becoming woody.

P. rhoeas
Field poppy/Corn poppy
Long, slender stem with solitary, dark-centred, red flower. Ripe seed capsule has ring of pores near top.

Leaf
Smooth, deeply lobed, unsymmetrical and pale grey-green. Upper leaves clasp the stem.

Stem
Tall, slightly hairy, rigid and occasionally branching.

 Lifespan
Hardy annual

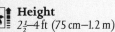 **Height**
2½–4 ft (75 cm–1.2 m)

CULTIVATION
Site Full sun.
Soil Well drained and cultivated.
Propagating Sow in spring or autumn in flowering site, just pressing seed into soil. Field poppy requires a cold spell to trigger germination. Self-seeds freely.
Growing Thin to 12 in (30 cm). Not suitable for indoor cultivation.
Harvesting Collect seed when capsule is ripe.
Preserving Dry seed heads; then shake to extract seeds.

USES
Decorative
● *Whole plant* (Field poppy) Make a "poppy doll": bend back petals and tie around stem with grass; for arms, push dried stalk through capsule "head".
● *Seed* Use dried seed heads for winter arrangements.

Culinary
● *Seed* Sprinkle on bread, cake and biscuits for a pleasant nutty flavour. Add to curry powder for texture, flavour and as a thickener. Gives a culinary oil from first cold pressing.

Household
● *Seed* Feed to birds. An artist's oil is made from the second pressing.
● *Flower* (Field poppy) Petals used to colour medicines and wines.

Medicinal
● *Seed* (Opium poppy) Latex from unripe capsule used originally to relieve pain, diarrhoea, and some coughs, but is now main source of morphine, which has not yet been synthesized. Morphine's derivative, heroin, is a most toxic poison.

Note: *All parts of opium poppy except ripe seed are dangerous and should be used only by trained medical staff.*

Pelargonium species

Scented geraniums *Geraniaceae*

Most pelargoniums originate from the Cape of Good Hope in Africa and although they were introduced to Britain in 1632, they remained relatively unknown until 1847, when the French perfume industry realized their aromatic potential. From the leaf of the rose-scented geranium, P. *graveolens*, the French distilled an oil with a delightful light rose perfume and a fresh green note. It is popular in cosmetics and important in aromatherapy. Unfortunately, it is an easy oil to adulterate, so purchase it from a reputable supplier.

In winter, the Victorians brought pot-grown pelargoniums indoors, and positioned them so that their long skirts would brush against the plants, thus scenting a room. In summer, they moved the pots outdoors and put them along paths for a similar effect.

A collection of potted pelargoniums.

Dried leaves
These retain their scent well, as do leaves that die on the plant.

**P. graveolens ×
tomentosum**
Rose-peppermint scent

P. quercifolium
"Oak" leaves smell of incense

P. crispum 'Prince of Orange'
Orange scent

P. radens
Rose-lemon scent

P. × fragrans
Piney-nutmeg scent

Flower
Fragrant, pink or white blooms appear in summer to autumn.

Seedhead
Stork's bill-shaped containing small black seed.

P. odoratissimum
Apple scent

P. capitatum
Rose scent

Stem
Hairy, round and green, becoming woody.

Leaf
Rose-scented, hairy, toothed, mid-green, with five to seven lobes.

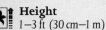 **Lifespan**
Tender evergreen perennial

Height
1–3 ft (30 cm–1 m)

CULTIVATION
Site Sunny, well-ventilated position.
Soil Well-drained potting compost.
Propagating Sow in early spring.
Take tip cuttings in spring (from over-wintered plants) or in late summer. May root well in sand.
Growing Grow pelargoniums in pots so they can be moved indoors in winter. Thin or transplant to individual pots. Pinch out growing tips when plants reach 6 in (15 cm). Cut back one-third of growth before bringing indoors.
Harvesting Pick leaves just before flowers open.
Preserving Dry leaves.

USES
Culinary
● **Flower** Toss in salads.
● **Leaf** Chop finely, or infuse in liquid then discard leaves, and use to flavour sauces, custards, jellies, buns, water ices, butters, jams, sugar, syrups and vinegars. Crystallize to decorate cakes. Lay leaves under baked apples or cakes to impart flavour (see p. 186). Infuse as a tea or add to a wine cup. (Rose-peppermint scented) Add to liver pâté. (Piney-nutmeg scented) Cook in watercress soup and Welsh rarebit. (Apple scented) Bake with fish in cider.

Cosmetic
● **Leaf** Add essential oil to perfume and face creams (to balance sebum of oily and dry or inflamed skin). Infuse as a mild astringent to clean and help circulation of pale, sluggish complexions. Add to bathwater.

Aromatic
● **Leaf** Use in potpourri and pillows.

Medicinal
● **Leaf** Essential oil used in aroma-therapy massages for premenstrual tension and fluid retention, dermatitis, eczema, herpes and dry skins. Add to massage oil for tonic to the nervous system.

Petroselinum crispum

Parsley *Umbelliferae*

Held in high esteem by the Greeks, parsley was used to crown victors at the Isthmian Games and to decorate tombs, being linked with Archemorus, the herald of death. The Greeks also planted parsley and rue along the edges of herb beds, thereby instigating the expression "being at the parsley and rue", meaning to be at the start of an enterprise. Although the Greeks used parsley medicinally, and Homer recorded that warriors fed parsley to their horses, it appears that the Romans were the first to use it as a food. They consumed parsley in quantity and made garlands for banquet guests to discourage intoxication and to counter strong odours.

There are many excellent parsley varieties, including Hamburg parsley (P.c. 'Tuberosum'). This has flat leaves and a large, edible, well-flavoured root. All parsleys are rich in vitamins, minerals and antiseptic chlorophyll, making it a beneficial as well as attractive garnishing herb. Set out a dish of the leaves each day and enjoy a flavour described as the "summation of all things green".

Seed
Small, grey-brown and sickle-shaped with cream ridges; contains apiole, which can be toxic.

Leaf
Finely cut, curled with toothed margins and bright green, with fresh taste; rich in vitamins A, B and C, salts of iron, calcium, magnesium and chlorophyll.

Dried leaves
These retain most flavour when dried quickly. Use in cooking and boil with stem for a yellow-green dye.

**P. crispum
Curled parsley**

**P.c.
'Neapolitanum'
Italian, or
French, parsley**
Flat, cut, dark green leaves with stronger, coarser flavour than the species, and edible, succulent stems. Ht: 2 ft (60 cm).

Stem
Solid, ridged, semi-circular, branching and mid-green; more strongly flavoured than leaves.

Root
Thin, brownish-yellow, smooth taproot with tiny hair-like roots; contains strongest parsley flavour.

 Lifespan
Hardy biennial

 Height
15 in (38 cm)

CULTIVATION
Site Full sun or light shade.
Soil Rich, moist and deeply dug.
Propagating Sow from spring to late summer. For fast germination: soak seed overnight in warm water, pour boiling water in drill before sowing or grow in seed tray and maintain 70 °F (21 °C). Self-seeds.
Growing Thin or transplant to 9 in (23 cm) apart. Protect in cold weather. Grows well indoors.
Harvesting Pick leaves during first year. Collect seeds when ripe. Dig up roots in autumn of second year.
Preserving Dry or freeze leaves. Dry or blanch and freeze roots.

USES
Culinary
● *Leaf* Add raw to salads. Finely chop and sprinkle over sandwiches, egg dishes, vegetable soups, fish, and boiled potatoes. Add to mayonnaise and many classic sauces. When cooked, parsley enhances other flavours, but add towards end of cooking time (see p. 165). Use in bouquet garni.
● *Root* Use in bouquet garni. Add to soups and stews. (Hamburg parsley) Boil as a root vegetable. Grate raw into salads.

Household
● *Whole plant* Grow by roses to improve their health and scent.

Cosmetic
● *Leaf* Infuse as a hair tonic and conditioner. Add to facial steam and lotion for dry skin and to minimize freckles. Use infusion as a soothing eye bath.

Medicinal
● *Leaf* Chew raw to freshen the breath and promote healthy skin. Infuse for a digestive tonic. Use in a poultice as an antiseptic dressing for sprains, wounds and insect bites.
● *Root* Decoct for kidney troubles and as a mild laxative. Apply juice to reduce swellings.

Pimpinella anisum

Anise/Aniseed Umbelliferae

This graceful feathery annual has been cultivated for centuries.
Around 1500 BC, the Egyptians grew their native anise in quantity to
supply food, drink and medicine from its leaves and seed. The fields
of Tuscany were planted with anise by the Romans, who developed
a special spiced cake, *mustaceus*, as a finishing dish for feasts. It was
baked with anise, cumin and other digestive herbs and established a
tradition thought to be the precursor of spiced wedding cakes.
Charlemagne's edict of the ninth century, that every herb growing in
St Gall's monastery should be planted on all his royal estates, spread
anise throughout Europe. It became so valued in England that its
import was taxed. Early colonists carried the seed to North America,
where Shakers grew it in their medicinal herb crops.

CULTIVATION

Site Sunny and sheltered.
Soil Well drained and alkaline.
Propagating Sow in situ in late
spring. Seed loses viability after
second year.
Growing Thin to 8 in (20 cm) apart;
do not transplant, so keep well
weeded. Can be grown indoors.
Harvesting Pick lower leaves as
required. Collect flowers as they
open. For seed, cut plant at ground
level when fruit begins to turn grey-
green at the tips. Gather stems and
dig up roots in autumn.
Preserving Dry seed by suspending
plant until ripe (see p. 270).

USES

Culinary
● *Seed* Use whole or crushed in
breads, cakes, apple pies, apple
sauces, creams and confectionery.
Add to cream cheese, pickles, curries
and water for boiling shellfish.
Chew slightly roasted seed after a
meal as a breath sweetener and
digestive. It flavours many liqueurs.
● *Flower* Mix into fruit salads.
● *Leaf* Add to fruit salads with figs,
dates and chestnuts. Use to garnish.
● *Stem and root* Mix into soups and
stews for a hint of liquorice.

Household
● *Seed* Set as a bait in mouse traps.

Cosmetic
● *Seed* Add ground to a face pack.
Seed oil is used in perfumes, tooth-
pastes, soaps and mouthwashes.

Aromatic
● *Seed* Use crushed in potpourri.

Medicinal
● *Seed* Infuse as a comforting
antiseptic tea for colds, coughs and
bronchial problems; to soothe colic
in babies, relieve nausea, and as a
gland stimulant for nursing mothers
to increase their milk supply.

Flower
*Small, star-like, white
blooms, in clusters,
appear in late summer.*

Seed
*Aromatic, light grey-
brown, ridged, elongated,
pointed egg-shape;
requires a sunny summer
to ripen fully.*

Stem
*Ridged, round,
branching and
mid-green.*

Leaf
*Aromatic, toothed, round,
lobed and mid-green lower
leaves; finely divided and
feathery upper leaves.*

Lifespan
Half-hardy annual

Height
12–18 in (30–45 cm);
erect or prostrate

Herbal trees

Although rarely considered for their herbal attributes, trees provide sap, bark, leaves, blossoms, berries and nuts – many of which have potent herbal properties. They have always supplied people's basic needs – fuel, food, building material and furniture – and given us herbal gifts such as dyes, medicines, salad and liqueur ingredients, household articles and aromatic items. Each month has its useful trees and the ancient Druids created a 13-month lunar calendar with a valued tree for each month, featuring oak for the summer solstice. Reaching great heights and extending deep into the earth, trees also give us spiritual sustenance as an almost universal symbol of wisdom and strength. They can provide an inspirational framework for a large herb garden.

Prunus dulcis
Sweet almond (above)
Yields rich almond oil, used in cosmetics and aromatherapy. (See p. 274.)

Sambucus nigra
Elder (left)
Flowers and fruit yield food, drinks, medicines, cosmetics, insect repellent and dyes. (See p. 115.)

Ginkgo biloba
Maidenhair tree (above)
Seeds and leaves are used medicinally in China. (See p. 273.)

Ilex aquifolium
Holly (right)
The tonic leaves have been used medicinally. Berries are toxic. (See p. 273.)

Betula pendula
Silver birch (right)
Birch leaves are antiseptic; all parts of the tree are useful. (See p. 112.)

Crataegus monogyna
Hawthorn (left)
The ripe fruits are an excellent tonic for the heart and circulatory system. (See p. 112.)

110

Picea abies
Norway spruce (above)
Yields a medicinal pitch and resin. Leaf tips used to make beer. (See p. 114.)

Tilia cordata
Lime (right)
Lime blossom tea is a popular remedy for nervous tension. (See p. 115.)

Quercus robur
Oak (above)
Oak bark yields dye and tannin. Highly valued for centuries. (See p. 274.)

Juglans regia
Walnut
(above)
Provides edible nuts and has other useful properties. (See p. 113.)

Cytisus scoparius
Broom (below)
Attractive flowering tree with many useful properties including a dye and fibrous bark. (See p. 113.)

Populus balsamifera 'Aurora'
Balsam poplar (left)
"Balm of Gilead" scented buds obtained from the species and this variegated form. (See p. 274.)

Juniperus communis
Juniper (above)
Berries are used as flavouring and are antiseptic. (See p. 114.)

Herbal trees

Betula pendula
Silver birch *Betulaceae*

An elegant and graceful tree, with its silvery bark and mid-green oval leaves, the silver birch has a lovely fragrance after rain. It grows to a height of 20–60 ft (6–18 m) with a spread of 8–12 ft (2.5–3.5 m) and bears male and female catkins in spring. In ancient times its softish wood was used in roof- and boat-building, and its bark served as a writing material.

CULTIVATION
Sow seeds in boxes in early spring. When large enough, prick out into nursery rows outdoors. After two to three years, plant out during autumn or winter in permanent positions. Thriving in any site and soil type, silver birch needs plenty of space to allow room for its wide-spreading surface roots.

USES
Birch twigs make strong, effective brooms, and are traditionally used in a sauna. Wine and vinegar can be made from the sap, and beer from the bark. Birch tea, made from the leaves, used to be recommended for rheumatism and gout. Oil extracted from the bark is used for dressing leather and in medicated soaps for skin conditions such as eczema.

Crataegus monogyna
Hawthorn *Rosaceae*

A tough, thorny perennial, the hawthorn grows very rapidly once established. It will thrive in semi-shade, but is happiest in an open, sunny position where it can reach a height of 30 ft (9 m) with a spread of 15–20 ft (4.5–6 m). Its dark-green leaves are lobed and toothed and, in late spring, it bears clusters of lovely, sweetly scented white flowers, followed by bright-red berries from late summer well into the autumn. Tradition links the tree with Christianity. Christ wore a crown of thorns and, according to legend, in AD 60 when Joseph of Arimathea came to Britain to bring the Holy Grail, he struck his staff into the ground at Glastonbury, where it took root, flowering twice a year, once in spring and once at Christmas.

CULTIVATION
Sow ripe seeds outdoors in late winter/early spring, or plant young shrubs from autumn until early spring. Protect with tree sleeves. For a hedge, plant shrubs at 12–16 in (30–40 cm) intervals and trim between midsummer and midspring.

USES
Hawthorn makes a good, thick hedge or an attractive specimen tree for a lawn. When burned, it gives off a great deal of heat. Today the flowers and especially the berries are used in cardiac tonics. A liqueur can be made from the berries mixed with brandy.

Cytisus scoparius
Broom *Leguminosae*

Honoured as a heraldic device of the medieval lords of Brittany and the Plantagenet rulers of England, common broom is a deciduous perennial shrub that could once be found extensively growing wild. With a height and spread of 8 ft (2.5 m), it has long, erect branches which remain bright green even in winter. In late spring and early summer the branches are covered with a mass of yellow, fragrant flowers, followed by black seed pods. The flowers, rich in pollen, attract bees, and hybrids are available in a variety of colours from white to red.

CULTIVATION
Although very adaptable, broom prefers full sun and a well-drained, slightly acid soil. Sow seeds as soon as they are ripe, and transplant the seedlings to their permanent position in autumn. Broom can also be increased by layering. Prune annually after flowering to prevent the plant becoming leggy.

USES
A colourful and useful addition to the garden, broom will bind the soil on a steep bank and provide shelter for other shrubs until they become established. It derives its common name from the fact that its tough and flexible branches were made into brooms. The tannin in its bark was once employed to tan leather and the seeds have been used as a substitute for coffee. Before hops were introduced to brewing, the young green tops added bitterness to beer, and broom buds were held to be a delicacy, often pickled to resemble capers. Known for its medical properties in Anglo-Saxon times, broom was thought to cure kidney and bladder complaints. Today it is an ingredient of a number of pharmaceutical drugs, including diuretics. Slightly narcotic, and dangerous if taken in large doses, broom is not suitable for domestic use.

Juglans regia
Walnut *Juglandaceae*

This handsome, hardy deciduous tree, with its massive trunk and large, spreading branches, can reach a height of 100 ft (30 m). It bears both male and female flowers in late spring: the insignificant tiny green female flowers in small clusters and the yellowish-green male flowers in catkins. The glossy, bright-green oval leaves have a strong aroma. Walnut trees are cultivated commercially for their timber as well as for their nuts.

CULTIVATION
Sow seeds in nursery beds in mid- to late autumn and leave for two or three years before transplanting during the autumn or winter. Choose an open site with fertile, well-drained soil, where the tree will be protected from spring frosts. Trees raised from seed will produce edible nuts after about 15 years.

USES
Green, unripe walnuts can be pickled in vinegar, preserved in syrup or made into a liqueur. Mature nuts are added to cake mixtures, stuffings and sauces. They are an essential ingredient of some salads and a variety of salad oil. The boiled green husks of the nuts give a yellow dye, and a brown hair dye can be obtained from the leaves and outer shells. An infusion of the dried leaves can help skin complaints such as eczema and herpes, while an infusion of the powdered bark is said to act as a laxative.

Herbal trees

Juniperus communis
Juniper Cupressaceae

This low, prickly bush or tree, between 4 and 10 ft (1.2–3 m) high, is a slow-growing coniferous evergreen. It has silvery-green spiny needles and, from late spring to early summer, bears small yellow flowers. The juniper is cultivated for its berries, which take up to three years to ripen, when they change from green to silvery-purple. The slightly resinous, sweetly flavoured berries are borne only by the female bush, and can be found in various stages of ripeness on the same plant. Their flavour is stronger the farther south the plant is grown. Many ornamental varieties are available.

CULTIVATION
Suitable for an exposed, sunny site, the juniper will tolerate an alkaline soil. Sow seeds taken from ripe berries in cold frames in early autumn. Grow the seedlings on in nursery rows outdoors for one or two years before planting in permanent positions. Both male and female plants are necessary for berry production. To be sure of the plant's gender, it is best to cultivate from semi-hardwood cuttings taken late summer to early autumn.

USES
As well as giving gin its characteristic flavour, juniper berries are used to flavour other spirits and beer. Crushed berries are added to marinades for game and stuffings for poultry (see p. 164). An infusion of the berries is thought to have diuretic properties and be good for cystitis. It also soothes aching muscles. Juniper berries should not be taken during pregnancy or by people with kidney problems.

Picea abies
Norway spruce Pinaceae

Familiar to millions of people as the traditional Christmas tree, the Norway spruce can reach a height of 50 ft (15 m) with a spread of 20 ft (6 m). Its evergreen, needle-like leaves appear on the upper side of its branches only. When the tree is about 40 years old, it begins to produce 6 in (15 cm)-long cylindrical cones, which hang downwards. Like many conifers, it is grown commercially for its light but strong timber.

CULTIVATION
Sow seeds in pots in early spring. Move the seedlings to nursery beds the following spring. Plant in their permanent positions during the winter two or three years later. Choose a sheltered site, where the soil is moist and acid.

USES
Oil of turpentine, rosin and oil of tar are all obtained from the resin of spruce and other members of the pine family. Its leaves and twigs fermented with yeast and sugar produce spruce beer.

Sambucus nigra
Elder Caprifoliaceae

A perennial, deciduous large shrub or small tree, with oval, serrated leaves, the elder has a height and spread of about 15 ft (4.5 m). Its spreading branches bear flat heads of small, star-shaped, creamy-white flowers in late spring and early summer. These are followed, in early autumn, by drooping bunches of purplish-black, juicy berries. A common wild plant, it is part of the folklore of several countries, where ancient legends link it with magic.

CULTIVATION
Sow ripe berries 1 in (2.5 cm) deep in a pot outdoors. Plant seedlings out in a semi-shaded position when large enough. Or plant 1 ft (30 cm) hardwood cuttings in a nursery bed in mid- to late autumn and plant out the following winter. Cut back hard in winter. Elders tolerate most soils; *S. nigra* is good for very chalky sites.

USES
This important and valuable tree, once called "the medicine chest of the country people", has innumerable uses. An infusion of the muscatel-scented flowers can be used to treat colds. Elderflower water is good for the complexion and the eyes. The flowers are also used in an ointment to treat burns, while an ointment made from the leaves is suitable for bruises and sprains. The berries are rich in vitamin C and are often the main ingredient of jams and cordials. For centuries, wine has been made from both the berries and the flowers (see p. 193).

Tilia cordata
Lime Tiliaceae

The small-leaved lime (above) is a fast-growing, hardy, deciduous tree, reaching a height of 35 ft (10 m). Its heart-shaped leaves are a glossy dark-green with serrated edges. The clusters of yellowish, heavily scented flowers, which appear in midsummer, have a sweet nectar that attracts bees. The leaves often harbour aphids which produce "honeydew", a sticky substance which also attracts bees but eventually drips off as an unpleasant residue.

CULTIVATION
Sow seeds in a cold frame in early spring. Plant out in nursery beds in midautumn. After growing on for at least four years, transplant to permanent positions, in full sun or semi-shade, in well-drained soil.

USES
Lime or linden tea, made from the dried flowers, is very popular in European countries, where it is drunk as a digestive and calming tonic. The flowers are also used to flavour sweets and liqueurs. Lime blossom is used in beauty preparations to soothe the skin. Although not particularly durable, the white, close-grained wood of the lime is the most suitable for intricate carving. Note that very old flowers should be avoided when making preparations as they may produce symptoms of mild intoxication.

Poterium sanguisorba (Sanguisorba minor)

Salad burnet *Rosaceae*

The dainty decorative leaves of this refreshing herb belie its hardiness – its leaves often survive a mild winter. Should they fail to do so, they are then among the earliest leaves to appear in spring. Salad burnet, which the Pilgrim Fathers carried to New England, was thought by Gerard to "make the hart merry and glad, as also being put in wine, to which it yeeldeth a certaine grace in the drinking". The young leaves have a pleasant if somewhat sharp cucumber flavour. The green flowering globes expand amid tiny red dots with the unfulfilled promise of an explosion of colour. This pretty plant was recommended by Francis Bacon to be set in alleys with wild thyme and water mint, "to perfume the air most delightfully, being trodden on and crushed".

Seed
$\frac{1}{8}$in (3 mm) long. Beige, ridged, oval shaped.

Flower
Tiny green blooms, with red points packed into a $\frac{1}{2}$in (13 mm) sphere, appear in early to midsummer. They contain no nectar and have to be wind-pollinated.

Leaf
Rosettes of hardy, lacy, graceful foliage, composed of finely toothed leaflets, survive mild winters.

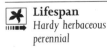

Lifespan
Hardy herbaceous perennial

Height
8–30 in (20–75 cm)

CULTIVATION
Site Sun or light shade.
Soil Prefers limy soil.
Propagating Sow seeds in spring or autumn. If allowed to flower, salad burnet will self-seed.
Growing Plant seedlings 12 in (30 cm) apart, when large enough to handle. Cut flowering stems and old leaves regularly to produce plenty of tender young leaves.
Harvesting Pick young tender leaves whenever required.
Preserving Dry leaves.

USES
Decorative
● *Whole plant* Plant as edging for formal herb garden designs.

Culinary
● *Leaf* Introduce this nutty and slightly sharp cucumber flavour into garnishes, salads, herb butters and soft cheeses, or sprinkle on vegetables. Add at beginning of cooking to casseroles and creamy soups. Combine with other herbs, particularly rosemary and tarragon. Serve in a sauce with white fish: add 2 tbsp (30 ml) each of chopped burnet and tarragon or mint to 4 oz (110 g) melted butter, simmer for 10 minutes. Use to flavour vinegar, salad dressing and to give a cooling effect to summer drinks and punch.

Household
● *Leaf* Press dried leaves into sides of slightly melted candles.

Cosmetic
● *Leaf* Infuse to make a facial wash for sunburn and for troubled skin.

Medicinal
● *Whole plant* Try as an infusion to relieve haemorrhoids or diarrhoea.
● *Leaf* Sprinkle fresh leaves, which contain vitamin C, on food to aid digestion. Use as a tonic and mildly diuretic tea.

Stem
Grooved, with branching flowering stems.

Primula veris *Primula vulgaris*

Cowslip & Primrose Primulaceae

These two flowers of spring never fail to gladden the heart. Favourite of favourites, the primrose is the first to appear. Although picked for jams and cosmetics, its real attraction is the soft yellow simplicity of its perfect flower. Its leaves are enjoyed by silkworms.

The cheerful, nodding cowslip, the "Keys of St Peter", has a unique milky scent likened to a cow's breath or to that of a new baby. In some areas, it has almost been picked to extinction, mainly to make seductive cowslip wine, but also for the childish delight of sucking the sweet nectar from the flowers. Successful conservation measures for wild cowslip, combined with many more home-grown plants, mean that all can continue to enjoy its pleasures.

Primrose.

Seed
Dark brown, faceted, $\frac{1}{16}$ in (1 mm) long.

Flower
Pale yellow, heart-shaped petals with deeper yellow centres. One flower per stalk; multiples are hybrids.

Leaf
Crinkled, oblong and yellow-green.

**Primula vulgaris
Primrose**

Dried flowers
These make a mild, sedative tea.

Root
Tan, aromatic rootstalk with small, pale yellow roots.

Dried leaves
Used occasionally as a medicinal tea.

**Primula veris
Cowslip**

Flower
Golden petals, each with an orange dot at the base, appear in spring.

Seed
Dark brown, faceted, $\frac{1}{16}$ in (1 mm) long.

Stem
Sturdy, solid, round stalk supports one to 30 flowers.

Dried flowers
Retain their colour well for dried decorations and potpourri.

Leaf
Bluer green than primrose, slightly crinkled and rosette forming.

Dried leaves
Used medicinally.

Lifespan
Hardy herbaceous perennial

Height
Cowslip 5–9 in (13–23 cm)
Primrose 3–6 in (8–15 cm)

CULTIVATION

Site Semi-shade or sun.
Soil Cowslip favours limy soil; primrose prefers moist soil.
Propagating Divide large plants in autumn. Seed picked in early autumn, when still slightly succulent, will germinate quickly; ripe, dry seed needs cold then warm temperatures to break its dormancy. Sow in autumn and cover with glass.
Growing Plant out in the following autumn, 6 in (15 cm) apart. Primrose, unlike cowslip, is not suitable for indoor cultivation.
Harvesting Pick leaves and flowers as they open. Harvest roots in autumn.
Preserving Crystallize flowers. Dry leaves and roots.

USES

Decorative
● **Flower** Include in spring posies.

Culinary
● **Flower** (Cowslip) Use for jam and wine, or pickle. (Primrose) Eat raw in salads. Crystallize for decoration. Once used in jams and an ancient dessert with rice, almonds, honey, saffron and ground flowers.
● **Leaf** (Cowslip) Use in salads and for meat stuffing. (Primrose) Boil as a vegetable.

Cosmetic
● **Flower** Soak in distilled water to make lotion for spots and wrinkles.

Aromatic
● **Flower and root** Use dried flowers and powdered roots in potpourri.

Medicinal
● **Whole plant** (Primrose) Infuse fresh plant to make a cough remedy and mildly sedative tea.
● **Flower** Try fresh or dried in tea as a sedative and for headaches.
● **Leaf** (Cowslip) May heal wounds in a salve. (Primrose) Use for a medicinal tea.
● **Root** (Primrose) Infuse as a tea for nervous headaches.

Rosmarinus officinalis

Rosemary Labiatae

Rosemary, "dew of the sea", holds a special place in the affections of many as the essence of a summer herb garden. It has been used by cooks and apothecaries from earliest times. With a reputation for strengthening the memory, it became the emblem of fidelity for lovers; some brides have even worn rosemary wreaths "richly gilded and tied with silken ribands of all colours". The Spanish revere rosemary as the bush that sheltered the Virgin Mary on her flight to Egypt. As she spread her cloak over the herb, the white flowers turned blue.

In times past, resinous rosemary was burned in sick chambers to purify the air and branches were strewn in law courts as a protection from "gaol fever". During the plague, it was carried in the hollow handles of walking sticks and in neck pouches to be sniffed when travelling through suspicious areas. In some Mediterranean villages, linen is spread over rosemary to dry, so the sun will extract its moth-repellent aroma.

Rosemary also makes a good garden hedge. In Shakespeare's time, it was used for topiary and clipped to a sphere or cone shape.

Apart from common rosemary, there are several named varieties, including a vigorous new upright form, 'Sawyer's Selection', with large, mauve-blue flowers, which can reach 8 ft (2.5 m) within three years. There is a variable gold-tipped form, and ancient texts mention a silver variegated form.

Seed
Tan, oily and small.

Leaf
Resinous, leathery, needle-like and dark green.

Lifespan
Hardy evergreen perennial

Height
3–6 ft (1–2 m) tall; a new variety now reaches 8 ft (2.5 m)

Dried leaves
These retain their flavour well and are convenient to store.

Dried stems
When stripped of leaves, rosemary stems can be burned on a fire or barbecue for a lovely aroma.

Stem
Squarish, turning woody from the second year.

OTHER VARIETIES

R. o. 'Prostratus'
A tender prostrate species with bright blue flowers and finer leaves.

R.o. 'Severn Sea'
Semi-prostrate, half-hardy cultivar, mid-blue flowers, fine leaves on arching branches.

R.o. 'Albus'
Hardy, white flowers occasionally with lavender veining.

R.o. 'Suffolk Blue'
Hardy, bright sky-blue flowers.

R.o. 'Majorca Pink'
Half-hardy, clear pink flowers, bright green leaves.

R.o. 'Miss Jessup's Upright'
Hardy, white flowers, tidy, vertical growth; useful for hedging.

Common rosemary has pale blue orchid-like flowers in early summer.

CULTIVATION

Site Sunny. Protect from cold winds. In cold or exposed gardens, grow in a large pot; sink it in outdoor soil in summer, but return it to the greenhouse or a sunny interior in winter.

Soil Needs excellent drainage. On limy soil, rosemary is a smaller but more fragrant plant. To provide additional lime, apply eggshells or wood ash.

Propagating Sow under heat in spring or outdoors in summer. Germination is erratic; needs at least 70 °F (21 °C). It is best to propagate by cuttings or layering.

Growing Transplant when large enough to handle, leaving 2–3 ft (60–90 cm) between plants. Rosemary can be container-grown indoors in a sunny position.

Harvesting Pick small amounts all year round. Gather main leaf crop before flowering.

Preserving Dry sprigs and branches. Strip off leaves before storing. To release the aroma, crush leaves only just before use.

USES

Decorative
● **Branch** Provides a fragrant "skeleton" when woven into wreaths and garlands.

Culinary
● **Flower** Toss fresh rosemary into salads. Crystallize for a garnish. Pound with sugar, mix with cream, and add to a fruit purée.
● **Leaf** Add sparingly to a wide range of meat dishes, especially lamb and pork. Use rosemary to flavour baked potatoes and to make a herb butter for vegetables.

Household
● **Branch** Place fresh boughs in a room to cool the air.
● **Leaf** Boil a handful of rosemary in 16 fl oz (475 ml) water for 10 minutes to yield an antiseptic solution for washing bathroom fixtures.
● **Stem** Shape into barbecue skewers.

Cosmetic
● **Flower** Use the essential oil in "Hungary water" (see p.223).
● **Leaf** Stimulates blood circulation in a bath. Use as a facial steam. Makes a rinse for dark hair.

Aromatic
● **Leaf** Use in potpourri. Lay sprigs amongst linen.
● **Stem** Scatter on a barbecue to discourage insects.

Medicinal
● **Leaf** Stimulates circulation and eases pain by increasing blood supply where applied. Aids fat digestion. Good for aching joints and rheumatic pains. Use as an antiseptic gargle and mouthwash.

Rosa species

Roses Rosaceae

For sheer fragrance and beauty, the rose reigns supreme. Its cultivation has spread from Persia, bringing inspiration to artists, warriors and lovers in every land. Cleopatra seduced Antony knee deep in roses, and Roman banquets were garlanded with petals. In 1187, on entering Jerusalem, the Muslim conqueror Saladin even had the Omar mosque washed in rosewater to purify it.

This "gift of the angels" was also popular for its gentle healing powers. Rose essence is among the safest healing substances known, and the delicate flavour of rosewater is excellent for cooking. Rose wine dates from ancient Persia, and the sweet Turkish delight is made with rosewater. Rose petals were historically valued for jam, vinegar, pies and as a garnish. Once again, all the myriad uses for the rose are being rediscovered and enjoyed.

Damask roses in bloom.

Dried hips
Hips from the wild (dog) rose are especially rich in vitamin C.

Leaf
Elliptical with finely serrated edges, five to seven mid-green leaflets on a stalk.

R. gallica 'Versicolor' Rosamundi *Attractive striped petals.*

R. damascena Damask rose

Stem
Green and densely covered with small thorns.

Dried petals and buds
Pick petals once flowers open as a main ingredient in potpourri and sweet bags.

Flower
Rose-pink, highly scented, semi-double flowers borne in summer. Source of rose oil and rosewater.

R.g. 'Officinalis' Apothecary's rose/ Red rose of Lancaster

R. canina Wild rose *Strong, arching, prickly stems, mid-green leaflets, pink or white fragrant flowers and bright red hips.*

R. eglanteria (R. rubiginosa) Sweetbrier/Eglantine
Small, pink, fragrant, single flowers with apple-scented leaflets, densely prickled, arching stems and bright red hips.

Fragrant old roses
Charles de Mills rose and petals of 'Maiden's Blush', 'Mme Isaac Pereire', 'Alba Maxima', 'Old Blush'.

Lifespan
Hardy shrub

Height
4–8 ft (1.2–2.4 m)

CULTIVATION
Site Sunny, or light shade, and open; not too windy.
Soil Well-drained loam.
Propagating Take cuttings in autumn. Plant seed for species.
Growing Thin or transplant from autumn to spring. Deadhead in summer. Prune lightly in spring. Do not grow indoors.
Harvesting Pick buds when formed, petals when first open, hips when ripe or, for wine, after the first frost when softened.
Preserving Dry petals and buds. Crystallize petals. Dry hips.

USES
Decorative
● **Flower** Use in arrangements.

Culinary
● **Flower** Use scented petals with bitter white heel removed. Sprinkle in salads, apple or cherry pie. Make syrup, vinegar, sorbets and sweets (see p. 183). Crystallize as a garnish. Flavour sweets and drinks with rosewater. Pickle rosebuds. Flavour pork with Chinese rose liqueur.
● **Hip** Remove irritant hairs first. Use in teas, wine, syrup and jams. Purée, sweeten and add lemon juice for a lamb sauce.

Cosmetic
● **Flower** Use rosewater as an antiseptic tonic to soothe skin, especially dry, inflamed, mature and sensitive skins. Use rose oil as perfume.

Aromatic
● **Flower** Add petals to potpourri.

Medicinal
● **Flower** Use blended oil in massage to aid circulation, cleanse the blood and tone capillaries. Soothes tension. Splash eyes with rosewater for conjunctivitis.
● **Leaf** Infuse for a tonic and astringent tea.
● **Hip** Contains vitamins B, E, K; high in C. Take as tea or syrup.

Rumex acetosa

Sorrel *Polygonaceae*

Prolific flowering stalks of sorrel, rising above grass on an acid soil, can cause a hay meadow to assume a reddish tint at harvest time. On a hot summer day, haymakers would frequently eat the succulent leaves to quench their thirst. Most sorrel leaves have an intriguing sharp acidic flavour, which is used to advantage in many dishes. However, buckler leaf sorrel (*R. scutatus*) boasts a milder lemony zest but still with an interesting sharpness. It is preferred by the French for sorrel soup. Confusingly, both species have been called French sorrel and garden sorrel.

Seed
Small, rich brown, shiny, pointed and ridged with three curved facets.

Flower
Whorled reddish-green spikes borne during summer. Remove to ensure continued supply of succulent young leaves.

**R. scutatus
Buckler leaf sorrel**
Silvery patches on light green leaves, which have sharp flavour; a "more grateful acidity" than broad leaf sorrel.

Leaf
Lance-shaped with broad base, containing potassium and vitamins A, B1 and C.

Stem
Juicy, ridged and reddish.

**R. acetosa
Broad leaf sorrel**
Fresh sap-green leaves that are almost tasteless in early spring: acidity develops as season progresses.

 Lifespan
Hardy perennial

 Height
R. acetosa 2–4 ft (60 cm–1.2 m); R. scutatus 6–18 in (15–45 cm)

CULTIVATION
Site (*R. acetosa*) Sun or light shade; (*R. scutatus*) Full sun; sheltered spot.
Soil (*R. acetosa*) Moist, rich with iron; (*R. scutatus*) Well drained.
Propagating Sow seed in spring; germination takes 7–10 days. Divide roots in autumn.
Growing Thin seedlings or transplant to 12 in (30 cm) apart. Water to keep leaves juicy; protect from snails. Divide and replant every 5 years. Grow indoors in pots.
Harvesting Gather leaves when young for culinary use. For a winter supply, cover sorrel with cloches.
Preserving Dried sorrel has little flavour. Best frozen in cooked dishes.

USES
Culinary
● **Leaf** Eat raw young leaves (especially *R. scutatus*) in salads (reducing vinegar or lemon in dressing) and in sorrel soup. Cook like spinach, changing the cooking water once to reduce acidity. Use to season vegetable soups, omelettes, lamb and beef dishes, and in sauces for fish, poultry and pork.

   To make a green sauce, wash a handful each of sorrel and lettuce leaves with half a handful of watercress. Cook in a little water with a whole onion until tender. Remove onion. Mix 1 tbsp (15 ml) olive oil with 1 tbsp (15 ml) wine vinegar, pepper and salt. Stir into sorrel mixture until creamy.

Household
● **Leaf** Use juice to bleach rust, mould and ink stains from linen, wicker and silver.

Medicinal
● **Leaf** Infuse as a tea to treat kidney and liver ailments. Apply to mouth ulcers, boils and infected wounds.
Note: *Large doses may damage kidneys.*

Ruta graveolens

Garden rue *Rutaceae*

Leonardo da Vinci and Michelangelo both claimed that, owing to rue's metaphysical powers, their eyesight and creative inner vision had been improved. Branches of rue were used to sprinkle holy water before high mass, and it was an important strewing herb and anti-plague plant. Robbers who stripped plague victims protected themselves with "Vinegar of the four thieves", rue being an ingredient, and it was also a main component of *mithridate*, a Greek all-purpose poison antidote. Rue is shown on the heraldic Order of the Thistle and inspired the design of the suit of clubs in playing cards.

Seed
Black and crescent-shaped; used in Roman cooking in the first century AD.

Dried leaves
These contain a powerful germ killer and insecticide; crush and sprinkle as insect repellent.

Flower
Frilled, slipper-shaped, greenish-yellow petals on flowers borne in late summer.

R.g. 'Variegata'
Bright cream splashes on leaf tips. Prune in spring to encourage new variegated foliage. May revert to green.

Leaf
Small, rounded, lobed and blue-green, dotted with oil glands.

Lifespan
Hardy evergreen subshrub

Height
2 ft (60 cm)

Root
Cream-coloured, branching and fibrous; thought to resemble the arrangement of blood vessels in the human eye.

Stem
Round and chalky blue-green, becoming woody in second year. Sap may cause a rash.

R.g. 'Jackman's Blue' *has compact, metallic blue leaves.*

CULTIVATION

Site Full sun. Tolerates light shade.
Soil Well drained and alkaline; poor to moderate fertility for hardiest plants.
Propagating Divide in spring. Take stem cuttings in late summer. (Species only) Sow in spring, slow to germinate.
Growing Thin or transplant to 18 in (45 cm) apart. Prune in late spring. In severe winters, give protection. Rue can be grown indoors.
Harvesting Pick young leaves just before flowers open. Collect seeds.
Preserving Dry leaves and seed.

USES

Decorative
● *Whole plant* (R.g. 'Jackman's Blue') Use as low hedge in knot gardens.
● *Leaf* Include in small posies and tussie-mussies.

Culinary
● *Seed* Infuse with lovage and mint as a marinade for partridge.
● *Leaf* Rue leaf tastes bitter but very small amounts give unusual muskiness to cream cheese, egg and fish dishes. Mix with damsons and wine for a delicious meat sauce.

Cosmetic
● *Leaf* Infuse to bathe tired eyes.

Medicinal
● *Leaf* Infused as a tea that acts as a menstruation stimulant, appetizer, perspiration inducer and bile stimulant. Added to compresses for wounds and skin ulcers. Drunk as a tonic for extra iron and mineral salts. Used by herbalists for hysteria, epilepsy and abnormal blood pressure. Fresh leaves used in a homeopathic tincture for rheumatism, arthritis and neuralgia.

Note: *Rue should be taken only under strict medical supervision and never during pregnancy. It may irritate some skins.*

Santolina chamaecyparissus (S. incana)

Santolina Compositae

Although it has long been known as cotton lavender, santolina is not a lavender but a member of the daisy family. The whole plant is highly aromatic and has been used to sweeten the air in Mediterranean regions for centuries. It is valued as an insect repellent and was much used medicinally in medieval times. Santolina was probably brought into Britain in the sixteenth century by French Huguenot gardeners, who were skilled in creating the popular knot gardens. It is neater than the thrift, germander, marjoram and thyme previously planted in such gardens. With three colour forms available, it is still a popular plant for edging and hedging.

S. rosmarinifolia
Yellow flowers and small, rosemary-like, willow-green leaves, which have a less pungent, sweeter scent than S.c.

Flower
Bright yellow button flowers, one on each stalk, borne from mid- to late summer.

Leaf
Pungent, finely divided, silver-grey, evergreen foliage forming low mounds.

S. virens (S. viridis)
Bright yellow button flowers and thread-like pungent, vivid green leaves.

Santolina chamaecyparissus

S.c. 'Lemon Queen'
Cream button flowers (the only cultivar that doesn't have lemon flowers!) and willow-green foliage with slightly fresher scent.

Stem
Soft, round and white felted; greenish-brown and woody in second season.

S. neapolitana
Bright yellow button flowers and silver-grey leaves which are longer, more feathery and slightly fruitier scented than S.c.
Ht: $2\frac{1}{2}$ ft (75 cm).

Lifespan
Hardy evergreen subshrub

Height
1–2 ft (30–60 cm)

A bed of flowering **S. chamaecyparissus**.

CULTIVATION

Site Full sun.
Soil Well drained, preferably sandy. If soil is too rich, santolina growth is soft and less silvery.
Propagating Take 2–3 in (5–8 cm) stem cuttings in spring or from midsummer to autumn (give protection in frosty weather).
Growing Transplant to 18 in–2 ft (45–60 cm) apart or, to 12–15 in (30–38 cm) apart, for hedging. Clip to shape in spring or summer; never in autumn in frosty climates. Deadhead in autumn. If temperatures drop below 5 °F (−15 °C), protect with a sleeve of two layers of chicken wire filled with straw, spruce or bracken, 5 in (13 cm) thick. Santolina can be grown indoors.
Harvesting Pick flowering stems in late summer. Gather leaves anytime.
Preserving Dry flowering stems and leaves.

USES

Decorative
● *Whole plant* Use for hedges, edging and knot gardens. Create patterns with the three colour forms available.
● *Flower* Dry for decorations.

Household
● *Branch* To deter moths and other insects, lay in drawers and under carpets, hang in closets and distribute among books.

Aromatic
● *Leaf* Add to potpourri.

Medicinal
● *Flower and leaf* A decoction was thought to kill intestinal worms and to give mild stimulation to menstrual flow. An infusion was taken to cleanse kidneys and to help jaundice. Wash with a decoction to heal ringworm and scab.
● *Leaf* Mix in herbal tobacco with chamomile and coltsfoot.

Salvia officinalis

Sage *Labiatae*

"The desire of sage is to render man immortal", instructs a late medieval treatise. Indeed, the sage plant has been praised highly throughout history and on many continents for its powers of longevity. "How can a man grow old who has sage in his garden?" is the substance of an ancient proverb much quoted in China and Persia and parts of Europe. It was so valued by the Chinese in the seventeenth century that Dutch merchants found the Chinese would trade three chests of China tea for one of sage leaves.

The name *salvia*, from the Latin *salvere*, to be in good health, to cure, to save, reflects its benevolent reputation. To the Romans it was a sacred herb gathered with ceremony. The appointed person would make sacrifices of bread and wine, wear a white tunic and approach with feet bare and well washed. Roman instructions advised against using iron tools, a sensible edict as iron salts are incompatible with sage.

This powerful healing plant is also a strong culinary herb, often best used on its own. As one chef wrote: "In the grand opera of cooking, sage represents an easily-offended and capricious prima donna. It likes to have the stage almost to itself." However, it is valuable as an aid to digesting fatty foods, both savoury and sweet.

To complete its commendation, sage is also a beautiful aromatic shrub, popular with bees yet often undervalued as a flowering garden plant.

Flower
Deep throated, two-lipped, generally mauve-blue. The white and pink forms are less common.

Dried leaves
Highly aromatic and pungent.

Seed
Dark brown, ovoid and tiny; form in fruits at the base of each flower.

Leaf
Set in pairs, grey-green often with yellow blotches on old leaves. Thick, downy and "pebbly" with pronounced veining on underside.

 Lifespan
Hardy evergreen shrub

 **Height**
1–2 ft 6 in (30–75 cm)

Stem
Square, green with fine hairs; woody from the second year.

OTHER VARIETIES

S. lavandulifolia
**Spanish sage/
Narrow leaf sage**
Slight balsamic
flavour; good for
teas.

S.o. 'Tricolor'
Half hardy.
Leaves green
splashed pink,
white margins.
Mild flavour.

**S.o. 'Purpurea
variegata'
Variegated
purple sage**
Strong flavour, good
for medicinal tea.

**S.o.
prostratus
Prostrate sage**
Most balsamic
flavour. Keeps
blue leaf colour
all summer.

**S.o. 'Icterina'
Gold variegated
sage** Milder
flavour than
common sage.

S. sclarea
Clary sage
Biennial. Large wrinkled
leaf, long-lasting lilac flowers.

**S.o. 'Purpurea'
Purple (or red)
sage**
Strongly
flavoured leaf. Use
in tea for sore
throats.

S. elegans (S. rutilans)
Pineapple sage
Half hardy. Scarlet
flowers late summer.
Pineapple flavoured
leaves.

**S.o. 'Broad leaf'
Broad leaf sage**
Seldom flowers in
cooler climates. Good
culinary and medicinal form.

A bed of sages, purple sage in the foreground.

CULTIVATION

Site Full sun.
Soil Light, dry, alkaline and well drained.
Propagating Grow common sage from seed. All forms
take easily from cuttings; rooting time is about four
weeks in summer.
Growing Cut back after flowering, replace woody plants
every four to five years. Plant 18–24 in (45–60 cm) apart.
Prune frequently to keep bushy. Yellowing leaves can
mean roots need more space. Small green caterpillar eats
leaves; remove by hand, or prune and burn leaves.
Suitable indoors with sun.
Harvesting Pick leaves just before flowers appear.
Preserving Dry leaves slowly to preserve best flavour and
avoid mustiness.

USES

Decorative
● *Leaf* Attractive in wreaths and tussie-mussies.

Culinary
● *Flower* Scatter in salads. Infuse for a light, balsamic tea.
● *Leaf* Mix with onion for poultry stuffing. Cook with
rich, fatty meats: pork, duck, sausage. Combine with
other strong flavours: wrap around tender liver and sauté
in butter; blend into cheeses. Dip and fry whole leaves in
batter (see p. 177) or young leaves in cream, and eat with
sugar and orange. Make sage vinegar and sage butter.

Household
● *Leaf* Put dried leaves among linen to discourage insects.
Burn on embers or boil in water to disinfect a room. Sage
smoke deodorizes animal and cooking smells.

Cosmetic
● *Leaf* Use in facial steams and astringent cleansing
lotion, and as a rinse to condition and darken grey hair.
Rub on teeth to whiten. Use in a mouthwash.

Medicinal
● *Seed* Clary sage seed infused in water may be used to
remove foreign matter from eyes painlessly.
● *Leaf* Aids digestion and is antiseptic, antifungal and
contains oestrogen. Helps to combat diarrhoea. A sage
sandwich or sage tea after a meal benefits digestion. Sage
tea and sage wine are nerve and blood tonics. Tea reduces
sweating, soothes coughs and colds and may be used to
treat irregular menstruation and menopause. Clary sage
beer was once famous for its intoxicating properties.
Note: *Sage should not be taken in large doses for a long period.*

Saponaria officinalis

Soapwort Caryophyllaceae

Soapwort is worth searching for, as it is a lovely garden herb. It yields a soapy sap which is excellent for laundering and revitalizing precious fabrics, and is now used in museums for this purpose. It also exudes the most delicious raspberry-sorbet scent with a hint of clove, thus revealing its family connection with pinks. This sweet fragrance will fill the air on hot summer evenings.

In the Middle East, soapwort has been used both as a cleaning agent and as a medicinal herb for skin problems such as eczema, acne and those caused by venereal diseases. For these qualities, as well as for its believed ability to help eliminate toxins, especially from the liver, and soothe poison ivy rashes, soapwort was grown on the nineteenth-century herb farms of the American Shakers.

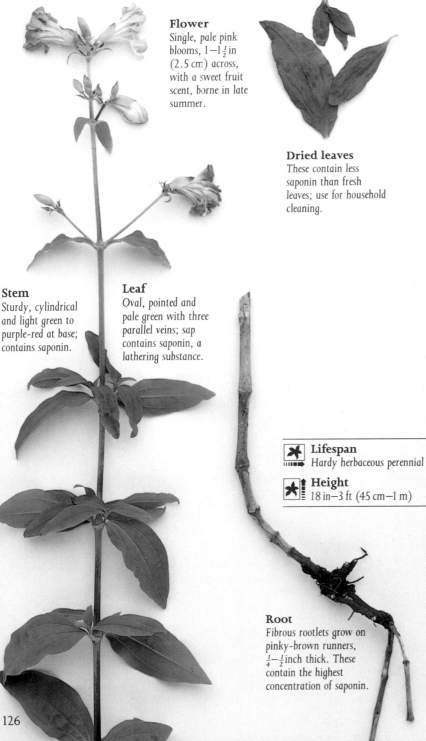

Flower
Single, pale pink blooms, $1-1\frac{1}{2}$ in (2.5 cm) across, with a sweet fruit scent, borne in late summer.

Dried leaves
These contain less saponin than fresh leaves; use for household cleaning.

Stem
Sturdy, cylindrical and light green to purple-red at base; contains saponin.

Leaf
Oval, pointed and pale green with three parallel veins; sap contains saponin, a lathering substance.

Root
Fibrous rootlets grow on pinky-brown runners, $\frac{1}{4}-\frac{1}{2}$ inch thick. These contain the highest concentration of saponin.

⊛ **Lifespan**
Hardy herbaceous perennial

⊛ **Height**
18 in–3 ft (45 cm–1 m)

CULTIVATION
Site Full sun or light shade.
Soil Fertile and moist.
Propagating Sow in spring. Divide plants or take pieces of underground runners in late autumn to early spring. Self-seeds.
Growing Thin or transplant to 2 ft (60 cm) apart. Use twiggy sticks to support stems. Cut back after flowering to induce second blooms. Scent strength varies according to where soapwort is planted. Do not grow near fish ponds as its root excretions can poison fish. Not suitable for indoor cultivation.
Harvesting Pick flowers, leaves, stems and roots in autumn or as required.
Preserving Dry flowers and leaves. Slice roots and and dry in the sun.

USES
Culinary
● **Flower** Toss on green and fruit salads. Sometimes used in brewing to produce a "head" on beer.

Household
● **Leaf, stem and root** Just cover in rain or soft water (not chemically-treated tap water) and boil for 30 minutes; then use soapy liquid to wash and miraculously revive delicate old fabrics. The Romans used soapwort as a water softener.

Cosmetic
● **Leaf, stem and root** Boil in soft water, strain and use to wash hair and sensitive skins (see p. 225).

Aromatic
● **Flower** Perfume a room with bouquets of soapwort. Use dried in potpourri, although only a little scent is retained.

Medicinal
● **Root** Decoct and use as a wash for acne and psoriasis.

Note: Soapwort root is poisonous and should not be taken internally.

Satureja montana (Satureia montana)

Winter savory *Labiatae*

Savory, with its peppery spiciness, is one of the oldest flavouring herbs and has long been considered an antiseptic herb beneficial to the whole digestive tract. It is also a stimulant and was in demand as an aphrodisiac – a possible reason why it was named *Satureia*, meaning satyr. Virgil, in a poem of country life, described savory as highly aromatic and valuable when planted near beehives. The Romans added savory to sauces and to vinegars which they used liberally as a flavouring. They also introduced savory into northern Europe, where it became a valued disinfectant strewing herb. Later, it was among the herbs listed by John Josselyn in *New England Rarities* (1672) as being re-exported to North America by the early settlers.

Tiny, pink to white flowers appear on winter savory in summer.

Seed
Shiny, mid-brown, elongated sphere, halved lengthways, with tiny tip.

Dried flowering tops
These contain an antiseptic that aids digestion and is used medicinally. Crumble leaves for cooking.

Leaf
Small, narrow, pointed and dark green, gland-dotted and aromatic with a distinctive central vein that creates a fold.

S. repandra
Creeping winter savory
Rockery carpet of strongly flavoured deep green leaves sprinkled with tiny white flowers in late summer. Ht: 3 in (8 cm).

Stem
Hairy, square, branching and green, turning reddish-brown; woody in second season.

S. hortensis
Summer savory
Annual. Sparser, slightly larger and more rounded leaves than winter savory and pale lilac to white flowers in late summer. Ht: 18 in (45 cm).

Root
Dark brown, dense and fibrous.

 Lifespan
Hardy evergreen subshrub

Height
15 in (38 cm)

CULTIVATION
Site Full sun.
Soil Well drained and alkaline. (Summer savory) Rich loam.
Propagating Sow in early autumn or late spring. Press lightly into soil. Divide plant in spring or autumn. Take stem cuttings in summer. (Summer savory) Sow in spring.
Growing Thin or transplant to 18 in (45 cm) apart. Prune in late spring. Winter savory may need some protection in winter. Can be grown indoors. (Summer savory) Thin or transplant to 9 in (23 cm) apart. Prune to prevent woody growth.
Harvesting Pick leaves just as flower buds are formed. Collect flowering tops in late summer.
Preserving Dry leaves. Infuse to make savory vinegar and savory oil.

USES
Decorative
● *Whole plant* A useful edging plant.

Culinary
● *Leaf* Cook with beans. Make into savory jelly using grape juice. Used commercially to flavour salami. Peppery winter savory is good for salt-free diets (see also p. 165).

Household
● *Branch and leaf* Throw on fires as an aromatic disinfectant.
● *Flower* Provides nectar for bees.

Cosmetic
● *Flowering top* Use as an astringent and antiseptic in facial steams or baths for oily skin.

Medicinal
● *Flowering top* Infuse as a tea to stimulate appetite, ease indigestion and flatulence; also use as an antiseptic gargle. Steep in wine as a tonic, especially good after fevers.
● *Leaf* Crush and apply to insect bites or wasp stings for pain relief.

Sempervivum tectorum

Houseleek *Crassulaceae*

According to legend, as a gift from Jupiter for protection from lightning, thunder, fire and witchcraft, houseleek has always been considered a form of home fire insurance. Its wild origins are unknown: even in the fourth century BC, the Greek botanist Theophrastus recorded its presence on walls and roof tiles. The Romans planted courtyard urns of houseleek, and Charlemagne ordered one plant to be grown on every roof. This spread the houseleek throughout Europe, and eventually to the New World.

In the language of flowers, houseleek symbolizes vivacity and industry. It is also one of the oldest first-aid herbs, with similar but reduced healing properties to aloe vera. Houseleek's advantage is that it will survive several degrees of winter frost.

CULTIVATION

Site Sunny; traditionally positioned on porches or roofs.
Soil Dry, well drained and thin; suitable for rock gardens.
Propagating In spring, take offsets and leaf cuttings (cut a leaf at the base with an eye from the stem); sow seed in spring.
Growing Thin or transplant to 9 in (23 cm) apart. Will grow indoors.
Harvesting Gather the thickest leaves for use.
Preserving Extract and freeze juice (no tests appear to have measured its properties after being frozen).

USES

Culinary
● *Leaf* The Dutch add it to salads.

Cosmetic
● *Leaf* Soak fresh leaves in a bath or facial steam to heal and nourish the skin. Apply juice (from sliced fresh leaf) or a decoction to warts and other skin blemishes.

Medicinal
● *Leaf* Relieves small injuries; either slice open fresh leaves to reveal their succulent interior and apply directly to skin, or pulp and use in a poultice or dressing. Apply to minor burns, wasp and nettle stings, cuts, ulcers, insect bites, itching burning skin and warts. To soften skin around corns, bind on leaves for a few hours, soak foot in hot water then attempt to remove corn. Repeat procedure as necessary.

Freshly crushed leaf may be helpful for thecal cyst and hygroma. These lumps can occur at the knee, heel, toe or wrist after a shock such as a fall. After repeated applications, grooves may be noticed in the cyst, which indicate it is breaking up.

Infuse as a tea for septic throats, bronchitis and mouth ailments.

Offset
Houseleek produces small rosettes which develop roots and become separate plants. Occasionally, in midsummer, a spray of 1 in (3 cm) rose-purple flowers will appear on an erect round stem covered with scale-like leaves. The rosette that produced the flower stem then dies.

Leaf
Fleshy and mid-green, forming rosettes 2–6 in (5–15 cm) wide, with spiny-pointed maroon tips.

Runner
Smooth red rootstalk which extends some of the offsets outward.

Root
Fibrous; clings to surfaces, especially to roofs.

Split leaf
Contains a succulent mucilage which has healing and soothing qualities.

 Lifespan
Hardy evergreen perennial succulent

Height
2–3 in (5–8 cm); flowering stem 8 in (20 cm)

128

Sium sisarum

Skirret *Umbelliferae*

This Chinese pot herb, grown for its aromatic edible root, was brought to Rome by early traders and became so valued by the Emperor Tiberius that he accepted skirret as tribute. In the sixteenth century, skirret was introduced to northern Europe as "the most delicious of root vegetables". As a perennial that multiplies quickly, it was an invaluable crop for peasants. Writing in 1699, John Evelyn praised skirret as "Exceedingly nourishing, wholesome and delicate; of all the root-kind, not subject to be windy. This excellent root ... is very acceptable to all palates."

Flowers
Small clusters of tiny, fragrant, white, five-petalled flowers, fragrant in evening in mid- to late summer.

Seed
Brown, ridged, crescent-shaped, $\frac{1}{8}$ in (3 mm) long.

Leaf
One to five pairs of narrow, pointed, finely toothed, mid-green leaflets and one terminal leaflet; older leaflets are more rounded. Some turn red in autumn

Stem
Sturdy, hollow, ridged, round, branching and light green; red toward the base.

Lifespan
Hardy herbaceous perennial

Height
2–4 ft (60 cm–1.2 m) in first two seasons; mature plants can reach 6 ft (2 m)

Root
Hair-like roots and numerous light brown, oblong tubers, 4–5 in (10–13 cm) long, with white flesh and pleasant aromatic smell and taste.

CULTIVATION
Site Full sun or light shade.
Soil Rich, well-drained, alkaline loam; but tolerates most soils.
Propagating In spring, sow seed or divide crown (stem base), leaving about three tubers to each piece. Plant each piece 3 in (8 cm) deep, 12 in (30 cm) apart.
Growing Thin or transplant seedlings to 12 in (30 cm) apart. Keep moist in summer, and feed with liquid comfrey fertilizer (see p. 131) or dilute liquid manure. Not suitable for indoor cultivation.
Harvesting Gather young shoots in spring. Dig roots as required or lift in autumn; sever from base of stem.
Preserving Store tuberous roots in sand until required, or lightly scrub, blanch for 1 minute, cool and freeze.

USES
Decorative
● *Whole plant* Boasts elegant foliage for back of herb or flower border.

Culinary
● **Shoot** Lightly steam or stir-fry young shoots.
● **Root** Lightly scrub, steam or boil and serve with butter and seasoning or with white sauce; or purée cooked root and serve with butter and nutmeg. Add sliced to meatballs and new potatoes for traditional German fare. Cook whole roots in stews, vegetable pies and Chinese stir-fried dishes. Pickle whole root and serve with salads or cold meats.

Medicinal
● **Shoot** Fresh young shoots said by Culpeper to be a "wholesome food, of a cleansing nature, and easy digestion, provoking urine".
● **Root** Boil and eat skirret root for, according to Culpeper, "opening and cleansing, to promote urine and to free the bladder of slimy phlegm; helps the jaundice and liver disorders". May also help relieve chest complaints.

Smyrnium olusatrum

Alexanders *Umbelliferae*

This aromatic plant resembles both lovage and angelica, which occasionally leads to mistaken identity, but its bright green glossy leaf has rounded tips and lacks the deep indentations of the other two. However, it is called black lovage by some. The medieval Latin name for this herb was *Petroselinum alexandrinum*, the parsley of Alexandria, illustrating its Mediterranean heritage, and it was one of many useful plants introduced by the Romans to northern Europe.

Although listed as an official medicinal plant for two centuries, its historical importance was more as a culinary herb: its leaves, root tops, stems and flower buds all feature in medieval recipes. The dried leaves were among the herbs taken on long sea voyages to prevent scurvy.

Flower
Greenish-yellow flowers, full of nectar, borne in early to midsummer.

Seed
Two ¼in (6mm) long, almost half-globular seeds, ridged, black and aromatic, form in each fruit.

Dried leaves
These retain slight flavour and can be used in cooking or medicinally.

Leaf
Glossy, serrated, and bright green. Lower leaves can reach 12 in (30 cm) in length.

 **Lifespan**
Hardy biennial; sometimes perennial

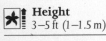 **Height**
3–5 ft (1–1.5 m)

Stem
Solid and furrowed.

Root
Thick at the top, branching to three or four main roots.

CULTIVATION

Site Sun or part shade. Grows wild near sea coasts.
Soil Grows readily in any soil.
Propagating In late summer or the following spring, sow ripe seed outdoors where it is to flower. Alexanders will self-seed readily.
Growing Thin out seedlings until 2–2½ft (60–75 cm) apart. In spring of second year, cover over with soil or straw for three or four weeks to blanch for a sweeter flavour. Alexanders is not suitable for indoor growth.
Harvesting Gather leaves in summer, and stems when young or blanched. Dig up roots in late summer of second year.
Preserving Dry only leaves gathered before flowering time.

USES

Decorative
● **Seed** Use dried seed heads for winter arrangements.

Culinary
● **Seed** Grind and use like pepper.
● **Flower** Toss buds in salads and flowers in savoury fritters.
● **Leaf** Eat raw young leaves in salads or use as flavouring in stew. Serve with fish. Include in a "Lenten potage" with watercress and nettles.
● **Stem** Stew, steam or braise young stems, which taste like asparagus; serve with a white sauce.
● **Root** Boil upper part, which tastes like parsnips. Crystallize as a sweet.

Aromatic
● **Seed** Grind coarsely and add to a potpourri.

Medicinal
● **Root** May be used in a decoction to improve jaded appetites.

Symphytum officinale

Comfrey _Boraginaceae_

Among plants, comfrey's claim to be a miracle worker must be preeminent. The list of beneficial substances in its leaves sounds impressive and includes calcium, potassium, phosphorous, vitamins A, C and B12 but not in sufficient amounts to meet our daily requirements. Comfrey has more protein in its leaf structure than any other known member of the vegetable kingdom and is cultivated in many countries. From two to five crops a year can be produced, depending on climate. Comfrey also sends down a 10 ft (3 m) taproot, or longer, to raise moisture and valuable minerals to the upper soil levels.

The leaf and roots contain allantoin, a protein that encourages cell division, and the plant is credited with some remarkable cures, from stubborn leg ulcers to broken bones.

S. x uplandicum, a rust-resistant hybrid.

CULTIVATION

Site Full sun. Position carefully as comfrey is difficult to eradicate.
Soil Rich in nitrogen; neutral pH.
Propagating Take root offsets (root section with growing tip) any time except midwinter.
Growing Transplant 2 ft (60 cm) apart. For a higher nutritious yield, give each plant a bucketful of crude manure in spring and late summer.
Harvesting Pick leaves in midsummer. Dig up roots in late autumn or winter.
Preserving Clean roots. Chop finely and dry. Dry leaves or make into a skin-healing "oil" (see below).

USES

Culinary
● **Leaf** Chop young leaves into salads. Cook as spinach or in fritters.
● **Stem** Blanch; cook like asparagus.

Household
● **Leaf** Soak in water for four weeks to make perfect fertilizer for tomato and potato plants, owing to high potash content. Pick leaves, allow to wilt for at least 48 hours then apply as a mulch. Boil fresh leaves for a golden fabric dye.

Cosmetic
● **Leaf and root** Infuse and add to baths and lotions to soften the skin.

Medicinal
● **Leaf** Make an "oil" to use externally on skin irritations. Pick clean dry leaves, cut into 1 in (25 mm) squares. Pack into a clean dark jar. Apply a screw-top lid, label and date. Store for two years; do not open. This results in an amber viscous liquid with some sediment. Decant "oil" into a smaller container. Use on eczema and other skin inflammations. Put fresh leaves in a poultice for rough skin, aching joints, sores, burns, cuts, sprains and to reduce swelling around fractures.
● **Leaf and root** Drink as a tea for stomach ulcers and coughs.

Flower
Blue-mauve bells in drooping clusters open along the spiral flower stem from late spring.

Leaf
Oval base, tapering to a point; rough, thick-ribbed and dark green.

Other species
Clockwise from the top:
S. grandiflorum _creamy red flowers; good ground cover._
S. officinale _white and pink flowers._ **S. asperum** _bright blue flowers._

Dried leaves
Infuse for a medicinal tea.

Stem
Squarish, rough, hairy and branching near top.

 Lifespan
Hardy herbaceous perennial

Height
3–4 ft (1–1.2 m)

Dried root
Useful medicinally.

Root
Brown-black, thick, tapering and penetrating.

Salad herbs

As culinary habits become more adventurous, herbs are being reintroduced, particularly in salads, giving us a range of flavours, colours and textures not experienced since the sixteenth century, when a salad might contain over 50 different leaves, buds, seeds, flowers, blanched stems and pickled roots.

Use leaves with a mild flavour such as lettuce, blanched chicory, summer purslane and chickweed to make up the bulk of the salad. Sharp flavoured leaves such as sorrel or nasturtium and those with great pungency such as basil should be shredded and used in small amounts as an accent. Flowers give special appeal but consider their colour when mixing ingredients so that they harmonize. Add other culinary herbs in small amounts: coriander, lemon balm, parsley, chervil, fennel stalks, leaves and bulb, thyme, lovage, tarragon, and seeds of sunflower or sprouted fenugreek.

Allium schoenoprasum
Chive flowers (*below*)
Sprinkle the flower petals of common chives in salads for a mild onion flavour. Try the white starry flowers of Chinese chives for a mild garlic flavour. (See p. 40.)

Lactuca sativa **'Lollo'**
Lettuce (*left*)
Succulent crunchy leaf in green and red forms; a decorative presentation leaf for pâté or around a salad bowl. (See p. 135.)

Lactuca sativa
'Salad bowl'
Red salad bowl lettuce (*right*)
A "heartless" form, and a useful plant as you pick only the number of leaves required. (See p. 135.)

Echium vulgare
Viper's bugloss (*right*)
Small blue or sometimes pink flowers with sweet nectar and a very mild taste. (See p. 275.)

Tropaeolum majus
'Variegata'
Variegated nasturtium (*right*)
Leaves add a sharp peppery zest to salads and sandwiches. Flowers and buds contribute a milder flavour. (See p. 137.)

Stellaria media
Chickweed (*below*)
Worth nurturing for its tender leaves available most of the year. (See p. 278.)

Brassica japonica **'Mizuna'**
Mizuna mustard greens (*right*)
An attractive cut leaf and tasty stalk with a fresh mild flavour; can be available all year from successive sowings.

Rosa species
Rose petals (*above*)
Use the petals of any scented rose. Remove the bitter white heel at the base. (See p. 120.)

Portulaca oleracea
Summer purslane
(right)
The perfect salad
herb: its crunchy leaves
have a succulent nutty
flavour. (See p. 137.)

Borago officinalis
Borage flowers (above)
Beautiful starry blue flowers.
To pick, grasp the black
stamens and gently wiggle
the flower away from the
green backing. (See p. 53.)

Calendula officinalis
Calendula petals (right)
The glamour herb
for salads; a mild
flavour and visually
stunning when
varnished with
salad oil.
(See p. 61.)

Alliara petiolata
Jack-by-the-hedge (above)
A wild plant with a hint
of garlic. Choose tender young
unblemished leaves and chop
finely. (See p. 134.)

Geranium pratense
Meadow crane's-bill
(above)
Mild flavoured blue
or crimson-veined blue
flowers most of the summer.

Bellis perennis
Lawn daisy (above)
Both the flowers and young leaves
can be used in salads. Separate
the petals or use small
flowers whole.
(See p. 275.)

Montia perfoliata
Winter purslane
(right)
Available almost
all year round. Second
stage leaves are shown;
early leaves are narrow.
(See p. 136.)

Lepidium sativum
Garden cress (right)
The hot flavoured
leaf is usually seen
in its seedling
stage as
"mustard and
cress". Allowed
to grow on, it is a
pretty salad crop.
(See p. 136.)

Atriplex hortensis
Orach (right)
Pick tender young
purple or gold leaves
for a colourful medium-mild flavoured
addition to salads. (See p. 134.)

*Eruca
vesicaria*
Salad rocket (above)
Young leaves have a hot spicy flavour,
older leaves become bitter. The flowers
can also be tossed in salads. (See p. 135.)

*Viola x
Wittrockiana*
Garden pansy
(right)
A colourful
addition to the
salad bowl.

Cichorium endivia
Endive (right)
Easy-to-grow salad leaf
with a bitter flavour
unless blanched or
picked young.

Brassica napus
Rape cabbage
(right)
Young leaves have a
mustardy-cabbage flavour.
Best grown as a seedling crop.

Salad herbs

Alliaria petiolata (Sisymbrium alliaria)
Jack-by-the-hedge Cruciferae

An early-flowering perennial or biennial found growing wild in hedgerows. It reaches a height of 2–3 ft (60 cm–1 m) and is topped by a cluster of small white flowers. The broad, somewhat heart-shaped, heavily indented leaves give off a strong smell of garlic when crushed. For this reason, the plant is also known as garlic mustard.

CULTIVATION
Rarely cultivated, the leaves of the wild plant were gathered by country people as and when they were needed. For garden cultivation, seeds can be obtained from a specialist in wild-plant seeds.

USES
The leaves make a tasty accompaniment for meat or cheese in a sandwich or, when finely chopped, add flavour to a salad. They can be eaten fried or boiled in sauces, although they lose flavour slightly when cooked. The juice of the leaves is said to be diuretic.

Atriplex hortensis
Garden orach Chenopodiaceae

This tall, erect hardy annual, also known as mountain spinach, was once commonly grown in the vegetable garden as a substitute for spinach. It grows to over 5 ft (1.5 m) high. The large leaves are indented and the whole plant resembles a large dock. Gold and purple varieties are available as well as green. A row of orach plants can be grown to form a temporary hedge.

CULTIVATION
Sow seeds in rows 2 ft (60 cm) apart in rich soil in late spring or early summer. Water freely to encourage quick growth. Pinch out the flower heads of all but a few plants, which will then seed themselves.

USES
No longer used medicinally, garden orach was once known to every housewife for its healing properties. It was prescribed for sore throats, gout and jaundice. Although considered inferior to spinach, it is now grown a great deal in France, where it is used in soups. The different forms, particularly the purple variety, make it a decorative salad ingredient. Young leaves can be eaten raw, older leaves should be cooked.

Eruca vesicaria (E. sativa)

Salad rocket *Cruciferae*

An easy-to-grow salad herb that can be found running wild on wasteland. The cultivated variety grows to a height of 2–3 ft (60 cm–1 m), with small creamy-yellow flowers that appear in late spring and early summer. The pointed, lance-shaped leaves are deeply indented near the base of the plant and have a characteristic smell when bruised and a peppery flavour.

CULTIVATION
Sow rows of seed in rich, moist soil in a lightly shaded position from early spring to early summer. Grow quickly for tender leaves, which are ready to pick within six to eight weeks of sowing and should be gathered before flowering.

USES
Once used medicinally in a cough syrup, salad rocket is now grown only as an edible herb. The Ancient Romans prized the flavour of its leaves and seeds. Added to a green salad, the leaves impart a pungent, spicy flavour, which is milder the earlier the leaves are picked. They can also be used in sauces or steamed as a vegetable. The flowers can be used to garnish a salad and in flower language, salad rocket means deceit.

Lactuca sativa

Lettuce *Compositae*

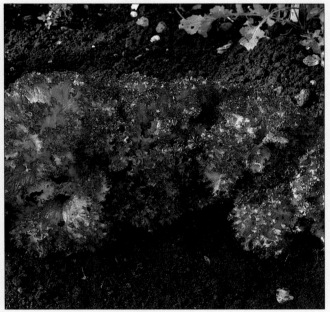

The best-known and most universally used of all the salad herbs, lettuce is now available in a variety of shapes, textures and colours as well as in all seasons. One of the most attractive and reliable is the 'lollo' (above). With its pretty frilled red leaves, this rosette type is almost completely pest- and disease-resistant. Other attractive forms are the red 'Salad bowl' and the cut-and-come-again varieties such as 'Saladisi'.

CULTIVATION
Lettuce needs a light, well-drained, fertile soil, which retains moisture. For a steady supply, sow seed little and often in an open site while the weather is cool. Thin as early as possible to 10 in (25 cm) apart.

USES
The Ancient Greeks and Romans were aware of its soporific and health-giving properties. In Greek mythology Aphrodite is said to have laid the dead Adonis on a bed of lettuce leaves. The juice is used in a cooling lotion for sunburn. Mainly eaten raw in green or mixed salads, lettuce can also be braised or made into soup.

Salad herbs

Lepidium sativum
Garden cress Cruciferae

Sown on a dish indoors, this is the cress of "mustard and cress". Outdoors it can reach a height of 18 in (45 cm) and bears small white flowers, typical of the crucifer family, in early summer. It is cultivated for its narrow, lance-shaped leaves, which have a biting, peppery taste.

CULTIVATION
Sow frequently in light, well-drained soil anytime from early spring to early autumn. Water freely and gather the young leaves before they have time to toughen in hot weather.

USES
Another favourite with the Ancient Romans, this useful cut-and-come-again crop adds piquancy to salads, garnishes and sauces. As a very young plant it gives a tang to mustard and cress, but the leaves develop a hotter flavour as the plant matures. Although it does contain a natural antibiotic, garden cress is not used medicinally.

Montia perfoliata
Winter purslane Portulacaceae

Also known as *Claytonia* or miner's lettuce, this hardy annual deserves more attention as a salad herb. It can provide several winter crops and is useful as a substitute when the soil is too poor for spinach. During spring it grows extremely rapidly, producing small white flowers on long stalks. The early leaves are narrow, while later leaves, just as succulent to eat, are rounded and become wrapped around the stem.

CULTIVATION
For winter use, sow very thinly in rows in late summer. Any soil is suitable, but the plants need protection in a severe winter. When they run to seed and die in midsummer, leave a few to seed themselves, then transplant seedlings that autumn, or the following spring for a summer crop.

USES
A cut-and-come-again crop that is indispensable for providing cool and juicy bulk in winter and early-spring salads. The stalks, leaves and flowers are all edible, and the leaves can also be cooked like spinach.

Portulaca oleracea
Summer purslane <small>Portulacaceae</small>

Cultivated for hundreds of years in India and the
Middle East, summer purslane was very popular in
Europe during the sixteenth century. There are
several varieties of this half-hardy annual, which
grows to a height of 6 in (15 cm) with rounded,
fleshy, green or, in some forms, golden leaves and
reddish stems. In midsummer it bears short-lived
small yellow flowers.

CULTIVATION
Sow each month during summer for a continuous
supply. Choose a sheltered, sunny site with light, well-
drained soil and sow in rows 1 ft (30 cm) apart with
6 in (15 cm) between plants. Water well and harvest
after six to eight weeks.

USES
The golden-leaved variety can make a very attractive
display in a more formal herb garden. The plant was
once thought to afford protection from evil spirits. It is
high in vitamin C and, eaten raw, has diuretic
properties. The thick leaves and stems can be pickled in
vinegar, but the plant is usually eaten cooked in the
East. With sorrel, it is one of the traditional ingredients
in the French dish *soupe bonne femme*. An excellent
crunchy salad plant, its cooling leaves blend well with
hotter-flavoured salad herbs.

Tropaeolum majus
Nasturtium <small>Tropaeolaceae</small>

There are many varieties of this colourful hardy
annual: climbers, semi-trailers, spreading and
compact dwarfs. It has round, flat leaves with
yellowy-green veins and red, yellow or orange,
trumpet-like flowers which appear from midsummer to midautumn.

CULTIVATION
Nasturtiums thrive in full sun or partial shade. Sow the
seeds singly 8 in (20 cm) apart in late spring in any
free-draining soil. In general, the poorer the soil, the
more flowers to expect.

USES
Both the leaves and flower buds have a cress-like
flavour and add bite to salads and sandwiches. The
young seeds have a stronger flavour and are sometimes
used chopped as a substitute for horseradish in sauce
tartare. Pickled in vinegar, they resemble capers. Used
whole, the flowers can make a stunning garnish. The
leaves have a high vitamin-C content and are thought
to relieve cold symptoms. The nasturtium seems to
attract hoverflies, which will attack aphids on nearby
plants, making it a useful companion plant.

Tagetes patula

French Marigold *Compositae*

Tagetes offers a unique asset to gardeners: it can deter eelworm. Its root secretions will deaden the detector mechanism of eelworms so that they don't "wake up" to the presence of their host plant. In Holland recent experiments have confirmed that eelworm among roses can be controlled by interplanting with French marigold. Tulip and potato growers also find it invaluable, and the foliage scent deters insects from tomato plants.

African marigold (*T. erecta*) has similar properties to French marigold, but most effective of all is the Inca marigold (*T. minuta*), which can grow to a height of 10 ft (3 m). For hundreds of years, South American Indians have grown potatoes on the same terraces and prevented eelworm attack by interplanting this "sacred weed".

Flower
Pungent-scented, vibrant dark orange, crimson or yellow flowers, double or single, borne from early summer to first frost.

Seed
Like miniature paintbrush: cream tipped, shiny, flat, dark "handle", ⅜in (10 mm) long, with cream "bristles".

Dried petals
These retain their rich colour for potpourri or for implanting in homemade papers.

Leaf
Finely divided and mid-green; bruised foliage emits pungent scent.

Stem
Sturdy, hollow (near base), round and green with pungent scent.

 Lifespan
Half-hardy annual

Height
T. patula 12 in (30 cm)

Root
Fine and beige.

CULTIVATION
Site Sunny and open.
Soil Well cultivated; prefers moderately rich loam but tolerates dry and poor soil.
Propagating Sow under glass in early spring.
Growing (*T. patula*) Transplant to 12 in (30 cm) apart in late spring. Deadheading improves growth. Can be grown indoors. (*T. minuta*) Start under glass, when 6 in (15 cm) tall, transplant 12 in (30 cm) apart.
Harvesting Gather open flowers.
Preserving Separate petals and dry.

USES
Decorative
● **Flower** Cut flowers are long lasting. Dry for potpourri.

Household
● **Whole plant** Emits scent which deters white fly from tomato plants.
● **Flower** Boil for a yellow dye with alum mordant for wool and silk.
● **Root** Exudes secretions which repel eelworm (*nematodes*). Grow T. patula and T. erecta as protection against most non-cyst-forming eelworms. The most damaging cyst-forming eelworms are clustered 90–500 in a chemical-proof cyst. They have a mechanism to detect potatoes which triggers their release. New research indicates that secretions of T. minuta deaden this detector (it does not eliminate the eelworm). T. minuta root secretions also kill certain weeds in a circle round it (the "Tagetes Effect"). It is strongest against ground elder (*Aegopodium podagraria*), quite strong against bindweed (*Calystegia sepium*) and slightly strong against couch grass (*Agropyron repens*).

Aromatic
● **Leaf** (*T. tenuifolia* var. *pumila* "Tangerine Gem") Plant for its orange scent. (*T. tenuifolia*) Cultivate for its fresh lemon verbena scent. Dry for potpourri.

Tanacetum parthenium (Chrysanthemum parthenium)

Feverfew Compositae

Some medicinal properties of this ancient herb have been known by herbalists, including Culpeper, for centuries. These were its ability to aid "melancholy and aches and pains in the head". However, feverfew's ability to soothe headaches was not given much attention until recently and, after detailed scientific analysis of the plant, several new healing substances have been discovered and patented. For example, in trials to prevent or reduce migraine, 70 percent of patients experienced some improvement after eating a number of feverfew leaves every day, while the best drug on the market currently has a 50 percent cure rate. Feverfew's success in combating migraines may be due to its accumulative effect in slowly reducing the smooth muscle spasms, which are implicated in many forms of migraine.

Seed
Small, beige-brown, narrow and flat.

Dried flowers
Add to potpourri for petal colour; also used medicinally in infusions, disinfectants, and as a mild sedative.

Dried leaves
Exude penetrating aroma, so store away from other herbs.

Flower
Small loose clusters of single white flowers with flat, yellow centres borne from midsummer. (Their flat centres distinguish them from chamomile flowers, which have conical ones.)

Leaf
Aromatic, divided and mid to yellow-green.

Stem
Slightly downy, ridged, round, branching and green.

Double-flowered form
White flowers resemble button chrysanthemums; very finely cut leaves. Lasts well in flower arrangements.

T.p. 'Aureum' Golden feverfew
Single white flowers and aromatic golden-green leaves; makes an attractive edging plant, especially in winter. Ht: 12 in (30 cm).

Lifespan
Hardy perennial

Height
2 ft (60 cm)

CULTIVATION

Site Prefers sunny position.
Soil Dry and well drained.
Propagating Sow in spring or autumn. (Feverfew self-seeds profusely.) Take stem cuttings in summer. Divide roots in autumn.
Growing Thin or transplant to 12 in (30 cm) apart. Feverfew can be grown indoors in cool air.
Harvesting Pick leaves and flowers anytime.
Preserving Dry leaves and flowers.

USES

Decorative
● *Whole plant* Cultivate golden feverfew for year-round colour.
● *Flower* Adds colour to potpourri.

Culinary
● *Leaf* Add small amounts to food to "cut" the grease; bitter flavoured.

Household
● *Leaf* Decoct or infuse for a mild disinfectant. Use dried in sachets to deter moths.

Cosmetic
● *Leaf* Used by Gervase Markham in the 17th century in the first commercial skin lotion reputed to remove freckles and blemishes.

Medicinal
● *Leaf* Eat three to five fresh leaves between slices of bread every day to reduce migraines. In trials, 70 percent of patients experienced reduced migraines, and 43 percent felt other beneficial side effects, including more restful sleep and relief from arthritis; while only 18 percent had unpleasant side effects. Research has not tested gold or double-flowered forms, but experience suggests they act similarly. Infuse as a mouth rinse after tooth extraction and as a mild laxative. Once used for fever, melancholy and vertigo.
● *Leaf and flower* Infuse as a mild sedative, a tonic to the appetite, and to relieve muscle spasms.

Tanacetum vulgare (*Chrysanthemum vulgare*)

Tansy *Compositae*

Tansy was believed to arrest decay, and its name derives from the Greek *athanatos*, meaning immortality. In some ancient cultures, its strong antiseptic properties were used to preserve the dead and, according to classical legend, a drink made from tansy was given to the beautiful young man Ganymede to make him immortal, so that he could serve as Zeus's cup bearer.

In the 1,100-year-old monastery plan of St Gall in Switzerland, tansy is shown in the physic garden. This monastery garden was Charlemagne's favourite, and he ordered that all its herbs should be grown on his imperial estates. Tansy was also popularly used as an insecticide, disinfectant and strewing herb, and, at Easter, was made into "Tansy", a rich custardy pudding. John Evelyn, in 1699, wrote that new leaves, stir-fried and eaten hot with orange juice and sugar, was a most agreeable dish.

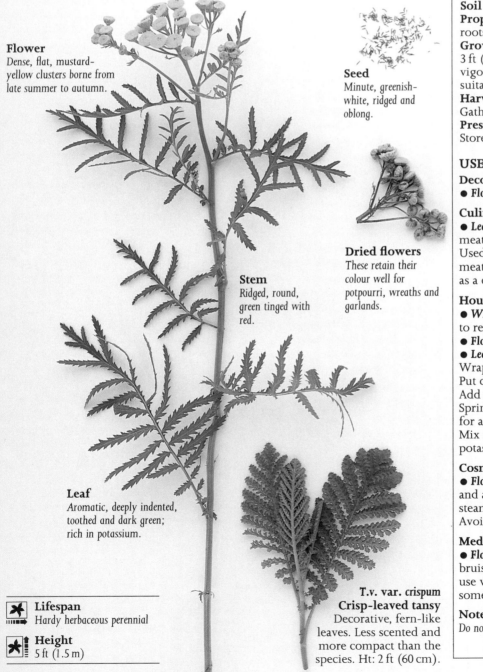

Flower
Dense, flat, mustard-yellow clusters borne from late summer to autumn.

Seed
Minute, greenish-white, ridged and oblong.

Dried flowers
These retain their colour well for potpourri, wreaths and garlands.

Stem
Ridged, round, green tinged with red.

Leaf
Aromatic, deeply indented, toothed and dark green; rich in potassium.

T.v. var. crispum
Crisp-leaved tansy
Decorative, fern-like leaves. Less scented and more compact than the species. Ht: 2 ft (60 cm).

Lifespan
Hardy herbaceous perennial

Height
5 ft (1.5 m)

CULTIVATION

Site Full sun or light shade.
Soil Any that is not too wet.
Propagating Sow in spring. Divide roots in spring or autumn.
Growing Thin or transplant to 2–3 ft (60 cm–1 m) apart; it is a vigorous spreader. Tansy is not suitable for indoor cultivation.
Harvesting Pick leaves as required. Gather flowers when open.
Preserving Dry leaves and flowers. Store away from other herbs.

USES

Decorative
● *Flower* Dry as an "everlasting".

Culinary
● *Leaf* Stew with rhubarb. Rub on meat for rosemary-like flavour. Used in the past to flavour sausages, meat pies, omelettes, stuffings, and as a colouring agent.

Household
● *Whole plant* Grow near fruit trees to repel insects.
● *Flower* Boil for golden yellow dye.
● *Leaf* Hang indoors to deter flies. Wrap meat in leaves to preserve. Put dried sprigs under carpets. Add to insect-repellent sachets. Sprinkle to deter ants and mice. Boil for a yellow-green woollen dye. Mix into compost heap for its potassium content.

Cosmetic
● *Flower and leaf* Use in stimulating and astringent baths and facial steams for mature and sallow skins. Avoid if you have sensitive skin.

Medicinal
● *Flower and leaf* Infuse as a wash for bruises, rheumatism and sprains, but use with caution as tansy can irritate some skins.

Note: Use in moderation, potentially toxic. Do not use during pregnancy.

Trigonella foenum-graecum

Fenugreek *Leguminosae*

Fenugreek is one of the herbs whose medicinal use and commercial cultivation is at present on the increase. Its seed contains not only mucilage but also diosgenin, which is important in the synthesis of oral contraceptives and sex hormone treatments. Its leaves contain coumarin, which gives them a sweet hay scent when dried, so they are sometimes used to mask inferior hay. *Foenum-graecum*, in fact, is the Latin for Greek hay and it is a well-known fodder crop.

Archaeological evidence suggests that the Egyptians valued fenugreek for eating, healing and embalming. The Greeks and Romans, too, enjoyed the seed as food and medicine. On the Indian subcontinent, its spicy seed has long been included in curry powder and its leafy shoots have been curried as a vegetable.

Seed
Yellow-brown, pebble-shaped, $\frac{3}{16}$ in (5 mm) long, divided into two unequal parts by a deep furrow. Smells of maple syrup with a hint of celery.

Flower
Yellow-white, pea-family-shaped blooms in midsummer. Each matures into a long narrow pod with 10–20 seeds.

Dried leaves
These often occur in hay mixtures and are well worth adding to "meadow" potpourri mixtures.

Leaf
Slightly toothed and mid-green with three oval leaflets, tasting of fresh French bean when young.

Stem
Slightly hairy, round, light green with very little branching; usually erect, occasionally prostrate.

Lifespan
Tender annual

Height
1–2 ft (30–60 cm); erect or prostrate

CULTIVATION
Site Full sun.
Soil Fertile, well drained, alkaline.
Propagating Sow thickly in rows 9 in (23 cm) apart in spring for main crop, and throughout summer for young salad leaves.
Growing Thin to 4 in (10 cm) apart; difficult to transplant. Small plants can be grown indoors.
Harvesting Pick young leaves as needed. Cut whole plant in autumn. Pick seed when ripe.
Preserving Dry leaves and seed.

USES
Culinary
● *Seed* Used as a spice in curries and chutneys. Roast gently to develop flavour before grinding (over-heating turns seed red and bitter). Sprout and use as a winter salad herb (ready in 4–6 days). As sprouts grow, curry flavour recedes.
● *Leaf* Toss sprouted seed leaves into salads. When fenugreek is 8 in (20 cm) tall, eat raw or boil or curry as a vegetable.

Household
● *Seed* Boil for a yellow dye.

Cosmetic
● *Seed* Contains up to 30 percent mucilage, protein, lecithin, vitamins and other valued conditioners. Infuse for a complexion wash. Powder and mix with oil for chapped lips, or use as a scalp massage for glossy hair. Try soaking seed until gummy and add to hand lotion recipes as an enriching, softening and thickening agent.

Medicinal
● *Seed* Grind coarsely, infuse and drink as a tonic tea to stimulate digestion and milk flow, ease coughing, flatulence and diarrhoea. Make a mushy poultice of crushed seed and hot milk for inflammation, ulcers, swollen glands, sciatica and bruises. Fenugreek is said to be effective in treating fevers.

Thymus species

Thymes Labiatae

Thyme has inspired poetic praise from Virgil to Kipling, who wrote of "wind-bit thyme that smells of dawn in Paradise". Its fragrance is particularly strong on the warm sunny hillsides of Mediterranean lands. To the Greeks, thyme denoted graceful elegance: "to smell of thyme" was an expression of stylish praise. After bathing, the Greeks would include oil of thyme in their massage.

Thymus is derived from the Greek word *thymon*, meaning "courage", and many traditions relate to this virtue. Roman soldiers, for example, bathed in thyme water to give themselves vigour. In the Middle Ages, European ladies embroidered a sprig of thyme on tokens for their knights-errant. A soup recipe of 1663 recorded the use of thyme and beer to overcome shyness, while Scottish highlanders drank tea made of wild thyme for strength and courage, and to prevent nightmares.

The powerful antiseptic and preservative properties of thyme were well known to the Egyptians, who used it for embalming. It is still an ingredient of embalming fluid, and it will also preserve anatomical and herbarium specimens, and protect paper from mould. Sprigs were included in judges' posies and clasped by nobility to protect themselves from disease and odour. Thyme is the first herb listed in the Holy Herb Charm recited by those with "herb cunning" in the Middle Ages, and it is featured in a charming recipe from 1600 "to enable one to see the Fairies".

THYME-SCENTED THYMES

**T. pulegioides
Broad leaf thyme**
Bushy shrub with mauve-pink flowers and strongly flavoured leaves, which are larger and rounder than common thyme's. Ht: 15 in (38 cm).

T.v. 'Silver Posie'
Shrub with pale pink to lilac flowers and green leaves edged in silver. Ht: 15 in (38 cm).

**T.p.a. 'Aureus'
Golden creeping thyme**
Rose-purple flowers with golden leaves, which fade with insufficient sun. Ht: 4 in (10 cm).

T. richardii (T. nitidus)
Neat shrub with pale lilac flowers and narrow, bright green leaves. Ht: 6 in (15 cm). (Similar T. carnosus has white flowers.)

Flower
Pale lilac blooms borne from early to midsummer.

Seed
Tiny, spherical, brown and shiny.

Dried leaves
These have stronger flavour than fresh winter leaves.

**T. pseudolanuginosus
(T. lanuginosus)
Woolly thyme**
Creeper with pale pink flower and very hairy, grey leaves. Ht: 3 in (8 cm).

Leaf
Aromatic, pointed oval and mid-green, covered in fine hairs.

Stem
Square, green-brown, becoming woody in second season.

**T. vulgaris
Common thyme**

Root
Fine and greyish-brown, forming dense mat.

T.p.a. 'Minus'
Creeper with pink flowers and tiny mid-green leaves. Ht: 2 in (5 cm).

**T.p.a. 'Snowdrift'
('Albus')**
Creeper with white flowers and small, faintly scented, bright green leaves. Ht: 3 in (8 cm).

T.p.a. 'Coccineus'
Creeper with crimson flowers and small, faintly scented, green leaves. Ht: 3 in (8 cm).

**T. praecox
arcticus
(T. serpyllum)
English wild thyme**
Very hardy creeper with mauve flowers and mildly scented leaves. Ht: 3 in (8 cm).

T. doerfleri
Creeper with mauve flowers and grey leaves, narrower and in closer clusters than woolly thyme's. Ht: 3 in (8 cm)

Lifespan
Evergreen shrub

Height
3–15 in (8–38 cm); creeping varieties make good ground cover

OTHER SCENTED THYMES

**T. caespititius
(T. azoricus)**
Creeper with pink flowers and narrow, pine-scented, green leaves. Ht: 2 in (5 cm).

T. herba-barona
Prostrate subshrub with rose flowers, arching branches and caraway-scented, dark green leaves. Ht: 4 in (10 cm).

**T. pallasianus
(T. odoratissimus)**
Shrub with pale pink flowers, long lax branches and citrusy leaves. Ht: 8 in (20 cm).

T.v. 'Fragrantissimus'
Shrub with pale lilac flowers and sweet, fruity, blue-grey leaves. Ht: 15 in (38 cm).

T.p.a. 'Doone Valley'
Creeper with pale purple flowers and lemon-scented, bright green leaves with gold splashes. Ht: 3 in (8 cm).

**T.p.a.
'Aureus'
Golden lemon
creeping thyme**
Creeper with pink flowers and golden-lemon leaves. Ht: 3 in (8 cm).

**T. × citriodorus
'Silver Lemon Queen'**
Shrub with pale pink flowers and lemony, silver-splashed leaves. Ht: 12 in (30 cm).

T.p.a. 'Lemon Curd'
Creeper with pink flowers, long wiry branches and narrow, sweet lemon-scented, green leaves. Ht: 2 in (5 cm).

T.p.a. 'Citriodorus'
Creeper with pink flowers and large, strongly lemon-scented, green leaves. Ht: 6 in (15 cm).

T. × citriodorus
Shrub with pale lilac flowers and lemon-scented, bright green leaves. Ht: 12 in (30 cm).

A bed of colourful thymes.

CULTIVATION

Site Full sun.
Soil Light and well drained, preferably alkaline.
Propagating Take 2–3 in (5–8 cm) stem cuttings with a "heel" anytime except winter. Divide roots or layer stems in spring or autumn. (Species only) Sow in spring.
Growing Thin or transplant to 9–15 in (23–38 cm) apart. In summer, prune frequently. In very cold areas, protect thyme in winter. Can be grown indoors.
Harvesting Pick leaves in summer. They are best while thyme is in bloom.
Preserving Dry leaves. Make thyme vinegar and oil.

USES

Decorative
● *Whole plant* Grow shrubs for low hedging and creepers for aromatic carpets.
● *Flower and leaf* Include in summer posies.

Culinary
● *Leaf* (Common thyme) Mix with parsley and bay in bouquet garni. Add to stocks, marinades, stuffings, sauces and soups, using cautiously as thyme is extra pungent when fresh. Aids digestion of fatty foods. Suits food cooked slowly in wine – particularly poultry, shellfish and game. Flavours Benedictine liqueur. (Lemon-scented thymes) Add to chicken, fish, hot vegetables, fruit salads and jams. (*T. herba-barona*) Use to flavour beef.

Household
● *Flower* Thyme is loved by bees. Its honey is esteemed.
● *Leaf* Make a strong decoction for a household disinfectant. Mix essential oil with alcohol, then spray on paper and herbarium specimens for mould protection.

Cosmetic
● *Leaf* Make a decoction to stimulate circulation; use in baths, facial steams and ointments for spots. Infuse with rosemary as a hair rinse to deter dandruff. Use essential oil as an antiseptic in toothpastes and mouthwashes.

Aromatic
● *Leaf* Use in potpourri.

Medicinal
● *Leaf* (English wild thyme) This has the strongest medicinal qualities, although any thyme can be used. Infuse as a tea for a digestive tonic and for hangovers. Sweeten infusion with honey for convulsive coughs, colds and sore throats. Apply infused thyme oil as a massage for headaches. Use essential oil in an antiseptic air spray. May also relieve insomnia, poor capillary circulation, muscular pain, and stimulate production of white blood corpuscles to resist infection.

Valeriana officinalis

Valerian *Valerianaceae*

This ancient medicinal herb, whose name derives from the Latin *valere* "to be in health", has long been valued around the world. Nordic, Persian and Chinese herbalists used the root, while the similar *V. sylvatica* was found in the medicine bag of Canadian Indian warriors as a wound antiseptic. Fresh valerian root smells like ancient leather but, when dried, it is nearer to stale perspiration. Its old name, *V. phu*, could be the origin of our expression for an undesirable scent. Nevertheless, valerian is still used to add a musky tone to perfume. Cats and rats are attracted to the smell, and the Pied Piper of Hamelin is said to have carried the root to lure the rats, his music being a decoy. Valerian returned to prominence in the First and Second World Wars for treating shell shock and nervous stress.

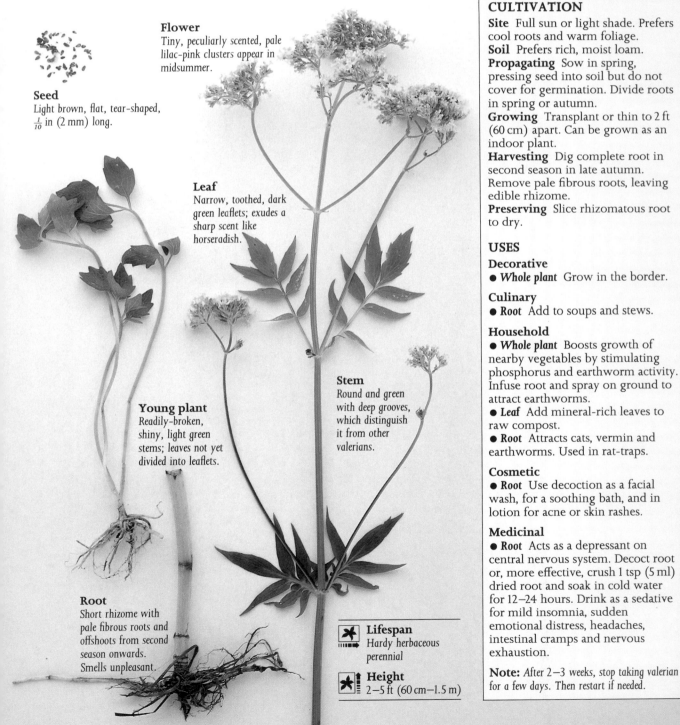

Flower
Tiny, peculiarly scented, pale lilac-pink clusters appear in midsummer.

Seed
Light brown, flat, tear-shaped, $\frac{1}{10}$ in (2 mm) long.

Leaf
Narrow, toothed, dark green leaflets; exudes a sharp scent like horseradish.

Young plant
Readily-broken, shiny, light green stems; leaves not yet divided into leaflets.

Stem
Round and green with deep grooves, which distinguish it from other valerians.

Root
Short rhizome with pale fibrous roots and offshoots from second season onwards. Smells unpleasant.

Lifespan
Hardy herbaceous perennial

Height
2–5 ft (60 cm–1.5 m)

CULTIVATION

Site Full sun or light shade. Prefers cool roots and warm foliage.
Soil Prefers rich, moist loam.
Propagating Sow in spring, pressing seed into soil but do not cover for germination. Divide roots in spring or autumn.
Growing Transplant or thin to 2 ft (60 cm) apart. Can be grown as an indoor plant.
Harvesting Dig complete root in second season in late autumn. Remove pale fibrous roots, leaving edible rhizome.
Preserving Slice rhizomatous root to dry.

USES

Decorative
● *Whole plant* Grow in the border.

Culinary
● *Root* Add to soups and stews.

Household
● *Whole plant* Boosts growth of nearby vegetables by stimulating phosphorus and earthworm activity. Infuse root and spray on ground to attract earthworms.
● *Leaf* Add mineral-rich leaves to raw compost.
● *Root* Attracts cats, vermin and earthworms. Used in rat-traps.

Cosmetic
● *Root* Use decoction as a facial wash, for a soothing bath, and in lotion for acne or skin rashes.

Medicinal
● *Root* Acts as a depressant on central nervous system. Decoct root or, more effective, crush 1 tsp (5 ml) dried root and soak in cold water for 12–24 hours. Drink as a sedative for mild insomnia, sudden emotional distress, headaches, intestinal cramps and nervous exhaustion.

Note: *After 2–3 weeks, stop taking valerian for a few days. Then restart if needed.*

144

Verbascum thapsus

Mullein Scrophulariaceae

A magical herb of antiquity, mullein was given to Ulysses to protect him from the sorcery of Circe, who changed his crew into pigs. This tall and imposing plant has attracted over 30 common names, including Aaron's rod, candlewick plant, hag's taper, cow lungwort and velvet dock. The soft fine hairs on verbascum's leaves and stems make superb tinder. They also protect the herb from moisture loss, creeping insects and grazing animals, as the down irritates their mucous membranes. This skilfully constructed plant drops rain from its small leaves on to larger leaves and down to the roots.

Seed
Tiny, brown, faceted and mildly toxic; many to a capsule.

Dried flowers
These exude honey-like scent. Keep their colour bright for optimum use.

Dried leaves
Can be used as tinder and in herbal tobaccos.

Stem
Sturdy, downy, round and fibrous, enclosing white pith.

Leaf
Large woolly and rosette-forming in first year, growing up stem in second year.

Flower
Bright yellow, stemless blooms open randomly from mid-summer to early autumn.

Lifespan
Hardy biennial

Height
7 ft (2.1 m)

CULTIVATION
Site Sunny and sheltered.
Soil Well drained; chalky or poor.
Propagating Sow in spring or summer. Self-seeds in light soils.
Growing Thin or transplant to 2 ft (60 cm) apart. Stake verbascum in exposed sites or on rich moist soil. Not suitable for indoor cultivation.
Harvesting Collect flowers as they open and leaves in their first season.
Preserving Remove green parts from flowers; then dry gently, without artificial heat, as its healing power is connected with the yellow colouring matter. Dry leaves.

USES
Decorative
● **Flowering top** Use in arrangements. Dry to add colour to potpourri.

Culinary
● **Flower** Use to flavour liqueurs.

Household
● **Flower** Verbascum pollen and nectar attract bees to gardens.
● **Leaf** Can be placed in shoes when soles become thin. The Romans wrapped figs in leaves to prevent them going bad. Use down stripped from leaves for tinder.
● **Stem** Dry and dip in suet or tallow for long-lasting iridescent torch.

Cosmetic
● **Flower** Use in a cream or facial steam to soften and soothe skin. Make a strong infusion to brighten fair hair.

Medicinal
● **Flower** Steep in hot water until water is yellow, then drink to relieve persistent coughs, respiratory mucus and hoarseness.
● **Leaf** Used in homeopathic products for migraine and earache. Infuse as a tea for coughs and strain through fine muslin to remove hairs or pollen, which can cause unpleasant itching in the mouth.

Note: *Take in small doses as all verbascum parts except the flower are mildly toxic.*

Verbena officinalis

Vervain Verbenaceae

It is curious that such an unassuming plant as vervain should have become sacred to so many cultures. In Egypt, for example, vervain was believed to have originated from the tears of Isis, and Greek priests wore its root with their vestments. Being sacred to Venus, vervain was used in love potions. The Chinese names for this herb, "dragon-teeth grass" and "iron vervain" suggest hidden powers.

Vervain was the Roman word for altar plants used for spiritual purification, and the Druids, too, washed their altars with a flower infusion and used vervain in their lustral water for visions. It was a herb of prophecy for the magi, the mystic sages of Persia. To the Anglo-Saxons vervain was a powerful protector and part of the Holy Salve against demons of disease.

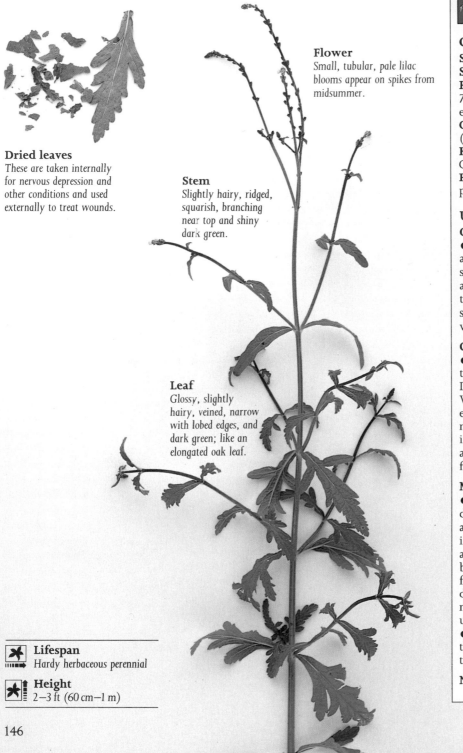

Flower
Small, tubular, pale lilac blooms appear on spikes from midsummer.

Dried leaves
These are taken internally for nervous depression and other conditions and used externally to treat wounds.

Stem
Slightly hairy, ridged, squarish, branching near top and shiny dark green.

Leaf
Glossy, slightly hairy, veined, narrow with lobed edges, and dark green; like an elongated oak leaf.

Lifespan
Hardy herbaceous perennial

Height
2–3 ft (60 cm–1 m)

CULTIVATION
Site Sun or light shade.
Soil Fertile, well-drained loam.
Propagating Sow in spring at 65–70 °F (18–21 °C). Germination is erratic and may take 3–4 weeks.
Growing Thin or transplant to 12 in (30 cm) apart. Can be grown indoors.
Harvesting Pick leaves as required. Cut whole plant when in bloom.
Preserving Dry leaves or whole plant if required.

USES
Culinary
● **Leaf** Because of its reputation as an effective love potion, vervain was sometimes included in dishes and added to homemade liqueurs. Note that vervain does not have a lemon scent and should not be confused with lemon verbena.

Cosmetic
● **Leaf** Infuse as an eye compress for tired eyes and inflamed eyelids. Decoct as an eye bath. The Victorians considered vervain an excellent hair tonic, especially when mixed with rosemary: massage infusion into the scalp and use it as a rinse. It was used in one of the first commercial hair tonics.

Medicinal
● **Whole plant** Infused as a tea for a digestive and for a sedative nightcap after nervous exhaustion, for detoxification and for promotion of urine; as an anticoagulant; or as a wash for bruising and to cool feverish foreheads. Chinese herbalists use a decoction to treat suppressed menstruation, liver problems and urinary tract infections.
● **Leaf** Infuse as a gargle for sore throats. A poultice of dried leaves treats wounds.

Note: *Use with caution.*

Viola odorata

Sweet violet *Violaceae*

A delightful herald of spring, this modest spreading plant is the most highly scented violet. It has long been cultivated for its perfume and colour and is added to cosmetics, drinks, sweets and syrups. Its seductive scent suggested strong emotions, and so sweet violet became a plant of Venus and Aphrodite, woven with other plants of love into the final scene of the famous Unicorn Tapestries, now held in The Cloisters in New York.

The Greeks chose sweet violet as their symbol of fertility, while the Romans enjoyed sweet violet wine; for Napoleon, it was the emblem of the imperial Napoleonic party. It was among the most popular scents in Victorian England, and the last Empress Dowager of China imported bottles of "Violetta Regia" from Berlin. Revered writers from Homer to Shakespeare and the old herbalists all speak with great affection of this charming flower. Its virtues were considered to be cool, moist and soothing.

Seed
Light tan, hard, round and small.

Flower
Scented, violet or white blooms from late winter to midspring. Provides nectar for early butterflies.

Dried leaves
Culpeper claimed that an infusion "doth purge the body of choleric humours".

Leaf
Heart-shaped, mid to dark green.

Crystallized petals
A delicious sweetmeat alone or as decoration for cakes.

Runners
Horizontal runners root every 3–5 in (8–13 cm).

Root
Yellowy brown, knobbly rootstalk with hair-like roots.

 Lifespan
Hardy perennial

Height
4–6 in (10–15 cm); good ground cover

CULTIVATION

Site Semi-shade. Benefits from sun either early or late in the day.
Soil Rich and moist.
Propagating Easy to propagate from runners. Seed germination is erratic as many early flowers miss pollination.
Growing Transplant in early spring, leaving 4–5 in (10–13 cm) between plants. Sweet violets are not suitable as indoor plants.
Harvesting Pick leaves in early spring. Gather flowers when newly opened, and roots in autumn.
Preserving Dry leaves, flowers and roots. Crystallize flowers.

USES

Decorative
● **Flower** Add to a spring posy.

Culinary
● **Flower** Use crystallized to decorate cakes, puddings and ice cream. Eat raw in salads or make into syrup: to 2 oz (50 g) fresh flowers add 3 fl oz (75 ml) boiling water. Cover and infuse for 24 hours. Strain. Add 3 oz (75 g) sugar and heat to dissolve. (The colour is maintained by not allowing it to boil.) Cool and bottle.

Cosmetic
● **Flower** Make a decoction for an eye bath or mouthwash.
● **Leaf** Add to a facial steam.

Aromatic
● **Flower** Use in potpourri, floral waters and perfumes.

Medicinal
● **Flower** Take fresh or dried in an infusion or syrup as a mild laxative; also helpful for coughs and bronchitis, and soothing for nerves, headaches and insomnia.
● **Leaf** A decoction or infusion with dried leaves may alleviate catarrh and bronchitis. Try fresh leaves in a poultice for bruising.
● **Root** A decoction or infusion of dried root is said to alleviate catarrh and bronchitis.

USING HERBS

For centuries, herbs were regarded as essential to daily life. They played a significant role in everyone's diet, were made into household products and cosmetics, and provided the main form of medical treatment. As manmade and chemical products were introduced and brought to the fore, the use of herbs fell into a decline. However, since some of these products have become the subjects of controversy, herbs are enjoying a revival. They are cheap, easy to grow and use, do not endanger the environment and are generally much less harmful than many of the synthetic ingredients found in commercial foods, household products and medicines.

The following chapters reveal a wealth of practical, herbal knowledge and provide an inspiring source of ideas for the many ways in which you can appreciate herbs. Arrange them indoors to scent and decorate your home. Taste their full flavours in mouthwatering recipes. Use them as cleaning and colouring agents. Add them to cosmetic preparations to soften the skin, bring lustre to your hair, brighten your eyes and whiten your teeth. Enjoy their aromatic oils in therapeutic massage treatments and reap the benefit of their healing properties in a wide range of simple home remedies.

A selection of colourful and aromatic herbs cut ready for use.

HERBAL DECORATIONS

One of the most delightful aspects of growing herbs is the many attractive ways in which you can display them and appreciate their fragrance indoors. Whether fresh or dried, herbs can be made into striking arrangements, colourful posies, or decorative wreaths and garlands to adorn your home or to present as gifts.

Fresh cut herbs brought straight in from the garden look best in natural, informal arrangements. A mass of summer herbal blooms and leaves in a simple vase can make a truly magnificent display. For added impact, position sweetly scented varieties near a window or in a place where they may be brushed against so their fragrance will waft through rooms.

Simple bunches of herbs hanging to dry look attractive, though they need to be in a warm, dry and dark place if you are drying to preserve them. Once they are dried, hang bunches on walls, from beams or shelves, around a window, or on the back of a door. For extra decorative effect, suspend them from ladders, on rake heads or from a mesh screen under a high ceiling – anywhere where they will look eyecatching and their scents can be appreciated. Tie small bunches of southernwood, lavender and other moth repellent herbs with ribbon bows and hang them in your wardrobe. Display groups of dried flowers in baskets, earthenware pots, wooden trugs and other suitably natural and complementary containers.

Herbs that you grow indoors can also be used for decorative effect. Evergreen shrubs like rosemary, bay and myrtle may be clipped as miniature topiary pieces, and at Christmas or on special occasions, you can add colour to their branches with ribbon bows and small trinkets.

The following pages show a range of delightful herbal arrangements that should tempt you into trying some floral creativity. Enchant a friend with a herbal posy which is both pretty and aromatic, and composed to bear a message in flower language (see p. 154). Celebrate a festive occasion by making a traditional wreath, or take a practical approach and make a wreath from culinary herbs for the kitchen, sweet-smelling herbs for the bedroom, and pretty, coloured herbs that complement your living areas (see p. 156). Use herbs in swags and garlands for their delicate foliage, flowers and fragrance (see p. 158). Arrange dried herbs that will extend the scents and colours of summer into the winter months (see p. 160). Make arrangements of culinary flavouring and garnishing herbs for the dinner table so guests can help themselves to tasty leaves and flowers or simply have their appetites sharpened by their refreshing scents (see p. 162).

A kitchen display
Dried summer herbs in a thyme basket set alongside bottles of herb oils and vinegars make an eyecatching feature in a kitchen corner.

HERBS FOR DECORATIONS

The following plants will add colour, interesting shapes and fragrance to arrangements when used fresh.

Those marked with an asterisk (*) also dry well for use in winter displays.

Flowers

*Alliums	*Elecampane	Lily of the valley	Poppies
*Angelica	Flax	Love-in-a-mist	Primrose
*Bergamot	Forget-me-not	Marigold	Pyrethrum
Betony	Foxglove	Marjorams	Rosemary
Borage	Honeysuckle	Meadowsweet	*Teasel
Chamomile	Jasmine	Melilot	Thymes
Columbine	Lady's mantle	Mints	Valerian
Cowslips	*Larkspur	Peony	Violet
Dill	*Lavender	Pinks	*Yarrow

Foliage

*Artemisias (all species)	Fennel	Myrtle	*Sages
Basils	Lungwort	Parsley	Salad burnet
*Bay	Marjorams	Pelargoniums	*Santolina
Eucalyptus	Mints	Rosemary	*Thymes
	Mullein		

Seed heads

*Alexanders	*Fennel	Lovage	*Sorrel
*Alliums	Good King Henry	*Love-in-a-mist	Sunflower
*Angelica	*Hops	*Poppy	*Sweet cicely

Fresh herbal arrangements

Often thought of as insignificant plants unworthy of inclusion in floral arrangements, herbs offer a wide choice of foliage and flowers as well as their refreshing aromatic qualities.

As the arrangements on these pages show, some herbal flowers have rich intense colours and intriguing shapes, others are delicate, inviting closer inspection. Use these to add highlights and focal points to arrangements.

Leaves may be feathery, lush, variegated, textured, soft or glossy. They come in all shades of green, and some are evergreen, providing year-round foliage to boost all arrangements. Many, such as the artemisias, have delicate fronds of silvery grey leaves. Fennel provides feathery leaves in green or bronze forms. Varieties of basil and sage offer deep purple-red leaves and there is a range of herbs with yellow variegated leaves,

including some of the highly aromatic mints, marjorams, pelargoniums, lemon balm and golden bay. Include such leaves in arrangements for their shape, form and colour as well as their fragrance, which will delight and freshen the senses.

Summer colour bowl (opposite)
A fragrant arrangement of summer blooms includes delicate pink honeysuckle, spiky red bergamot, starry blue borage, white double-headed feverfew and sprays of lady's mantle amidst sprigs of foliage including rosemary and mints. The simple vase and setting focus attention on the mixed rich colours and delicate shapes of the herbs.

A loose and light display (below)
Frothy sprays of lady's mantle and meadowsweet blossoms, white deutzia flowers, spikes of sorrel buds and feathery fennel leaves give this arrangement a light, airy feel. The grey leaves of artemisia 'Silver King' provide extra highlights and a trailing stem of ivy extends the line of the display.

Tussie-mussies

Fragrant posies filled with aromatic herbs and flowers were popular accessories in the sixteenth century, carried through the streets to disguise unpleasant smells and protect the owner from the many virulent diseases that plagued those times. Consequently, they were named nosegays, or more curiously, tussie-mussies.

Apart from their aromatic and disinfectant attributes, tussie-mussies became increasingly popular for their hidden messages based on the symbolic meanings bestowed on individual plants. This tradition can turn a pretty bouquet into a charming and unique personal gift.

Before making a tussie-mussie, consider its theme and select ingredients for their appearance and symbolism. Start with a central bloom and encircle it with contrasting flowers and leaves. Bind the stems with florist's tape as you go to keep the posy tight. Build up the layers and emphasize the outer rim with a large-leafed herb. Tussie-mussies stay fresh in water for about a week and can be dried by hanging in a warm, dark place.

The language of plants
A selection of meanings bestowed on some garden plants: agrimony (gratitude); bay (nobility); broom (humility); lavender (luck); lily of the valley (return to happiness); pansy (thoughts); parsley (festivity); poppy (consolation); rue (repentance); sweet basil (good wishes); vervain (enchantment); wormwood (absence).

Birthday tussie-mussie (below)
A pretty arrangement with a garden daisy (innocence) centrepiece surrounded by feathery mugwort (happiness); thyme (courage); angelica (inspiration); southernwood (jesting); marjoram (blushes); pink sweet peas (delicate pleasures). Rounded leaves and flowering sprigs of lady's mantle (protection) form the edging.

Angelica seed head

Garden daisy

Lady's mantle

Sweet pea

Thyme

Mugwort

Golden marjoram

Southernwood

Ivy

Pink rose

Forget-me-not

Golden marjoram

Myrtle

Rosemary

Sage

Variegated mint

Lime blossom

Bridal tussie-mussie (left)
Centred around a pale pink 'New Dawn rose (pure and lovely) are sprigs of mint (virtue); sage (domestic virtue); forget-me-nots (true love); golden marjoram (blushes); myrtle (love); lime blossom (conjugal love); rosemary (remembranc A rim of variegated ivy (fidelity) completes the posy.

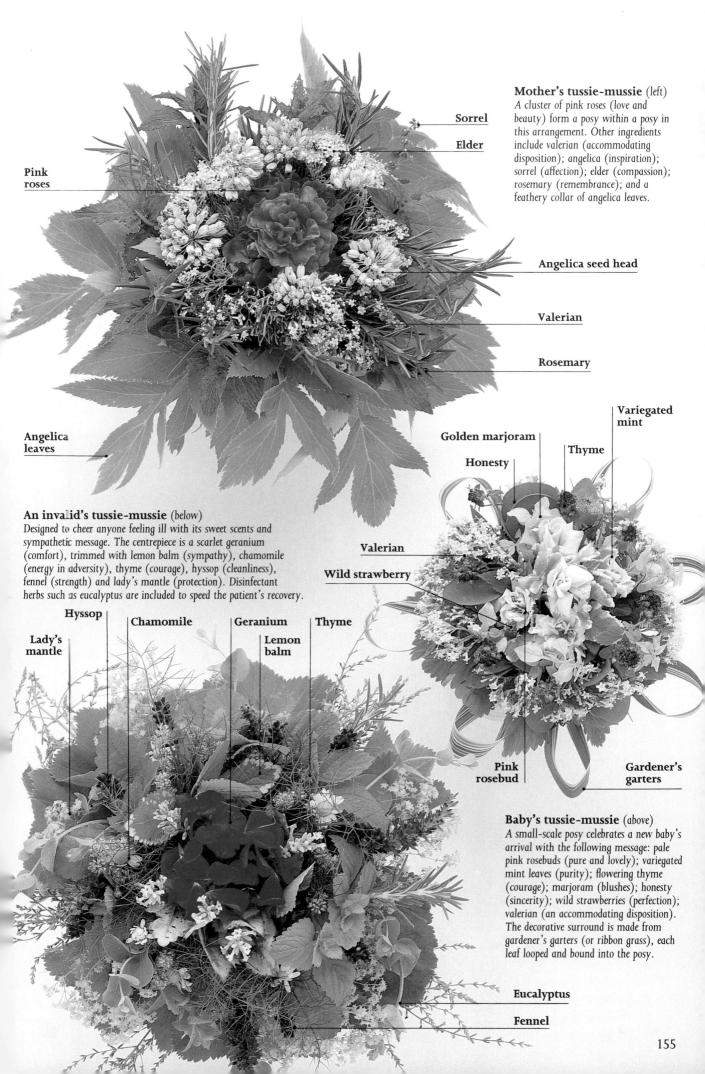

Sorrel

Elder

Pink roses

Mother's tussie-mussie (left)
A cluster of pink roses (love and beauty) form a posy within a posy in this arrangement. Other ingredients include valerian (accommodating disposition); angelica (inspiration); sorrel (affection); elder (compassion); rosemary (remembrance); and a feathery collar of angelica leaves.

Angelica seed head

Valerian

Rosemary

Angelica leaves

Golden marjoram

Variegated mint

Honesty

Thyme

Valerian

Wild strawberry

An invalid's tussie-mussie (below)
Designed to cheer anyone feeling ill with its sweet scents and sympathetic message. The centrepiece is a scarlet geranium (comfort), trimmed with lemon balm (sympathy), chamomile (energy in adversity), thyme (courage), hyssop (cleanliness), fennel (strength) and lady's mantle (protection). Disinfectant herbs such as eucalyptus are included to speed the patient's recovery.

Hyssop

Chamomile

Geranium

Thyme

Lady's mantle

Lemon balm

Pink rosebud

Gardener's garters

Baby's tussie-mussie (above)
A small-scale posy celebrates a new baby's arrival with the following message: pale pink rosebuds (pure and lovely); variegated mint leaves (purity); flowering thyme (courage); marjoram (blushes); honesty (sincerity); wild strawberries (perfection); valerian (an accommodating disposition). The decorative surround is made from gardener's garters (or ribbon grass), each leaf looped and bound into the posy.

Eucalyptus

Fennel

155

Wreaths and hangings

One of the most traditional and attractive ways of displaying herbs is in a wreath. Hanging from a wall or door, a wreath adds colour and fragrance to any interior. It is also potentially long-lasting and lends itself to an infinite variety of styles.

For the base, which you can make yourself or buy from a florist, use plain or moss-covered wire, plaited raffia or twisted vines. On top of this, wire on bunches of selected herbs. Pick from bay, thyme, sage, lavender, rosemary, savory and artemisias for scent and shape. Fresh material is easier to handle than dry, and you can always

make up a wreath and then leave it to dry in a dark, well-ventilated place for later use. For interest, add colourful drying flowers such as yarrow, santolina, roses, bergamot or larkspur; or make a theme-wreath like the hanging below using kitchen herbs such as sage, marjoram, parsley, mint and rosemary, adding bunches of spices for extra effect. Expand your repertoire by making seasonal wreaths for spring, summer, autumn or winter, and festive wreaths for weddings, anniversaries and Christmas. The possibilities are endless and always rewarding.

A fresh summer wreath
Echoing the profusion of a summer garden, this wreath is alive with interesting detail and informality. The base is a circle of florist's foam set in a round plastic container and soaked with water. Madonna lilies form the sweetly-scented focal points, with bergamot, borage, daisy-like feverfew, and other colourful blooms. Set in amidst the flowers are tiny green unripe cherries and filberts.

Spearmint

Golden marjoram

Garlic

Madonna lily

Bergamot

French tarragon

Parsley

Curry plant

A kitchen hanging
Bunches of culinary herbs adorn a looped length of plaited raffia, making a convenient yet ornamental way of drying herbs for the kitchen. Clusters of exotic spices add colour highlights to the hanging and further enhance its store of aromas. Each bunch is bound and secured to the base with a twist of wire. Any of these ingredients, used singly or in combination, will make a delightful and practical wreath to hang in the kitchen.

Feverfew

Borage

Meadowsweet

1 Cover a wire base with sphagnum moss, pressing a handful at a time into the frame. Bind on with reel wire, wrapping it over and pulling from underneath. When the base is covered, cut the wire and secure the end by bending it back into the moss.

Vanilla pods

Rosebuds

A festive wreath
Simple to make, as the steps at right show, this stunning wreath has a lush covering of traditional bay, with tiny red rosebuds giving rich points of contrasting colour, accentuated by the decorative red satin ribbon.

Bay

Variegated mint

Hyssop flowers

Bay leaves

2 Cut small branches of bay to the same length. Place them in overlapping groups all facing the same way and bind in place with wire until the base is covered.

Rosemary

ge

Cinnamon

Chili pepper

Thyme

Juniper

3 Wire together small bunches of rosebuds (or berries): place a medium stub wire against the stems and bend it round about halfway up. Twist over the stems, leaving a length to pin the bunch in place.

Garlands

Hanging bunches of dried herbs look attractive in their own right: combined into small posies and wired together to form a thick "rope" of foliage, seed heads and flowers, they can look truly spectacular. A garland of herbs such as the one below will transform any room into a setting suitable for a special event. Using dried herbs gives such a garland long-lasting appeal. Drape it over a fireplace or a mirror, around a picture or window frame, over a door, along shelves or beams.

Choose your ingredients to reflect the occasion, whether it be a wedding, a christening, a seasonal festival or some other celebration. Select items that add colour, delicacy, texture and fragrance. Ensure that you have enough materials and assemble them all with the required tools (fine reel wire, scissors, length of string) before you start. Once you are underway, it is very hard to move or put aside the extending length of overlapping posies until the decoration is completed. Experiment with your assembled ingredients, trying out different combinations of colour, texture and shapes and seeing how a change in order or composition can alter the overall effect. Once you have settled on your scheme, lay out the herbs in groups within arm's reach so they are easy to combine and wire in position. Add ribbons, baubles and other ornaments as finishing touches.

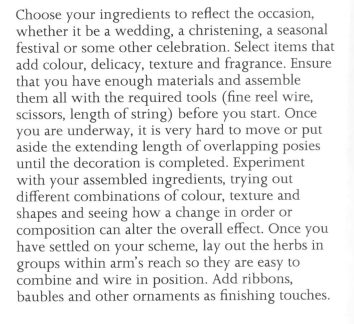

Lady's mantle

Thyme

Peach-coloured roses

Blue lavender

Sweet summer garland
Delicately coloured and highly fragrant, this striking garland of dried summer herbs makes a spectacular decoration. It is scented with thyme, lavender and eucalyptus. The curled satin ribbons have a softening effect and unite the whole arrangement by their colour.

Eucalyptus leaves

Blue larkspur

Love-in-a-mist seed heads

MAKING A GARLAND

1 Cut string to the required length and knot a loop at one end. Take a length of fine wire and attach one end to the string by wrapping it around a few times. Make up a small bunch from your ingredients and lay it on the string to hide the loop. Bind in place with wire.

2 Turn your hand so the first bunch lies under the string and position a second bunch on top, so it overlaps the stems of the first bunch and covers the string loop. Bind in place by wrapping over the wire, always pulling it tight from underneath after each turn.

3 Keep turning your hand and securing bunches one overlapping the other, always covering the string and the stems of the bunch above. Follow this procedure until you reach the end of the string. Make a hanging loop with the end piece of wire. Finish with ribbons.

159

Herbal baskets

Baskets make naturally complementary and highly attractive containers for dried herb displays, particularly as they are constructed from plant materials. The texture of woven stems or branches echoes that of many dried herbs, while the natural colours of baskets show off the range of hues found in dried herbs. Baskets made from the aromatic stems of lavender and thyme are also available, as shown below. Alternatively, attach aromatic stems to a basket's rim or handle to give an arrangement extra appeal.

To arrange dried herbs in a basket, you need to prepare a base which will sit in the container area and hold stems in place, as shown opposite. Select herbs for their colours, shapes and textures so they make striking contrasts or subtle blends. Try to incorporate any handles in your design to add height or extra shape to the arrangement.

Pink bergamot

Artemisia 'Silver King'

Chive flower

Pink larkspur

Blue lavender

Thyme

Double-headed feverfew

Pink lavender

A dainty floral basket
Aromatic flowers in delicate shades of pink, lilac, lavender and white make a pretty arrangement in this thyme basket. The handle is embellished with lavender and feverfew.

Alexanders seed head

Teasel

Red bergamot

Elecampane

Fennel

Tansy

Yarrow

A basket of colour and contrast
*This striking arrangement is packed with bold,
coloured flowers, delicate florets and interesting
seed heads.*

Blue lavender

Red roses

MAKING A HERBAL BASKET ARRANGEMENT

1 Press a block of florist's foam into
the basket. Secure in place with
wire and cut to shape with a sharp
knife so that its surface is slightly
higher than the basket's rim.

2 Form a base of colour by lightly
covering the foam with small
flowers and leaves such as artemisia,
thyme, lavender and melilot. Leave
space for the feature plants.

3 Add height, texture and solidity
to the arrangement with larger seed
heads and flowers such as teasel,
alexanders, elecampane, fennel
and bergamot.

161

Table decorations

Fresh herbal arrangements are the perfect way to decorate a dinner table. Their fragrance awakens the senses, while their flowers and leaves provide colour and interest as well as instant garnishing material. For a simple supper party, a spray of parsley, mint, marjoram or thyme by each place setting looks attractive and can be nibbled to freshen the palate betwen courses, to sharpen the appetite or aid digestion.

The table below is lavishly decorated for a special dinner party. Fresh garnishing herbs are set in pre-soaked, cone-shaped florist's foam. Selected for their colours and flavours, they include mints, parsley, basils, fennel, purple sage, curry plant, rosemary and lemon verbena, which also makes an effective finger freshener after a sea food or fish dish. A fragrant garland made from wired posies of lavender and thymes links the herbal cones and encloses the sumptuous candelabra centrepiece. The effect is stunning, both visually and aromatically.

A herbal dinner table
An arrangement of fresh flavouring herbs sits within reach of each place setting. These are interlinked by a delicate garland of lavender and scented thymes, which release their fragrance when touched or brushed against. The central candelabra is covered in dried golden yarrow and contains a colourful central spray of sweetly scented garden flowers.

HERBS IN THE KITCHEN

Herbs have been described as the soul of cookery and the praise of cooks. Used judiciously, they can transform a routine meal into a sensuous experience of tangy, spicy, refreshing flavours and crunchy textures. The aromatic leaves of rosemary and thyme delicately permeate cooked dishes; the seeds of dill, fennel and anise add piquancy to fish, salads and vegetables, while the earthy flavoured leaves of lovage and smallage lend body to soups and casseroles.

Many herbs make foods more palatable by easing digestion. Angelica, anise, balm, basil, caraway, coriander, dill, fennel, mint, rosemary and sage have long been eaten for their carminative qualities. The Romans traditionally finished their banquets with small aniseed cakes. Indians frequently serve a plate of roasted seeds at the end of a rich meal. The famous Greek mathematician, Pythagoras, used to nibble a nutritious mixture of herbs and seeds consisting of poppy and sesame seeds, mallow leaves, sea onion skin, barley and peas, all mixed to a paste in honey.

Herbs were used to preserve foods: in medieval times meat was wrapped in tansy both to deter flies and to give the flesh a spicy flavour; minty pennyroyal was added to kegs of fresh water on long sea voyages to help keep it sweet. However, the range of edible herbs and the number of ways of using them was much greater in the past than today. A salad for King Henry VIII included over 0 leaves, buds, flowers and roots. Thomas Tusser's sixteenth-century garden plan for farmers' wives recommended the planting of no less than 70 salad and pot herbs. After the Industrial Revolution and the move from the countryside into the towns, herbs became less important in the kitchen. Now, with a fresh interest in the culinary arts, herbs are enjoying a revival.

Most fruit and vegetable growers today tailor their crops to meet the demands of packaging and supermarket shelf-life rather than taste, so flavouring herbs and spices must come to the rescue. They enliven any dish, snack or drink. They can also supply extra nutrition to everyday meals, as many herbs, such as parsley, watercress and comfrey, contain a small but rich balance of vitamins, minerals and trace elements.

Using and storing herbs

The emphasis in the following recipes is on fresh herbs. As a guide, 1 tsp (5 ml) dried herb is equivalent to 1 tbsp (15 ml) fresh. Always store fresh cut herbs in a plastic bag in the bottom of the refrigerator. Don't set them in a jar of water in the sun or they will wilt before your eyes. Store dried herbs in dark airtight jars. Try preserving the flavour of herbs in oils and vinegars for use in dressings (see p. 188). Add them to butters, and use them to flavour savoury jellies.

The following pages list a selection of useful culinary herbs with guidelines on their attributes and complementary foods.

Popular culinary herbs

ANGELICA
A strong, clean flavour that pierces through heavy syrup makes angelica an excellent candidate for crystallization. Dilute angelica syrup for summer drinks and use to give character to fruit salads and ice cream. Cook leaves with acidic fruits to reduce tartness and sugar consumption.
Angelica and mint sandwich p. 182
Crystallized angelica p. 190
Angelica, mint and sweet cicely yogurt drink p. 191

BASIL
Indispensable for many Mediterranean dishes, the fresh leaf has a sweet clove-like spiciness and is superb on fresh tomatoes with a little salad oil, and in hot tomato dishes. Basil adds interest to rice salads and combines well with courgettes, marrows, beans and mushrooms. It has a powerful enough flavour to stand up to garlic, and together they make the classic pesto sauce. Basil's pungency increases with cooking. The fresh leaves keep their flavour if preserved in oil or vinegar (see p. 188).
Split pea and basil soup p. 166
Pancakes with basil stuffing p. 176

BAY
Bay is one herb that is better dried than fresh. Use it with parsley and thyme to make a bouquet garni. Add a leaf or two to marinades, stock, pâtés, stuffings and curries. When poaching fish, add a bay leaf to the water. A leaf in a storage jar of rice will impart its flavour to the rice. Add at the start of cooking and remove before serving.
Game soup with bay p. 166
Escalope of veal with bay p. 170
Marinated venison fillet p. 170

CHERVIL
Chervil is one of the classic *fines herbes* much used in French cuisine. It has a delicate flavour and is suitable wherever parsley is used. Chop the fresh leaf into omelettes, salads, dressings and add to chicken before roasting. Add at the end of cooking so its flavour is not lost. Preserve in vinegar and oil (see p. 188).
Carrot and chervil soup p. 166
Chervil stuffed trout p. 168
Globe artichokes with ravigote sauce p. 178
Violet herb salad p. 180

CHIVES
Freshly chopped chives lift many foods above the mundane. Sprinkle them on soups, salads, chicken, potatoes, cooked vegetables and egg dishes. Blend chopped chives with butter to garnish grilled meats and fish. Use them in place of raw onion in hamburgers for a milder flavour. Blend with butter (see p. 190), mix in cream cheese, yogurt sauces and baked potatoes. Add at the end of cooking. Chives freeze well but are poor dried.
Bass with ginger and chives p. 167
Potato salad with dill and chives p. 182
Cheese balls p. 182
Cheese bread with chives p. 186

CORIANDER
The leaves and ripe seeds have two distinct flavours. The seeds are warmly aromatic and indispensable in tomato chutney and curries. They provide an excellent flavouring for vegetables, especially stir fried, and in soups, sauces and biscuits. The leaves have an earthy pungency, delicious in salads, vegetables and poultry dishes.
Lentil and coriander soup p. 166
Persian chicken with herbs p. 170
Mediterranean vegetables p. 177
Hot salad p. 180

DILL
Frequently described as similar in flavour to caraway, aniseed and fennel, dill is like none of these. It has a totally unique, spicy green taste. Add whole seeds to potato salad, pickles, bean soups, salmon dishes, and apple pies. Ground, they can flavour herb butter, mayonnaise and mustard. The leaves go well with fish, cream cheese and cucumber.
Gravlax p. 168
Potato salad with dill and chives p. 182
Pickled cucumbers p. 188

FENNEL
With its pronounced aniseed flavour, fennel is an excellent digestive and reputed to be a slimming aid. Chop the stems when tender into salads. Stuff the leaves into oily fish such as mackerel, and sprinkle finely chopped on salads and cooked vegetables. Add the seeds to sauces, breads, savoury biscuits and the water for poaching fish. The swollen bulb of Florence fennel can be eaten raw in salads or cooked.
Fennel soup p. 166
Fennel flan p. 176
Fennel with Roquefort sauce p. 178
Fennel salad with orange p. 180

GARLIC
A strong flavouring for all savoury dishes, hot and cold. Rub a clove around a salad bowl to subtly flavour salads; add one or two cloves to dressings and marinades, or make garlic vinegar and oil (see p. 188). Mash with butter and bake in a French loaf or on grilled meat or fish. Insert sliced cloves into joints of meat before roasting. It can even be baked as a vegetable. The leaves have a lighter flavour.
Pork chops marinated with juniper and garlic p. 173
Mediterranean vegetables p. 177
Spicy aubergines p. 178
Aioli (garlic mayonnaise) p. 182

JUNIPER
The crushed berries of the juniper tree have an aromatic resinous flavour often featured in pâtés, marinades and stuffings for pork, venison and other game. They are a popular flavouring for sauerkraut, sauces, ham and cabbage.
Lamb's kidneys sautéed with juniper p. 173
Pork chops marinated with juniper and garlic p. 173
Cabbage and juniper p. 177
Mulled pears with juniper p. 183

LEMON BALM
Use the refreshing, lemon flavoured leaves fresh in salads; to make a pleasant herbal tea or to give a lemon flavour to Indian tea. Add generously to a white sauce for fish and spread over chicken before roasting. Finely chopped leaves add a lemony sweetness to sauerkraut, mayonnaise, sauces, and stuffings as well as fruit salads and custards. Freeze in ice cubes to add to drinks (see p. 192).
Spicy lemon balm kebabs p. 172
Lemon balm cheesecake p. 185
Sweet herb sorbet p. 185

LOVAGE
The leaves and stems have a meaty flavour, but use sparingly until familiar with their potency. Fresh leaves make an interesting base on which to serve strong flavoured pâté. Young leaves and blanched stems are good steamed as a vegetable and served with a white sauce. A brew of the leaves is like a yeast extract broth.
Lovage soup p. 166
Stuffed lovage and vine leaves p. 172
Lovage and lentil roulade p. 174
Lovage seed bread p. 185

MINTS

With their clean, sharp flavours, the mints are an aid to the digestion and can be used individually or blended. Excellent in mint sauce, syrups, vinegar and in teas. Add to new potatoes, to a garlic and cream cheese dip and to a yogurt dressing or drink. Also mix with chocolate cakes, rich desserts and bake with raisins or blackcurrants in pastry. Crystallize the leaf for a sweet decoration.

Persian chicken with herbs p. 170
Melon, tomato and mint salad p. 180
Angelica and mint sandwich p. 182
Mint and chocolate ice cream p. 183
Sweet herb sorbet p. 185
Raspberry and mint yogurt drink p. 191
Mint julep p. 192

OREGANO and MARJORAM

Marjoram has a distinctive savoury flavour, while oregano is slightly stronger. Both dry well. Marjoram is suitable for thick vegetable soups, pasta, fish, game, beef, chicken, sausages and meat loaf. Tomatoes, courgettes, potatoes and peppers are enhanced by its flavour. It is also used in omelettes and cheese dishes. Oregano is good with pizzas; it can be used like marjoram, but more sparingly.

Oregano cheese pie p. 174
Oregano tomatoes p. 178

PARSLEY

The mild flavour and bright green leaves of parsley make it the most useful and popular kitchen herb. Add it to a bouquet garni with bay and thyme. When cooked, it serves to enhance the flavour of other foods and herbs. To increase its potency, use generous amounts and include the stems, which are more strongly flavoured. Feature it in bland dishes and add toward the end of cooking. Use in salads, sandwiches, soups, sauces, mayonnaise and egg dishes. Fry whole sprigs briefly to serve with fish.

Sardines in wine with parsley p. 167
Herby hamburgers p. 173
Green herb omelette p. 174
Mediterranean vegetables p. 177
Green mayonnaise p. 182
Parsley and chive butter p. 190

ROSEMARY

This aromatic resinous leaf aids the digestion of fats, and traditionally is sprinkled on roast lamb and pork or added to chops, pigeon, sausage meats, pâtés and stuffings. Crumble dried leaves and chop fresh, or remove them before serving as they can be tough. Put a whole sprig in the oven to flavour baking bread. Put a sprig in oil or vinegar. Add leaves, pre-soaked in hot water, to oranges soaked in wine.

Rosemary kebabs p. 172
Sweet herb sorbet p. 185
Rosemary cheese fingers p. 185
Sweet rosemary slices p. 186

SAFFRON

Saffron is our most expensive seasoning due to the labour required for harvesting the individual stamens. Fortunately, only a pinch is needed to colour and flavour a large dish. Good saffron should be less than a year old and a brilliant orange colour. It has a strong aroma and a pungent, warmly bitter flavour. When using threads, crush the required number and infuse in hot milk or liquid from the recipe. If using powder (which is easily adulterated), infuse in liquid or add it with the flour for cakes.

Paella p. 167
Mussels in saffron p. 168
Saffron fruit bread p. 186

SAGE

Sage is a strongly flavoured, pungent herb which complements strongly flavoured foods and aids the digestion of fats. It makes a good flavouring for cheese and cream cheese dips. Use leaves in onion soup, with stewed tomatoes, omelettes, herb scones and bread. Try them in a sage jelly, butter or vinegar (see pp. 188, 190). If dried, sage must be of top quality as otherwise it acquires an unpleasant musty flavour.

Hazelnut and sage pâté p. 174
Leek and sage croustade p. 176
Herb leaf fritters p. 177
Sage oat cakes p. 185

SUMMER and WINTER SAVORY

The two savories have a similar flavour to thyme, with winter savory being marginally milder. Cook with fresh or dried beans and lentils or in a white sauce for bean dishes. Mix with parsley and chives for roasting duck. Sprinkle finely chopped fresh leaves on soups and sauces. Use to flavour vinegar (see p. 188).

Barbecued monkfish with savory p. 167

SCENTED GERANIUMS (PELARGONIUMS)

The many scented geranium leaves can flavour teas and drinks (see p. 191), cakes, custards, fruit and sorbets. Experiment with them in savoury dishes too.

Sweet rice with rose geranium p. 183
Sweet herb sorbet p. 185
Scented geranium leaf sponge p. 186

SORREL

A sharp flavoured leaf with the tangy zest of lemon, sorrel adds piquancy to bland dishes and sauces. Sorrel soup is a classic, and sorrel is often cooked and served like spinach.

Pork and sorrel terrine p. 172
Sorrel and parsnip mousses p. 178

SWEET CICELY

This is a mild flavoured leaf with a hint of aniseed. Add to tart fruit when stewing or making jam to reduce acidity and cut sugar requirements. Use fresh chopped leaves in salads, avocado dressing and cabbage water, and to garnish puddings, cakes, cold drinks and punches. Add green, unripe seeds to fruit salads. Boil the root, slice and serve cold with salad oil or add chopped root to stir-fried dishes.

Sweet cicely baked mackerel p. 167

TARRAGON

An aristocratic herb with a savoury flavour and hidden tang; one of the *fines herbes* with chervil and parsley. It is indispensable for Béarnaise and hollandaise sauces, soups, fish dishes and any delicate vegetables. It is particularly good stuffed in a roasting chicken and added to egg dishes.

Tarragon baked chicken p. 172
Tarragon stuffed mushrooms p. 177
Tarragon vinegar p. 188

THYME

Common thyme is used in a bouquet garni with parsley and bay and has a long history of culinary use. It stimulates the appetite and aids digestion of fatty food; useful with meat, shellfish, poultry and game. It is very pungent when fresh, so use with discretion. Try the lemon thymes in fish and poultry dishes.

Sole en croûte with thyme p. 168
Pheasant pot roast with thyme p. 170
Rabbit with mustard and thyme p. 170

Soups

Game soup with bay

2 pints (1 litre) beef stock
1 pheasant, partridge, pigeon or other game bird carcase
1 rabbit or hare forequarters
1 medium carrot, quartered
1 medium onion, quartered
4 bay leaves
juice of 1 lemon
salt and black pepper
2 fl oz (50 ml) port

Serves 4–6

1 Place the stock, carcase, forequarters, carrot, onion and bay leaves in a saucepan. Bring to the boil, cover and simmer for about 1 hour until the meat is tender.

2 Strain through a sieve, reserving the carrot, onion and any pieces of meat.

3 Purée the meat, carrot, onion and stock in a blender. Return to a clean pan with the lemon juice, seasoning and port. Reheat and serve with croûtons of bread.

Carrot and chervil soup

2 oz (50 g) butter
10 oz (275 g) carrots, chopped
2 oz (50 g) plain flour
2 pints (1 litre) chicken stock
salt and black pepper
½ cup (100 ml) chopped chervil

GARNISH
cream or natural yogurt
sprigs of chervil

Serves 4–6

1 Melt the butter in a saucepan and gently sauté the carrots for 5 minutes. Stir in the flour, then the stock and seasoning. Bring the soup to the boil, cover and simmer gently for 30 minutes.

2 Allow to cool slightly, then purée the soup in a blender. Return to the pan with the chopped chervil and slowly bring back to the boil. Serve hot or chilled with a swirl of cream or yogurt and sprigs of chervil.

Fennel soup

1 oz (25 g) butter
4 bulbs of Florence fennel, sliced
1 large onion, chopped
2 pints (1 litre) vegetable stock
1 pint (570 ml) milk
1 bay leaf
salt and black pepper
2 egg yolks
5 fl oz (150 ml) single cream

GARNISH
fennel leaves

Serves 8

1 Melt the butter in the base of a large saucepan. Sauté the fennel and the onion to soften; do not brown.

2 Add the stock, milk, bay leaf and seasoning. Bring to the boil, cover and simmer for 30 minutes.

3 Remove the bay leaf, then strain the soup by passing it through a metal sieve.

4 Mix the egg yolks and cream together in a bowl. Whisk in about half a cup of the strained soup. Then add this mixture to the rest of the soup and reheat, taking care not to let it boil or it will curdle. Garnish with chopped fennel leaves.

Split pea and basil soup

1 tbsp (15 ml) vegetable oil
1 large onion, chopped
1 clove garlic, crushed
8 oz (225 g) split peas, soaked overnight
1 tsp (5 ml) tomato purée
1 tbsp (15 ml) vegetable stock concentrate
1 large potato, diced
4 pints (2.3 litres) water
3 tbsp (45 ml) basil leaves
salt and black pepper

GARNISH
4 fl oz (110 ml) single cream
8 basil leaves

Serves 8

1 Heat the oil in a large saucepan and sauté the onion and garlic for 5 minutes. Add the drained split peas, tomato purée, stock concentrate, potato and water.

2 Bring to the boil, add the basil leaves and seasoning, cover and simmer for 40 minutes until the peas soften.

3 Allow to cool slightly, then purée the soup in a blender. Return to the pan to reheat for serving. Garnish with a swirl of cream and a basil leaf.

Lentil and coriander soup

1 tbsp (15 ml) vegetable oil
1 large onion, chopped
4 oz (110 g) split red lentils
1 pint (570 ml) tomato juice
½ pint (275 ml) water
salt and black pepper
1 tbsp (15 ml) ground coriander seeds
1 tbsp (15 ml) chopped coriander

Serves 4

1 Heat the oil in a saucepan and sauté the onion for 5 minutes. Add the lentils and sauté for a few minutes.

2 Stir in the tomato juice, water, seasoning and ground coriander. Bring to the boil, cover and simmer for 20 minutes. Serve very hot, sprinkled with coriander.

Lovage soup

For a sharp lemony soup, try using sorrel instead.

1 oz (25 g) butter
2 medium onions, finely chopped
4 tbsp (60 ml) finely chopped lovage leaves
1 oz (25 g) plain flour
1 pint (570 ml) chicken or vegetable stock
½ pint (275 ml) milk
salt and black pepper

Serves 4

1 Melt the butter in a saucepan and gently sauté the onions for 5 minutes until soft. Add the lovage, stir in the flour and cook for 1 minute, stirring constantly.

2 Gradually stir in the stock, cover and simmer gently for 15 minutes. Add the milk and seasoning. Reheat slowly; do not boil the soup or it will curdle.

HERBS FOR SOUPS
General: chervil, garlic, juniper berries, lemon balm, lovage leaf and seed, marjorams, mint, onion green and bulb, parsley leaf, stem and root, rosemary, savories, smallage, sorrel, tarragon, thyme
Minestrone: basil, rosemary, thyme
Pea: basil, borage, dill, marjoram, mint, parsley, rosemary, savory, thyme
Potato: bay, caraway, parsley
Tomato: basil, dill, marjoram, oregano, tarragon, thyme

Fish

Barbecued monkfish with savory

1½ lb (700 g) monkfish
grated rind and juice of 1 lemon
8 fl oz (225 ml) olive oil
salt and black pepper
a good handful of winter savory (or rosemary)

Serves 4

1 Remove any bones from the monkfish and cut the flesh into ½ in (1 cm) cubes. Lay the cubes in a deep dish.

2 Mix the lemon rind and juice, olive oil and seasoning together in a bowl. Break the winter savory into small sprigs and add to the mixture.

3 Pour this marinade over the fish and leave for 6 hours or overnight in the refrigerator.

4 Thread the monkfish on to 4 skewers. Cook over a barbecue (or under the grill) for 5–10 minutes, turning often and using the marinade for basting. Serve on a bed of boiled rice and accompany with a green salad.

Sardines in wine with parsley

3 tbsp (45 ml) olive oil
16 sardines, cleaned
2 cloves garlic, crushed
4 tbsp (60 ml) chopped parsley
1 tbsp (15 ml) lemon juice
¼ pint (150 ml) white wine

Serves 4

1 Heat the oil in a deep frying pan and add the sardines, garlic, parsley, lemon juice and wine.

2 Simmer for 5–6 minutes or until cooked. Serve hot with French bread or cold as a starter.

Sweet cicely baked mackerel

Fennel leaves also work well in this recipe.

2 oz (50 g) butter
8 oz (225 g) onion, thinly sliced
1 clove garlic, crushed
2 oz (50 g) fresh root ginger, grated
1 cup (225 ml) finely chopped sweet cicely
4 mackerel, about 8 oz (225 g) each, or 2 larger fish, cleaned

Serves 4

1 Preheat the oven to 350 °F (180 °C) Gas 4.

2 Melt the butter in a saucepan and gently sauté the onion for about 5 minutes. Add the garlic, ginger and sweet cicely and sauté until soft but still moist.

3 Cut deep slits diagonally from head to tail on both sides of the mackerel.

4 Divide the onion and sweet cicely mixture between the fish and spoon it into the cavities.

5 Lay the fish on a baking tray. Bake for 15 minutes or 25 minutes if the fish are larger.

6 If you like, you can crisp the fish by browning for about 2 minutes on each side either under the grill or over a barbecue.

Bass with ginger and chives

2 lb (900 g) bass
salt
1 tbsp (15 ml) soya sauce
1 tsp (5 ml) sesame oil
1 tbsp (15 ml) grated fresh root ginger
4 tbsp (60 ml) chopped chives

Serves 6

1 Put the fish into a saucepan of boiling salted water to cover. Simmer for 5 minutes. Drain the fish and arrange on a serving dish.

2 Mix the soya sauce, oil and ginger together and pour over the fish. Sprinkle with the chopped chives and serve with plain boiled rice or new potatoes.

Paella

Any kind of shellfish can be used in this dish, although squid and mussels are traditional.

4 tbsp (60 ml) olive oil
4 chicken drumsticks or other small portions, about 3 oz (75 g) each
2 oz (50 g) red pepper, cut into strips
2 large tomatoes, skinned and chopped
12 oz (350 g) Valencia or short grain rice
4 baby squid, ink sacs and eyes removed
8 oz (225 g) unshelled prawns or 8 large Mediterranean prawns
1 lb (450 g) mussels scrubbed and cleaned
¼ tsp (1.25 ml) saffron, infused in 2 tbsp (30 ml) hot water
2 pints (1 litre) water

Serves 4

1 Heat the oil in a large paella dish or heavy-based frying pan and gently fry the chicken until golden brown. Remove the chicken from the pan.

2 Add the pepper and tomatoes to the pan and fry for a few minutes. In stages, add the rice, squid, prawns, mussels, saffron and finally the water, mixing well all the time. Return the chicken pieces to the pan and bring to the boil.

3 Cover and simmer for 30 minutes or until the water has been absorbed and the rice is fluffy. If the water evaporates before the rice has cooked, add more water. However, if the rice has cooked and there is still water, boil rapidly until the rice is dry. Each grain of rice should be separate, so stir with a fork only when absolutely necessary. Serve from the pan and accompany with a crisp green salad.

HERBS FOR FISH

General: alexanders, basil, bay, caraway, chervil, chives, dill, fennel, lemon balm, lemon thyme, lovage, marjoram, mint, parsley

Baked or grilled: all the above, savory, tarragon, thyme

Oily fish: fennel, dill

Salmon: dill seed, rosemary

Seafood: basil, bay, chervil, chives, dill, fennel seed, marjoram, rosemary, tarragon, thyme

Soups: bay, lovage, sage (though this should be used sparingly), savory, tarragon, thyme

Mussels in saffron

6 pints (2 kg) mussels	1 oz (25 g) butter
1 tbsp (15 ml) olive oil	1 oz (25 g) plain flour
1 tbsp (15 ml) oats	$\frac{1}{4}$ pint (150 ml) milk
2 small onions, sliced	$\frac{1}{4}$ tsp (1.25 g) saffron,
2 tbsp (30 ml) finely	infused in 1 tbsp (15 ml)
chopped parsley	hot water
2 fl oz (50 ml) dry white wine	2 oz (50 g) breadcrumbs

Serves 4–6

1 Soak the mussels for about 2 hours in a bowl of fresh water with the oats added to plump them up. Carefully scrub all the mussels under running water and remove their beards.

2 Heat the oil in a large saucepan and sauté the onion until soft. Add the parsley, mussels and wine. Cover the saucepan and leave the mussels to steam open (about 5 minutes), stirring occasionally. As the mussels open, remove them from the pan.

3 Preheat the oven to 400 °F (200 °C), Gas 6.

4 Melt the butter in a saucepan and stir in the flour to make a roux. Add the milk and liquid from the cooked mussels and the saffron infusion. Stir well to make a smooth sauce and remove from the heat.

5 Stir the cooked mussels into the sauce, then pour into a deep 10 in (25 cm) square ovenproof dish. Sprinkle with breadcrumbs and bake for about 10 minutes. Serve with garlic bread.

Sole en croûte with thyme

4 fillets of sole	5 fl oz (150 ml) dry white wine
1 oz (25 g) butter	8 oz (225 g) puff pastry
salt and black pepper	1 egg, beaten

STUFFING

1 oz (25 g) butter	3 oz (75 g) raisins
1 medium onion, finely	1 tbsp (15 ml) chopped
chopped	thyme
2 oz (50 g) mushrooms,	1 egg, beaten
finely chopped	salt and black pepper
4 oz (110 g) soft breadcrumbs	

Serves 4

1 Preheat the oven to 325 °F (170 °C) Gas 3.

2 Put the sole fillets in a baking dish, dot with butter, season and pour over the wine. Bake gently for about 15 minutes. Drain, retaining the fish juices.

3 Melt the butter and sauté the onion. Add the finely chopped mushrooms and fry for a few minutes until just soft.

4 Mix the onion and mushrooms with the rest of the stuffing ingredients and set aside.

5 Turn up the oven to 375 °F (190 °C) Gas 5.

6 Divide the puff pastry into four portions. Roll out each one to the size of a small plate. Place one sole fillet with a quarter of the stuffing on each round of pastry. Roll over, moisten the pastry edges with beaten egg and seal.

7 Glaze with beaten egg and bake for about 20 minutes, or until golden brown. Delicious served with a thyme-flavoured cream sauce.

Gravlax

2 lb (900 g) fresh salmon	black pepper
5 tbsp (75 ml) sugar	5 tbsp (75 ml) dill leaves
5 tbsp (75 ml) sea salt	

SAUCE

2 tbsp (30 ml) French mustard	salt and black pepper
1 tsp (5 ml) clear honey	6 tbsp (90 ml) olive oil
1 egg yolk	2 tbsp (30 ml) chopped
2 tbsp (30 ml) white wine	dill leaves
vinegar	

Serves 6

1 Cut the salmon in half lengthways and remove all the bones.

2 Mix together the sugar, salt and black pepper. Rub the mixture over the fish.

3 Place a layer of dill in the bottom of a dish and lay half the salmon, skin side down, on the dill. Cover with more dill and lay the other half of salmon on it skin side up. Coat with the rest of the dill and any of the remaining sugar mixture.

4 Cover the dish with cling film and a weighted plate. Leave in a cool place for 24 hours.

5 Make the sauce by putting all the ingredients except the oil and dill in a bowl and beating with a whisk. Slowly beat in the oil and then add the chopped dill.

6 Scrape the marinade off the salmon. Slice the flesh away from the skin, across the grain, and serve with the sauce and a garnish of lemon and dill leaves.

Chervil stuffed trout

2 oz (50 g) butter	juice and rind of 1 lemon
3 oz (75 g) onion, finely	1 cup of chopped chervil
chopped	salt and black pepper
4 oz (110 g) soft	4 trout, about 8 oz (225 g)
breadcrumbs	each, or 1 large fish,
3 oz (75 g) mushrooms,	2–4 lb (1–2 kg), gutted
finely chopped	and cleaned

Serves 4

1 Preheat the oven to 350 °F (180 °C) Gas 4.

2 Melt the butter and gently sauté the onion until golden but not brown.

3 Combine the breadcrumbs, mushrooms, lemon rind and juice, chervil and seasoning in a large bowl. Add the cooked onion and mix together.

4 Divide the stuffing mixture between the trout, spooning it into each stomach cavity. Put a knob of butter on top of each fish and then wrap in a square of lightly greased kitchen foil. Bake for 15 minutes.

5 Remove the fish from the oven, open the foil and grill or barbecue for 5 minutes on each side.

Clockwise from the top: Chervil stuffed trout; Sole en croûte with thyme; Mussels in saffron; Gravlax.

Meat

Pheasant pot roast with thyme

This is a succulent way of cooking any type of game, just adjust the cooking time accordingly.

2 tbsp (30 ml) vegetable oil	4 oz (110 g) button
1 pheasant	mushrooms
2 oz (50 g) streaky bacon, cut	1 medium onion,
into 2 in (5 cm) pieces	thickly sliced
8 oz (225 g) carrots, cut into	6 large sprigs of thyme
2 in (5 cm) chunks	2 tbsp (30 ml) plain flour
4 oz (110 g) celery, cut into 2 in	½ pint (275 ml) red wine
(5 cm) lengths	½ pint (275 ml) water
	salt and black pepper

Serves 4

1 Preheat the oven to 350 °F (180 °C) Gas 4.

2 Heat the oil in a heavy-based casserole and quickly brown the pheasant on all sides. Remove from the casserole and set aside.

3 Add the bacon to the casserole and fry until lightly browned. Add the carrots, celery, mushrooms, onion and 3 sprigs of thyme and gently sauté until browned.

4 Stir in the flour, then add the red wine and water. Stir well and gently bring to the boil. Add the pheasant and remaining thyme. Season to taste.

5 Cover and pot roast for 1½ hours. When cooked, remove the pheasant from the casserole and place it on a serving dish. Strain the sauce into a sauce boat.

Rabbit with mustard and thyme

The mustard and thyme coating forms a delicious crust. For chicken, try savory or chives instead of thyme.

2 tbsp (30 ml) mustard powder	salt and black pepper (optional)
2 tbsp (30 ml) plain flour	about 6 tbsp (90 ml) water
1 tbsp (15 ml) chopped thyme	1 rabbit, jointed

Serves 4

1 Preheat the oven to 350 °F (180 °C) Gas 4.

2 Mix the mustard powder, flour and thyme together in a bowl. Season if liked. Gradually add the water, mixing the mustard and flour to a smooth paste. Using a pastry brush or the back of a spoon, spread the paste all over the surfaces of the jointed rabbit.

3 Arrange the joints on a greased baking tray. Bake for 1–1½ hours or until tender. Serve hot or cold.

HERBS FOR GAME AND POULTRY

Venison: bay, juniper, lovage seed, rosemary, sage, savory, sweet marjoram
Rabbit/Hare: basil, bay, lovage seed, marjoram, rosemary, sage
Pigeon: juniper berries, rosemary, thyme
Chicken: chervil, chives, fennel, lemon balm, marjoram, mint, parsley, savory, tarragon, thyme
Duck: bay, rosemary, sage, sweet marjoram, tarragon
Goose: fennel, sage, sweet marjoram,
Turkey: parsley, sage, sweet marjoram, tarragon, thyme

Marinated venison fillets

MARINADE

8 fl oz (225 ml) wine	1 branch thyme
vinegar	1 branch parsley
8 fl oz (225 ml) red wine	6 tarragon leaves
3 tbsp (45 ml) olive oil	1 tsp (5 ml) juniper berries
3 bay leaves	1 small onion, chopped
4 venison fillets	1 tbsp (25 g) flour
1 oz (25 g) butter	2 tbsp (30 ml) brandy

Serves 4

1 Boil all the marinade ingredients together for 5 minutes. Allow to cool.

2 Place the fillets in a deep ovenproof dish. Pour the marinade over and leave to steep for 24 hours, turning from time to time.

3 Remove from the marinade and fry in butter for about 10 minutes. Keep warm while you make a sauce.

4 Stir the flour into the butter, then gradually stir in about half of the marinade mixture and the brandy. Pour over the fillets and serve.

Escalope of veal with bay

1 oz (25 g) butter	4 dried bay leaves
1 small onion, finely chopped	8 fl oz (225 ml) dry white wine
4 veal escalopes, about	¼ pint (150 ml) single cream
4 oz (110 g) each	salt and black pepper

Serves 4

1 Melt the butter in a large frying pan and sauté the onion for about 5 minutes until soft.

2 Add the veal escalopes and crush the bay leaves over them. Turn the escalopes over and add the wine to the pan. Cook, uncovered, for 5 minutes. Pour in the cream and stir well. Season to taste. Serve on a bed of rice.

Persian chicken with herbs

4 oz (110 g) butter	¼ cup (50 ml) chopped mint
2 medium onions, sliced	¼ cup (50 ml) chopped
1 boiling chicken	coriander leaves
¾ pint (425 ml) chicken stock	2 oz (50 g) walnuts,
salt and black pepper	chopped
1 cup (225 ml)	6 fl oz (175 ml) orange juice
chopped parsley	grated rind of 2 oranges
1 cup (225 ml) chopped chives	2 eggs, beaten (optional)

Serves 4–6

1 Melt 1 oz (25 g) of the butter in a large saucepan and sauté the onions until golden.

2 Add the chicken to the pan with the stock and seasoning. Cover and simmer for 1 hour until tender.

3 Melt the remaining butter in a pan and lightly cook the parsley, chives, mint and coriander to flavour the butter. Add to the chicken, then stir in the chopped walnuts, orange juice and rind. Simmer for 30 minutes.

4 If liked, stir in the beaten eggs just before serving. Accompany with noodles or rice.

Clockwise from the top: Spicy lemon balm kebabs (p. 172); Rosemary kebabs (p. 172); Stuffed lovage and vine leaves (p. 172); Pork and sorrel terrine (p. 172); Persian chicken with herbs.

Tarragon baked chicken

Parsley, chives, thyme or chervil can be substituted for the tarragon.

8 chicken thighs or	2 tbsp (30 ml) chopped
drumsticks, 3 oz (75 g) each	tarragon
2 oz (50 g) butter	salt and black pepper

Serves 4

1 Preheat the oven to 375 °F (190 °C) Gas 5.

2 To remove the bones from the chicken pieces, use a sharp knife and run it downward between the bone and the flesh until the bone comes loose. Gently twist the bone with your hands and it will come out easily.

3 Soften the butter a little and work to a paste with a wooden spoon. Mix in the tarragon and seasoning.

4 Divide the flavoured butter between the chicken pieces, filling each cavity with a generous amount. Seal the open ends of each chicken piece using a wooden cocktail stick or small skewer.

5 Lay the pieces in a 9 in (23 cm) square ovenproof dish and cover with foil. Bake for 40 minutes, removing the foil for the last 10 minutes. The chicken can also be finished off over a barbecue.

Spicy lemon balm kebabs

1 clove garlic	1 large onion, sliced into
1 leg of lamb, about 3 lb	chunks
(1.5 kg), boned and cut into	2 good handfuls of lemon
1 in (2.5 cm) cubes	balm leaves

MARINADE

2 fl oz (50 ml) wine vinegar	1 tbsp (15 ml) brown sugar
1 tsp (5 ml) ground coriander	1 tbsp (15 ml) mango chutney
1 tsp (5 ml) ground cumin	2 bay leaves
½ tsp (2.5 ml) chili powder	2 chilies (optional)
1 tsp (5 ml) ground turmeric	salt and black pepper

Serves 6

1 Rub the surface of a deep dish with the cut clove of garlic. Arrange the lamb cubes on the base of the dish. Cover with a layer of onion and top with the lemon balm leaves.

2 For the marinade, boil the vinegar, coriander, cumin, chili, turmeric, brown sugar, chutney and bay leaves together for 5 minutes. Leave to cool. Pour the cooled marinade over the meat. Add the chilies and seasoning. Cover and leave overnight in the refrigerator.

3 Drain the lamb and onion pieces and thread them on to metal skewers. Barbecue or grill for 15–20 minutes until browned, basting with the marinade. Discard the bay leaves before serving. Serve with hot garlic bread or on a bed of rice accompanied by a crisp green salad.

Rosemary kebabs
To make a marinade for 1 lb (450 g) chopped lamb or pork, mix 4 tbsp (60 ml) olive oil, the juice of 2 lemons and the grated peel of 1 lemon, a crushed garlic clove and 4 sprigs of rosemary, or 2 tsp (10 ml) dried leaves. Marinade the meat for at least 4 hours, then thread it on to skewers, or woody rosemary stalks, alternating it with chunks of red and green pepper and onion. Use the marinade to baste the meat as it grills.

Pork and sorrel terrine

1½ lb (700 g) lean pork	2 cloves garlic
4 oz (110 g) fresh	salt and black pepper
breadcrumbs	about 60 sorrel leaves,
1 medium onion	washed and drained

Serves 8

1 Mince or blend the pork with the breadcrumbs, onion and garlic. Mix very well and season to taste.

2 Preheat the oven to 375 °F (190 °C) Gas 5.

3 Grease a 2 lb (1 kg) loaf tin and press a third of the pork mixture into the base. Next make a layer of half the sorrel leaves. Add another third of the pork mixture, then the rest of the sorrel leaves, pressing each layer down well. Finish with a layer of the remaining pork mixture.

4 Cover with foil and stand the tin in a roasting tin half filled with water. Bake for 1½ hours.

5 Let it cool in the tin; slice and serve with hot toast.

Stuffed lovage and vine leaves

about 8 large stalks of	1 tsp (5 ml) chopped
lovage	rosemary
1 tbsp (15 ml) olive oil	salt and black pepper
1 small onion, finely chopped	8 oz (225 g) lean minced lamb
2 oz (50 g) pine kernels	8 vine leaves
1 oz (25 g) raisins	

Serves 4

1 Cut the lovage leaves as close to the small groups of leaves as possible and lay them in a large heatproof dish. Cover with boiling water, leave for 10 minutes, drain and rinse under cold water. Set aside to cool.

2 Preheat the oven to 400 °F (200 °C) Gas 6.

3 Heat the oil in a large saucepan and gently sauté the onion for about 5 minutes until soft. Add the pine kernels, raisins, rosemary and seasoning. Remove from the heat and leave to cool.

4 Mix the lamb into the cooled onion mixture.

5 Lay out the vine leaves and put 2–3 lovage leaves on each one.

6 Place about 1 tbsp (15 ml) of the lamb stuffing on the leaves and roll them up. Place the rolls in a greased 8 in (20 cm) square ovenproof dish. Cover and bake for about 30 minutes.

HERBS FOR MEAT

Beef: basil, bay, caraway seed, chervil, lovage seed, marjoram (pot roasts), mint, oregano, parsley, peppermint, rosemary, sage, savory, tarragon, thyme
Lamb: basil, chervil, cumin, dill, lemon balm, lovage seed, marjoram, mints, parsley, rosemary, savory, thyme
Pork: chervil, coriander, fennel, lovage seed, marjoram, rosemary, sage, savory, thyme
Liver: basil, dill, marjoram, sage, tarragon
Ham: juniper berries, lovage, marjoram, mint, mustard, oregano, parsley, rosemary, savory

Lamb's kidneys sautéed with juniper

8 lamb's kidneys	1 tsp (5 ml) tomato purée
2 tbsp (30 ml) vegetable oil	2 tbsp (30 ml) dry sherry
4 oz (110 g) button mushrooms	½ pint (275 ml) brown stock
6 juniper berries, crushed	1 dried bay leaf
2 tbsp (30 ml) plain flour	salt and black pepper

Serves 4

1 Using a sharp knife, skin the kidneys, cut them in half lengthways and remove the cores.

2 Heat the oil in a large frying pan and gently sauté the kidneys and mushrooms for 2–3 minutes. Add the juniper berries and gently sauté for 2–3 minutes. Remove the mushrooms and kidneys, leaving the juniper berries in the pan.

3 Stir the flour into the remaining juices and add the tomato purée, sherry, brown stock, bay leaf and seasoning. Heat through, stirring.

4 Strain the sauce through a sieve and make up to 1 pint (570 ml) with water.

5 Return the liquid to the pan with the mushrooms and kidneys. Retrieve the juniper berries from the sieve and add to the pan. Simmer for 20 minutes, uncovered, stirring occasionally.

Baked ham with marigold glaze

Marigold (calendula) petals and violets were commonly used in ham or meat glazes in the seventeenth century.

5 lb (2.25 kg) middle leg   or corner gammon

GLAZE

2 oz (50 g) brown sugar	salt and black pepper
½ tsp (2.5 ml) mustard powder	3 tbsp (45 ml) dry breadcrumbs
4 tbsp (60 ml) milk	
1 cup (225 ml) marigold (calendula) petals	

Serves 12

1 First, soak the gammon for 24 hours in cold water. Change the water at least two or three times, keeping the gammon covered.

2 Preheat the oven to 350 °F (180 °C) Gas 4. Wrap the gammon in kitchen foil, enclosing it completely. Stand the gammon in a roasting tin containing about 8 fl oz (225 ml) water. Bake, allowing 45 minutes per 1 lb (450 g), turning half way through the cooking time.

3 When cooked, leave the gammon to stand for 30 minutes. Remove the foil and cut off the rind while it is still warm.

4 Score the fat into diamond shapes and replace the gammon in the roasting tin, this time without water.

5 Mix all the glaze ingredients together and spread across the gammon. Increase the oven temperature to 400 °F (200 °C) Gas 6 and bake for a further 10 minutes.

Pork chops marinated with juniper and garlic

2 tbsp (30 ml) olive oil	4 pork chops, ¾ in (2 cm) thick, about 8 oz (225 g) each
6 juniper berries, crushed	
2 cloves garlic, crushed	1 oz (25 g) plain flour
salt and black pepper	½ pint (275 ml) dry cider

Serves 4

1 Mix the oil, juniper berries, garlic and seasoning together in a bowl.

2 Lay the pork chops in the base of a shallow dish and cover them with the marinade, making sure all the surfaces are coated. Cover and leave for at least 3 hours, preferably overnight.

3 Drain the chops and reserve the marinade.

4 Heat a large frying pan and add the reserved marinade. When hot, add the pork chops and cook over a moderate heat for about 10 minutes on each side. To test if the chops are cooked, insert a sharp knife between the thickest part of the meat and the bone; all traces of pink should have gone. Remove the chops from the pan.

5 Leave the frying pan over the heat and stir the flour into the remaining juices. Add the cider and bring to the boil. Return the chops to the sauce in the pan. Heat through and serve.

Herby hamburgers

1 lb (450 g) lean minced beef	black pepper
1 egg, lightly beaten	1 tsp (5 ml) soya sauce
2 tsp (10 ml) equal parts basil, sweet marjoram, thyme and lovage or smallage leaves	1 large onion, minced
	2 tbsp (30 ml) butter
1 tbsp (15 ml) chopped parsley	approx ¼ cup (50 ml) breadcrumbs
½ tsp (2.5 ml) salt	

Serves 4

1 Mix the meat, egg, herbs, salt and pepper and soya sauce together in a large bowl.

2 Sauté the onion in the butter until golden. Stir into the stuffing mixture. Add enough breadcrumbs to make the mix hold together.

3 Shape into flattened patties and grill or barbecue until cooked through (about 5 minutes each side). Serve on a seeded bun with crisp lettuce, fresh tomato, and mayonnaise.

HERBS FOR CASSEROLES

Borage, bay, chicory, chives, coriander seed, dill seed, fennel, garlic, good King Henry, lemon balm, lovage, marjorams, mint, oregano, parsley, sage, savory, smallage, thyme

---

HERBS FOR MARINADES

Basil, bay, coriander seed and leaves, cumin, dill, fennel, garlic, juniper berries, lemon balm, lovage, mint, onion greens and bulbs, parsley stems, rosemary, tarragon

Savoury main dishes

Green herb omelette

6–8 eggs
2 leeks, washed and chopped
4 spring onions, chopped
4 oz (110 g) spinach, washed and chopped
3 tbsp (45 ml) chopped parsley
3 tbsp (45 ml) chopped herbs, such as tarragon, coriander, chives, chervil, dill
1 tbsp (15 ml) chopped walnuts
salt and black pepper

Serves 4

1 Heat the oven to 350 °F (180 °C) Gas 4.

2 Beat the eggs in a large bowl. Add the chopped vegetables, herbs and walnuts. Season to taste and mix the ingredients together thoroughly.

3 Butter a large ovenproof dish and pour in the mixture. Cover and bake for 30 minutes. Remove the cover and bake for a further 15 minutes until the top is golden. Serve hot or cold.

Lovage and lentil roulade

The lovage can be replaced by spinach, sorrel or any other leafy herb.

2 oz (50 g) bacon, chopped
6 oz (175 g) split red lentils
1 small onion, finely chopped
½ pint (275 ml) water
1 tbsp (15 ml) tomato purée
4 oz (110 g) lovage leaves
2 oz (50 g) margarine
2 oz (50 g) plain flour
½ pint (275 ml) milk
2 eggs, separated
salt and black pepper
1 oz (25 g) dry breadcrumbs

Serves 6

1 Place the bacon, lentils and onion in a saucepan and cover with the water. Simmer, uncovered for 15 minutes. Add the tomato purée and simmer for a further 15 minutes until the mixture has thickened and absorbed the liquid.

2 Place the lovage leaves in a pan with just a sprinkling of salt, no water. Cover and cook for 5 minutes.

3 Preheat the oven to 400 °F (200 °C) Gas 6.

4 Melt the margarine in a pan, add the flour and cook for 2–3 minutes, stirring until smooth. Gradually add the milk and simmer for 2 minutes, stirring to make a smooth sauce. Remove from the heat and add the egg yolks to the sauce.

5 Purée the cooked lovage and add to the sauce. Season to taste.

6 Whisk the egg whites until stiff and fold into the lovage mixture.

7 Grease and line an 11 in (28 cm) Swiss roll tin and spread the lovage mixture into the tin. Bake for 25 minutes until golden and well risen.

8 Scatter the breadcrumbs on to a sheet of greaseproof paper and turn out the cooked lovage mixture on to it.

9 Spread over the lentil filling, then roll up like a Swiss roll. Return to the oven and bake for a further 10 minutes. Serve hot or cold.

Hazelnut and sage pâté

5 oz (150 g) hazelnuts
2 oz (50 g) sesame seeds
8 oz (225 g) cream cheese
2 cloves garlic, crushed
⅓ tsp (2 ml) salt
½ tsp (2 ml) black pepper
1 tbsp (15 ml) chopped sage
2 tbsp (30 ml) olive oil
about 4 tbsp (60 ml) milk

Serves 4–6

1 Preheat the oven to 350 °F (180 °C) Gas 4.

2 Place the hazelnuts and sesame seeds on separate baking trays. Lightly roast in the oven for 5–10 minutes. When the nuts are cool, rub off the skins.

3 Grind the nuts and seeds together until they resemble fine crumbs. Or, if you prefer a coarse pâté, grind half the nuts and seeds finely and half coarsely.

4 Beat the cream cheese, garlic, salt, pepper, sage and oil together in a bowl.

5 Add the nut and seed mixture, combining well. Add the milk to give a moist consistency. The mixture needs to be fairly wet as the nuts will absorb some liquid.

6 Serve chilled in ramekins or on small individual salads with toast.

Oregano cheese pie

PASTRY
8 oz (225 g) plain flour
pinch of salt
4 oz (110 g) butter, cut into pieces

FILLING
8 oz (225 g) ricotta cheese
1 tbsp (15 ml) chopped onion
2 oz (50 g) Parmesan cheese, grated
2 eggs
black pepper
2 tbsp (30 ml) chopped parsley
1 tbsp (15 ml) olive oil
1 clove garlic, crushed
2 tbsp (30 ml) chopped oregano
7 oz (200 g) tomato purée
2 oz (50 g) black olives, stoned and sliced
4 oz (110 g) Mozzarella cheese, thinly sliced
1 large green pepper, deseeded and sliced
a little beaten egg

Serves 6

1 For the pastry, sift the flour and salt into a bowl. Rub in the butter until the mixture resembles fine breadcrumbs. Add enough water to bind to a dough.

2 Roll out half the dough and use to line an 8 in (20 cm) greased deep pie dish.

3 Preheat the oven to 400 °F (200 °C) Gas 6.

4 For the filling, mix the ricotta cheese, onion, Parmesan, eggs, plenty of black pepper and parsley.

5 Heat the oil in a small pan and sauté the garlic with the oregano. Stir in the tomato purée and olives.

6 Spread half the ricotta mixture on the pastry base, cover with half the Mozzarella slices, then half the tomato mixture and half the pepper slices. Repeat.

7 Roll out the remaining dough to make a lid. Seal the edges. Brush the top of the pie with beaten egg and slash 4 times with a knife because the pie rises during cooking. Bake for 30–40 minutes.

Clockwise from top right: Tagliatelle with marigold sauce aurore (p. 176); Oregano cheese pie; Green herb omelette; Herb leaf fritters (p. 177).

Tagliatelle with marigold
sauce aurore

12 fl oz (350 ml) milk
1 large onion, quartered
4 tbsp (60 ml) marigold
(calendula) petals,
fresh or dried
2 large carrots, sliced
lengthwise

1 bay leaf
4 oz (110 g) butter
4 oz (110 g) plain flour
6 oz (175 g) cheese, grated
salt and black pepper
8 oz (225 g) tagliatelle
verde

Serves 4

1 Place the milk, onion, marigold petals, carrots and bay leaf in a saucepan. Cover and simmer gently for about 10 minutes until the carrots are soft.

2 Pour through a sieve into a jug and reserve the carrot and onion pieces.

3 Melt the butter in a pan, add the flour and cook for 2–3 minutes, stirring until smooth. Gradually add the flavoured milk and simmer for 2 minutes, stirring to make a smooth sauce.

4 Press the cooked carrot and onion through a sieve and add to the sauce. Fold in the cheese and seasoning.

5 Cook the tagliatelle in a pan of boiling salted water until al dente. Serve topped with the marigold sauce.

Leek and sage croustade

4 oz (110 g) fresh breadcrumbs
4 oz (110 g) mixed
chopped nuts
1 clove garlic, crushed
1 tsp (5 ml) basil

1 tsp (5 ml) rosemary,
chopped
1 tsp (5 ml) oregano
2 oz (50 g) butter
4 oz (110 g) cheese, grated

SAUCE

2 oz (50 g) butter
4 leeks, washed and finely
chopped
1 oz (25 g) plain flour
½ pint (275 ml) milk

2 tomatoes, skinned and
chopped
2 tbsp (30 ml) chopped sage
salt and pepper

Serves 6

1 Preheat the oven to 350 °F (180 °C) Gas 4.

2 Mix the breadcrumbs, nuts, garlic and herbs together in a bowl. Rub in the butter, then stir in the cheese. Press this mixture firmly into the base of an 8 in (20 cm) flan dish. Bake for 20 minutes until golden.

3 For the sauce, melt the butter in a saucepan and fry the leeks for about 10 minutes until soft. Stir in the flour, then add the milk and cook for 5 minutes, stirring. Add the tomatoes, sage and seasoning.

4 Spread the leek sauce over the cooked croustade. Bake for a further 20 minutes.

HERBS FOR EGGS AND CHEESE
Eggs, general: basil, chervil, chives, dill, parsley, tarragon
Devilled eggs: the above, marjoram, rosemary
Scrambled eggs and omelettes: the above, sweet marjoram, oregano
Cheeses, hard: caraway, dill seed, rosemary, sage
Cheeses, soft: caraway, chervil, chives, dill seed, fennel, marjoram, mints, rosemary, sage, savory, thyme
Fondues: basil, garlic, mint
Welsh rarebit: basil, parsley, sweet marjoram, tarragon

Fennel flan

PASTRY

6 oz (175 g) plain flour
pinch of salt

3 oz (75 g) butter, cut
into pieces

FILLING

2 tbsp (30 ml) vegetable oil
1 large onion, chopped
1 clove garlic, crushed
1 bulb Florence fennel, sliced
1 tbsp (15 ml) fennel seeds

2 tbsp (30 ml) chopped
fennel leaves
4 eggs
½ pint (275 ml) single cream
salt and black pepper

Serves 6

1 For the pastry, sift the flour and salt into a bowl. Rub in the butter until the mixture resembles fine breadcrumbs. Add enough water to bind to a dough. Roll out and use to line an 8 in (20 cm) flan dish.

2 Preheat the oven to 350 °F (180 °C) Gas 4.

3 For the filling, heat the oil in a pan and sauté the onion and garlic for about 5 minutes until soft. Remove and drain on kitchen paper.

4 Repeat with the fennel.

5 Spread the onion and fennel over the pastry base. Scatter the fennel seeds and leaves on top.

6 Beat the eggs with the cream, season well and pour over the filling.

7 Bake for 30 minutes. Serve hot or cold.

Pancakes with basil stuffing

BATTER

4 oz (110 g) plain flour
4 fl oz (110 ml) beer
4 fl oz (110 ml) milk

2 eggs
2 oz (50 g) butter, melted
salt

FILLING

1 oz (25 g) butter
1 small onion, finely chopped
1 clove garlic, crushed
8 oz (225 g) button
mushrooms, chopped

8 oz (225 g) cream cheese
2 eggs, beaten
1 tbsp (15 ml) shredded
basil
salt and black pepper

TOPPING

3 tbsp (45 ml) grated
Parmesan cheese

¼ pint (150 ml) single cream

Serves 4

1 Put all batter ingredients in a blender and blend for about 1 minute. Leave to stand for at least 1 hour.

2 For the stuffing, melt the butter in a pan and sauté the onion and garlic for about 5 minutes. Add the mushrooms and sauté for 1 minute. Leave to cool. Mix with the remaining filling ingredients. Chill.

3 Preheat the oven to 350 °F (180 °C) Gas 4.

4 For the pancakes, melt a little butter in a small frying pan. Add about 2 tbsp (30 ml) of batter and swirl round the pan. Cook for about 2 minutes until the underside is golden, then turn the pancake and cook the other side for about 1 minute. Put the pancake on a tea towel. Use the remaining batter to make 7 more pancakes.

5 Fill the 8 pancakes with the cream cheese and mushroom mixture. Roll up and place in an ovenproof dish. Sprinkle with Parmesan cheese and pour over the cream. Bake for 20 minutes.

Vegetable side dishes

Herb leaf fritters

Any of the stronger tasting herb leaves can be used. Salad burnet leaves have a delicate shape and good flavour, or try sage, basil or sorrel.

20–30 herb leaves depending on size   oil for deep frying

BATTER
4 oz (110 g) plain flour   4 tbsp (60 ml) warm water
pinch of salt   1 large egg white
2 tbsp (30 ml) olive oil

Serves 4

1 Carefully rinse and dry the herb leaves.

2 For the batter, mix the flour and salt together in a bowl. Blend in the oil and water until smooth and creamy. Leave to stand for 1–2 hours in a cool place.

3 Whisk the egg white until stiff, then fold it carefully into the batter.

4 Heat the oil until a drop of batter crisps and browns quickly but does not burn. Dip the leaves, one at a time, into the batter. Fry, several at a time, for 2–3 minutes until golden brown.

5 Carefully remove the fritters and drain on kitchen paper. Keep warm in the oven until all the fritters are cooked. Serve immediately.

Cabbage and juniper

1½ lb (700 g) white cabbage   1 clove garlic, crushed
1 tbsp (15 ml) olive oil   8 juniper berries, crushed
1 onion, finely chopped   salt and black pepper

Serves 4–6

1 Preheat the oven to 400 °F (200 °C) Gas 6.

2 Remove and discard the outer leaves from the cabbage and cut out the centre stalk. Finely shred the cabbage, then rinse in a colander. Drain well.

3 Heat the oil in a flameproof casserole and gently fry the onion and garlic for about 10 minutes until soft. Stir in the juniper berries, then add the cabbage and mix well. Season to taste.

4 Cover with a tight-fitting lid. Bake for about 35 minutes. Check that the cabbage is cooked but still crisp before serving.

Tarragon stuffed mushrooms

1 lb (450 g) large mushrooms   2 tbsp (30 ml) finely
6 oz (175 g) fresh   chopped tarragon
breadcrumbs   2 eggs
2 cloves garlic, crushed   salt and black pepper
1 small onion, very finely   4 oz (110 g) dry breadcrumbs
chopped   oil for deep frying

Serves 4–6

1 Wipe the mushrooms clean. Carefully remove the stalks without damaging the caps. Finely chop the stalks and set aside.

2 Place the fresh breadcrumbs in a bowl and add the garlic. Stir in the onion, tarragon, 1 egg, seasoning and chopped mushroom stalks. Mix very well to form a soft stuffing.

3 Divide the mixture between the hollows of the mushroom caps, carefully pressing in well.

4 Beat the remaining egg in a dish and dip each stuffed mushroom into it.

5 Place the dry breadcrumbs in a dish and dip the egg-coated mushrooms into them, ensuring that they are evenly coated.

6 Heat about 2 pints (1 litre) oil in a heavy-based pan. Deep fry the mushrooms for 4 minutes in about 4 batches. Drain on kitchen paper. Serve immediately with a herb mayonnaise (p. 182).

Mediterranean vegetables

4 fl oz (110 ml) olive oil   8 oz (225 g) okra, trimmed
2 cloves garlic, chopped   4 oz (110 g) onion, sliced
8 oz (225 g) potato, cubed   1 tbsp (15 ml) coriander,
8 oz (225 g) green beans   chopped
8 oz (225 g) courgettes,   juice of 1 lime
sliced   juice of 1 lemon

GARNISH
2 tbsp (30 ml) chopped parsley

Serves 4

1 Heat the oil in a large saucepan and sauté all the vegetables and the coriander for about 5 minutes.

2 Add the lime and lemon juices, then cover and cook gently for 30 minutes, stirring occasionally to prevent the mixture from sticking to the bottom of the pan. Garnish with parsley.

HERBS FOR VEGETABLES	
Artichokes: bay, savory, tarragon **Asparagus:** chervil, chives, dill, lemon balm, salad burnet, tarragon **Avocado:** dill, marjoram, tarragon **Brussels sprouts:** dill, sage, savory **Cabbage:** borage, caraway, dill seed, marjoram, mint, oregano, parsley, sage, savory, sweet cicely, thyme **Carrots:** chervil, parsley **Cauliflower:** chives, dill leaf and seed, fennel, rosemary **Celeriac:** chervil, parsley, tarragon **Green beans:** dill, marjoram, mint, oregano, rosemary, sage, savory, tarragon, thyme **Lentils:** garlic, mint, parsley, savory, sorrel **Marrow:** basil, dill, marjoram, rosemary, tarragon **Mushrooms:** basil, dill, lemon balm, marjoram, parsley,	rosemary, salad burnet, savory, tarragon, thyme **Onions:** basil, marjoram in soup, oregano, sage, tarragon, thyme **Peas:** basil, chervil, marjoram, mint, parsley, rosemary, sage, savory **Potatoes:** basil, bay, chives, dill, lovage, marjoram, mint, oregano, parsley, rosemary, savory, thyme **Sauerkraut:** dill, fennel seed, lovage, savory, tarragon, thyme **Spinach:** borage, chervil, marjoram, mint, rosemary for soup, sage, sorrel, tarragon **Tomatoes:** basil, bay, chervil, Chinese chives, chives, dill seed, garlic, marjoram, mint, oregano, parsley, sage, savory, tarragon **Turnips:** dill seed, marjoram, savory

Spicy aubergines

2 large aubergines
1 tbsp (15 ml) olive oil
1 tsp (5 ml) cumin seeds
1 tsp (5 ml) fennel seeds
1 lb (450 g) tomatoes, skinned and chopped
1 in (2.5 cm) fresh, ginger, grated

4 cloves garlic, crushed
1 tsp (5 ml) ground coriander
1 tsp (5 ml) ground cardamom
½ pint (275 ml) water
salt and black pepper

GARNISH
fresh coriander leaves

Serves 4

1 Wipe the aubergines, remove the stalks and cut into finger-sized pieces. Fry them in the oil for about 5 minutes until brown. Drain on kitchen paper.

2 Fry the cumin and fennel seeds for about 2 minutes, stirring all the time, until they turn a shade darker. Stir in the chopped tomatoes, grated ginger, crushed garlic, coriander, cardamom and the water. Simmer for about 20 minutes until the mixture is a thick sauce.

3 Return the aubergines to the pan and heat through, turning them carefully. Garnish with coriander leaves.

Globe artichokes with ravigote sauce

4 artichokes

SAUCE
mixed bunch of parsley, tarragon, watercress
a bunch of chervil
a few chives
1 tbsp (15 ml) capers

2 gherkins, finely chopped
4 tbsp (60 ml) olive oil
1 tbsp (15 ml) tarragon vinegar
a little lemon juice

Serves 4

1 Wash the artichokes and soak in salted water to clean. Trim the stalks close to the base.

2 Place the artichokes in a large pan of boiling salted water and simmer for about 30 minutes until cooked. Remove the artichokes and drain upside down.

3 For the sauce, finely chop all the herbs. Add the capers and gherkins, then the oil, vinegar and lemon.

4 Transfer the sauce to individual pots. To serve, dip the artichoke leaves into the sauce.

Oregano tomatoes

4 large tomatoes
2 oz (50 g) butter
1 tbsp (15 ml) chopped oregano or 1½ tsp (7.5 ml) dried oregano

1 clove garlic, crushed
black pepper
pinch of salt
2 tbsp (30 ml) grated Parmesan cheese

Serves 4

1 Cut the tomatoes in half horizontally and place in a shallow flameproof dish.

2 Beat the butter with the oregano, garlic, pepper, salt, and Parmesan in a bowl. Spread the mixture over the cut side of each tomato.

3 Cook the tomatoes under a medium grill for about 5 minutes until the topping is just turning golden.

Sorrel and parsnip mousses

1 lb (450 g) parsnips, peeled and cut into large pieces
about 36 sorrel leaves
2 oz (50 g) butter
2 oz (50 g) plain flour

½ pint (275 ml) milk
1 egg, separated
1 tbsp (15 ml) chopped chives
salt and black pepper

Serves 6

1 Place the parsnips in a saucepan, cover and simmer for 20 minutes until tender.

2 Preheat the oven to 375 °F (190 °C) Gas 5.

3 Very quickly dip each sorrel leaf into a bowl of boiling water to blanch. Use these leaves to line the bases and sides of 6 ramekin dishes. (You will need about 6 leaves for each dish.)

4 When the parsnips are cooked, drain and mash them into a smooth purée.

5 Melt the butter in a pan, add the flour and cook for 2 minutes, stirring until smooth. Gradually add the milk and simmer for 2 minutes, stirring to make a smooth thick sauce.

6 Beat the egg yolk into the sauce. Whisk the egg white in a bowl until soft peaks form.

7 Mix the sauce and parsnip together. Add the chives and seasoning. Fold in the egg white.

8 Divide the mixture between the lined ramekin dishes. Place the dishes into a deep roasting tin half filled with hot water.

9 Bake for 50 minutes until golden and puffy. Turn out and serve hot.

Fennel with Roquefort sauce

4 bulbs of Florence fennel

SAUCE
1 oz (25 g) butter
1 oz (25 g) plain flour
½ pint (275 ml) mixed milk and fennel stock

3 oz (75 g) Roquefort cheese, grated
black pepper
1 tbsp (15 ml) plain yogurt

GARNISH
1 tbsp (15 ml) chopped parsley
1 tbsp (15 ml) chopped fennel leaves

Serves 4

1 Halve the fennel bulbs vertically, put in a saucepan and cover with water. Bring to the boil and simmer for about 15–20 minutes or until tender. Drain, reserving ¼ pint (150 ml) of the cooking liquid.

2 For the sauce, melt the butter, add the flour and cook for 2 minutes, stirring until smooth. Gradually add the milk and stock and simmer for 2 minutes, stirring to make a smooth sauce.

3 Add the grated cheese and black pepper to taste. Do not allow the sauce to boil. Stir in the yogurt and cook gently for a few minutes, stirring.

4 Place the fennel in a serving dish and pour over the Roquefort sauce. Garnish with the parsley and fennel.

Clockwise from the top: Globe artichokes with ravigote sauce; Oregano tomatoes; Fennel with Roquefort sauce; Sorrel and parsnip mousses.

Salads and snacks

Salad herbs can be divided into three groups. First are those selected for their crunchy texture and mild flavour, so any amount can be used. These include the ornamental lettuces, forced chicory, and blanched leaves such as dandelion and summer purslane. Second are the flavouring herbs. This includes most of the savoury leaves and seeds listed in the box below and pickled herbs and buds. Use these in small quantities as they can taste sharp. The third group consists of herb flowers, which have subtle flavours and are employed more for their beauty than taste. Be selective: a hotchpotch of every flower will diminish the impact of one or two. Try to keep within one range of colours, say blue borage and sage flowers, or golden calendula and gold variegated lemon balm.

Melon, tomato and mint salad

Try replacing the mint with lemon balm or fresh basil leaves for a different combination.

8 oz (225 g) canteloupe or ogen melon	½ cup (125 ml) finely chopped mint
8 oz (225 g) firm tomatoes, cut into thin wedges	½ pint (275 ml) natural yogurt
6 oz (175 g) cucumber, peeled and grated	salt and black pepper

GARNISH
mint leaves

Serves 4

1 Cut the melon flesh into balls with a ball cutter. Alternatively, cut the melon into cubes.

2 Combine the melon, tomato and cucumber in a large salad bowl.

3 Stir the mint into the yogurt to make a dressing, then pour over the salad. Season to taste and garnish the dressed salad with mint leaves.

Fennel salad with orange

1 bulb of Florence fennel, thinly sliced	1 bunch of watercress
1 lettuce	fennel leaves, chopped

DRESSING

4 fl oz (110 ml) olive oil	1 tsp (5 ml) fennel seeds
juice of 1 large orange	salt and black pepper
1 tsp (5 ml) French mustard	

Serves 6

1 First make the dressing. Put all the ingredients in a screw top jar and shake well. Leave to stand for at least 30 minutes.

2 Arrange the fennel, lettuce and watercress in a salad bowl. Scatter with the fennel leaves.

3 Shake the dressing, then pour over the salad just before serving.

Hot salad

2 onions	grated rind and juice of 1 large lemon
2 radishes	1–2 chilies, chopped (seeded if preferred)
2 large carrots	
1 large tomato, chopped	salt and black pepper
1 small lettuce, shredded	
bunch of coriander, chopped	

Serves 4–6

1 Grate the onions, radishes and carrots and place in a salad bowl.

2 Add the remaining ingredients and toss together well. Add extra lemon juice to taste.

Violet herb salad

1 head of chicory	1 tbsp (15 ml) chopped parsley
1 tbsp (15 ml) finely chopped celery	1 tbsp (15 ml) chopped chervil
1 tbsp (15 ml) finely chopped tender fennel stalks (peeled if necessary)	2 olives, finely chopped
	salad dressing to taste
	petals of 30 sweet violets

Serves 4

1 Separate the chicory leaves and place in a salad bowl. Add the remaining salad ingredients, including the herbs, and gently mix well.

2 Add the dressing and toss the salad. Sprinkle on the sweet violet petals.

Sweet anise salad

3 red apples	2 bananas, sliced
3 tbsp (45 ml) lemon or orange juice	4 oz (110 g) walnuts, coarsely chopped
1 tsp (5 ml) sugar	4 fl oz (110 ml) mayonnaise
6 oz (175 g) anise stalks, sliced	lettuce leaves

GARNISH
parsley

Serves 4

1 Core the apples and dice, leaving the peel on. Reserve some apple to use as a garnish.

2 Mix the lemon juice and sugar together in a bowl, then toss the apple in the mixture.

3 Add the anise stalks, banana and walnuts to the apple. Mix in the mayonnaise and chill.

4 Serve the salad in a lettuce lined salad bowl and garnish with the reserved apple and parsley.

SALAD HERBS

General: alexanders, angelica, basil, bistort, borage leaves, caraway, chervil, chicory, Chinese chives, chives, coriander leaves, corn salad, dill, fennel, lemon balm, lovage, marjoram, mint, mustard seedlings, nasturtium leaves, orach, parsley, purslane (summer and winter), salad burnet, salad rocket, savory, smallage, sorrel, sweet cicely, tarragon, thyme, watercress.
Floral additions: bergamot, borage, calendula, chives, nasturtium, primrose, rose petals, sweet rocket, violet.

Clockwise from the top: Mixed flower and leaf salads; Hot salad; Melon, tomato and mint salad; Herb spread sandwiches (p. 182); Fennel salad with orange.

Potato salad with dill and chives

4 medium potatoes	finely chopped or 1 tsp (5 ml)
1 tbsp (15 ml) chopped onion	dill seed
1 tbsp (15 ml) chopped parsley	3 tbsp (45 ml) mayonnaise
	1 tbsp (15 ml) cream or
1 tbsp (15 ml) chopped chives	yogurt
1 flowering head of dill	salt and black pepper

Serves 4

1 Boil the potatoes in their skins until just tender. Cool, peel and slice them.

2 Sprinkle on the onion, parsley, chives and dill.

3 Blend the mayonnaise and cream, season with salt and pepper. Add to the potato mixture and stir gently. Leave to stand a few hours so the flavours mingle.

Cheese balls

8 oz (225 g) cream cheese	herbs: chives, parsley,
1 cup (225 ml) finely chopped	rosemary, sage, thyme

Shape the cheese into plum-sized balls and then roll them in the chopped herbs. Serve with salads, on hot vegetables or as a spread.

Herbal vinaigrette

One of the simplest dressings to make and one that is infinitely variable. Select herbs from those listed to vary the emphasis. Substitute a herbal oil or vinegar for extra pungency.

3 tbsp (45 ml) olive oil	3 tbsp (45 ml) fresh chopped
1 tbsp (15 ml) wine vinegar	herbs (basil, chervil, chives,
$\frac{1}{4}$ tsp (1.2 ml) mustard	dill seed, lemon balm,
salt and black pepper	marjoram, rosemary, salad
1 clove garlic, crushed	burnet, tarragon, thyme)

Makes about 3 fl oz (80 ml)

Mix all the ingredients together in a screw-top jar or bottle and shake well.

Green mayonnaise

Use the following herbs, either singly or in combination: garlic, lemon balm, lovage, salad burnet, tarragon, thyme.

1 egg yolk	2 tbsp (30 ml) chopped
$\frac{1}{2}$ pt (275 ml) olive oil	parsley
1 tbsp (15 ml) wine vinegar	1 tbsp (15 ml) selected herbs

Makes $\frac{1}{2}$ pint (275 ml)

1 Beat the egg yolk for a minute or so, then start adding the oil, drop by drop, beating continuously.

2 When over half the oil has been added and the mixture has started to thicken, beat in the vinegar.

3 Add more oil drop by drop until it thickens again, then slowly pour in the rest. (If the mixture refuses to thicken or curdles, break a fresh egg yolk into a clean basin and slowly stir in the first mixture.)

4 Stir in the chopped herbs.

Aioli (garlic mayonnaise)

1 egg yolk	salt and black pepper
$\frac{1}{2}$ pint (275 ml) olive oil	4 cloves garlic
1 tbsp (15 ml) wine vinegar	

Makes $\frac{1}{2}$ pint (275 ml)

1 Make up the mayonnaise as described before.

2 Crush or pound the garlic in a pestle and mortar. Mix into the mayonnaise.

Tartare sauce

1 cup (225 ml) mayonnaise (see above)	3 shallots or tree onions, finely chopped
2 tbsp (30 ml) chopped green herbs (chervil, chives, parsley, tarragon)	$\frac{1}{2}$ tsp (2.5 ml) mustard
	1 tbsp (15 ml) capers, chopped

Makes $\frac{1}{2}$ pint (275 ml)

Mix all the ingredients together.

Horseradish sauce

2 tbsp (30 ml) wine vinegar	$\frac{1}{2}$ tsp (2.5 ml) black pepper
1 tsp (5 ml) sugar	4 tbsp (60 ml) finely grated
$\frac{1}{2}$ tsp (2.5 ml) salt	horseradish
1 tsp (5 ml) mustard	3 tbsp (45 ml) cream

Makes about $\frac{1}{4}$ pint (150 ml)

1 Heat the vinegar in an enamel pan. Add the sugar, salt, mustard and pepper and stir over a low heat for 2 minutes.

2 Add the horseradish and heat for 2 minutes more. Leave to cool then blend in the cream. Chill to serve.

HERB SPREADS

These make a delicious snack served with biscuits, bread or sticks of raw vegetables.

Mix equal quantities of mayonnaise with chopped chervil, chives, coriander, dill, fennel, nasturtium petals parsley, tarragon. The following mixture is a favourite.

Angelica and mint sandwich

Choose a variety of mint with a clean spearmint flavour such as Moroccan mint or Red raripila spearmint.

a good handful of fresh young angelica leaves	1–2 tbsp (15–30 ml) mayonnaise
a good handful of fresh mint leaves	2–4 slices of wholewheat or rye bread

Serves 2

1 Pass the leaves through a herb mouli or chop very finely by hand. Mix the two herbs together.

2 Toast the bread then spread with mayonnaise.

3 Sprinkle a thick layer of the herb mixture on top. Cut into quarters and serve.

Desserts

Gooseberry and elderflower cream

1 lb (450 g) fresh washed gooseberries
½ cup (125 ml) water
5 elderflower heads or 1 tbsp (15 ml) orange-flower water
6 oz (175 g) sugar (or to taste)
2 oz (50 g) butter
3 eggs, beaten
whipped cream for topping

DECORATION
borage flowers

Serves 4

1 Cook the gooseberries and elderflowers in the water until soft. Remove the flowers and purée the fruit.

2 Return the mixture to the saucepan. Add the sugar and heat to dissolve. (At this stage, the mixture can be strained, bottled and kept in the freezer as a delicious muscatel-flavoured syrup for serving on fruit dishes or diluted with soda water as a summer drink.)

3 To make the cream dessert, stir in the butter until melted. Cool a little and slowly add the beaten eggs, stirring constantly until thick. Do not boil.

4 Spoon into serving glasses, top with cream and garnish with borage flowers.

Rose layered dessert

1 cup (225 ml) loosely packed scented rose petals, white heels removed
4 bananas, mashed
approx. 4 oz (110 g) chopped dates (equal volume to banana)
2 tbsp (30 ml) mincemeat
4 tbsp (60 ml) rose petal jam (see p. 190)
juice of 2 oranges
small carton whipped cream

DECORATION
crystallized rose petals   sweet cicely seeds (optional)

Serves 4

1 Cover a dish with pink and red rose petals.

2 Mix the banana, dates and mincemeat and make a layer over the petals, leaving the petals protruding around the edge. Cover with a layer of rose petal jam.

3 When ready to serve, pour over the orange juice. Add a layer of whipped cream and garnish with crystallized rose petals and sweet cicely seeds.

Mulled pears with juniper

4 firm pears
¼ pint (150 ml) red wine
¼ pint (150 ml) fresh orange juice
2 oz (50 g) dark brown sugar
4 juniper berries, crushed

Serves 4

1 Either peel the pears whole, leaving the stalks intact, or peel, core and quarter them.

2 Mix the red wine, orange juice, brown sugar and juniper berries together in a saucepan. Bring to simmering point.

3 Add the pears and simmer, uncovered, for 15 minutes or 25 minutes if the pears are whole. Turn and baste from time to time.

Sweet rice with rose geranium

4 oz (110 g) pudding rice
1½ pints (800 ml) milk
8 scented rose geranium leaves
1 oz (25 g) desiccated coconut
2 oz (50 g) flaked almonds
2 oz (50 g) raisins
2 oz (50 g) soft brown sugar

Serves 6

1 Mix the rice and milk together in a saucepan. Add 4 geranium leaves to the pan. Cover and simmer very gently for 30 minutes.

2 Remove from the heat and take out the leaves. Preheat the oven to 375 °F (190 °C) Gas 5.

3 Add the coconut, almonds, raisins and sugar to the milk mixture, stirring well.

4 Transfer the mixture to a large 8 in (20 cm) oven-proof dish. Arrange the remaining 4 geranium leaves across the top. Bake for 45 minutes.

Mint and chocolate ice cream

1 cup (225 ml) mint leaves, preferably spearmint
2 oz (50 g) caster sugar
3 oz (75 g) plain chocolate
2 eggs, separated
½ pint (275 ml) double cream

DECORATION
mint leaves   1 oz (25 g) plain chocolate

Serves 6

1 Mix the mint leaves with 1 oz (25 g) of the sugar and chop as finely as possible.

2 Set a bowl over a pan of simmering water and melt 2 oz (50 g) of the chocolate. Remove from the heat. Add the egg yolks and whisk until creamy. Leave to cool.

3 Whip the cream until soft peaks form, then fold in the chopped mint. Fold the whipped mint cream into the cooled chocolate mixture. Freeze the mixture in a 1¾ pint (1 litre) freezer tray.

4 When the ice cream becomes crisp at the edges, whisk for 2 minutes. Return to the freezer, then whisk the ice cream every 45 minutes until it is just set.

5 Whisk the egg whites until soft peaks form. Fold in the remaining sugar, then fold carefully into the frozen ice cream. Finally grate the remaining 1 oz (25 g) chocolate and stir into the ice cream. Return the ice cream to the freezer until completely set.

6 Serve decorated with mint leaves dipped in melted chocolate (leave to set on greaseproof paper).

HERBS FOR DESSERTS
General: angelica, aniseed, bergamot, elderflower, lemon balm, lemon verbena, pineapple sage, rosemary, saffron, sweet cicely leaves and green seeds
Custards: bay, lemon thyme, mint, rose petals, scented geraniums (pelargoniums)
Fruit salads: aniseed, lemon balm, mints, rosemary, sweet cicely leaves and green seeds
Fruit compotes: dill, mint with pears; aniseed, caraway, coriander, dill with apples; savory with quinces; angelica, sweet cicely with acidic fruits

Lemon balm cheesecake

PASTRY
4 oz (110 g) plain flour 2 oz (50 g) margarine, cut
pinch of salt into pieces

FILLING
2 oz (50 g) margarine 2 eggs, beaten
2 tbsp (30 ml) honey 6 tbsp (90 ml) very finely
12 oz (350 g) cream cheese chopped lemon balm

Serves 6

1 Preheat the oven to 400 °F (200 °C) Gas 6.

2 For the pastry, sift the flour and salt into a bowl. Rub in the margarine until the mixture resembles fine breadcrumbs. Add enough water to make a soft dough. Roll out to line a 7 in (18 cm) flan dish. Bake blind for 15 minutes.

3 For the filling, cream the margarine, honey and cream cheese together in a bowl until soft and creamy. Beat in the eggs and fold in the lemon balm. Reduce the oven temperature to 350 °F (180 °C) Gas 4.

4 Pour the filling into the pastry case. Bake for 45 minutes until the filling is golden and set. Serve with whipped cream or yogurt.

Sweet herb sorbet

3 oz (75 g) caster sugar lemon balm, scented
½ pint (275 ml) water geranium or rosemary)
¼ cup (50 ml) spearmint juice of 1 lemon
leaves (or apple mint, 1 egg white

DECORATION
spearmint leaves

Serves 4

1 Place the sugar in a saucepan and add the water. Bring to the boil, stirring, until the sugar is dissolved.

2 Chop the herb leaves and add to the pan. Cover, then remove from the heat. Leave to infuse for 20–30 minutes. Test for flavour, if it is too light, bring to the boil again then leave to infuse for 15 minutes.

3 Strain the liquid and add the lemon juice. Transfer the mixture to a freezer tray and freeze for 2–3 hours.

4 When the sorbet is semi-frozen, whisk the egg white until stiff and fold it into the mixture. Return to the freezer for a further 3–4 hours or until frozen.

5 Serve the sorbet in individual dishes and decorate each serving with extra herb leaves.

Breads, cakes and biscuits

Lovage seed bread

Try with poppy seeds or sweet cicely seeds instead.

½ oz (15 g) fresh yeast 12 oz (350 g) strong white
½ tsp (2.5 ml) sugar flour
¾ pint (425 ml) warm water 1 tbsp (15 ml) vegetable
2 tsp (10 ml) salt oil
12 oz (350 g) plain 1 medium onion, grated
wholemeal flour 1 tbsp (15 ml) lovage seeds

Makes about 14 rolls or two 1 lb (450 g) loaves

1 Mix the yeast, sugar and warm water together in a bowl. Leave in a warm place until frothy.

2 Mix the flours, salt and oil together in a bowl. Add the yeast and onion, kneading to make a soft dough.

3 Knead lightly on a floured surface for 10 minutes until the dough is smooth and elastic. Place the dough in a bowl, cover with a damp cloth and leave to rise in a warm place for about 1½ hours until doubled in size.

4 Turn out the dough on to a floured surface and knead for about 5 minutes. Shape into rolls or loaves and place on a baking tray or greased loaf tins.

5 Brush the dough with a little water and sprinkle with the lovage seeds. Leave to prove for 20 minutes.

6 Preheat the oven to 450 °F (230 °C) Gas 8.

7 Bake for 10 minutes, then reduce the oven temperature to 400 °F (200 °C) Gas 6 for a further 5–20 minutes. Turn out on to wire racks to cool.

Rosemary cheese fingers

2 oz (50 g) butter 1 tbsp (15 ml) chopped
5 oz (150 g) oat flakes rosemary
6 oz (175 g) Cheddar pinch of cayenne
cheese, grated salt
1 egg, beaten

Makes 12 slices

1 Preheat the oven to 350 °F (180 °C) Gas 4.

2 Melt the butter in a saucepan. Place the remaining ingredients in a bowl and mix in the butter.

3 Press the mixture into a greased 8 in (20 cm) square tin. Bake for 30–40 minutes. Cut into fingers.

Sage oat cakes

1 oz (25 g) lard ¼ tsp (1.25 ml) bicarbonate
6 tbsp (90 ml) boiling water of soda
8 oz (225 g) medium oatmeal pinch of salt
½ tsp (1.25 ml) dried sage

Makes 8 slices

1 Preheat the oven to 350 °F (180 °C) Gas 4.

2 Place the lard and water in a small pan and heat until the lard has melted. Cool.

3 Mix the oatmeal, sage, bicarbonate of soda and salt together in a bowl. Stir in the cooled liquid and mix to a soft dough, adding a little more water if necessary.

4 Pat the dough into a round about 8 in (20 cm) in diameter. Place on an ungreased baking tray.

5 Bake for about 40 minutes. Cut into 8 wedges, then leave to cool slightly before turning on to a wire rack.

Clockwise from top centre: Sweet herb sorbet; Mulled pears with juniper (p. 183); Lemon balm cheesecake; Mint and chocolate ice cream (p. 183).

Cheese bread with chives

½oz (15 g) fresh yeast or   pinch of salt
1 oz (25 g) dried yeast and   12 fl oz (350 ml) water,
     1 tsp (5 ml) sugar   heated to blood temperature
     2 fl oz (50 ml) water   2 oz (50 g) butter
     1 lb (450 g) plain flour   9 oz (250 g) cheese, grated
     4 oz (110 g) plain   3 tbsp (45 ml) chopped chives
     wholemeal flour   1 egg, beaten

Makes 2 lb (900 g) loaf

1 Put the yeast into a cup and stir in the 2 fl oz (50 ml) water. If using dried yeast, add the sugar. Leave in a warm place until frothy.

2 Put the flours and salt into a large bowl. Pour the yeast mixture into the centre of the flour and mix together well with a knife, adding some of the warm water. Add the rest of the water, then knead the dough for 2 minutes.

3 Form the dough into a ball and sprinkle with flour. Cover the dough with a damp cloth and leave to rise in a warm place for 1½–2 hours until doubled in size.

4 Knead the dough lightly. Roll into a rectangle and dot with butter. Fold into 3, then roll out to the same size again. Sprinkle with the cheese and chives to within 1 in (2.5 cm) of the edge. Roll up from the short end, like a Swiss roll.

5 Place in a greased 2 lb (900 g) loaf tin and score the top with a sharp knife. Leave to prove in a warm place for about 30 minutes.

6 Preheat the oven to 425 °F (220 °C) Gas 7.

7 Brush the loaf with beaten egg. Bake for 35–40 minutes. Best eaten when warm.

Sweet rosemary slices

     2 eggs   8 oz (225 g) raisins and
5 oz (150 g) soft brown sugar   candied fruit, such as
¼ tsp (1.25 ml) vanilla essence   angelica, glacé cherries,
     5 oz (150 g) plain flour   or candied pineapple
1 tsp (5 ml) baking powder   6 oz (175 g) pecan
     pinch of salt   nuts, chopped, or
1 tbsp (15 ml) rosemary leaves   sunflower seeds
     or 2 tsp (10 ml) dried

Makes 24 slices

1 Preheat the oven to 375 °F (190 °C) Gas 5.

2 Beat the eggs in a bowl, then gradually add the sugar and vanilla essence. Mix well.

3 Sift in the flour, baking powder and salt. Add the rosemary leaves, then fold in the fruit and nuts.

4 Spoon the mixture on to a greased and floured 8 in (20 cm) baking tin and spread evenly.

5 Bake for 30 minutes. Remove from the tin while still warm. Allow to cool, then cut into squares.

HERBS FOR BREADS
Aniseed, basil, caraway, chives, dill, fennel, lovage seed, poppy seed, rosemary, sunflower seed, thyme

Saffron fruit bread

8 fl oz (225 ml) milk,   1 lb (450 g) plain flour
     warmed   4 oz (110 g) butter
1 oz (25 g) fresh yeast   2 oz (50 g) caster sugar
1 tsp (5 ml) sugar   6 oz (175 g) currants
¼ tsp (1.25 ml) saffron   4 oz (110 g) chopped
     powder or strands   mixed peel
¼ pint (150 ml) boiling water   1 tsp (5 ml) dried thyme

Serves 10

1 Place the milk in a bowl and dissolve the yeast and the 1 tsp (5 ml) sugar in it. Leave in warm place for about 10 minutes until frothy.

2 Steep the saffron in the boiling water, then leave the mixture to cool.

3 Sift the flour into a large bowl. Rub in the butter. Add the rest of the sugar, the currants, peel and thyme, mixing well.

4 Add the yeast liquid and saffron liquid to the flour mixture. (Strain the saffron mixture if using strands.) Mix until smooth with a wooden spoon; it should look like a very thick batter.

5 Pour the batter into a greased and lined 10 in (25 cm) round cake tin. Cover with a damp cloth and leave in a warm place for about 1 hour until the mixture rises to the top of the tin.

6 Preheat the oven to 375 °F (190 °C) Gas 5.

7 Bake the bread for 1 hour. Leave to cool in the tin. Slice and serve with butter.

Scented geranium leaf sponge

20 scented geranium leaves   4 eggs, beaten
     8 oz (225 g) butter   8 oz (225 g) self-raising
     8 oz (225 g) caster sugar   flour, sifted

DECORATION
scented geranium leaves   icing sugar

Serves 6

1 Grease and line two 8 in (20 cm) sandwich tins. Arrange the geranium leaves on the lining paper.

2 Preheat the oven to 375 °F (190 °C) Gas 5.

3 Cream the butter and sugar together in a bowl until light and fluffy. Add the beaten eggs, a little at a time, to the creamed mixture, beating well. Fold in the flour.

4 Divide the mixture between the prepared tins. Bake for 20–25 minutes until golden.

5 Turn out of the tins and cool on wire racks. Remove the leaves and lining paper.

6 Sandwich the sponges with a filling: sweet geranium jelly and whipped cream are excellent. Arrange some geranium leaves on top of the sponge, then sift over some icing sugar. Carefully remove the leaves before eating.

Clockwise from top centre: Saffron fruit bread; Cheese bread with chives; Sage oat cakes (p. 185); Herb butter (p. 190); Sweet rosemary slices; Cheese balls (p. 182); Scented geranium leaf sponge.

Preserves

HERBAL OILS

To make a herb oil, loosely fill a clear jar with freshly picked herbs and cover with unheated safflower or sunflower oil. (Any oil can be used but avoid strongly flavoured ones.) Cover with muslin and place on a sunny window sill. Allow to steep for 2 weeks, stirring daily. Strain through the muslin, and check the flavour. If it is as strong as you wish, bottle and label. If you want a stronger flavour, repeat the process with fresh herbs. Use herb oils in salad dressings, marinades, for browning meats and softening vegetables.

For sweet oils, use almond oil with scented flowers.

HERBS FOR OILS
Savoury: basil, garlic, fennel, marjoram, mint, rosemary, tarragon, thyme, savory **Sweet:** clove pinks, lavender, lemon verbena, rose petals

HERBAL VINEGARS

Use cider or wine vinegar as a base. Bruise the freshly picked herbs and loosely fill a clean jar. Pour on warmed but not hot vinegar to fill the jar and cap with an acid-proof lid. Set in a sunny window and shake daily for 2 weeks. Test for flavour; if a stronger taste is required, strain the vinegar and repeat with fresh herbs. Store as it is or strain through double muslin and rebottle. Add a fresh sprig to the bottle for identification and visual appeal. Use in salad dressings, marinades, gravies and sauces.

Tarragon vinegar

Follow the above instructions and add a sliced clove of garlic to the steeping tarragon and vinegar. Remove the garlic after one day and replace with 2 cloves for the remaining 2 weeks. Strain and bottle.

Floral vinegars

Floral vinegars are made in the same way and are used with fruit salads and in some cosmetic recipes. Select from the list below, removing stems and any green or white heels from the petals.

HERBS FOR VINEGARS
Basil, bay, chervil, dill leaves, fennel, garlic, lemon balm, marjoram, mint, rosemary, savory, tarragon, thyme

FLOWERS FOR VINEGARS
Carnations, clover, elderflowers, lavender, nasturtiums, primroses, rose petals, rosemary flowers, thyme flowers, sweet violets

Blended vinegars

With imagination and skill many other interesting flavours can be created using the method described above.
Try the following savoury combinations:
1 part tarragon to 2 parts lemon balm
1 part basil to 2 parts salad burnet
1 part each of tarragon, basil, chives and 2 parts each of lemon thyme and salad burnet and 1 clove garlic.
1 part each crushed seed of anise, caraway, celery, coriander, cumin, dill, salad burnet and 1 clove garlic.

Floral bouquet vinegars: Follow the method described for savoury blends using these combinations:
1 part lavender flowers to 1 part lemon verbena
1 part lavender flowers to 3 parts rose petals
1 part each clove pinks and rosemary, 2 parts each rose petals and elderflowers.

Pickled horseradish

Pick good sized roots, wash and scrape off the skin. Mince in a food processor or grate and pack loosely into small jars. Cover with salted vinegar made from 1 tsp (5 ml) salt to half a pint (275 ml) vinegar. Seal and leave for about a month before using.

Pickled alexanders buds

Pick young dry buds and pack loosely in a small earthenware jar. Cover with boiling white wine vinegar and seal. Leave at least 2 weeks before using. Try this with green seeds of sweet cicely or dry elderflowers, picked as the flowers open.

You can adapt this recipe to make a sweet pickle using flowers such as rosebuds, violets, rosemary blooms or cowslips. Follow the same procedure but sprinkle sugar over each layer.

Pickled nasturtium seeds

These can be used as a substitute for capers. Pick nasturtium seeds on a dry day while they are still green. Steep in brine made from 4 oz (110 g) salt to $1\frac{3}{4}$ pints (1 litre) water for 24 hours. Remove and dry the seeds, then pack into small jars. Make a strong spiced vinegar to fill the jars, using white wine vinegar and salt and a selection from tarragon leaves, mace, nutmeg, shallots, garlic, peppercorns and horseradish slices. Pour the hot vinegar into the jars then seal and leave for about a month. After opening the jar, use up the contents quickly.

Pickled cucumbers

about $2\frac{1}{2}$ lb (1 kg) small cucumbers, 3–5 in (8–12 cm) long
2 cloves garlic
2 dill flower heads with leaves
7 tbsp (105 ml) coarse salt
6 peppercorns
8 fl oz (225 ml) white wine vinegar
$1\frac{1}{4}$ pints (750 ml) water

Makes approx. $2 \times 1\frac{3}{4}$ pints (1 litre) jars

1 Scrub the cucumbers and soak overnight in salted cold water. Drain.

2 Place 1 clove garlic and a dill flower head in each sterilized jar.

3 Either leave the cucumbers whole or cut in quarters lengthways. Pack them into the jars.

4 Place the salt, pepper, vinegar and water in a saucepan and bring to the boil. Pour over the cucumbers. Seal, label and date. Store in a cool place for 6 weeks before using. Keep in the refrigerator once the jars have been opened.

From left to right: Savoury herb jelly (p. 190); Rose petal jam (p. 190); Tarragon vinegar; Thyme oil; Basil oil; Lemon verbena vinegar; Lavender vinegar; Pickled cucumbers.

HERB BUTTERS

Herb butters are a delicious way of adding the full flavours of fresh herbs to savoury snacks and dishes. Spread on sandwiches, toast and biscuits; use to add piquancy to grilled meats and fish, and vegetables.

Try the blend below or make up your own. Choose from well-flavoured herbs such as chervil, chives, garlic, parsley, rosemary, sage, salad burnet, tarragon and thyme.

Follow the same method, substituting soft cheeese for the butter to make a flavoursome spread.

Parsley and chive butter

2 tbsp (30 ml) chopped parsley
1 tbsp (15 ml) chopped chives
8 oz/1 cup (225 g) butter, slightly softened
juice of 1 lemon
salt and black pepper

1 Beat the herbs into the butter and then add the lemon juice and seasoning. Mix until smooth.

2 Chill before serving. Shape in a mould if desired. Store in a cool place, or freeze in an ice-cube tray for handy portions.

JELLIES

The flavour of most aromatic herbs can be captured in a jelly to serve with cold meats, pâté, game, roasts, salads and sandwiches, and even to garnish soups and vegetables. An apple or crab apple jelly makes a suitable base.

Savoury herb jelly

4 lb (2 kg) tart cooking apples or crab apples roughly chopped
1½ pints (800 ml) water
½ pint (275 ml) wine vinegar
a good handful of fresh herbs
12 oz (350 g) sugar per pint (570 ml) of juice

Makes about 4 lb (1.8 kg)

1 Boil the cooking apples with the water and vinegar in a large preserving pan. Add the fresh herbs and simmer. Cook until the apples are soft. Strain through a jelly bag overnight.

2 Measure the juice, return to the saucepan and add the sugar. Stir to dissolve the sugar, then boil until setting point is reached, taking care not to let it boil over. Allow to cool a little for 10 minutes.

3 Pour into clean, sterilized jars and add a few leaves as decoration, if desired. Seal, label and date. Store in a cool, dark cupboard.

Sweet jelly

Follow the same procedure for sweet jellies but omit the vinegar and use 2 pints (1 litre) water.

HERBS FOR JELLY
Savoury: basil, mint, rosemary, sage, savory, thyme
Sweet: bergamot, marigold (calendula), lavender flower petals, lemon balm, lemon verbena, scented geranium leaves (rose, apple, peppermint, lemon), sweet violet

Rose petal jam

1 lb (450 g) heavily scented, red or pink rose petals
1 pint (570 ml) water
1 lb (450 g) caster sugar
juice of 2 lemons
1 tbsp (15 ml) rosewater

Makes approx. 2 × 1 lb (450 g) jars

1 Remove the bitter white base from each petal. Rinse and drain the petals.

2 Bring the water to the boil in a large, heavy saucepan. Reduce to simmering point then add the rose petals. (The mixture will froth up considerably so do not have the pan more than half full.) Simmer gently for 5 minutes until the petals are soft.

3 Add the sugar and lemon juice. Bring back to the boil and simmer for about 30 minutes, stirring until the sugar has dissolved and the mixture begins to thicken. Add the rosewater.

4 Allow the mixture to bubble up well. When the bubbles have turned more to foam, test for setting point. To do this, first remove the pan from the heat. Put a spoonful of the jam on a cold saucer, allow to cool and push the surface; if it wrinkles it is ready.

5 Allow the jam to cool slightly, then pour into sterilized jars, label and seal.

CRYSTALLIZED FLOWERS AND LEAVES

Crystallized flowers and leaves can make wonderful decorations for cakes, desserts and summer drinks. The method is time-consuming but relaxing. Pick leaves or flowers on a sunny, dry day. Remove stalks and the white bases from petals, then commence.

Lightly beat an egg white until it starts to foam. Dip each flower or leaf into the egg white to coat, then dip it into a dish of caster sugar. Once coated, place on a sheet of greaseproof paper on a wire cooling rack. Cover with another sheet of paper and place in a dry airing cupboard or very low oven, with the door left ajar. Store in an airtight tin when dry.

Flowers to crystallize

Borage, cowslips, lavender, lilac, pinks, primroses, rose petals, rosemary, sage

Leaves to crystallize

Bergamot, lemon balm, lemon verbena, mint

Crystallized angelica

1 lb (450 g) angelica stalks
1 lb (450 g) sugar
½ pint (275 ml) water

1 Wash the stalks and cut them in 3 in (8 cm) lengths. Boil in a little water until tender.

2 Drain, remove the outer skin and place in a shallow dish. Sprinkle the sugar, cover and leave on for 2 days.

3 Transfer into a pan with the water. Bring to the boil, stirring all the time. Simmer until all the syrup is absorbed and the stalks are clear. Drain and cool.

4 Sprinkle the stems with sugar to coat. Spread them out on a cake rack and allow to dry thoroughly. Store in airtight containers.

Herbal drinks

HERBAL TEAS

Teas made of aromatic leaves, flowers or roots steeped in boiling water are the most ancient and the most commonly consumed liquid after pure water. Most herb teas are infused: the leaves or flowers are put into a warm teapot, boiling water is poured over and the tea is brewed for 3–5 minutes. Alternatively add 1 tsp (5 ml) of dried or 3 tsp (15 ml) of fresh herb to a cup of boiling water. Grind or pulverize seeds and root just before use and then make into a decoction; simmer 1 tbsp (15 ml) of crushed root or seeds in 2 cups (450 ml) of boiling water until the water is reduced to 1 cup (225 ml). This takes from 5–20 minutes, depending on the herb used.

Many people find herb teas bland by comparison to coffee and black tea but there are some intermediate steps you can take. Mix China tea with herbs or, to supply some of the "bite" we get from regular tea and coffee, add dried leaves of raspberry, strawberry, or lady's mantle, which have a high tannin content.

Start with herbs which have strong, familiar flavours: anise, chamomile, lemon verbena, lime blossom, mint, rose hip and sage are all refreshing.

China tea blends

Infuse the herbs for 5 minutes in 2 cups (450 ml) boiling water and strain before drinking.

Herbal "Earl Grey"

1 tsp (5 ml) China tea	3 tsp (15 ml) young fresh bergamot leaves

Spicy geranium

1 tsp (5 ml) China tea	(Also try 3 cloves with rose geranium leaves)
1 blade cinnamon	
3 apple geranium leaves	

Hibiscus

A pleasant lemony flavour with a beautiful amber-ruby colour. Also refreshing as an iced tea.

1 tsp (5 ml) China tea	1 tsp (5 ml) hibiscus flowers

YOGURT DRINKS

These are nutritious, easy to digest and refreshing to drink. They can be savoury or sweet.

Raspberry and mint yogurt drink

8 fl oz (225 ml) natural yogurt	3 oz (75 g) raspberries or 1 tbsp (15 ml) raspberry syrup
4 fl oz (100 ml) mineral water	1 tsp (5 ml) mint syrup

DECORATION
2 sprigs of mint

Serves 2

1 Purée all the ingredients in a blender.

2 Pour the drink into 2 glasses and decorate each with a sprig of mint. Serve chilled.

Angelica, mint and sweet cicely yogurt drink

¾ pint (450 ml) natural yogurt	1 medium angelica leaf
8 fl oz (225 ml) mineral water	4 medium sweet cicely leaves
	1 tsp (5 ml) mint syrup

DECORATION
4 sprigs of mint

Serves 4

1 Purée all the ingredients in a blender.

2 Pour the drink into 4 glasses and decorate each with a sprig of mint. Serve chilled.

SYRUPS

Herb and fruit syrups are a convenient way of capturing a seasonal crop for year-round use. They can be diluted for drinks, poured over ice creams and puddings, and used as a base for jellies and sorbets.

Spearmint, lemon verbena, rose petals, apple, lemon or rose geranium, elderflowers, rose hips and all soft fruit and berries are suitable. For hips and fruit, leave in the jelly bag overnight to collect the juices.

Peppermint syrup

2 pints (1 litre) loosely packed peppermint leaves	green food colouring (optional)
white sugar	

1 Place the leaves in a saucepan with just enough water to cover. Simmer for 30 minutes.

2 Strain through a jelly bag for 1 hour.

3 For each pint (570 ml) liquid, add 12 oz (350 g) sugar. Place the mixture in a pan and simmer for 15 minutes. Add food colouring, if using.

4 Bottle, label and date. Alternatively, freeze in convenient portions.

Lemon verbena and lime cordial

10 lemon verbena leaves	1 oz (25 g) sugar
juice of 1 lemon	1 pint (570 ml) water
2 fl oz (50 ml) lime juice	

DECORATION
lemon verbena leaves	slices of lime
slices of lemon	

Makes about 1 pint (570 ml)

1 Either finely chop the lemon verbena leaves or pound in a pestle and mortar.

2 Place all the ingredients in a saucepan and heat until the sugar is dissolved, stirring. Leave to cool in the refrigerator for 2–3 hours or overnight.

3 Strain the drink and serve with ice cubes in tall glasses or a jug, decorated with lemon verbena leaves and lemon and lime slices.

HERBS AND ALCOHOL

Herbs have long been used to improve the flavour of alcoholic drinks. Some of the most exotic and revered liqueurs derive their character from herbal ingredients. Many of these are produced in monasteries and their recipes are a closely guarded secret. However, we know that Benedictine and Chartreuse both contain a huge range of herbal flavourings; crème-de-menthe is flavoured with mint, and Kümmel with caraway and cumin. You can make your own by steeping a handful of fresh herb leaves in a pint (570 ml) of brandy or kirsch, following the method on p. 193.

Many apéritifs also contain herbs: anise flavours Pernod; wormwood flavours vermouth; and a range of bitter herbs characterize Campari.

Herbs make attractive garnishes in drinks and cocktails. Try freezing borage flowers or mint leaves in ice cubes to add to summer drinks.

HERBS FOR WINE CUPS

Angelica leaves (bestow a muscatel flavour), bergamot leaves and flowers, borage leaves and flowers, clary sage leaves, lemon balm leaves, lemon verbena leaves, mint leaves, all varieties, rosemary leaves, salad burnet leaves, sweet woodruff leaves

From left to right: Loving cup; Herbal tea (p. 191); Spicy geranium tea (p. 191); Raspberry and mint yogurt drink (p. 191); Hock cup (p. 193); Lager cup (p. 193); Angelica, mint and sweet cicely yogurt drink (p. 191).

Mint julep

¼ pint (150 ml) water	juice of 1 lemon
4 tbsp (60 ml) chopped mint leaves	¾ pint (450 ml) soda water
2 tbsp (30 ml) sugar	4 fl oz (100 ml) whisky
	sprigs of mint

1 Bring the water to the boil and pour over the mint. Stir in the sugar until it dissolves. Leave to cool.

2 Add the lemon juice then strain. Just before serving, pour in the soda water and the whisky. Add a sprig of mint to each glass as decoration.

Loving cup

2 lemons	1½ pints (800 ml) water
6 sprigs of lemon balm	½ bottle dessert wine
6 sprigs and flowers of borage or viper's bugloss	¼ pint (150 ml) French brandy
4 oz (110 g) sugar	1 bottle champagne or sparkling dry white wine

DECORATION
borage flower ice cubes

1 Remove the thin rind (zest) from one of the lemons with a zester. Peel and thinly slice the lemons.

2 Put the lemon balm, borage, sliced lemon, lemon zest and sugar into a jug. Stir in the water, wine and brandy. Cover and chill for 1 hour.

3 Chill the champagne and mix in just before serving. Decorate with borage flower ice cubes.

Four flower liqueur

2 pints (1 litre) brandy, vodka, kirsch or white "eau de vie"
1 in (2.5 cm) piece cinnamon stick
2 cloves
8 oz (225 g) scented rose petals, white heels removed

8 oz (225 g) clove pink petals
8 oz (225 g) orange blossoms or 3 oz (75 g) dried orange blossoms
8 oz (225 g) sweet violet flowers
sugar to taste

Makes about 2 pints (1 litre)

1 Put the alcohol, spices and flowers in a large glass jar with a tight-fitting lid or cork. Place in a sunny or warm position to infuse for 1 month.

2 Filter through coffee filters. Add sugar, stirring until dissolved. Bottle in strong glass or pottery

Hock cup

1 bottle hock
2 × 70 cl bottles soda water
1 liqueur glass brandy
½ liqueur glass Curaçao or Benedictine

finely grated rind of 1 lemon
finely grated rind of 1 orange
12 young salad burnet leaves
sprinkling of marigold (calendula) petals

1 Chill the hock and soda water for 1 hour.

2 Place the brandy, liqueur, lemon and orange rind and salad burnet leaves in a jug. Pour in the chilled hock, add the soda water and decorate with calendula petals. Serve immediately.

Lager cup

thinly peeled rind of 1 lemon
a few mint leaves
pinch of grated nutmeg
2 tbsp (30 ml) vodka
¼ pint (150 ml) water

juice of 2 lemons
1 tbsp (15 ml) caster sugar
crushed ice
½ pint (275 ml) soda water
1½ pints (800 ml) lager

Makes about 2 pints (1 litre)

1 Put the lemon rind, mint, nutmeg and vodka in a jug. Cover and steep for 20 minutes.

2 Add the water, lemon juice and sugar. Strain and add some crushed ice, the soda water and lager.

Elderflower fizz

Elderflowers must be picked on a dry, sunny day, as the yeast is mainly in the pollen.

1 gallon (4.5 litres) water
1½ lb (700 g) sugar
juice and thinly peeled

rind of 1 lemon
2 tbsp (30 ml) cider or wine vinegar
12 elderflower heads

1 Bring the water to the boil. Pour into a sterilized container, add the sugar, stirring until dissolved.

2 When cool, add the juice and rind of the lemon, vinegar and elderflowers. Cover with several layers of muslin and leave for 24 hours.

3 Filter through muslin into strong glass bottles. This drink is ready after 2 weeks. Serve chilled.

HERBS FOR THE HOUSEHOLD

In days gone by, herbs were central to household economies. As well as being used to flavour and preserve food, and to make medicine for people and livestock, herbs were incorporated in roof thatch, they were used to cover floors, to clean, polish and disinfect utensils, and to sweeten and purify musty air.

Each nation used its native plants with creative ingenuity, as many countries still do. The Chinese use bamboo for food, medicine, clothing, paper and pens, musical instruments and the intriguing bamboo wife – a basketwork cylinder designed to bring solace on hot summer nights, as the sleeper embraces it and receives the cooling breezes that pass through its frame. To give another example, North American Indians use birch bark to make canoes, baskets, documents, snow-shoes, medicine, syrup, tea and, as it prevents decay, to wrap meat and embalm the dead.

Tudor stillroom

In Tudor England so many activities centred around processing and preserving herbs that a special room, the stillroom, was set aside for this purpose. Here a small still made spirits for medicinal purposes and floral waters, like lavender water, to scent the laundry. Herbs were dried and tucked into clothes, chests to protect and perfume linen, or added to wax to make aromatic furniture polish. Roots and seeds of angelica were dried to burn on a chafing pan to disinfect a room. Leaves and berries were collected to dye spun wool.

Favourite and valued recipes were passed along from mother to daughter in the form of "A household book of receipts", although new skills were always welcomed. When a certain Mistress Dinghen arrived in England from Holland in the sixteenth century, Elizabethan ruffs were in vogue. She found many customers who were willing to pay her to teach them the art of making and using perfumed starch.

Perhaps the most pleasurable stillroom activity for the lady of the household was the blending of herbs, flowers and spices to make potpourri. She would escape to her warm and private stillroom, rich in sweet and pungent aromas, and gather together the aromatic leaves and flowers dried through the summer, remembering the day and the circumstances when each was picked; then she would measure and blend until she had created a mixture that pleased her.

Modern uses

It is not only historical interest or nostalgia that makes the idea of using herbs attractive to us today. Herbal dyes are still unsurpassed for subtlety of colour, and aromatic herbs contain antiseptic oils useful for cleaning.

But beyond this, the fresh fragrance of herbs has a way of pushing our thoughts past the strictly utilitarian. To fold sheets scented with lavender water or to polish furniture with sweet marjoram scented wax changes the chore to a pleasure. Perhaps it reminds us of the seasons or gives us a sense of continuity with the past. Whatever the reason, herbalists through the ages have told us that fresh sweet scents will lift our spirits and modern research confirms this assertion.

Herbal household products

HERBS FOR CONTROLLING PESTS

Herbs can be used effectively to keep unwanted insects and mice at bay. They have the advantage that they are completely safe compared to chemical poisons, which is especially important in the kitchen and other places where food is kept.

Ants Place sprigs of pennyroyal, rue or tansy on shelves or in cupboards to deter ants. Disturb the leaves occasionally to release more scent. This doesn't kill ants but encourages them to go away.
Flies Many herbs help to deter flies, including elder, lavender and mint, mugwort, peppermint, pennyroyal, rue and southernwood (but see also p. 210). Use them in arrangements, wreaths or potpourri. Hang pieces of sticky elecampane root around windows and doors.
Fleas and lice Burn the leaves of common fleabane (*Pulicaria dysenterica*), greater fleabane (*Inula conyza*), mugwort or wormwood on an open fire over low embers, to destroy fleas and lice. Encourage the fumes to fill the room but try to avoid breathing them in.
Mice Mint and tansy in your store cupboard will deter mice.
Preserving wraps Wrap dried nettle leaves around stored apples and pears, root vegetables and moist cheeses to preserve them and keep off pests. The wraps will keep vegetables and fruit skins smooth and moist for 2 or 3 months. Wrap figs in mullein leaves to preserve them.
Strewing In the Middle Ages, herbs were often strewn on the floor, to repel fleas, lice, moths and insect pests. They also masked unsavoury smells and provided insulation against the cold in winter and the heat in summer. This practice is unsuitable today but sprigs of herbs can be placed under doormats or carpets, or perhaps on the porch. Choose from the following:
alecost, balm, basil, chamomile, cowslip, daisies, fennel, germander, hop, marjoram, meadowsweet, mint, pennyroyal, pine, rose, rosemary, sage, southernwood, sweet flag, sweet woodruff, tansy, thuja, thyme, sweet violet or winter savory.
Wasps Burn dried leaf of *Eupatoria cannabinum* to drive away wasps.
Weevils Place a few bay leaves in flour and rice bins, and with dried pulses to prevent weevils.

HOUSECLEANING

These herbal products make polishing and cleaning an aromatic pleasure. They are also kinder to your skin and to the environment than many chemical household cleansers.

Lemon disinfectant Mix 6 drops of essential oil of lemon with 1 tsp (5 ml) of isopropyl alcohol to aid dispersal, and add to 4 pints (2 litres) of tepid water (hot water would make the oils evaporate too quickly). You can also use essential oils of tea tree, thyme, orange, bergamot, juniper, clove, lavender, niaouli, peppermint, rosemary, sandalwood or eucalyptus – listed in descending order of their antiseptic powers.
Rosemary disinfectant Simmer some leaves and small stems for 30 minutes in water; the less water, the more concentrated the disinfectant will be. Strain and use to clean sinks and bathrooms or to give a fresh scent to other rooms. Add washing-up liquid to get rid of grease on surfaces. Store any excess in the fridge for up to one week. Disinfectants can also be made with the leaves and flowering stems of eucalyptus, juniper, lavender, sage and thyme and with angelica roots.
Pot scourer The precursor to wire-wool, horsetail stems (*Equisetum arvense* or *E. hyemale*) have a fine sandpaper surface of silica crystals which will clean pots and pans. Rub a handful of dried, leafless stems on surfaces, then rinse to remove any residual green stains.
Metal polish Make a strong infusion of fresh horsetail, using 1 oz (25 g) to each pint (570 ml) of water. Soak for at least 2 hours, then simmer in the same water for 15 minutes and strain. Pour over metal or pewter articles and soak for 5 minutes. Remove the articles, allow them to dry slowly then polish with a soft cloth. If the article is too large to soak, like a suit of armour, wipe it with a cloth dipped in the solution, allow to dry and then polish with a soft cloth.

Sweet marjoram furniture wax

4 oz (110 g) beeswax	½ oz (15 g) olive-oil
1 pint (570 ml) turpentine	based soap
12 fl oz (350 ml) strong	essential oil of sweet
infusion of sweet marjoram	marjoram (optional)

1 Grate the beeswax into the turpentine and leave to dissolve, which may take a few days. Alternatively, warm the beeswax and turpentine carefully over a flameless heat until the wax melts. Turpentine can easily burst into flames so it's safest to warm it over boiling water.

2 In a separate pan, bring the infusion to boiling point and stir in the grated soap until melted.

3 Allow both mixtures to cool then blend slowly, stirring until it resembles thick cream. Stir in a few drops of essential oil. Pour into a wide-topped container and label.

Leaves of mock orange, lemon balm, lemon verbena, or rosemary, or lavender flowers can be used instead of sweet marjoram.

Sweet cicely polish Pound aromatic, fresh, soft sweet cicely seeds in a mortar. Pick up a handful in a cloth and rub on wood as a polish.

Herbal dyes

Plant dyes are unsurpassed for richness and
subtlety of colour, and often have an individual
fragrance too. They are created by boiling fresh or
dried pigment plants in water; the material is then
put in the dye bath, as described on p. 198. Dyes
take best on wool and silk but can be used on
unbleached cotton or linen with a more complex
process; they do not colour synthetics except
rayon. The white fleece, spun wool, silk cloth and
silk thread shown here have been dyed with light-
fast and washfast herbal colours. Each batch has
been dyed in the same dye bath and displays the
range of tones obtainable on different materials.

Nettle
Shades of dark grey-
green on wool and cream
on silk from a dye
bath of nettle with a
mordant of alum.

Woad
A range of soft
blues from a double-
strength dye vat of
woad leaves.

Elder leaves
Shades of yellow-
green from a dye
bath of elder leaves
with a mordant of
copper and
acetic acid.

Woad
A rich blue obtained
from a quadruple-
strength dye vat of
woad leaves.

Elder leaves
Shades of grey-green
from the dye bath above,
double strength, with a
pinch of iron added 30
minutes before
the end.

Bramble shoots
Shades of oatmeal
from a dye bath of
bramble shoots with a
mordant of alum and
cream of tartar.

Alkanet root
Shades of pink-
brown from a dye
bath of alkanet root
with acetic acid.

Weld
Soft green-yellows from a
dye bath of weld plant with
a mordant of copper and
acetic acid.

Onion skins
Rich browns from a
dye bath of red onion
skins with a mordant of
copper and acetic acid.

Chamomile
Bright yellow-gold
from a dye bath of
dyer's chamomile flowers
with a mordant of alum
and cream of tartar.

Madder root
Rich russet-red from
a dye bath of madder
root with a mordant of
alum and cream of
tartar.

Making herbal dyes

No two batches of herbal dyes will be identical: the final colour depends on the plant variety used, how much sunlight the plant received when growing, the chemicals in the water, the type of pan used (iron, copper and aluminium can alter the colour), the mordant, or fixative (see the box at right), and the immersion time. This unpredictability restricts large-scale commercial use of herbal dyes but adds interest to home experiments.

There is an optimum time to pick each herb, usually when it is about to flower or in autumn for roots (see p. 269). Use the same weight of herb as the weight of wool to be dyed; for silk, use twice the weight.

EQUIPMENT FOR HOME DYEING

Glass rod or wooden dowels	Stainless steel or unchipped
Pestle and mortar	enamel bath or large pan to
Pillow case or muslin bag	use as a dye bath
Rubber gloves	Thermometer
Sink or buckets for rinsing	Water, soft or filtered, or
	rain water
	Weighing scales

PROCEDURE FOR DYEING

Dyeing with herbs is a time-consuming but fascinating process. The fabric must be prepared to receive the dyes, which involves scouring and mordanting, and the dyes have to be extracted from the herbs. The process is explained below.

Avoid exposing wool and silk to sudden changes in temperature. For instance, when lifting wool from a hot bath, don't put it on a cold surface. Always handle wool very gently. To dry wool at any stage for storage, spin dry in a muslin bag at half speed and dry away from direct heat. If you dry wool after scouring, you must wet it again in 1 gallon (5 litres) of water at 120–125 °F (50 °C) with a drop of washing-up liquid for an hour before mordanting.

Scouring

Soak wool for several hours or overnight in 4 gallons (20 litres) of water at 120–125 °F (50 °C) with 1 tbsp (15 ml) of liquid detergent or a proprietary scouring agent to remove oil. Squeeze the wool gently, remove, then repeat. Give a final rinse in warm water with 2 fl oz (50 ml) of vinegar. Follow the same procedure for silk but have the water at 195 °F (90 °C).

Mordanting

Dissolve the mordant in a little hot water, then stir into 4 gallons (20 litres) of water at 120–125 °F (50 °C). Submerge the wet wool. Take an hour to bring to the boil and simmer at 180–200 °F (82–93 °C) for a further hour. Immerse silk at 140 °F (60 °C) and steep for 24 hours. Then rinse and dye immediately in a prepared dye bath.

MORDANTS

Colour is influenced by the choice of mordant. A mordant (from the Latin *mordere*, to bite) is used to help "fix" the dye. Some common mordants are listed below and are available from chemists or dye suppliers. Quantities recommended are for use with 1 lb (450 g) of dry wool:
- **Alum** (aluminium potassium sulphate); 1 oz (25 g). Often combined with cream of tartar (tartaric acid); $\frac{3}{4}$ oz (20 g). Alum gives bright, clear colours.
- **Iron** (ferrous sulphate); $\frac{1}{8}$ oz (5 g). Dulls and deepens colours and is called a "saddening" agent. Use alum first, add wool to the dye bath, simmer for 45 minutes, remove the wool, add the iron, replace the wool and simmer for a further 30 minutes.
- **Copper** (copper sulphate); $\frac{1}{2}$ oz (15 g) with $\frac{1}{2}$ pint (275 ml) vinegar gives a blue-green tint to colours. Copper is poisonous so handle it with care.
- **Chrome and tin**; Chrome gives colour depth and greater permanence, and tin brightens tones. Both are poisonous and require careful handling.

Dye bath

Chop or crush the plant material. Place loosely in a muslin bag and soak in 4 gallons (20 litres) of soft, tepid water overnight. Then simmer at 180–200 °F (82–93 °C) for about 1–3 hours, until the desired colour is reached. Remove the herbs, cool the liquid to hand heat, and gently add the wool. Take 1 hour to return to a simmer and simmer for a further hour. Leave to cool to hand heat then remove the wool or silk and rinse in warm, tepid and finally cold water. Leave silk to cool overnight, then rinse. Hang to dry.

Woad (or indigo) dye bath
(for 8 oz/250 g wool)

Woad and indigo require a different process to yield their rich, blue dyes. Pick 2 lb (1 kg) fresh leaves, chop and boil in 2 gallons (10 litres) of water for 7 minutes. Strain, squeeze the leaves and discard. Cool the liquor and add a few drops of liquid ammonia. Aerate by whisking or pouring liquid from one bucket to another for 10–15 minutes until the froth becomes pale blue. Warm the liquor until hand hot. Sprinkle 1 tsp (5 ml) of sodium dithionite (obtainable from a pharmacist or craft shop) over its surface to remove oxygen; do not stir. This turns the dye yellow. Leave to stand for 30 minutes to cool to room temperature.

Pre-wet the wool in water with a pinch of sodium dithionite, then slide it very gently into the dye so no air enters. Soak for 20 minutes. Remove gently and catch any drips with a cloth or they will oxidize the water. Shake out and hang the wool for 10–15 minutes and watch it turn blue. Add more sodium dithionite and repeat 3 to 6 times. Finally, wash in soapy water at the same temperature, rinse and dry.

DYE HERB CHART

The chart below provides a selection of dye-yielding herbs and tells you which part of the plant to use ("whole plant" means all the parts above ground), and which mordant combination for specific colours.

COMMON NAME	BOTANIC NAME	PLANT PART USED	MORDANT	COLOUR
Agrimony	*Agrimonia eupatoria*	flowering tops	alum	butter yellow
Alkanet	*Anchusa officinalis*	root	acetic acid	soft pink-brown
Bearberry	*Arctostaphylos uva-ursi*	dried leaves	alum	violet grey
Bearberry	*Arctostaphylos uva-ursi*	dried leaves	iron	charcoal black
Blackberry	*Rubus species*	young shoots	alum	creamy fawn
Bloodroot	*Sanguinaria canadensis*	root	alum	reddish orange
Bracken	*Pteridium aquilinum*	young shoots	alum	yellowish green
Coltsfoot	*Tussilago farfara*	whole plant	alum	green-yellow
Comfrey	*Symphytum officinale*	fresh green plant	alum	yellow
Chamomile, dyer's	*Anthemis tinctoria*	flowers	alum & cream of tartar	bright yellow
Chamomile, dyer's	*Anthemis tinctoria*	flowers	copper, acetic acid	olive
Dog's mercury	*Mercurialis perennis*	plant tops	alum	greyish yellow
Dyer's greenweed	*Genista tinctoria*	flowering tops	alum	yellow
Elder	*Sambucus nigra*	leaves	alum & cream of tartar	greenish yellow
Elder	*Sambucus nigra*	leaves	copper, acetic acid	olive (pinch of iron for grey green)
Elder	*Sambucus nigra*	berries	alum, salt	purple
Heather	*Calluna vulgaris*	young tips	alum	yellow
Heather	*Calluna vulgaris*	fresh branches	alum, pinch of iron	green
Horsetail	*Equisetum arvense*	fresh sterile stems	alum	creamy yellow
Juniper	*Juniperus communis*	crushed berries, fresh	alum	strong yellow
Juniper	*Juniperus communis*	crushed berries, dried	alum, cream of tartar, copper	olive-brown
Lady's bedstraw	*Galium verum*	roots	alum	coral pink
Madder	*Rubia tinctorum*	roots	alum, cream of tartar	rich tomato red
Marigold	*Calendula officinalis*	petals	alum, cream of tartar	pale yellow
Meadowsweet	*Filipendula ulmaria*	roots	alum	black
Nettle	*Urtica dioica*	whole plant	alum, cream of tartar, pinch of iron	greeny grey
Nettle	*Urtica dioica*	whole plant	copper	soft grey green
Onion	*Allium cepa*	skins	alum, cream of tartar	orange
Onion	*Allium cepa*	skins	copper, acetic acid	deep brassy yellow (tan on silk)
Parsley	*Petroselinum crispum*	fresh leaves, & stems	alum	cream
Privet	*Ligustrum vulgare*	leaves, young shoots	alum	strong yellows
Privet	*Ligustrum vulgare*	ripe berries	alum	greyish green
Safflower	*Carthamus tinctorius*	flowers	alum	yellows & tan
St John's wort	*Hypericum perforatum*	flowers	alum	beige
Sorrel	*Rumex acetosa*	whole plant	alum	greyish yellow
Sorrel	*Rumex acetosa*	roots	alum	soft pink
Tansy	*Tanacetum vulgare*	flowering tops	alum	mustard yellow
Turmeric	*Curcuma domestica*	powdered root	alum	gold-orange
Walnut	*Juglans regia*	leaves	no mordant	creamy fawn
Walnut	*Juglans regia*	green husks & shells	no mordant	light to dark browns
Weld	*Reseda luteola*	whole plant	alum	lemon yellow
Weld	*Reseda luteola*	whole plant	copper, acetic acid	green-yellow
Woad	*Isatis tinctoria*	leaves	sodium dithionite, ammonia	blue
Yew	*Taxus baccata*	heartwood chips	alum	orange-brown

Herbal papers

Paper can be scented with herbs, decorated with herbs, have herbs embedded in its fibres and even be made exclusively from herbs.

The cellulose in plants forms the raw material for paper, and herbs such as nettles, chamomile, dandelions and fennel all yield fibrous pulps. However, successful paper-making from herbs requires dedication, time and space. A simpler route is to recycle existing paper, adding herb leaves and petals when mixing the pulp, as described on p. 202. Some results are shown here. Each sheet of recycled herb paper will have its own character; no two are ever alike. Even the two surfaces have distinctive qualities, one being smooth and one having more texture, allowing scope for endless experimentation.

Use these textured herbal papers for mounting drawings or photographs; as a base for pressed herb and flower collages, or for charcoal, crayon or watercolour work.

You can also enhance your personal letters by adding the fragrance of lavender or a herb sachet to a box of writing paper. For a more subtle effect, scent ink as described on p. 203.

Potpourri paper
Full of rich colour and scent, this makes an attractive drawer liner.

Cornflower paper
Cornflower florets, added at the final stage of paper-making, give a dainty finish.

Dandelion paper
The leaves and petals of dandelions create subtle flecks of grey, green and yellow.

Lavender paper
Scent a box of writing paper with grains of lavender or other sweet-smelling herbs.

Scented ink
Add fragrance to ordinary ink with a decoction of lavender, rosemary or lemon verbena.

Sunflower stem paper
The pale gold fibres of dried sunflower stems are embedded in the pulp.

Fern paper
Dried fern leaves add an earthy accent to a delicate paper.

Onion skin paper
Crushed onion skins add subtle tints of mauve and burgundy.

Petal paper
Delicate petals from lavender, rose and other garden flowers make a colourful addition.

Hop vine paper
A fine-textured paper with silver-grey speckles.

201

Making herbal papers and ink

The Chinese invented paper-making around 105 AD using flax with tree bark, and paper is still made from the cellulose fibres of plants. Excellent herbs are flax, straw, nettles and rush. Others of use are bamboo, broom, chamomile, cow parsley, dandelion, dill, fennel, iris, mullein, pampas grass, sunflower and most cereal grasses.

EQUIPMENT

For making plant pulp
2 gallon (10 litre) bucket
Pestle and mortar or mallet
2 gallon (10 litre) stainless steel or galvanized pan
Rubber gloves

Wooden spoon
Metal sieve
Strong nylon net bag
Liquidizer

For making paper
Large plastic basin
Wooden frames, A5 or A4, with waterproof joints and strong nylon net stapled taut to the frames

One extra frame of the same size, without netting
Newspapers

Preparing plant pulp

2 gallons (10 litre) fresh herbs   2 tbsp (30 ml) caustic soda
2 pints (1 litre) water

1 Gather a 2 gallon (10 litre) bucketful of herbs and cut or tear them into 1–2 in (2.5–5 cm) square pieces. Crush thick pieces with a mallet or a pestle and mortar to speed the breakdown process.

2 Put 2 pints (1 litre) cold water into a stainless steel pan and stir in the caustic soda using a wooden spoon. Avoid breathing the fumes, wear rubber gloves and rinse off any splashes with cold water immediately. Add the herbs, cover with extra warm water if necessary and mix well. Simmer for 1½–2 hours or until the plant fibres feel soft.

3 Rinse the plants thoroughly to remove all traces of caustic soda. Then strain them through a metal sieve.

4 Gather the pulp (much reduced) into a net bag and rinse in water, squeezing the fibres repeatedly for several minutes.

5 Liquidize 2½ tbsp (35 ml) fibres with 25 fl oz (¾ litre) water for 20 seconds. The finer the plant fibres are liquidized, the finer the paper will be. This pulp can be used as it is or added to recycled paper pulp.

6 Writing paper needs to be treated or "sized" to receive ink. Mix ⅕ tsp (1 ml) cold water laundry starch with a little water and mix into the pulp.

Recycled paper pulp
You can use old papers to make fresh paper which you can then embellish with herbal additions or mix with plant pulp. Try absorbent papers such as newspapers, wallpaper, blotting paper or computer printout. Soak small pieces of paper overnight in warm water. Liquidize 2½ tbsp (35 ml) paper with 25 fl oz (¾ litre) water for 15 seconds. "Size" as above.

Making paper

pulp (recycled paper, plant or mixed)

optional additions
flowers, petals, stalks, essential oil

1 Fill the basin with pulp to just below the rim.

2 Place the empty frame over a net frame, hold together and dip vertically into the basin. Tilt to horizontal below the water, and raise slowly, keeping the frame horizontal.

3 Lay on newspaper to drain. Remove the empty top frame, scatter on petals or leaves for decoration and leave the pulp to dry.

4 When completely dry, slide a palette knife under the sheet to loosen it from the frame. Clean the frame and re-use following the same process.

Scented paper
Scent paper by storing it with aromatic herbs in an enclosed space. Lay lavender bundles or envelopes of your favourite herb blend in a box of writing paper. Wallpaper absorbs scent well and can be used to line drawers. Slip thin muslin bags of potpourri laced with extra essential oils between layers of drawer-lining paper, roll up and cover with cling film for 6 weeks to scent.

Paper decorations
Press flowers of borage, daisy, forget-me-not, primrose or sweet violet; leaves of alpine lady's mantle, chervil, pelargonium or salad burnet; or sprigs of lemon thyme, rosemary or myrtle between sheets of blotting paper or newsprint in a heavy book. When they are dried, use a small amount of latex-based glue to fix the herbs to writing paper, greeting cards and gifts.

MAKING INK
Black ink is made from pigments which are dark and contain tannin to prevent fading. These can be found in oak galls (formed by gall wasp larvae on oak trees) and the bark of blackthorn, alder and dogwood. A red ink can be made from field poppy petals, as described below. Alternatively, you can scent inks with fragrant herbal infusions.

Scented oak gall ink

This recipe is adapted from an eleventh-century recipe.

8 oz (250 g) bruised oak galls   a few drops of tincture of myrrh
4 pints (2.25 litres) boiling   1½ oz (45 g) gum arabic
water or herbal decoction   3 oz (80 g) sulphate of iron
a few drops of essential oil   (ferrous sulphate)

1 Steep the galls in water for 24 hours. Strain.

2 Add essential oil to the tincture of myrrh, then add the gum arabic.

3 Stir this with the sulphate of iron into the gall infusion. Bottle and label.

Scented ink

Give ink a sweeter fragrance with an infusion of
strongly scented herbs.

1 oz (25 g) dried aromatic
flowers or leaves (lavender
flowers; lemon verbena,
rose geranium, rosemary,

or sweet myrtle leaves)
½ cup (100 ml) water
1 small bottle of ink

1 Immerse the herbs in the water, bring to the boil
and simmer for 30–45 minutes, covered with a lid.
Take care that the mixture does not boil dry and reduce
the decoction to make about 4 tsp (20 ml) of strong-
smelling dark liquid.
2 Strain, allow to cool and mix with the ink.

Red ink

Take 1 cup (225 ml) field poppy petals and pour
on a small amount of boiling water just to cover
the petals. Steep overnight. Add 15 percent
isopropyl alcohol to preserve. Strain and bottle.

Herbal toys and trinkets

Children and adults alike will love these scented
beads and quaint, fragrant toys. They are fun to
make, whatever your age, and are excellent gifts.

Aromatic beads

(makes 75 large pea-sized beads)
Paint the finished beads or tint them with food
colouring to make them more decorative.

1½ tbsp (22 ml) each of
powdered orris root,
sweet flag and basil
1 tbsp (15 ml) each of
powdered gum benzoin,
cinnamon and mace
½ tsp (2.5 ml) ground cloves
½ nutmeg, freshly grated

3 drops of essential oil of
sandalwood
3 drops of essential oil of
cedarwood
3 drops of essential oil of myrrh
1 tsp (5 ml) gum tragacanth
powder
3–4 tbsp (45–60 ml) triple
strength rosewater

1 Mix the dry herbs and spices and add the oils,
stirring gently.

2 Mix the gum tragacanth with 3 tbsp (45 ml) of the
rosewater and stir into the first mixture to form a
paste. Add more rosewater if necessary.

3 Dampen your hands with rosewater and roll the
paste into beads. To increase their scent, use a darning
needle dipped in essential oil to pierce the beads and
thread onto strong oiled thread. Dry slowly. Paint with
food dyes or ink.

Rose beads

Place finely chopped scented red and pink rose
petals in a saucepan – a rusty pan will give a rich,
dark colour. Just cover with water, heat for 1 hour
but keep below boiling point. Cool for 24 hours.
Repeat four times. Dampen your hands with
rosewater, roll the pulp into beads, pressing hard,
then roll in powdered spices (cinnamon, cloves,
nutmeg). Thread with a darning needle onto thick
thread and dry in a warm place. Originally,
rosaries were made with 165 rose petal beads.

Herbal dough toys

Combine 1 unit of plain, white flour, ½ a unit of
salt and ½ a unit of strong herbal infusion. Knead
for at least 5 minutes into a smooth pliable dough.
Working on a piece of greaseproof paper, shape
the dough into a flat-backed doll (use a cookie-
cutter or a cut-out picture as a guide if it helps).
Make some hair for the doll by pushing dough
through a sieve or cutting thin strands, and shape
an apron with a pocket, or form clasped hands to
push dried herbs into. When joining the pieces of
dough, moisten each end before pressing together.
Transfer the paper with dough to a baking sheet.
Bake at 300 °F (160 °C) for 1 hour. Cool and apply
paint sealer or thick acrylic paints. Dry thoroughly
and varnish. Sprinkle essential oil onto the surface.

Alternatively, make a basket with a flat slab back
and a shallow lattice-work curved front. Plait a
handle and insert a wire in the back of the base as
a hanging hook. Bake and finish as described
above. Hang and fill with dried herbs.

Spiced apple granny doll

This may seem a slightly gruesome idea, but
children seem to love it. Peel a firm cooking apple.
Carve a face in the flesh then soak and keep
submerged in brine (5 percent salt by volume)
overnight. Remove, drain, then mount on a
wooden dowel. Add cloves for eyes and a cloth
headscarf. Dress the dowel body and add an apron
with pockets containing different spices such as
cardamoms, coriander and nutmegs. As the apple
face dries it wrinkles and "ages".

Lavender Bo-Peep mobile

This is a delightful idea for a mobile in a child's
bedroom based on a nursery rhyme character.

Make a small cloth doll, stuff the body with
lavender, then make a few cloth sheep, and fill
each with aromatic herbs. Make a circular hoop
with wire and use nylon thread to hang the doll
and sheep at different lengths. The movement of
the mobile will spread the soothing fragrance of
herbs and lavender around the bedroom.

Toys

Aromatic stuffed toys and animal-shaped herb
pillows delight children and bring comfort at
night or during periods of illness.

Potpourri

The traditional way to capture the essence of a summer herb garden and bring it indoors is to make a potpourri, a mixture of fragrant, colourful flowers and leaves displayed in a bowl.

Potpourri has become a term for many aromatic mixtures, but the original French means "rotten pot", a moist mixture of pickled flowers and leaves. This older, "moist" method gives a longer-lasting perfume but it is more difficult to do and visually less attractive. The dry method is popular as it is easier and the colourful result can be displayed in bowls or potpourri balls, and used in herb pillows.

The basic ingredients fall into four categories: flowers for scent or colour; aromatic leaves; spices and peel; and fixatives to preserve the blend. Many herbs are available as essential oils, a great asset to modern mixtures, but they must be used with discretion to avoid dominating subtler scents.

The leisurely activity of creating the mixture, focusing intently on scent and colour, gives as much pleasure as the finished product. As you become familiar with your herbs and their seasons, you can preserve a few leaves here and a few blossoms there, slowly building up a store of aromatic ingredients. When you wish to create a mixture, assemble your aromas and consider how each will blend and harmonize with the others.

The recipes on p. 207 provide guidelines but experience is the best teacher.

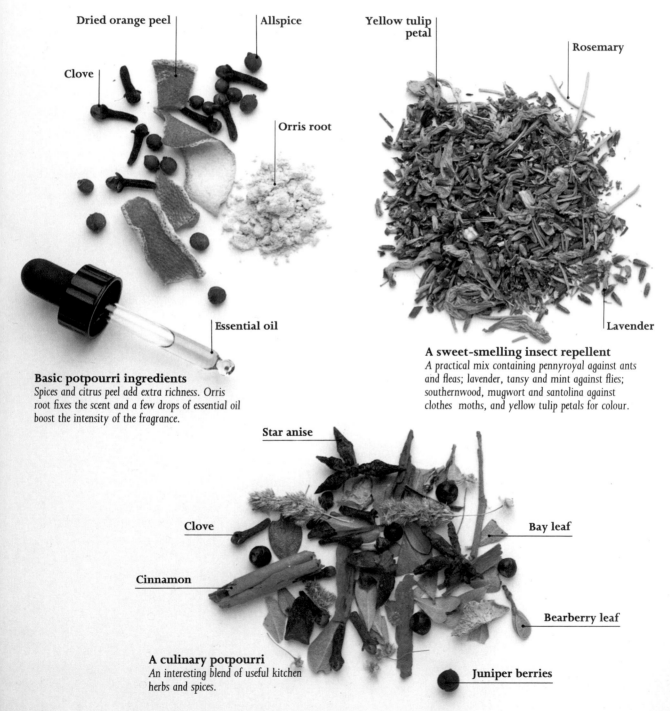

Dried orange peel

Allspice

Clove

Orris root

Yellow tulip petal

Rosemary

Lavender

Essential oil

Basic potpourri ingredients
Spices and citrus peel add extra richness. Orris root fixes the scent and a few drops of essential oil boost the intensity of the fragrance.

A sweet-smelling insect repellent
A practical mix containing pennyroyal against ants and fleas; lavender, tansy and mint against flies; southernwood, mugwort and santolina against clothes moths, and yellow tulip petals for colour.

Star anise

Clove

Bay leaf

Cinnamon

Bearberry leaf

Juniper berries

A culinary potpourri
An interesting blend of useful kitchen herbs and spices.

Cottage garden potpourri
All the colours of a cottage garden are found in this mixture of rosebuds, larkspur, love-in-a-mist, daisies, lavender, pelargoniums and helichrysum.

Strawflower

Love-in-a-mist

Hop

Blue delphinium

Rosebud

Helichrysum

Pink rose petal

Calendula petal

Lemon verbena

A soothing potpourri
This mixture of rose petals and calendula with soothing lavender, meadowsweet, angelica and lemon verbena is ideal for creating a calm atmosphere.

Elizabethan blue potpourri
A courtly mixture of royal blue delphinium, mallow and lavender with lemon verbena and bearberry leaves, and raspings of rosewood.

Larkspur

Blue mallow

Bearberry leaf

Lemon verbena

Potpourri balls
Mount a polystyrene ball on a toothpick or sturdy needle, paint or dip the ball in white glue, then roll it in potpourri to coat the entire surface.

Rosebud ball
Wire rosebuds of uniform or graded size together to form a sphere. Alternatively, insert short wired buds into a polystyrene ball.

Making potpourri

INGREDIENTS

To blend your own potpourri, select ingredients from each of the categories below. Use one of the recipes opposite as a guide for quantities.

Flowers for scent

Traditionally, flowers dominate any mixture, especially rose petals and lavender, as they retain their perfume the longest. For fragrance, select perfect, whole flowers just before they fully open. Dry by laying as flat as possible on stretched muslin to allow air to circulate. Large flowered roses and thick petalled lilies and hyacinths should have their petals separated. Small rosebuds can be dried whole and look exquisite but have little scent at this stage. Select from:

acacia, broom, carnations, elder, freesias, honeysuckle, hyacinth, jasmine, lavender, lilac, lily-of-the-valley, lime, Madonna lily, meadowsweet, Mexican orange blossom, mignonette, mock orange, musk mallow, narcissus, nicotiana, orange blossom, roses, stocks, sweet rocket, violets, wallflowers.

Flowers for colour

Choose from the following to include in display mixtures for extra colour:

bergamot, borage, calendula, chicory, cornflowers, delphinium, feverfew, forget-me-not, foxglove, larkspur, lawn daisy, poppy, sage, tansy, tulip petals, viper's bugloss, zinnias, and any of the small "everlasting" flowers. Use pussy willow catkins and sweet myrtle buds to give extra texture.

Aromatic leaves

These represent the second largest group in a potpourri mixture and as their scent is often more powerful than that of flowers, select those that will harmonize. Dry leaves whole and then break or crush them in the blend to release their scent. Choose from:

alecost, balm of Gilead, balsam poplar buds, basil, bay, bergamot, lady's bedstraw, lemon balm, lemon verbena, melilot, mints, patchouli, scented pelargoniums, rosemary, sage, southernwood, sweetbrier, sweet cicely, sweet marjoram, sweet myrtle, sweet woodruff, tarragon, thymes, and wild strawberry.

Spices, peel, roots and wood chips

These have a strong aroma and are used sparingly; about 1 tbsp (15 ml) to 4 cups (1 litre) of flowers and leaves. Selected spices are usually added in equal proportions. The best scent is obtained by freshly grinding whole spices in a pestle and mortar or pepper grinder; grate nutmeg. To make dried peel, take a thin layer of peel with a zester, grater or potato peeler, avoiding any white pith. Dip in orris root powder to intensify the scent. Dry slowly, then crush or mince if desired. Roots should be cleaned, carefully peeled, sliced and dried slowly. Then chop, crush, mince or powder them. Select from:

alexanders (seed), allspice, aniseed, cardamom, cinnamon, cloves, coriander, dill seed, ginger, juniper, nutmeg, star anise, vanilla pods; dried peel of citrus fruits; roots of angelica, cowslip, elecampane, sweet flag, valerian and vetiver, and shreds or raspings of cedarwood, sandalwood or cassia chips.

Fixatives

These are available as powders and are used to absorb and hold the other scents so they last longer. Most have their own perfume, which enters into the aromatic equation. The most popular vegetable fixative is orris root as its sweet violet scent doesn't affect a blend strongly: use 1 tbsp (15 ml) per cup (225 ml) of flowers and leaves. Gum benzoin has a sweet vanilla scent; use about $\frac{1}{2}$ oz (15 g) to 4–6 cups (1–1$\frac{1}{2}$ litres) of flowers and leaves. The tonka bean from *Dipteryx odorata* also has a strong vanilla scent; use one or two crushed beans per recipe.

Some fragrances act as fixatives including oakmoss or chypre, sandalwood, sweet flag root, sweet violet root, and frankincense and myrrh. Use $\frac{1}{2}$ oz (15 g) to 4 cups (1 litre) of potpourri.

Essential oils

Many of the above are available as essential oils (see pp. 228–237). This is a great boon to present day potpourri blenders for adding intensity and depth to a fragrant mixture. Oils are particularly good for reviving an old potpourri which has lost its scent; but only a few drops should be added to each mixture or you will overpower the blend.

METHODS
Moist potpourri

In traditional recipes, this is made from highly fragrant damask or cabbage rose petals which are partly dried until leathery and halved in bulk: it takes about two days of dry weather. Then layer the petals with dry non-iodized sea salt (half coarse and half fine), using 1 cup (225 ml) to 3 packed cups (700 ml) of petals. Alternate every $\frac{1}{2}$ in (1 cm) of petals in a bowl until two-thirds full. Stand it in a dark, dry, well-aired space for 10 days until caked together. If it froths, stir daily and allow another 10 days.

Break up the caked petals into small pieces, mix with the other ingredients and seal in an airtight container for six weeks to "ferment". Stir daily. Add dried flowers and essential oils, seal again for two weeks to complete blending. Transfer to a decorative opaque container with a lid and cover when not in use. Moist potpourri will keep its fragrance for several years.

Dry potpourri

Select a theme for the scent such as woodland or citrus, and assemble paper dry flowers and leaves. Gently combine the flowers and leaves, then mix the fixative with the spices and blend in with your hands. Sprinkle on essential oils if desired, a drop at a time, stirring between each drop. Seal and store in a warm, dry, dark place for six weeks to "cure".

Place the mixture in open bowls to display. Choose a container with colours that harmonize with the potpourri or use clear glass containers to show off the potpourri between layers of lavender or rose petals. A lid will prolong its scented life.

POTPOURRI RECIPES

Traditional rose and spice mixture
(moist method)

4 cups (1 litre) "fermented" rose petals	2 tbsp (30 ml) ground mace
1 tbsp (15 ml) crushed bay leaves	2 tbsp (30 ml) ground allspice
1 tbsp (15 ml) crushed orange peel	1 tbsp (15 ml) ground cloves
$\frac{1}{2}$ cup (100 ml) orris root powder	1 nutmeg, grated
	1 cinnamon stick, crushed
	1 cup (225 ml) dried rosebuds

Rondeletia potpourri
(moist method)

This is based on a nineteenth-century perfume.

4 cups (1 litre) "fermented" rose petals	1$\frac{1}{2}$ oz (40 g) tonka bean, crushed
4 cups (1 litre) lavender flowers	7 drops of bergamot oil
2 tbsp (30 ml) cloves	3 drops of clary sage oil

Culinary potpourri
(dry method)

Crush half of each ingredient for scent, leave the other half whole for texture and use.

2 cups (450 ml) sweet marjoram	2 tbsp (30 ml) sweet myrtle leaves
$\frac{1}{2}$ cup (100 ml) lemon thyme flowering tops	2 tbsp (30 ml) orange peel
$\frac{1}{2}$ cup (100 ml) basil	20 cardamom seeds
2 tbsp (30 ml) bearberry leaves	20 star anise pods
20 bay leaves	20 juniper berries
	2 tbsp (30 ml) cloves
	2 cinnamon sticks

Fresh citrus blend
(dry method)

2 cups (450 ml) lemon verbena	$\frac{1}{2}$ cup (100 ml) peppermint
1 cup (225 ml) lemon thyme	$\frac{1}{2}$ cup (100 ml) alecost leaves
1 cup (225 ml) spearmint	$\frac{1}{2}$ cup (100 ml) thyme (pine-scented)
1 cup (225 ml) variegated applemint	$\frac{1}{2}$ cup (100 ml) calendula petals
1 cup (225 ml) young bergamot leaves	20 crushed juniper berries
$\frac{1}{2}$ cup (100 ml) basil	$\frac{1}{4}$ cup (50 ml) lemon peel
$\frac{1}{2}$ cup (100 ml) pelargonium (lemon and peppermint)	2 drops each lemon, orange and bergamot oil

Soothing potpourri
(dry method)

2 cups (450 ml) lemon verbena	1 cup (225 ml) meadowsweet florets
2 cups (450 ml) rose petals	1 cup (225 ml) chamomile flowers
1 cup (225 ml) lavender flowers	1 oz (25 g) angelica root
1 cup (225 ml) calendula petals	4 tbsp (60 ml) orris root

Cottage garden potpourri
(dry method)

2 cups (450 ml) rose petals	1 cup (225 ml) pinks
1 cup (225 ml) rosebuds	1 cup (225 ml) larkspur flowers
2 cups (450 ml) lavender	$\frac{1}{4}$ cup (50 ml) daisies
1 cup (225 ml) mock orange flowers	8 love-in-a-mist seed capsules or hop flowers
1 cup (225 ml) scented pelargonium leaves	8 helichrysum
1 cup (225 ml) bergamot leaves	5 tbsp (75 ml) orris root

Elizabethan mixture
(dry method)

2 cups (450 ml) lemon verbena	$\frac{1}{2}$ cup (100 ml) violets
2 cups (450 ml) lavender flowers	$\frac{1}{2}$ cup (100 ml) blue mallow flowers
1 cup (225 ml) bearberry leaves	$\frac{1}{2}$ cup (100 ml) crushed roseroot
1 cup (225 ml) sweet myrtle leaves	1 oz (25 g) rosewood
1 cup (225 ml) delphiniums	4 tbsp (60 ml) orris root
	1 tbsp (15 ml) gum benzoin

Fly away potpourri
(dry method)

Sweet scented insect repellent.

2 cups (450 ml) lavender flowers	$\frac{1}{4}$ cup (50 ml) tansy
1 cup (225 ml) rosemary	$\frac{1}{4}$ cup (50 ml) mugwort
1 cup (225 ml) southernwood	$\frac{1}{4}$ cup (50 ml) cedarwood chips
$\frac{1}{2}$ cup (100 ml) spearmint	10 yellow tulips
$\frac{1}{2}$ cup (100 ml) santolina	3 tbsp (45 ml) orris root
$\frac{1}{4}$ cup (50 ml) pennyroyal	

Woodland blend
(dry method)

2 cups (450 ml) wild strawberry leaves	$\frac{1}{4}$ cup (50 ml) patchouli
1 cup (225 ml) pine needles	$\frac{1}{4}$ cup (50 ml) rosewood
$\frac{1}{2}$ cup (100 ml) violets	2 tbsp (30 ml) sweet violet root
$\frac{1}{2}$ cup (100 ml) rosemary	3 drops cypress oil
$\frac{1}{4}$ cup (50 ml) cedarwood chippings	2 drops pine oil
	1 oz (25 g) oakmoss

Family Heirloom
(dry method)

Begin with a simple blend of rose petals, lavender flowers, rosemary leaves, allspice and orris root. Whenever you have a special occasion involving flowers, dry the petals and add them to the potpourri. As scent fades it can be revived with essential oils. The character of the potpourri will develop with your family history and each petal will have a story to tell.

Herbal fragrance for the bedroom

Discover refreshing new ways of using herbs in the bedroom. All the pretty things shown on these pages are enhanced with herbal fragrance of different kinds. A scented sachet can be slipped under your pillow so that turning over in the night produces a soothing drift of bergamot. A lingerie drawer can be perfumed with the sweet scent of rose potpourri. Or a scented hanger can give a shirt the clean, fresh aroma of lemon verbena. See the following pages for more ideas.

Classic potpourri
Countless possibilities for recipes make concocting potpourri an absorbing art. A classic rose-scented mix has an intoxicating perfume.

Colourful potpourri
Tossing in a few vivid, dried flower heads for their colour makes mixtures more decorative.

Lavender bundle
Pretty be-ribboned bundles of lavender make enchanting presents and are easy to slip into drawers and cupboards. Fresh-cut stalks of lavender are used, and pastel ribbon holds the flower heads in place.

Herb pillow
Especially treasured by those confined to bed, a herb pillow is easily constructed with a muslin inner slip. This holds the herbs, allowing the outer case to be laundered. A sleep pillow could include the heady-scented flowers of golden hop.

Country scent potpourri
The English garden mixture includes lavender, bergamot, rose petals, mock orange and eau de clogne mint. A hay-scented meadow mixture can be made from melilot, lady's bedstraw and sweet woodruff.

Lavender bags

Tiny and neat, hand-made lavender bags have a peaceful fragrance. They can be stitched from fabric and lace scraps, or made up to match a scented hanger. Different shapes can be filled with dried lavender or a fragrant mixture of your choice.

Scented hanger

The floral fabric covering this padded coat hanger encloses a selection of fragrant dried herbs, caught beneath muslin strips wound round the hanger. Rose and lavender mixtures are suitable, or, for a man's hanger, a minty citrus blend of spearmint, alecost, lemon verbena and pine-scented thyme.

Pomander

This traditional aromatic pomander is made with an orange, some spicy cloves and a length of ribbon to hang it by.

Perfumed box

The old-fashioned fragrance of lavender can be used for a new idea. A pretty, fabric-covered box for keepsakes or handkerchiefs conceals a secret — padded, lavender-filled panels in the lid and base.

209

Herbal fragrance in the home

LIVING ROOM

Fresh, scented flowers and herbs arranged in a vase are one of the easiest ways to fill a room with scent. Other ways to freshen or perfume the air are listed below. All are based on simple ideas that have been practised for centuries and are now enjoying something of a revival.

Herbal decorations Generous bunches of fresh herbs in vases or garlands will cool and perfume a room (see pp. 150–162). Herbs that sweeten the air include:

alecost, basil, bay, germander, hyssop, lavender, lemon balm, lemon verbena, mints, rosemary, roseroot, santolina, sweet myrtle, thyme, woodruff and wormwood.

Essential oils Add a few drops of lavender oil to a bowl of near-boiling water and place in the room. Alternatively, moisten a sponge with boiling water and add a few drops of an essential oil. Place the sponge in a dish in the room, and moisten it with boiling water twice a day, adding a few drops of oil twice a week (also see p. 235).

Chafing pan Use a heavy pan to burn aromatic herbs and spices over a low heat for fragrance and fumigation. Try angelica seed, dried angelica root, elecampane root, roseroot, sweet violet root, and cloves or mixed spices. When the dry ingredients begin to smoulder, remove the pan from the heat and carry it around to freshen the air.

Scented water Mix $\frac{1}{2}$ cup (100 ml) triple strength rosewater with 1 tbsp (15 ml) powdered allspice or cloves. Store for a week to mature, then sprinkle a few drops on a hot pan or fire grate to scent a room.

Scented wood Keep any prunings of herbs like lavender and rosemary in a jar by the hearth to sprinkle on the fire and scent the room. For special occasions burn scented wood such as apple, cedar, cherry, cypress, juniper, larch, lilac, pear or pine.

Lavender incense Soak dried lavender stems in 1 tbsp (15 ml) saltpetre dissolved in 1 cup (225 ml) of warm water for 30 minutes. Dry out and light for a slow smouldering scent.

Potpourri Try out recipes on p. 207 and display in pretty bowls, inviting the potpourri to be touched so the scent is released.

Lavender soother Put a dish of lavender by the telephone for its soothing fragrance.

Herb cushions Fill two rectangular muslin bags with favourite potpourri blends. Cover each with material to match your sofa or chair. Join the two bags with two straps of fabric and hang over the back of the sofa so the fragrance is released whenever anyone rests against them. Swap the bags around occasionally.

Scented books Put small sachets of lavender, southernwood, santolina or wormwood and cinnamon or cloves on your bookshelves to scent and protect books from pests.

Scented candles The easiest way to make candles is to buy a candle-making kit. Add small pieces of dried alecost, bergamot, germander, lavender heads, lemon thyme, mint, rosemary, sweet myrtle, powdered cinnamon or a few drops of essential oil to the melted wax just before pouring it into the mould.

For decoration, apply aromatic leaves to the outside. Hold a candle by the wick, dip it in hot water for a few seconds to soften the outside, then roll it over dried herb leaves, pressing gently. Alternatively, put the leaves round the edge of the mould. Salad burnet is a very pretty and delicate leaf to apply.

If you want to make a herbal wax, boil the leaves of bog myrtle (*Myrica gale*) or the pale grey berries (nutlets) of bayberry for about 15 minutes to extract their wax. Skim it off, remelt and strain. This wax burns with a mild spiciness.

HERBS FOR THE KITCHEN

Use herbs in the kitchen to freshen the air and disguise cooking fumes. Make decorative hangings (see pp. 156–7) and incorporate those herbs listed below to deter flies.

Kitchen potpourri Try the recipe on p. 207 or the following blend to reduce kitchen smells and deter flies. Use 4 parts lemon verbena, 2 parts mints, 2 parts bay leaves, 1 part tansy leaves and flowers, 1 part lovage, a few crushed cloves and orris root. Handle the leaves when you pass by.

Fly-away posies Kitchen bouquets of chamomile, hemp agrimony, mugwort, pennyroyal, peppermint, rue, tansy or wormwood, or pot plants of basil and shoo-fly (*Nicandra physaloides*), should deter flies.

Oven gloves Sew rosemary, thyme or spices into the padding of oven gloves so they release their scent when warm.

Pot cover Make pockets in a teapot cover and fill with lemon verbena, rose petals or jasmine; the warmth of the teapot will activate their perfume.

Scented oven Whenever baking, place a sprig of rosemary or any savoury herb in the oven to scent the kitchen.

HERBS FOR THE BEDROOM

Fragrant herbs can help you sleep, sweeten the air and your clothes, and are particularly welcome in a bedroom where someone is ill.

Herb pillows Make a small muslin or cotton cover and fill with your favourite potpourri mixture. Keep it under your normal pillow. As you turn in the night, soothing wafts of herbal fragrance will aid your sleep. Fresh scents, not overly sweet, are best for the sickroom or a convalescent. Hops have sleep-inducing properties but not everyone enjoys their beery scent; adding a little lavender, lemon verbena, mint or rosemary helps to counteract the aroma. Another sleep mixture includes 1 part chamomile (to dispel nightmares), 2 parts each rosemary and pine needles (both refreshing), 2 parts lavender (alleviates sadness) and a little sweet marjoram (a sedative) with crushed aniseed or dill, orris root and a few drops of bergamot oil.

Drawer bags (sweet bags) Use lavender, lemon verbena, mint or rose petals to fill individual sachets of lace, silk or cotton to lay among lingerie, sweaters, gloves and linen. Add a loop to hang sachets on hangers under dresses and shirts. Choose more robust materials for sachets to store herbs inside shoes, boots and suitcases so they stay sweetly scented. Tuck small sachets in pockets or hems of winter coats in storage.

Perfumed boxes Make thin rectangular lavender pillows and tack them into the lid and base of a small box for storing jewellery or mementos.

Scented hangers Add herbs with the padding when making fabric-covered coat hangers.

Lavender bundles To make lavender bundles you need an odd number, 13 or more, of long stems of lavender, freshly picked on a dry day, and about 3 ft (1 m) of lavender or blue $\frac{1}{4}$ in (6 mm) ribbon. Make a bunch, lining up the base of the flower heads. Leave an 8 in (20 cm) length of ribbon free at one end, then tie the stems together just below the heads. Gently bend back each stem until the flower heads are enclosed by the stems. Take the length of ribbon you saved and weave it under and over each stem, travelling around the bundle several times until the flower heads are covered with ribbon. Tuck in the short end of the ribbon and tie a bow with the other end. Trim the stalks and the ribbon.

Pomanders Press cloves into the skin of an orange, pricking the skin with a darning needle first if necessary. Either cover the whole orange with cloves, allowing a clove space between each to allow for shrinkage as the orange dries, or set them in patterns round the orange. Roll the finished orange in a mixture of orris root and spices – cinnamon or allspice. Tie a ribbon round to suspend the pomander, which should hold its scent for a year or more.

Pomanders can also be made with apples but they bruise and shrivel more than oranges. Select a large firm cooking apple for the best results. A cidery clove scent eventually develops.

CLOTHING AND HOUSEHOLD LINEN
Scented bed-linen and sweet-smelling clothes add a touch of luxury to your life at very little cost of time or money.

Sweet rinse waters Make a strong infusion of aromatic leaves or flowers by simmering them for 15 minutes in a lidded pan. Strain and use the liquid as the final rinse for hand-washed articles or add it to the washing machine final rinse cycle.

Single herbs or mixtures can be used: rosemary with lavender is very refreshing. Choose from the following:

leaves of alecost, angelica, bay, bergamot, eau de cologne mint, lemon verbena, rosemary, sweet marjoram or sweet myrtle; powdered root of roseroot; or flowers of cottage pinks, lavender, rose petals or violets.

A small teaspoon of powdered orris root can be dissolved in the mixture to fix the scent. The solution can also be sprinkled on clothes before ironing. Alternatively, add a few drops of essential oil to the final rinse.

Herbs to protect and scent fabrics Make up small bags of your favourite aromatic herbs (see pp. 206–7). Alternatively, you can use individual herbs to lay among your clothes. Choose from:

sprigs of alecost, lavender, rosemary or southernwood; dried lemon peel; or root pieces of elecampane, orris, roseroot or sweet flag.

HERBS FOR SMOKERS
Mixtures of herb leaves and seeds have been smoked for centuries, long before the commercial domination of the tobacco plant. Indeed, in times past, herbal mixtures were smoked to relieve chest complaints.

Scented tobacco An aromatic mixture of aniseed, balsam, cinnamon, clove oil and gum benzoin can be made into peppercorn-sized balls and matured for a month. Add one piece to a pipeful of tobacco to perfume a room.

Herbal tobacco There is now a revival of interest in herbal tobacco, in response to the dangers inherent in smoking tobacco leaves. Most herbal tobaccos are based on coltsfoot, and can be bought from herbal suppliers. Other herbs added include arnica, betony, buckbean, annual chamomile, eyebright, lavender, mallow, mugwort, rosemary, thyme and yarrow. Final blending includes liquorice, salt, saltpetre and sugar.

HERBS
FOR BEAUTY

The cosmetic use of plant material runs through all ancient cultures. Seven thousand years ago, the early tribes of the Nile Valley painted and anointed their dead both to preserve the body and make it more attractive for the world beyond. The Egyptians who followed assimilated their practices and developed them into an elaborate routine of beauty preparations for religious rituals and ceremonial occasions.

The ancient Greeks changed the focus of cosmetics from ceremonial to personal, developing a philosophy of all-round health and beauty akin to modern concepts. The famous physician Hippocrates formulated the study of dermatology and recommended diet, exercise baths and massage for improving physical health and beauty. The Romans indulged further in aromatic rituals and body pampering. Citro, a Roman writer in the first century AD, wrote four books on cosmetics with a range of recipes for bleaching, tinting and greasing hair, avoiding wrinkles, and dealing with body odours.

By the time of the Renaissance there was an awareness of skin care as separate from medicinal disorders. Recipes for soaps, creams, and herbal waters were collected and recorded in herbals and still-room books, which were handed down from mother to daughter for generations.

Commercial beauty products
During the nineteenth century, cosmetics became an organized industry in America. In 1846 Mr Theron T. Pond offered his "Pond's Extract" to the public and other manufacturers soon followed. The innovative use of preservatives and mass production created an unprecedented choice.

Today's commercial products are often expensive, having vast amounts of money spent on advertising, packaging, distribution and testing (which can involve cruelty to animals). Allergies have increased along with the use of chemical preservatives, synthetic perfumes and artificial colourings. As a result, demand has risen for natural ingredients, and since research has demonstrated the remarkable therapeutic properties of herbs, many firms are rushing to create their own ranges of herbal cosmetics.

Homemade herbal cosmetics
By making your own cosmetics, you can be sure of their contents. You select each ingredient and have control over its freshness and purity. The following recipes combine present-day knowledge with traditional ingredients and methods inherited from past ages, including the first face cream recipe recorded by Galen, a Roman doctor in the second century. This recipe used a formula of oil, water and wax and has formed the basis of day creams ever since. Some preparations take no longer than boiling a kettle, others require heating and blending but are no more complicated or time-consuming than preparing a simple sauce.

Note: *Before using any herbal preparations, you are advised to sample a small amount first, particularly if you have had allergic reactions in the past.*

USEFUL EQUIPMENT FOR HERBAL COSMETICS

This list is meant as a guide only but do avoid using aluminium, copper and non-stick pans as their chemical contents can affect the ingredients' beneficial properties.

All containers and utensils must be scrupulously clean. Ideally they should be sterilized by being boiled or placed in a hot oven for 10 minutes. Have hot soapy water standing by to wash off wax before it hardens. Otherwise, stand bowls over boiling water to remelt traces of contents and wash immediately.

Heatproof glassware or pottery cookware (to sit in or above pans of boiling water)
Enamel double boiler
Wire whisk or electric whisk
Measuring spoons
Measuring jug
Small glass 1 oz (25 ml) measure
Small funnel
Nylon sieve
Pestle and mortar
Set of small measuring scales
Electric blender/grinder

Juice extractor
Glass dropper
Wooden spoons
Glass rods
Spatula
Clean dark glass bottles and jars with airtight lids
Labels
Indelible pen
A notebook for recording recipes

BASIC HERBAL PREPARATIONS

Most of the recipes in this section use one of these methods to extract the therapeutic properties from herbs.

Infusing Put one and a half handfuls of fresh herbs or 1 oz (25 g) of dried into a heatproof container (not aluminium or copper). Bring 1 pint (570 ml) distilled water to the boil. Pour over the herb immediately, cover with a lid to prevent the loss of any volatile elements through evaporation. Steep for at least 30 minutes. Strain and store in a refrigerator for up to three days.

Decocting This method is usually employed for the tougher parts of herbs, for example roots, bark, stems or seeds. Put 1 oz (25 g) of the herb, cut up if necessary, into a saucepan (not aluminium or copper). Add 1 pint (570 ml) distilled water, bring to the boil and simmer for 30 minutes. By this time the liquid should have reduced by half. If more has evaporated, top up with water to make half a pint (275 ml). Cool, strain and bottle. Keep in the refrigerator and use within a few days.

Macerating Herbs likely to lose some of their therapeutic value if heated should be steeped in oil, vinegar or alcohol. Pack a glass jar with the crushed, fresh herb. Cover with vegetable oil, cider vinegar or pure alcohol. Seal and leave for two weeks, shaking the jar each day. Strain and top up with fresh herbs. Repeat until the liquid smells strongly herbal. Strain, seal and bottle. Keeps well.

Pulverizing Grind, bruise or mash plant fibres and seeds in a pestle and mortar or electric blender.

NON-HERBAL INGREDIENTS

The following can be bought from any good pharmacist.

Agar agar Derived from seaweed. Used to make gels.

Alcohol A colourless, flavourless preservative and solvent. The best alcohol for perfumery and least irritating to skin is ethyl alcohol. Isopropyl alcohol (surgical spirit) is second best but has a medicinal scent. Vodka can be used sometimes instead.

Beeswax Acts as an emulsifier for oil and water in creams. Usually sold in blocks. To ease measuring, line egg box compartments with foil, melt the wax gently and put 1 tsp (5 ml) or 1 tbsp (15 ml) in each compartment. When it has cooled and solidified, remove, wrap in foil and store until required.

Benzoin A preservative, astringent and antiseptic.

Borax A white, crystalline, mineral powder used as an emulsifier. May be omitted from recipes.

Bran Used in face masks, soaps and body scrubs as a cleanser.

Buttermilk Available from health-food shops. Soothing and astringent.

Calamine lotion A soothing alkaline lotion useful for skin problems.

Castile soap A pure white soap with no added colour or perfume. Makes a useful base for homemade soaps.

Cocoa butter A thick fat from the cocoa bean, which makes a rich emollient in creams.

Distilled water Only pure water is suitable for making cosmetics. Piped water and rain water contain too many impurities.

Emulsifying wax A wax used to emulsify oil and water in creams.

Fuller's earth A fine grey powder derived from single-cell algae found on sea beds. Its absorbent properties and mineral richness make it an excellent face mask.

Gelatine A colourless, odourless, tasteless glue and a rich source of water-soluble protein, obtained by boiling animal bones. Used in eye ointments and nail hardening lotions. Agar agar is a vegetable substitute.

Glycerine A thick, colourless, odourless syrup and by-product of soap manufacture. It mixes with water, is soluble in alcohol and has softening properties.

Honey Softening, healing and binds other ingredients together.

Iodine Used as an antiseptic.

Kaolin The purest form of clay, useful in face masks.

Lanolin A thick, sticky fat obtained from sheep's wool. Softens and nourishes the skin.

Liquid paraffin A mineral oil which is not absorbed by the skin, making it useful in barrier creams.

Oatmeal See **Bran**

Oils See p. 230 for notes on essential oils and vegetable oils. Almond, avocado, wheatgerm, carrot, coconut and nut kernel oils are particularly skin-enriching. Castor oil disperses in water, making a good vehicle for scented bath oils.

Oleic acid An emulsifying liquid that can rescue separated creams.

Petroleum jelly A pale yellow translucent mineral jelly insoluble in water. Does not turn rancid when exposed to air. Used in lip salves.

Vinegar Used in cosmetics to soften, cleanse and soothe the skin.

Vitamin capsules A convenient way of adding vitamins to skin creams.

Zinc oxide A white powder derived from zinc which has mild antiseptic and astringent qualities. Usually available as an ointment.

Knowing your skin

To appreciate how herbs can benefit your skin, it helps to know something about why skin deteriorates. Like eyes and hair, skin is a reflection of your general health, so diet and lifestyle are major contributors to its appearance. Its surface needs to be kept moist and clean to protect it from drying winds, the sun and environmental pollution. The first line of defence is to avoid as many of these factors as possible; the second is to clean and nourish your skin with care.

SKIN TYPES

To give your skin the correct treatment you need to ascertain your skin type. Test by cleaning your face thoroughly, rinse well and dry with a towel. Allow it to rest for two hours or overnight and then press a tissue onto your face. If the tissue comes away full of grease, you have oily skin; if there is grease on only parts of it (usually from around the forehead, nose and chin), you have combination skin. If the tissue comes away unmarked, wash your face with soap and water. If your skin feels supple and smooth afterwards, it's normal; if it feels taut, it's dry.

Normal skin is soft, smooth and springy with a translucent glow. Why it is called normal when it is the rarest form is a mystery. A simple care routine is sufficient.

Dry skin feels taut and dry and has no shine. All types of skin become drier and more sensitive to changes as they age. This type of skin requires moisturizer at an earlier age. It should be treated with mild cleansers and gentle care.

Oily skin has a definite shine and is supple. The pores are open and the skin may look coarse and sallow. An oily skin is less vulnerable to sun and winds, and a further benefit comes later in life as it appears supple for longer. It needs thorough cleansing as the greasy surface acts like a magnet to dirt and a breeding ground for spots, but cleansing must be gentle to avoid stimulating the sebaceous glands into yet further oil production.

Combination skin is the most common type as the pores on the forehead, nose and chin are usually larger than those on the rest of the face. This "T" panel is oily and the remainder of the face is dry. It is best treated as two types of skin, using different recipes for the appropriate areas.

Skin creams and lotions

All skin creams are based on a combination of melted waxes, oils and scented waters, which must all be a similar temperature. The waxes are melted together over a low heat, the oils are warmed and beaten into the waxes, then the heated waters are dribbled slowly into the blended wax and oil, and the mixture is stirred until cool. It is like making mayonnaise only easier – a 10-minute operation.

The proportions of the ingredients govern a cream's consistency and are easy to adjust. To make a cream firmer, add more beeswax; to make it softer, add more oil. Adding more water will make it lighter and fluffier but also makes the ingredients more prone to separation. The addition of herbs such as marsh mallow and houseleek, which contain an emollient mucilage (a sticky substance in the roots, stems or leaves), will make a cream spongier. Add a few drops of essential oil for both the fragrance and its beneficial properties. Rose, geranium and lavender are particularly good for all skin types.

Spooning creams into small jars is an acquired skill. It's best to begin with a small spoon and to use a knife around the inside edge to remove any air pockets. Some lotions become firmer after a few hours so until you are familiar with a recipe put your creams into wide-necked jars. What you pour into a bottle may become too thick to pour

out. (Gently reheat to remove if this does happen.)

Always label and date products immediately, keeping a record of each recipe and its success. As perishable ingredients are involved, refrigerate creams and use within a few weeks. To prevent the possibility of introducing bacteria, make sure your hands are clean before dipping into your creams, or use a small spatula.

ALLERGY

No cosmetics can claim to be non-allergenic because every ingredient holds the possibility that someone might be allergic to it. One of the main benefits of making your own cosmetics is that if you do have an allergic reaction you know what ingredients you have used and can soon find the culprit. Test for a reaction by placing a spot of any ingredient on the inner gauze area of a piece of sticking plaster and attaching this to your inner arm, between the wrist and elbow. Leave in place for 24 hours, by which time any reaction you may have will show.

Some essential oils can irritate sensitive skins, particularly on the face. Oils to watch out for are bay, bergamot, geranium, neroli, pennyroyal, peppermint, sage, and spearmint.

For those with highly sensitive skins, the following ingredients can cause allergic reactions:

Agrimony	Glycerine	Lovage
Almond oil	Henna	Nettles
Cocoa butter	Ivy	Pennyroyal
Cowslips	Lanolin	Primrose
Cucumber	Lime blossom	Violet leaves

CLEANSING CREAMS

These are more efficient than soap and water at removing heavy dirt and makeup, which can lodge in skin crevices, aging the skin more quickly and making it seem dull and lifeless. Massage into the skin and then wipe off with cotton wool or tissue. Avoid dragging the skin; stroke lightly upwards and across the face.

Glycerine and rosewater cleansing cream
(for dry and normal skins)

Most recipes for creams follow this procedure. Waxes are melted in one container while oils are warmed in another. All ingredients should be about the same temperature when you mix them together or the mixture may curdle. You can substitute any suitable herbal infusion for the rosewater.

4 tbsp (60 ml) lanolin	3 tbsp (45 ml) rosewater
2 fl oz (50 ml) almond oil	1 tsp (5 ml) zinc oxide
1 tbsp (15 ml) glycerine	ointment
⅛ tsp (0.65 ml) borax	6 drops essential oil of rose

1 Melt the lanolin and gently heat the almond oil and glycerine together. Slowly pour the oil and glycerine mixture into the lanolin, beating constantly.

2 Dissolve the borax in the warmed rosewater and add gradually to the lanolin and oil mixture, beating all the time. Leave to cool.

3 When cool and creamy, beat in the zinc oxide and rose oil. Spoon into prepared jars and label.

PLANTS TO USE IN CREAMS AND LOTIONS

Many plants and herbs have beneficial cosmetic uses. Those listed here are particularly effective in skin creams. Follow the preparation instructions on p. 213. For equivalent strengths, use half the quantity of dried herbs as fresh. Many of these herbs are also beneficial in face packs, baths and hair treatments and are listed in those sections of the chapter.

Aloe vera The sap from the leaves is soothing and healing.

Avocado An excellent skin food with high vitamin E and A content.

Borage Good for dry, sensitive skins.

Calendula A healing herb for rough, damaged and problem skin.

Chamomile A gentle, soothing herb that also softens and whitens skin.

Comfrey A healing and soothing herb that contains allantoin, a protein which speeds up cell renewal. Good for rough and damaged skin.

Cucumber A cleansing agent and toner. Soothing and healing.

Dandelion Contains a rich emollient useful in cleansing lotions for dry, mature and sallow skins.

Elderflower A good tonic for all skins, especially mature or sallow skins. Reputed to soften skin and smooth wrinkles, fade freckles and soothe sunburn.

Essential oils These are excellent additions to creams and lotions. See p. 236 for details of their properties.

Fennel Cleansing and soothing. Add crushed seeds to face packs.

Houseleek A healing, softening and soothing herb especially good for dry, sensitive skins.

Ivy Relieves sunburn; helps to disperse trapped fluids and toxins in the fight against cellulite.

Lady's mantle A healing herb for soothing dry, sensitive skin and rough hands, makes a good astringent for large pores.

Lavender A healing and gentle cleanser and tonic for all skin types.

Lemon An astringent that restores the skin's natural acid balance.

Lime tree blossom Soothes and softens the skin. Deep cleansing.

Lupin seed A cleanser and pore refiner for oily skin.

Marsh mallow A healing softener for dry skins, chapped hands and sunburn.

Nettle A deep cleanser, particularly good for oily skin.

Orange flower An excellent skin tonic, said to help restore the skin's acid barrier. Also treats dry skin and broken capillaries and stimulates cell replacement.

Parsley A conditioner for dry, sensitive and troubled skins.

Peppermint A stimulating astringent which clears the complexion.

Rose A soothing and gentle cleanser which has a refining and softening effect on the skin.

Rosemary An invigorating tonic and antiseptic which boosts circulation and deep skin cleansing.

Sage A cleansing, stimulating astringent which also tightens pores.

Thyme A stimulating but gentle antiseptic cleanser.

Violet A gentle, soothing astringent.

Watercress Expressed juice can help to clear blemishes.

Witch hazel Soothing and astringent. Distilled witch hazel contains 15 percent alcohol.

Yarrow A healing and cleansing astringent.

Chamomile cleansing milk
(for dry and sensitive skins)

Use elderflowers, sweet violets or lime blossom
in place of chamomile.

½ cup (125 ml) creamy milk   2 tbsp (30 ml) chamomile
flowers, fresh or dried

1 Heat together in a double boiler for 30 minutes. Do
not let the milk boil or form a skin.

2 Leave to infuse for 2 hours then strain. Keep
refrigerated and use within 1 week. Apply with cotton
wool and remove excess with tissues.

Orange-flower cleansing cream
(for dry and normal skins)

Essential oil of neroli (extracted from the orange
flower) is used to stimulate the loss of old skin
cells and their replacement with new ones.

1 fl oz (25 ml) soya oil   1 fl oz (25 ml) orange-flower
1 fl oz (25 ml) almond oil   water
1 oz (25 g) cocoa butter   ⅛ tsp (0.65 ml) borax
1 tbsp (15 g) beeswax   5 drops essential oil of neroli

1 Mix and warm the oils. Melt the cocoa butter and
stir it into the oils. Melt the beeswax then beat it into
the oil mixture, a little at a time.

2 Warm the orange-flower water and dissolve the
borax in it. Beat this into the main mixture. Leave to
thicken and cool.

3 As the mixture starts to thicken, stir in the essential
oil. Once cool, spoon into prepared jars and label.

Cucumber and yarrow cleanser
(for oily skins)

Cucumber is an active cleanser while yarrow is
both cleansing and astringent.

1 tsp (5 ml) emulsifying wax   6 tbsp (90 ml) yarrow
4 tbsp (60 ml) soya oil   infusion
¼ cucumber, liquidized and   5 drops tincture of myrrh
strained to make 2 tbsp (30 ml)

1 Melt the wax over a low heat. Warm the soya oil
and then slowly add the oil to the wax, beating well.

2 Heat the cucumber juice with the yarrow infusion
then blend into the oil and wax. Take off the heat and
beat until the mixture cools. Once cool, stir in the
myrrh. Spoon into jars and label.

Buttermilk and fennel cleansing milk
(for oily skins)

Fennel helps to remove impurities from oily skins
with a deep cleansing action.

½ cup (125 ml) buttermilk   2 tbsp (30 ml) fennel seed,
crushed

1 Gently heat the milk and crushed seed together in a
double boiler for 30 minutes.

2 Leave to stand and infuse for a further 2 hours.
Strain, bottle, refrigerate and use within 1 week.

Lemon cleansing cream
(for oily skins)

Lemon has a reputation for clearing greasy skin
and smoothing wrinkles, as well as having a
mildly antiseptic quality.

1 tbsp (15 ml) beeswax   1 tbsp (15 ml) lemon juice,
1½ tbsp (22 ml) petroleum jelly   strained
3 tbsp (45 ml) mineral oil   ⅛ tsp (0.65 ml) borax
1 tbsp (15 ml) witch hazel   6 drops essential oil of lemon

1 Melt the beeswax and petroleum jelly together over
a low heat. Warm the mineral oil, then gradually add it
to the wax mixture, beating for 3–5 minutes.

2 Add the witch hazel to the lemon juice. Warm
gently then stir in the borax until dissolved. Slowly add
this to the wax mixture, beating steadily until it is
creamy and cool.

3 Once cool, stir in the lemon oil. Spoon into clean
jars and label.

TONERS

Called variously astringents, refreshers and skin
tonics, these are important for removing any
remaining trace of cleansing cream. They also
tighten the pores and impart a clean refreshing
feeling to the skin. Toners can also be used as a
pickup or quick cleanser during the day.

Elderflower water, lavender water, orange-
flower water and rosewater are four classic tonics
still valued today for all skin types. They can be
purchased as distilled waters, which will keep
(avoid synthetics), or made as a strong infusion to
be refrigerated and used within three days.

Rosewater toner
(for dry skins)

The soothing properties of rose make this a good
tonic for dry, sensitive and mature skins.

just over a ¼ pint   just under a ¼ pint
(160 ml) rosewater   (140 ml) witch hazel
6 drops glycerine

Blend all the ingredients in a bottle and shake well
before use.

Sage astringent
(for oily skins)

4 tbsp (60 ml) dried sage   ¼ tsp (1.25 ml) borax
4 tbsp (60 ml) ethyl alcohol   3 tbsp (45 ml) witch hazel
(or 6 tbsp (90 ml) vodka)   10 drops glycerine

1 Macerate the sage in the alcohol for 2 weeks and
then strain.

2 Dissolve the borax in the witch hazel. Stir into the
alcohol. Mix in the glycerine and decant into a bottle
with a tight-fitting lid. Shake before use.

*Clockwise from the top: Light rose moisturizer (p. 218); Ivy cellulite cream
(p. 218); Orange-flower cleansing cream; Comfrey and calendula cream
(p. 218); Avocado and nettle moisturizer (p. 218); Lemon cleansing cream.*

MOISTURIZING CREAMS

After the skin has been cleansed and toned it is ready for a protective film of moisturizer. The main function of a moisturizer is to maintain the skin's natural moisture level. It also protects from external dirt and drying atmospheres, and some formulations will add moisture to the epidermis (the skin's outside layer). Recent research has shown that massaging moisturizer into the skin regularly helps to speed the renewal of skin cells.

Light rose moisture cream
(for all skin types)

A pleasant light cream for daytime use.

1 tsp (5 ml) beeswax	3 tbsp (45 ml) rosewater, warmed
1 tsp (5 ml) lanolin	
1 tbsp (15 ml) almond oil	6 drops essential oil of rose, or rose geranium
$\frac{1}{2}$ tsp (2.5 ml) wheatgerm oil	
$\frac{1}{4}$ tsp (0.65 ml) borax	a few drops of red food colouring if desired

1 Melt the beeswax and lanolin together, stirring constantly.

2 Warm the oils gently and gradually beat them into the waxes. Dissolve the borax in the rosewater and slowly add to the oil and wax mixture, beating constantly until cool. Stir in the rose oil as the mixture begins to thicken.

3 Spoon into jars and label.

Rich moisturizing cream
(for dry skins)

Very penetrating if applied before a bath as the steam will help the skin absorb the oils and moisture in the cream.

2 tsp (10 ml) beeswax	$\frac{1}{2}$ tsp (2.5 ml) glycerine
2 tsp (10 ml) emulsifying wax	4 tbsp (60 ml) rosewater
1 tbsp (15 ml) lanolin	$\frac{1}{4}$ tsp (1.25 ml) borax
$2\frac{1}{2}$ tsp (12 ml) avocado oil	6 drops essential oil of neroli
$\frac{1}{2}$ tsp (2.5 ml) wheatgerm oil	a few drops of red food colouring, if desired

1 Melt the beeswax, emulsifying wax and lanolin in a double boiler. Warm the avocado and wheatgerm oils with the glycerine and then gradually beat into the waxes until creamy. Remove from the heat.

2 Warm the rosewater and dissolve the borax in it. Dribble the rosewater into the cream, beating all the time. Keep stirring until the mixture cools and thickens. As it cools stir in the neroli oil.

3 Spoon into jars and label.

Avocado and nettle moisturizer
(for oily skins)

1 tsp (5 ml) beeswax	$\frac{1}{8}$ tsp (0.65 ml) borax
2 tsp (10 ml) emulsifying wax	2 tbsp (30 ml) strong nettle infusion, warm
8 tsp (40 ml) hazelnut oil	
4 tsp (20 ml) avocado oil	4 drops cedarwood essential oil

1 Melt the waxes together. Warm the oils and gradually beat them into the waxes.

2 Dissolve the borax in the warm infusion. Slowly beat this into the first mixture.

3 Allow to cool then mix in the essential oil. Spoon into jars and label.

Comfrey and calendula cream
(nourishing cream for all skin types)

Especially good for rough, dry skin as these herbs are nourishing and healing. This also makes an excellent hand cream for sore, chapped hands. Comfrey contains a substance that helps cell renewal.

1 tbsp (15 ml) beeswax	$\frac{1}{4}$ tsp (1.25 ml) borax
1 tbsp (15 ml) lanolin	2 tbsp (30 ml) comfrey leaf infusion
1 tbsp (15 ml) cocoa butter	
$1\frac{1}{2}$ tbsp (22 ml) calendula oil	6 drops essential oil of petitgrain
1 tsp (5 ml) glycerine	

1 Melt the beeswax. Melt the lanolin and cocoa butter and gradually stir into the beeswax.

2 Warm the calendula oil and glycerine and slowly stir into the first mixture.

3 Dissolve the borax in the warm comfrey infusion and then add this to the main mixture, stirring well. Continue stirring until thick and cool, then mix in the essential oil.

4 Spoon into jars and label.

Ivy cellulite cream

Some doctors and scientists dispute the concept of cellulite; many women look at their skin and think otherwise. Whatever the outcome of this argument, the fatty "orange peel" deposits on the thighs and buttocks can benefit from extra attention. Massage into areas of cellulite.

2 tsp (10 ml) beeswax	4 tbsp (60 ml) double strength ivy decoction
1 tsp (5 ml) emulsifying wax	
3 tsp (15 ml) almond oil	8 drops each essential oils of oregano, fennel, rosemary
1 tsp (5 ml) avocado oil	

1 Melt the waxes in a double boiler. Warm the oils and then stir them in well.

2 Beat in the ivy decoction and allow the mixture to cool before stirring in the essential oils.

3 Spoon into jars and label.

HERBAL SUN LOTIONS

Herbal sun products are suitable for skin that tans easily. Homemade products do not provide the heavy screening necessary for fair skin, young children, or protection against very hot sun.

Sesame suntan lotion

Bergamot improves the skin's ability to produce melanin, the substance which darkens the skin, but after a report suggesting it may have harmful effects, the research body for the world's perfumers recommended a maximum of 2 percent bergamot as a safe level.

1 tbsp (15 ml) lanolin	1 tsp (5 ml) cider vinegar
4 tbsp (60 ml) sesame oil	2 drops essential oil of
6 tbsp (90 ml) rosewater	bergamot

1 Melt the lanolin. Warm the oil, then gradually blend the two together.

2 Add the rosewater and vinegar, beating vigorously to create the lotion.

3 When cool, add the oil of bergamot. Bottle and label for use as required.

Lavender sunburn oil

Lavender oil is healing and soothing. Add a few drops more to lessen the pain (for serious burns consult a doctor).

6 tbsp (90 ml) olive oil	$\frac{1}{2}$ tsp (2.5 ml) iodine
3 tbsp (45 ml) cider vinegar	10 drops lavender oil

Blend all the ingredients together and bottle. Apply very gently to relieve sunburn.

Herbal baths

Cleansing is the first and primary activity of external skin care, and an aromatic herbal bath is one of the most pleasurable and therapeutic ways of accomplishing this. You can add herbs to invigorate and stimulate circulation, or to relax and soothe muscles, unwinding the body for a peaceful night's rest (see p. 220). Select them for healing treatments to help a skin complaint, or simply for the pleasure of their aroma. Try to keep the water temperature around body heat. If it is too hot, the skin will perspire and not absorb any of the therapeutic herbal properties. To get most benefit, relax in the water for at least 10 minutes.

Although it is a romantic idea to sprinkle scented leaves and flowers directly onto the water, it's not advisable – you will emerge from such a bath like a creature from the swamp, with plant bits clinging to every part of your body.

Herbal bath bags

The easiest way of adding herbs to a bath is to hang three or four herbal tea bags from the tap, or to place a small herb-filled tea infuser in the water. Alternatively, put a handful of herbs in the centre of a square piece of muslin or fine gauze, gather up the corners to make a pouch and tie securely, adding a long loop to hang over the hot tap so the water will run through the bag. For a more permanent container, make simple drawstring bags from 4 × 3 in (10 × 8 cm) squares of muslin or gauze sewn together. Fill with the herbs of your choice, fresh or dried, and suspend from the hot tap. Make the loop long enough to immerse the bag in the water so it continues to release its goodness. Use a single herb or mix up to four in one bath. For a body scrub, add a little fine oatmeal or bran to the herb bag. Rub this over the body near the end of the bathing time. Herbal bath bags are reusable. Dry thoroughly after each bath and discard once the scent becomes faint.

Herbal bath infusions

Instead of adding the herb, you can extract its therapeutic properties by infusing 10 oz (275 g) dried herb or a large handful of fresh herbs in a pint (570 ml) of boiled water. Leave for at least 10 minutes then strain and pour into the bath. Select from the list on p. 220.

Skin-soothing vinegar baths

A vinegar bath soothes itchiness and aching muscles and softens the skin. Add a cupful (225 ml) of the following mixture to your bath for its beneficial effects. Bring 1 pint (570 ml) cider vinegar and a handful of fresh bath herbs slowly to the boil then infuse overnight. Strain and bottle.

Skin-softening milk baths

Add 3 tbsp (45 ml) of powdered milk (not skimmed as it does not have the same healing qualities) to a fine gauze or muslin bag along with 2 oz (50 g) dried or 4 oz (110 g) fresh elderflowers, chamomile or fresh lime blossom. Alternatively, infuse fresh flowers in $\frac{1}{2}$ pint (275 ml) cold milk for 2 hours, strain and add to the bath.

Therapeutic oil baths

The addition of 5–10 drops of essential oil to your bath allows you to lie in an envelope of fragrance and feel their beneficial power. Make your selection from the list on p. 236. Sprinkle the oil on hand-hot water after it has settled and gently swish around. Don't add oils under running hot water or they will evaporate. The temperature of the water will affect you as well. A relaxing sedative bath should be just under blood heat. For a stimulating bath, use a temperature below 85 °F (29 °C). If it is too low (below room temperature), the oils will not evaporate readily. A very hot bath is debilitating, even with relaxing oils, as well as aging for your skin.

● For dry skin, add the oils in a tablespoon (15 ml) of almond oil.

● For a more dispersible preparation, add the oil with a tablespoon (15 ml) of milk.

● For a bubble bath, add the oils with a tablespoon (15 ml) of mild liquid soap or baby shampoo.

Herbal saunas

Herbs rich in essential oils will release their properties in the heat of a sauna. Sprinkle in the water bucket a selection from basil, eucalyptus, lavender, lemon verbena, pine, rosemary, rose petals, sage, or thyme.

THERAPEUTIC BATH HERBS	
Relaxing bath herbs	
Chamomile	Lime flowers
Hops	Meadowsweet
Jasmine	Valerian
Stimulating bath herbs	
Basil	Mint
Bay	Pennyroyal
Eucalyptus	Pine
Fennel	Rosemary
Ivy	Sage
Lavender	Tansy
Lemon balm	Thyme
Lemon verbena	
Healing bath herbs	
Calendula	Lady's mantle
Comfrey	Spearmint
Houseleek	Yarrow
Spring tonic bath herbs	
Blackberry leaves	Lawn daisies
Dandelion	Nettle

Facial steams

A facial steam provides a thorough deep cleansing easily and inexpensively. The heat produces perspiration, which aids the elimination of toxins and stimulates circulation. The steam softens the skin and opens the pores, which helps the skin absorb the beneficial properties of the herbs.

Normal skin benefits from a weekly facial steam, oily skin from a steam two or three times a week, while those with dry skin should not have one more often than once every two weeks. Do not have a facial steam if you have thread veins, serious skin disorders, asthma, other breathing difficulties or heart problems.

To prepare a facial steam, assemble 2 handfuls of fresh herbs or 3 tbsp (45 ml) dried herbs. Tie back your hair, remove makeup and clean your face in your normal fashion. Place the herbs in a bowl or jug and pour over 3 pints (1½ litres) of boiling water. Stir briefly with a wooden spoon or chopstick. Hold your face 12 inches (30 cm) away (or 18 inches (45 cm) if you have sensitive skin) and make a tent over your head and the bowl with a towel. Keep your eyes closed and maintain this position for 10 to 15 minutes.

Rinse with tepid to cool water and a few minutes later splash with cold water or witch hazel. A diluted herbal vinegar or an infusion of elderflower, peppermint, sage or yarrow dabbed on with cotton wool will tighten the pores. Avoid strong changes of temperature and don't go outdoors for an hour or so.

HERBS FOR FACIAL STEAMS	
Use leaves unless otherwise indicated.	
To remove impurities	
Fennel	Nettle
Lime blossom	
To boost circulation and aid deep cleansing	
Nettle	Rosemary
For soothing and gentle cleansing	
Applemint	Lemon balm
Chamomile	Rose petals
Chervil	Spearmint
Lavender	Thyme
For healing	
Comfrey (roots and leaves)	Fennel
For oily skin	
Calendula flowers	Crushed lupin seeds
Geranium (herb-robert)	Sage
Horsetail	Yarrow
For dry, sensitive skins	
Borage	Parsley
Cornflower	Salad burnet
Houseleek	Sorrel
Lady's mantle	Sweet violet (flowers and
Marsh mallow (roots and	leaves)
leaves)	
For mature or sallow skins	
Dandelion	Red clover (flowers and
Elderflowers	leaves)
Lemon verbena	Tansy (flowers and leaves)

A selection of herbal bath products including floral waters (p. 223); herbal bath bag (p. 219); face mask (p.222); aromatic bath oils (p. 219) and a facial steam

Face packs

A face pack or mask draws impurities to the skin's surface, stimulates the circulation and tightens the skin. It is doubly effective if applied after a facial steam before the pores have closed. Apply the mixture to slightly moist skin and then rest with your feet higher than your head so gravity forces blood to the facial skin. Make cooling eye pads of cucumber or cotton wool soaked in a herbal infusion and place them against your eyelids to increase the absorption. Leave the mask on for 20 to 30 minutes before removing with warm water. Finish with a pore-closing infusion such as elderflower water, and then a moisturizer.

Do not apply a face mask just before preparing for a special occasion as the drawing power of the mask, particularly one with a cereal or clay base, can flush the skin.

Green herbal mask

Any of the herbs recommended for a facial steam can be used to create a green mask. Take 2 handfuls of fresh leaves or 3 tbsp (45 ml) of dried (softened by soaking in boiled water overnight). Add 2 tbsp (30 ml) of distilled or mineral water and liquidize at high speed for a few seconds.

This makes a rather wet mixture but if you are in a bath or lying on a towel it can be applied as it is. To thicken, add fuller's earth or ground almonds until it reaches the desired consistency.

Paste face packs

Ground oatmeal, ground almonds or fuller's earth used either singly or in combination form the basic carrier of a paste face pack. Each has the ability to draw impurities from the skin.

To 2 tbsp (30 ml) basic carrier, add 2–3 tbsp (30–45 ml) of a strong herbal infusion, or the juice of the herbs obtained using a juice extractor.

HERBS FOR FACE PACKS

For normal skin fennel, juniper berries, lady's mantle, lime flowers, mint, nettle

For dry and sensitive skin comfrey, houseleek, marsh mallow, pounded flax or quince seed (which contain a softening mucilage).

For oily skin sage, yarrow; 2 tbsp (30 ml) of pounded fennel or lupin seed to exfoliate dead skin and refine pores.

NON-HERBAL INGREDIENTS FOR FACE PACKS

● Milk products have softening and mild bleaching properties. Substitute 1 tbsp (15 ml) of the herbal infusion for 1 tbsp (15 ml) of creamy milk, or sour cream for dry skin, or yogurt or buttermilk for oily skin.

● Add 1 tsp (5 ml) honey for its healing properties.

● A few drops of lemon juice or cider vinegar help to restore the skin's acid mantle.

● Eggs are an excellent binding agent. Add an egg yolk for dry skin and a beaten egg white for oily skin.

● Mashed cucumber, strawberries, tomatoes, lemon juice and grapefruit juice are all good astringents. Avocado and ripe peach are rich moisturizers.

A deep pore cleansing mask

This recipe is based on an expensive face pack offered by a famous salon – so treat yourself!

1 tsp (5 ml) beeswax   2 fl oz (50 ml) rosewater
1 tbsp (15 ml) lanolin   1 tbsp (15 ml) fuller's earth
optional additions
1 tsp (5 ml) Irish moss or pounded quince or flax seed

1 Melt the wax and lanolin together over a gentle heat, stirring continuously.

2 Remove from the heat and add the rosewater, stirring until it has cooled.

3 Mix in the fuller's earth (and optional additions), stirring until you have a smooth paste.

Herbal soaps

Making soap from scratch involves the use of caustic soda – a dangerous ingredient to work with. It is much safer and easier to start with a bar of pure castile soap as a base.

Lemon and rosemary wash-balls

This recipe is based on the 16th-century method of soap making. Lemon is cleansing and toning, and rosemary is an astringent for all skin types.

5 oz (150 g) bar of castile soap, grated   1 tsp (5 ml) dried, powdered lemon peel
3 tbsp (45 ml) lemon juice   6 drops essential oil of lemon
4 tbsp (60 ml) calendula infusion   4 drops essential oil of rosemary
1 tbsp (15 ml) rosemary leaves, pulverized   1 tbsp (15 ml) calendula infusion to moisten hands

1 Place the grated soap, lemon juice and calendula infusion in an enamel saucepan and heat gently until the soap has melted, stirring with a wooden spoon.

2 Leave to cool for 10 minutes, or until cool enough to touch, and knead with your hands to make a smooth paste. Add the rosemary leaves, lemon peel and oils.

3 Leave for 10 minutes until it has begun to dry and is malleable. Form into approximately 6 plum-sized balls. Leave in a warm place for 2 hours covered with clingfilm so the outside does not crack. Then remove the clingfilm, moisten your hands with the remaining calendula infusion and smooth the balls until shiny.

4 Cover with clingfilm and return them to a warm place to dry completely (approximately 24 hours). Wrap in tissue paper and store in a warm, dry place for a month before using.

Lavender and oatmeal soap

The healing and soothing qualities of lavender make it useful for many skin conditions, especially acne. The grittiness of the oatmeal removes dead skin cells; the coarser the oatmeal, the stronger the exfoliant action. For a whiter soap, substitute triple-strength rosewater for the lavender infusion and add either the lavender oil or a rose oil.

5 oz (150 g) bar of castile soap, grated
12 fl oz (350 ml) lavender infusion

1 oz (25 g) ground oatmeal
a few drops of lavender oil

1 Put the grated soap flakes and the lavender infusion in an enamel saucepan and heat gently until the soap has melted. Stir occasionally.

2 Remove from the heat and cool a little, then stir in the oatmeal and add the lavender oil.

3 Pour into small oiled moulds and allow to set. This can take from a few hours to a week. When dry, unmould, wrap in tissue and leave for a month in a dry cupboard.

Floral waters

Scent stirs the imagination as no other stimulus can, and aromatic leaves and flowers picked at perfection on a summer's day can be captured in a floral water (see right) to provoke pleasant memories throughout the year.

Herbs infused in water will not keep, so some form of alcohol or oil must be employed in order to preserve the scent. Use alcohol for a stronger scent. A floral water can be made with a strong infusion, adding 20 percent by volume of a 90° proof alcohol (ethyl alcohol) or 30 percent by volume of a 60° proof alcohol such as vodka.

Hungary water

Named after Queen Isabella of Hungary who is said to have used this secret formula to restore her youth and beauty with such success that the King of Poland proposed marriage to her when she was 72. The original was made by distilling rosemary flowering tops, lemon verbena, rose and possibly sage.

2 fl oz (50 ml) ethyl alcohol mixed with the following essential oils:
30 drops of rosemary
12 drops of lemon

5 drops of rose
5 drops of neroli
2 drops of sage
2 drops of mint

Store in a screw-top bottle and shake before use.

Eau de Cologne

2 fl oz (50 ml) ethyl alcohol mixed with the following essential oils:
44 drops of bergamot

15 drops of lemon
4 drops of neroli
1 drop of lavender
1 drop of rosemary

Store in a screw-top bottle and shake before use.

Floral waters

Suitable for use as a skin toner, scent or perfume.

1 cup lavender flowers, scented rose petals or orange blossom

¼ cup ethyl alcohol at room temperature

1 Steep for 6 days in a screw-top jar, shaking vigorously each day.

2 Strain and decant into a dark glass bottle.

Alternative method

If flowers are not available, use essential oils. Mix 25 drops of essential oil (traditionally lavender, rose or neroli) with 2 fl oz (50 ml) ethyl alcohol (or isopropyl or vodka). Shake them together in a screw-top bottle. Leave the mixture to settle for 2 days then shake again. To store, decant into a dark bottle with a tight-fitting lid and leave almost no air space.

Roger's choice

This recipe was created in response to the challenge of a man who liked none of the scented products available for men. The basil makes it wonderful for clearing mental fatigue.

2 fl oz (50 ml) ethyl alcohol mixed with the following essential oils:
16 drops of basil
20 drops of bergamot
20 drops of frankincense
20 drops of lemon

20 drops of petitgrain
10 drops of coriander
5 drops of cloves
5 drops of black pepper
5 drops of patchouli
1 drop of sage
3 drops oil of benzoin

Store in a screw-top bottle and shake before use.

Aftershave

The above recipe made with witch hazel instead of ethyl alcohol makes a delicious aftershave.

Hands

The skin of our hands is subject to adverse weather conditions, hot water, detergents, polishes and garden soil. The best defence is to wear either cotton or rubber gloves, or gardening gloves, as appropriate and to make lavish use of hand creams. Make up several bottles of your chosen recipe and leave them wherever you wash your hands. If you dislike wearing gloves or find that you keep removing them unconsciously, apply a barrier cream before doing any dirty work.

To make a particularly healing barrier cream, follow the recipe for Comfrey and calendula nourishing cream on p. 218, and add 1 tbsp (15 ml) warmed liquid paraffin to the wax mixture before adding the comfrey infusion. The recipe below is for a much stronger barrier cream.

Regular herbal hand treatments

To soften and soothe hands, soak them in an infusion of lady's mantle, fennel, comfrey, yarrow, or marsh mallow; an infusion of calendula or chamomile flowers is also effective.

Heavy duty barrier cream

4 tbsp (60 ml) petroleum jelly	2 handfuls fresh elderflowers

1 Gently melt the petroleum jelly then add the elderflowers.

2 Leave to macerate for 45 minutes, reheating the jelly each time it solidifies.

3 Warm to a liquid and strain through a sieve into a screw-top jar. Cool and then seal.

Glycerine and rosewater hand cream

A useful everyday skin softener.

4 tbsp (60 ml) glycerine	3 drops essential oil of rose
1 cup (225 ml) rosewater	
4 tbsp (60 ml) cornflour	

1 Blend the glycerine, rosewater and cornflour. Heat the mixture over a double boiler until it thickens.

2 Allow to cool then add the rose oil, stirring well. Pour into screw-top jars and label.

Dill and horsetail nail bath

Both these herbs contain silicic acid, which helps to strengthen nails. Warm the mixture before using and soak your nails in it for 10 minutes every other day.

2 tbsp (30 ml) chopped horsetail	2 tbsp (30 ml) dill seed
	1 cup (225 ml) boiling water

1 Pour the water over the two herbs and steep for at least an hour.

2 Strain the liquid into a bottle.

Lady's mantle hand lotion

2 tbsp (30 ml) glycerine	10 drops essential oil of lemon, rose, geranium or sandalwood
2 tsp (10 ml) carragheen moss melted in a little hot water	
4 tbsp (60 ml) alcohol	2 tbsp (30 ml) strong infusion of lady's mantle

1 Stir the glycerine into the melted moss.

2 Add the essential oil to the alcohol, mixing well, and then blend the two mixtures. Stir in the herbal infusion, blending well.

3 Pour into a screw-top jar and label. Shake before use if necessary.

Hand mask

Once a week treat your hands to this mask to whiten and soften the skin. Apply to the hands for 20 minutes, preferably just before going to bed. Wash off, then apply a rich moisturizing cream for the night (and wear cotton gloves while you sleep). Wash off the cream the following morning.

2 tbsp (30 ml) finely ground oatmeal	1 tsp (5 ml) avocado oil
	1 tsp (5 ml) lemon juice
1 tbsp (15 ml) calendula petals or lady's mantle infusion	1 tsp (5 ml) glycerine

Mix the ingredients together to form a smooth paste. Use as instructed above.

Feet

Any of the above treatments for hands can also be applied to feet. The enriching mask is particularly beneficial, but remember to wear cotton socks if you put moisturizer on your feet overnight.

Herbal foot baths

The traditional foot bath is one of the most therapeutic treatments.

To refresh tired feet choose from the following: bay, lavender, sage, sweet marjoram, thyme. Place a large handful of fresh or $\frac{1}{4}$ cup of dried herb and 1 tbsp (15 ml) sea salt in a bowl of hot water. For convenience, these can be loose in the water.

● **To make a warming foot bath,** add 1 tbsp (15 ml) black mustard seed, bruised, to the water.
● **To soothe itchy feet,** add 4 tbsp (60 ml) cider vinegar to your foot bath.
● **To deodorize feet,** soak them in a strong decoction of sage or lovage.

Cold feet

Add 1 tsp cayenne pepper to talcum powder or fuller's earth and sprinkle on your feet to get a quick warming sensation.

Hair care

Although most aspects of hair, its colour, rate of growth, thickness and curliness are hereditary, a wide range of herbal ingredients has been used through the ages to improve and enhance what nature provided.

Advertising agents have decided we all fall into one of four hair types: dry, greasy, normal or "problem" hair, but herbal trichologists state that all hair is normal for that person and problems should first be dealt with by looking holistically at a person: that is, looking at his or her lifestyle. Too many spicy foods, fats and sugars can be responsible for greasy hair and synthetic shampoos can create dry hair. There is also concern about the effects that medicated shampoos can have on the hair and scalp if used routinely. Stress, hormonal changes, lack of sleep, too much sun, chemical hair treatments, rinses and dyes all cause hair problems too.

HERBS USED IN HAIR CARE

To condition dry hair burdock root, comfrey, elderflowers, marsh mallow, parsley, sage, stinging nettle.

To condition greasy hair calendula, horsetail, lemon juice, lemon balm, lavender, mints, rosemary, southernwood, witch hazel and yarrow.

To prevent dandruff burdock root, chamomile, garlic and onion bulbs (powerful but unpleasantly scented), goosegrass, parsley, rosemary, southernwood, stinging nettle and thyme.

To soothe scalp irritation catmint (leaves and flowering tops), chamomile, comfrey.

To provide a hair tonic (giving body and lustre) calendula, goosegrass, horsetail, lime flowers, nasturtium, parsley, rosemary, sage, southernwood, stinging nettles and watercress.

To dispel lice an infusion of quassia chips, poke root, or juniper berries with a tablespoon of cider vinegar. Apply at two-week intervals, three times.

Hair treatments

Dry hair and any hair lacking lustre will benefit from a warm oil treatment before a shampoo.

Make a herbal oil using one of the above herbs and a polyunsaturated vegetable oil such as peach kernel, almond or sunflower. Alternatively, add 6 drops of essential oil to 2 tbsp (30 ml) of almond oil or any vegetable oil. Warm the oil, pour a small amount into your palm and rub your hands together. Massage well into the scalp and along the hair strands. Repeat as necessary. Cover the head with foil and a plastic shower cap and wrap in a hot towel (wrung out in hot water), replacing the towel when it cools. Try to leave on for 20 to 30 minutes for greatest penetration, then wash off with a mild shampoo.

A quick herbal shampoo
Pour one application of a mild baby shampoo into a cup and add 2 tbsp (30 ml) of a strong decoction of your selected herb, or 4 drops of essential oil. Mix together and use in the normal manner.

Soapwort shampoo

A very gentle cleansing shampoo which doesn't make much lather, but then lather does not equal cleaning power.

| 2 tbsp (30 ml) finely chopped soapwort root or a handful of leaves and stems | 1 large handful of herb (see box) 1 pint (570 ml) boiling water |

1 Pour the boiling water over the soapwort and herb and infuse for at least 30 minutes.

2 Strain and use when cool. About half a cup (125 ml) should be enough for average length hair.

Soapbark shampoo
Good for greasy hair. Simmer 2 tbsp (30 ml) soapbark chips (available from many health shops) in 1 pint (570 ml) water for 30 minutes.

Dry shampoo

| 2 tbsp (30 ml) powdered orris root | 2 tbsp (30 ml) powdered arrowroot |

Mix together. Part the hair in narrow regular bands and sprinkle the powder along each row. Leave on for 10 minutes to absorb any grease and then brush out vigorously and thoroughly until the hair is shiny.

Herbal hair rinses

Use these after your shampoo as the quickest and easiest way to improve hair shine. Prepare the herbal rinse before shampooing so it will have cooled when you are ready to use it.

| 1 tbsp (15 ml) selected herb 1½ pints (850 ml) boiling water | 1 tbsp (15 ml) cider vinegar (or lemon juice for fair hair) |

1 Infuse the herb in water until cool. Strain well. Add the vinegar.

2 Pour through the hair, massaging the scalp. Catch the drain-off in a bowl and repeat until either your patience or arms give out. If the final rinse is of cool rather than warm water, it makes all the outer cells on the hair strands lie flat, giving a smooth, shiny finish.

Rosewater pick-up
This is an excellent way to clean and revive your hair between shampoos. Orange-flower water can be used instead, or lavender water for greasy hair.

You will need a number of 4 in (10 cm) squares of muslin or gauze dipped in rosewater. Force the muslin over a natural bristle brush and stroke through the hair in sections, removing dirt as you brush. Repeat with fresh muslin squares until the cloth picks up no more dirt. This treatment also gives a lovely fragrance to the hair.

Herbal hair colourants

Make your selection from the herbs listed in the box below. Unless otherwise stated, make a strong decoction, simmering 2 oz (50 g) herb in 2 pints (1 litre) of water for 20 minutes keeping the lid on the pan. Cool, strain and pour through the hair, catching the rinse in a bowl. Repeat as many times as possible. Use an old towel to pat hair dry as some colour will come off. These are progressive dyes, so the more you use them, the stronger the effect.

For a more intense colour, make the rinse into a paste. Use only 1 cup (225 ml) of water for the decoction and 1 oz (25 g) of herb. Boil, strain and add kaolin powder to make a smooth paste. Apply to the hair roots wearing thin plastic gloves and gradually work down the hair strands. Cover the head with a small hot towel and a plastic bag to retain the heat. Leave on for 20 minutes then rinse off. If further colour is required, leave the paste on for longer next time.

HERBS TO COLOUR HAIR

To lighten hair
Chamomile: infuse 8 tbsp (120 ml) and use regularly.
Mullein flowers: make a decoction.
Rhubarb root: make a decoction.
Privet leaves: make a decoction.
Hollyhock (blue-purple flowers): improve dingy yellow hair. Use as a decoction.

To darken hair
Sage: make a decoction.
Sage and rosemary leaves: make a decoction.
Sage and dried raspberry leaves: make a decoction.
Green outer shells of unripe walnuts: crush in a pestle and mortar, add a pinch of salt, cover with water and soak for 3 days. Then add 3 cups (675 ml) water and simmer for 5 hours, adding more water as necessary to maintain at least 1 cup liquid. Strain and reduce to 1 cup by boiling.
Ivy berries: make a decoction.

To redden hair
Alkanet root: make a decoction.
Calendula: make a decoction.
Henna: follow product instructions carefully as results are variable.
Red hibiscus: make a decoction.
Saffron: make a decoction.

For black hair
Elderberries: make a decoction.
Indigo leaves and henna in equal quantities: make a decoction.

For grey hair
Hollyhock (blue-purple flowers): remove yellow tones. Use as a decoction.
Betony: highlights yellow tones. Use as a decoction.
Sage: darkens grey hair and adds lustre. Use as a decoction.

Eye care

The best recipe for clear bright eyes is a good night's sleep. "Just enough regular and natural sleep is the great kindler of woman's most charming light" wrote a famous beauty of the nineteenth century. Failing that, eyes which are tired, irritated or bloodshot can often be soothed with a cooled herbal decoction. However, if you experience frequent or continuing eye irritation, it is advisable to consult a doctor.

When you are dealing with the delicate eye area, scrupulous cleanliness is vital. Sterilize all utensils and fabrics and use only absolutely fresh decoctions. Always boil herbs for an eye bath for 20 minutes to kill the greatest number of bacteria. Then filter the solution three times through a coffee filter paper to ensure no small bits remain to irritate the eye.

The most famous reputation for giving a brilliance and sparkle to the eyes goes to the modest little plant, eyebright (*Euphrasia rostkoviana*). It is called *Augentrost* (consolation to the eyes) by the Germans, *luminella* (light for the eyes) by the Italians, and *casse-lunette* (discard your spectacles) by the French. It can relieve tiredness and soreness, and halt running eyes from a cold or hay-fever.

Eyebright eye bath
Boil 2 tbsp (30 ml) fresh plant or 2 tsp (10 ml) of dried herb in 2 cups (450 ml) water for 20 minutes. Cool, strain and use immediately in an eye bath.

Agrimony eye bath
This herb is second to eyebright in its fame for adding lustre to eyes. Boil a handful of fresh tops in a pint (570 ml) of water for 20 minutes. Cool, strain and use immediately.

Eye compresses
The following herbal tea bag compress refreshes tired eyes at work.

Make 2 cups of chamomile or rosehip tea, using 2 tea bags, and brew for 3 minutes. Remove the bags and cool. Place the tea bags over your eyes for 15 minutes, put your feet up and rest. This can also be done with black tea bags.

Eye gels
Lotions or gels for the delicate, thin skin around the eye must be light so that the application does not drag or pull it. The ingredients should treat only the surface of the skin. Rich penetrating oils can contribute to a puffy appearance around the eyes.

Eyebright or elderflower gel
Dissolve a strong decoction of eyebright or elderflower water in gelatine (following manufacturer's instructions) for a soothing and cooling eye gel.

Soothing eye gel
Use equal quantities of chamomile, calendula and cornflower flowers and mallow leaves to make a strong decoction.

6 tbsp (90 ml) decoction
2 tbsp (30 ml) witch hazel
¼ tsp (1.25 ml) agar agar

pinch of sodium benzoate if required to improve keeping qualities

1 Heat the herbal decoction and witch hazel until just below boiling point. Stir in the agar (and benzoate) to dissolve. The agar agar must be thoroughly dissolved or it will feel grainy.

2 Leave to cool and thicken. If it forms a solid gel, put into a blender for a few seconds to thin. Store in screw-top jar in refrigerator.

HERBAL EYE REFRESHERS

Make a strong decoction of the herb. Strain, then soak sterilized squares of lint in the solution and apply over closed eyes while resting.

Calendula Soothes sore or inflamed eyes
Chamomile Reduces inflammation and removes a "tired look"
Cornflower Soothes and helps-reduce puffiness
Fennel seed Removes inflammation and gives sparkle
Horsetail Reduces redness and swollen eyelids and can be effective for styes. (Must boil for 30 minutes.)
Mallow Softens skin around eyes
Mint Minimizes dark circles under the eyes
Rose Softens and soothes skin around the eyes
Wormwood Reduces eye inflammation and redness; dab on a decoction with cotton wool.

For an extra refreshing application, freeze any of the above strained decoctions in icecube trays and rub a cube over the eyelids and around the eyes.

Teeth

Most commercial toothpastes contain damaging abrasives, detergents and sweetening agents. Homemade products can achieve a better result without the harmful ingredients.

Instant tooth cleansers
● Rub a sage leaf over the teeth and gums to make them feel polished and clean.
● Peel a twig of flowering dogwood, chew the end to create a brush and rub on the teeth and gently on the gums.

Peppermint toothpaste
To make your own cleansing paste, take 1 tsp (5 ml) bicarbonate of soda, charcoal or powdered strawberry roots and 2 drops essential oil of peppermint. Add enough drops of water to create a paste. Mix and use.

Stain removers
Strawberry: rub half a strawberry (alpine is best) over the teeth.
Lemon peel: rub the wet side on the teeth. The blanching property of lemon is good for removing tea and other brown stains.

Mouthwashes
Commercial mouthwashes are often so powerful that they damage the proper balance of digestive juices and can irritate the lining of the mouth. Seek further help for persistent bad breath as the digestive system may not be functioning properly. To sweeten the breath, chew fresh parsley, liquidized nettle leaves or watercress, which are all high in chlorophyll, a green plant pigment used in many commercial breath sweeteners. For a quick mouthwash, gargle with a peppermint infusion, rosewater, lavender water, or dilute witch hazel (1 part witch hazel to 6 parts water).

Toothache
To ease the pain, apply a drop of oil of cloves.

Mint and rosemary mouthwash
Both herbs sweeten the breath and rosemary has antiseptic properties. If you wish to make up larger quantities, add 1 tsp (5 ml) tincture of myrrh for its preservative properties.

1 pint (570 ml) distilled or mineral water
1 tsp (5 ml) fresh mint leaves
1 tsp (5 ml) rosemary leaves
1 tsp (5 ml) aniseed

1 Boil the water and infuse the mint, rosemary and aniseed for 20 minutes.

2 When cool, strain and use as a gargle.

Apricot and lemon lip balm
A delicious, protective and healing gloss, especially good for chapped lips.

1 tsp (5 ml) beeswax
1 tsp (5 ml) apricot kernel oil
1 tsp (5 ml) calendula oil
a few drops essential oil of lemon or orange

1 Melt the beeswax. Add the apricot and calendula oils, stirring constantly.

2 Remove from the heat while stirring, and when partly cooled add the essential oil. Store in a small pot.

ESSENTIAL

OILS

Essential oils are the concentrated vital essences of aromatic plants. They contain potent therapeutic properties and are much used in cosmetics, perfumes and flavorings, and in aromatherapy – a system of healing the body through massage, inhalation or bathing with blended essential oils. Although called "oils," they are more like water, being a liquid that readily evaporates.

Essential oils are found in minute glands in one or more parts of aromatic plants: in leaves (basil), flowers (rose), fruit (lemon), seed (coriander), wood (sandalwood), resin (frankincense), bark (cinnamon) and roots (calamus). Heat causes these essences to evaporate, creating a protective aura around the plant which seems to fight bacteria, fungi and pests, and also seems to act as a buffer against extremes of temperature.

Historical background
Aromatic oils have a long, rich history and were highly valued in ancient cultures in the Far and Middle East, including Egypt, China and India. *Ayur veda*, a system of traditional Indian medicine dating back to 1000 B.C., includes these oils in many healing and rejuvenating recipes.

Numerous papyri and temple reliefs show us that the Egyptians used them to perfume their clothes and bodies, to preserve and flavor food and drink, to heal, and most famously, to embalm. When the tomb of Tutankhamen was entered in 1922, the scent of herb oils was still perceptible.

Over two thousand years ago, the Greek physician Theophrastus wrote a study of scent and its healing effects entitled *Concerning Odors*. In this, he laid the early groundwork for some of our current understanding of aromatherapy. He described the effects of different flower essences and noted that an aromatic plant poultice applied to a leg could produce fragrant breath – its essences could permeate the skin and enter the circulatory system.

In Arabia, the technique of distillation was perfected centuries ago. This method of extracting plant essences by steaming is still the most useful in terms of preserving a plant's fragrance and healing properties. During the eleventh century A.D., Persian chemists distilled highly exotic and sophisticated essences, including the famous attar of roses. Crusaders learned these skills and brought them back to Europe.

For the past few centuries, the world's essential-oil industry has been centered in Grasse, in southern France. With the sixteenth-century fashion for scented gloves, local glovers were licensed to scent their own leather and sell perfumes, and their use of lavender oil appears to have rendered them immune to an outbreak of cholera.

Today essential oils have an enormous range of uses, in food, cosmetics and medicines. Most research is into their remarkable healing potential.

Healing properties
The revival of essential oils for healing in the West was instigated by a French chemist, Professor René-Maurice Gattefosse, who originated the term "aromatherapy." He conducted experiments with

essential oils on wounded soldiers during World War I. At this time, the most commonly used antiseptic was phenol, which was good for cleaning hospital floors but not very effective for healing wounds. The soldiers Gattefosse was treating had badly infected wounds, which often resulted in serious poisoning as the body reabsorbed harmful substances produced by decaying tissue. His work proved that essential oils, particularly lavender, are superior to chemical antiseptics in their ability to detoxify and speed up the elimination of these substances. Gattefosse was convinced of the power of lavender after he accidently burned his hand in his laboratory. The wound became gangrenous and he applied lavender oil. The pain went almost immediately and the skin soon healed, perfectly cured.

Another attractive feature of the antiseptic essential oils is that they do not appear to lose their effect with repeated applications.

More recent experiments have shown that essential oils are carried through the circulatory system to all the organs and eventually through the elimination system, the process taking anywhere from 30 minutes to 12 hours. To appreciate this, rub the sole of your foot with a slice of garlic, then smell your breath several hours later. It seems that each organ takes from the essential oils the components it needs.

Both directly in the pleasure they give and indirectly, essential oils are therapeutic. The sense of smell is our most ancient sense and yet the one we know least about. A scent travels from the olfactory nerves in the nose directly to the part of the brain concerned with intuition, emotions and creativity. It registers almost twice as fast as a pain sensation. Because the sense of smell is so immediate, substances administered by scent are likely to affect the body's chemical balance. For this reason, psychiatrists and psychologists are taking great interest in the safe mood-changing potential of essential oils.

Aromatherapy

Madame Maury, a biochemist and student of Gattefosse, recognized the potential of plant essences for skin care and developed the massage techniques and formulae now usually associated with aromatherapy.

Trained aromatherapists draw on several diagnostic and treatment systems. Their approach is usually holistic (looking at how all aspects of a person's life affects their well-being), and is based on the idea that the most effective way to prevent illness is to strengthen the body's own defence systems. Essential oils are applied mostly through massage but also through baths and inhalations.

These techniques are all easy to use at home as long as you follow the recommended number of drops for treatments. The oils are so concentrated that even a few drops too many can reverse their beneficial effects and provoke a bad reaction.

HOW ESSENTIAL OILS ARE PRODUCED AND SOLD

The extraction of oils is a highly complex and expensive business. Most oils are collected by distillation (steaming) or enfleurage (in grease). Both methods are time-consuming, labour-intensive and require expert use of complicated equipment and top quality materials. Huge amounts of plant stock are needed to distil minute quantities of oil: it takes about 250 pounds (115 kg) of rose petals to produce 1 fl oz (25 ml) of essential oil. For these reasons it is not worth attempting to extract essential oils at home.

Pure essential oils versus synthetic

Continuous attempts are being made to create synthetic essences as substitutes for essential oils. Some scents have been reproduced quite successfully, but it is only the scent. This is often acceptable to the food and cosmetic industries but it is of no use to anyone interested in the therapeutic value of an essential oil. Each essential oil is composed of many active and effective ingredients so that it can have many functions; one oil may soften the skin, act as a preservative, and deter insects. No synthetic substances can replicate all these aspects.

Buying essential oils

As the popularity of essential oils swells, so a wave of new firms has appeared each selling its own labelled oils. When you are buying oils, check that the supplier runs tests on them for purity, that staff are knowledgeable about their qualities and uses, and that they handle and store them correctly. Never buy oils that have been displayed in a hot sunny window or in clear glass. They must be stored in airtight, dark glass containers in a cool, dark place but not a refrigerator. The ideal storage temperature is about 65 °F (18 °C).

Many shops sell oils labelled "aromatherapy oils", a mixture of about two percent essential oil in a carrier oil (a lubricating vegetable oil), which is meant for massage. Once essential oils are added to carrier oils, their shelf life is reduced from years to a few months.

As a further guarantee of quality, get to know the price range of essential oils. At the time of writing, jasmine, neroli and rose are 150 to 175 times more expensive than camphor, sweet orange and eucalyptus, with most oils being in the range of two, three and four times the price of camphor. If a selection of essential oils is offered all at the same price, be suspicious.

Essential oils in massage

Massage is the primary method of application in aromatherapy. Essential oils are selected and blended with a carrier oil before the massage, as described in the box below. When undergoing a massage, you first notice the fragrance but soon become aware of the many other benefits. Essential oils penetrate the skin more effectively than vegetable oils, taking from 20 to 70 minutes to enter the bloodstream. However, their benefits to the body and emotions go on for far longer.

General benefits of aromatherapy massage
● Depending on the oils selected and the individual, the fragrance can have a relaxing or stimulating effect on the mind and spirits. The sense of smell is our most immediate sense – an unpleasant smell can cause nausea within seconds. It is closely linked to memory and emotional responses. Because of the fragrance alone, a massage can have considerable effect.
● The oils combined with the massage help to relieve stress and tension by their effect on the mind, the nerve endings, and the muscles.
● Many oils are antibacterial and work to relieve or heal certain internal conditions as well as skin problems (see the chart on p. 236).
● The combination of massage and oils improves blood circulation.
● The combination of oils and massage is thought to improve cell growth on the skin and give the surface a smooth appearance by speeding up the elimination of old skin cells.
● The oils combined with the massage help to accelerate the elimination of wastes through the body's lymph system, which cleanses and nourishes the blood.

Specific benefits
Here are some ideas for using oils to treat a number of common problems. For further ideas on the specific treatments and the relevant oils to use, see the recipes on the following page and the charts on p. 236 and p. 258.
● Use of the correct oils can normalize an oily or dry skin (for oily: try cedarwood, juniper, lemon, ylang-ylang; for dry: try chamomile, geranium, clary sage, jasmine, lavender, neroli).
● To soothe acne and other skin eruptions, try juniper, chamomile, cedarwood, eucalyptus, lavender, lemongrass.
● To increase the elasticity of the skin and promote the growth of new skin cells, try lavender, chamomile, calendula, jasmine, frankincense, myrrh.
● Cellulite seems to improve with aromatherapy massage (try cypress, fennel, geranium, juniper).
● To eradicate feelings of apathy, try jasmine or rosemary.
● To lift depression, try camphor, chamomile, jasmine, thyme, basil, bergamot, clary sage.

CARRIER OILS FOR MASSAGE

As essential oils are highly concentrated they are used by the drop and must be diluted in a carrier oil for skin applications. A carrier oil is a lubricating oil, used in massage to allow the hands to glide smoothly over skin. Aromatherapy uses only vegetable oils, mainly cold pressed from seeds. These do not evaporate when warmed, unlike essential oils, but they become rancid on exposure to air and do so more quickly once mixed with essential oils.

A blend will be at its best for two or three months, so it is wise not to mix more oil than you may use in that time. Store it in an airtight bottle in a cool, dark place.

A good carrier oil has penetrative properties to assist the essential oils; it is 100 percent pure; it should have little or no smell, an attractive texture for massage and should benefit the skin. Select from the following:

Almond oil The most popular carrier oil as it has little smell, is rich in protein and is emollient, nourishing and slow to become rancid.

Apricot kernel and peach kernel oils Both have the same properties as almond oil but are more expensive.

Grapeseed oil Very fine and clear, it gives a satin smooth finish without a greasy touch.

Hazelnut oil Hazelnut penetrates the most easily and deeply. It stimulates the circulation and nourishes the skin.

Jojoba oil Keeps well and gives a satin smooth feel to the skin. Treats acne.

Olive oil Calming, good for rheumatism and to relieve the itching of skin ailments. Unfortunately the scent of olives can overpower the fragrance of the essential oils.

Sesame oil Keeps well but the rich colour and odour can be off-putting. Used in Scandinavia to treat cases of dry eczema and psoriasis.

Corn, soya and sunflower oils Acceptable. Soya has a nice feel and doesn't become sticky with pressure. Sunflower has least keeping qualities but contains vitamin F.

The following oils are often added in small quantities to a massage mix for their special qualities.

Avocado oil Nourishing and penetrating; useful for fatty areas and muscle preparations. Becomes sticky when massaged into a large area.

Calendula Macerated calendula petals. Beneficial in any cosmetic preparation for chapped and cracked skin.

Carrot oil Tonic and rejuvenating and particularly good for neck massage. Rich in many vitamins.

Evening primrose oil Useful for scaly skin and dandruff. Recent research has shown that oil extracted from borage seed has a similar composition.

Wheatgerm oil Nourishing, rich in vitamin E, but would be rather "oily" on its own. It is a natural antioxidant (preservative), a teaspoonful (5 ml) added to 2 fl oz (50 ml) massage oil will extend its keeping time.

MIXING ESSENTIAL OILS FOR MASSAGE

Most essential oils are sold in bottles measured in millilitres. One millilitre equals about 20 drops of essential oil. To a 2 fl oz (50 ml) bottle of carrier oil, add between 15–30 drops of essential oil. The usual amount is 25 drops. Trial and error teaches that some problems and some people respond to more dilute solutions while others require greater strength. Start with the average amount or less. Lower concentrations often give the best results for emotional problems whereas higher concentrations are often more successful for helping physical problems.

One full body massage uses 2 to 4 tsp (10 to 20 ml) of a blend, which can be mixed in an egg cup or gill measure. For a deluxe massage oil in a 2 fl oz (50 ml) bottle, add 1 tsp (5 ml) wheatgerm oil for keeping quality, 1 tsp (5 ml) avocado oil for greater penetration, then top up with your chosen carrier oil and drops of essential oil.

When you make up a blend, label and date the bottle, reminding yourself who it was blended for and for what conditions.

Selecting the oils

Decide which conditions you want to treat and then refer to the chart on p. 236. Usually two or three oils are added, occasionally four. Each oil has different properties so select those that are most appropriate and appealing.

For example, if you have a dry, mature skin and wish to make a facial oil as a night treatment, you will find quite a bewildering choice of oils. Think about their additional properties and select scents that appeal to you.

You may also want to consider an oil's "note". Essential oils, like perfumes, are described as having a top, middle or base note. In aromatic terms, top notes are noticed first; they are stimulating and uplifting. Middle notes form the character of a perfume and last longer. Base notes are mainly sedative and calming, and are very long-lasting. You may prefer to select one oil from each group to make a balance but it is not essential. When I made a massage oil for one son's aching muscles after an over-exuberant day of sports, I assembled eucalyptus, juniper, lavender, marjoram, rosemary, sage and thyme (all good for muscular aches and pains) and invited him to choose three. He selected (by sniffing preference) eucalyptus, sage and thyme, which are all top notes, but which helped to clear his head cold at the same time as soothing his muscles.

The box (right) shows a suggested list of recipes for drops added to 2 fl oz (50 ml) of carrier oil. To make less, cut all ingredients proportionally.

THERAPEUTIC BLENDS	
TREATMENT	**FORMULAE (in drops)**
Skin facial oils	
Normal skin	6 frankincense 6 geranium 3 jasmine 12 lavender
Dry skin	8 chamomile 8 rose 8 sandalwood
Oily skin	8 cedarwood 10 lemon 6 ylang-ylang
Massage oils	
Stretch marks	10 frankincense 15 lavender 5 neroli
Post-diet saggy skin	8 lemongrass 8 pine 8 sage
Cellulite (use hazelnut oil)	8 oregano 8 fennel 8 rosemary
Muscular cramp	10 basil 8 cypress 8 sweet marjoram
Muscular aches (use hazelnut oil)	8 bergamot 8 coriander 6 eucalyptus 8 rosemary
Arthritis	10 juniper 10 lemon 5 thyme
Arthritis (before sleep)	6 benzoin 6 chamomile 8 cypress 8 sage
Rheumatism, acute	9 ginger 9 pine 9 rosemary
Rheumatism, chronic	6 eucalyptus 8 juniper 8 rosemary 6 thyme
Colds and flu	7 cinnamon 7 eucalyptus 7 tea tree 7 pine
Bronchitis	10 eucalyptus 5 hyssop 10 niaouli 5 sandalwood
Asthma	4 hyssop 8 lavender 8 pine 8 rosemary
Eczema (dry)	10 calendula 5 chamomile 5 geranium 5 lavender
Eczema (weeping)	5 bergamot 10 calendula 10 juniper
High blood pressure	10 clary sage 10 lavender 10 ylang-ylang
Sinusitis	7 basil 7 eucalyptus 7 lavender 7 peppermint
Circulation, poor	12 black pepper 12 juniper 8 cypress
Nausea and diarrhoea	9 lavender 9 peppermint 6 sandalwood
Menstrual pain	7 chamomile 7 clary sage 7 cypress 4 jasmine
Mosquito repellent	5 clove 10 eucalyptus 5 geranium 5 peppermint
Massage or inhalation (see p. 235)	
Cough and cold	3 benzoin 2 cypress 3 eucalyptus 2 hyssop
Head cold	3 basil 3 eucalyptus 3 ginger
Bronchitis	4 eucalyptus 4 niaouli 2 hyssop
Sinus	2 basil 2 eucalyptus 2 lavender 2 peppermint

GIVING A MASSAGE

With a friend, it is easy to enjoy and give a beneficial massage using therapeutic oils and basic massage strokes. A warm quiet room with soft lighting, no draughts or interruptions and perhaps the addition of some gentle meditation music (without sudden changes in tempo) will provide the atmosphere for a deeply relaxing experience.

Make sure your friend has plenty of space to lie comfortably full length on a firm surface. Professional masseurs use a massage table which is level with the upper thigh and about 2′6″ (75 cm) wide. Ideally, the height should be level with the flat of your hand when holding your arm down at your side. You can use a long table with a padded covering; a narrow, very firm bed; a thin foam mattress or blankets on the floor as a substitute for a massage table. Protect whatever you use with a towel as you will probably spill some oil. You'll also need somewhere less than an arm's length away to put the oil bottle between applications, to enable you to keep in continuous contact with your friend's skin, even if with your elbow.

The less clothing your friend wears, the easier you will find it to do long flowing strokes but it's important that your friend feels comfortable. Cover any bare parts that you're not working on with a towel to keep them warm.

Before starting the massage, ensure that your hands are clean and warm. Rub them together for a second or two if they feel cold. A cold hand on the back is not a good way to start a massage.

WHEN MASSAGE IS INAPPROPRIATE

Although there are many benefits to an aromatherapy massage, the effects can be so far-reaching that sometimes it should be avoided.

● After a very hot bath, steam bath or sauna, the skin will be eliminating excess heat, toxins and surplus moisture for up to an hour. When the body is eliminating, it is not absorbing, so except for giving a pleasant fragrance, the therapeutic benefits of the oils would be wasted.

● Do not massage any area if it causes discomfort either to you or your friend.

● Do not massage if the person has a temperature, fever or viral disease as this may spread the infection further via the lymphatic system. For the same reason do not massage if cancer is suspected.

● Do not massage someone who has recently undergone a serious operation.

● Avoid areas where there are fractures, broken skin, sprains, bruises, swelling, rashes, torn muscles or ligaments, or varicose veins.

● Do not massage anyone who has heart trouble.

● Do not massage someone who has acute back pain.

● Do not massage the abdomen straight after a meal.

● If in doubt, don't massage.

MASSAGE STROKES

Aromatherapy massage employs a range of different strokes. Three of the easiest techniques to use are:

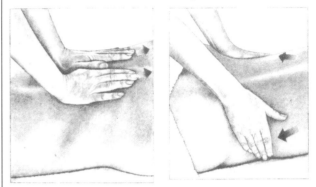

Effleurage This long stroking movement makes up most of aromatherapy massage. It helps movement in the veins and allows fresh blood to circulate more freely. The movement begins with a deep stroke made with pressure in the direction of the heart. The return journey is a light stroke moving away from the heart over a large area. The whole hand must be relaxed and moulded to the shape of the body as it glides rhythmically over the skin.

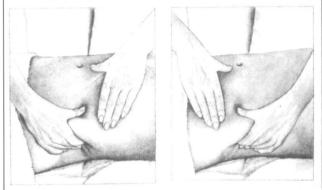

Kneading A vigorous movement, this stimulates muscle tissue, increases circulation and helps reduce fatigue by facilitating the removal of waste products. Pick up a handful of flesh and squeeze or roll it with one hand, then pass it to the other. Pick up the adjacent skin and repeat to make a rippling movement as if you were kneading dough. Do this slowly and rhythmically after relaxing the area with effleurage.

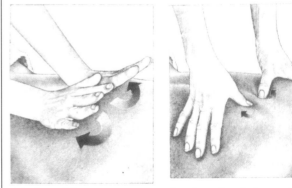

Frictions These movements stimulate circulation and help to remove excess fluid. Press the heel of the hand into the skin and move it in deep circles using a little pressure. After several circles, slide gently to the next area, always keeping in contact with the skin. On small areas of skin, use your thumbs instead of the heel of the hand.

Back massage

The back is a good area to start exploring the power of massage. It provides an expanse for your hands to experiment on and the opportunity to try out different massage strokes. It is also the area most people enjoy having massaged.

Have your friend lie on his or her front with arms comfortably positioned at the side or acting as a cushion under the forehead.

Start by placing one of your hands on the crown of your friend's head and the other at the base of the spine for a few seconds to establish contact. Breathe slowly and deeply, and relax. Take your selected oil and pour about a teaspoonful (5 ml) into one hand (it may be more fluid than you anticipate when you first pour). Take more later as you need it: 2 to 4 teaspoons (10–20 ml) should be sufficient for a back, depending on the dryness of the skin. Rub your hands together and cover the whole back with the oil.

The following is a suggestion of strokes for you to adapt or build on as you wish.

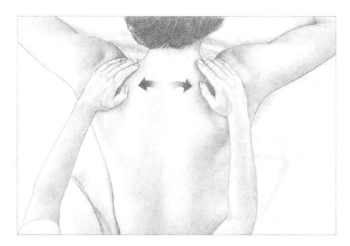

1 Start at the base of the back with your hands either side of the spine, fingers pointing upward. Move them up the centre to the base of the neck, then slide them across the shoulders and bring them down lightly to your starting position. Repeat these long effleurage strokes until the back is oiled. Apply a series of dinner-plate size circular movements up both sides of the spine, then glide your hands slowly and rhythmically back down to the base of the spine.

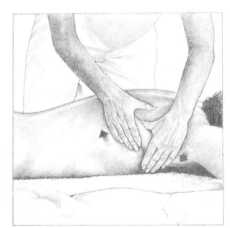

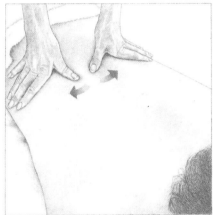

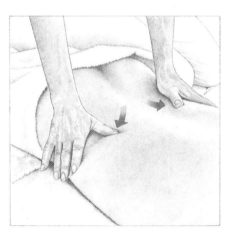

2 Move your hands to one side of the body and start to knead the flesh, working up the back and across the top of the shoulders. On the less fleshy areas knead more lightly, using just your thumb and fingers, not the whole of your hand. Be careful not to pinch. Repeat on the other side of the spine, then lightly slide your hands down, without dragging the skin.

3 Starting again at the base of the spine, make small friction movements with your thumbs along either side of the backbone, working up to the neck and over the shoulder blades. Press into the muscles and outward, not into the bones, and work with both hands simultaneously. Return to the base of the spine, gliding your hands down the back in long, rhythmic strokes.

4 Make small friction movements with your thumbs, starting from the backbone at waist level and moving in an outward curve over the hip bone. Make three concentric curves. Complete the massage with a series of long, slow effleurage strokes, then finish by resting both hands lightly on the small of the back. Hold this position for a few seconds then slowly lift your hands away.

Arm massage

Use a small drop of oil for each arm. Hold one hand in your hand and stroke from the wrist up the outside of the arm with your other hand. Repeat the stroke on the inside of the arm. Knead any areas of cellulite on the backs of the upper arms and make friction circles on any rheumatic areas. Knead into the shoulder muscles and finish with a few effleurage strokes up and down the arm, letting your hand trail off from the fingertips. Repeat the movements on the other arm.

Leg massage

Start on the backs of the legs so have your friend lie on his or her stomach. Put a drop of oil in one palm, rub your hands together lightly and place your palms over the soles of your friend's feet to establish contact. Now run your hands up the backs of the legs to the knees, pause and continue upward. Stroke firmly toward the tops of the legs and lightly back down several times until you have covered the legs in oil. Never apply pressure to the backs of the knees. Use kneading on any cellulite in the thighs followed by effleurage. Finish the backs of the legs by running your hands up to the tops of the thighs and sliding them off outwards.

Turn your friend over, using the towels to keep him or her warm, and massage the front of each leg. Place your hands across the first leg, stroking sideways up to the top, one hand after the other. Go firmly upward, lightly downward. Repeat the treatment on the other leg. Make circular movements with the fingers (or lightly with the thumbs) around the ankles and the knees. Finish with relaxing effleurage strokes, working from the ankle up to the tops of the legs.

Foot massage

For a real treat, give yourself or a friend a foot massage. First bathe the feet to freshen them and then pat them dry. Pour about a teaspoonful (5 ml) of oil into your palm, rub your hands together and then take one foot in your hands. Place one hand under the sole of the foot and the other on top. Start to spread the oil by moving both hands up to the heel and down to the big toe. Work the oil well into the foot by repeating this stroke several times. Stroke each toe separately, running your fingers from the tip to the base. Work from the big toe to the little toe.

Repeat the routine with the other foot. Then take the tops of both feet in your fingers, and rest your thumbs on the heels. Slide your thumbs along from the heel to the toes and repeat several times, moving from the sides of the feet to the centre of the soles. All movements on the feet should be done with confidence. If strokes are too light you will simply cause tickling.

Self face massage

Prepare by cleaning your face well, then pour 2 teaspoons (10 ml) of your oil mix into a saucer. Before oiling your hands, place them over your face, fingers on your forehead and palms over your cheeks and chin. Hold this for a few moments and then slowly draw your fingers out to your ears as if ironing out creases and tension from the forehead.

Now dip your fingers into the oil (very little is needed) and lightly rub your hands together. Always use gentle strokes on the face, particularly around the delicate eye skin. Start under the chin, glide up the face, then circle the eyes in the direction the eyebrows grow.

Add a little more oil and go very gently over the throat and up the face again. Place your fingers at the centre of the forehead. Press lightly, then slide them apart toward the temples and off at the hairline. Repeat this movement, placing your fingers slightly higher up the forehead each time until you reach the hairline. Finish by pressing your fingers down harder in the centre of your forehead for a few seconds. Repeat this movement along the brow bone until you reach the outer corner of the eyes.

Place your thumbs on your chin and pull them slowly along the jawline up to the ear. Repeat, moving slightly upward each time until you are just below the cheekbone. Then gently stroke the entire face with upward movements.

Work behind the ears making small circular movements with your fingers. Then gently pinch the outer semi-circle of the ear, starting at the top. Finish by pulling on the ear lobes three times.

Complete a face massage by "palming" the eyes. Press the base of your palms over your eyes to exclude the light for about 20 seconds. Do not lift away your hands immediately, let them slide down so they cover your face, hold them there for a few moments, then gently take them away.

Facial massage strokes
The drawings below show some of the basic facial massage strokes. To give yourself a soothing facial massage, follow the procedure described above.

Ease away tension by stroking outward from the centre of your forehead.

Lightly stroke up your neck and along your jawline to your ears.

Smooth your fingers across your forehead, moving from the centre outward along your hairline.

Draw your thumbs up along your jawbone, from your chin out to your ears. Repeat, moving upward.

OTHER WAYS OF USING ESSENTIAL OILS

You can experience the beneficial properties of essential oils by trying one of a number of other methods of application apart from massage. Use the chart on the following pages to select your oils.

Air purification
Essential oils have active antiseptic, antibacterial and even anti-viral properties to differing degrees (see chart on p. 236). Some essential oil companies now sell various antiseptic oils in atomizers which are excellent for domestic use, especially in a sick room, and for use in hospitals and other public places.
● To make your own air purifier, half fill an atomizer with isopropyl alcohol and add 200 drops of essential oils per 25 ml. Try 65 drops bergamot, 25 drops lemon, 25 drops lavender, 15 drops orange, 15 drops thyme, 15 drops clove, 10 drops juniper, 10 drops tea tree, 5 drops peppermint, 5 drops rosemary, 5 drops sandalwood, 5 drops eucalyptus. (If you don't have all these oils, any combination of them will be effective). Top up with distilled water and spray as required.
    You can make up the mixture without the alcohol, but the oils will not disperse so you'll have to shake the atomizer before each spray, and the keeping qualities will be reduced.

Room fresheners
● Add a few drops of oil to a dish of warm water set on a radiator or in a sunny window. As it evaporates, its aroma will fill the room.
● Alternatively, place drops of one or more oils in a crucible over a small lamp, taking care that they don't burn or the scent will spoil and the therapeutic qualities will be lost. Try thyme, lavender, pine or eucalyptus for their fresh fragrance.

Potpourri revitalizer
● A favourite use for essential oils is to top up the scent of fading potpourri. Lavender, rose, bergamot, pine, cedarwood, the citrus oils, and spice oils add intensity and freshness to other ingredients.

Car fresheners
● Sprinkle a few drops of an essential oil on a tissue and place it in an air vent inside the car. Use basil or peppermint to remain alert for long distances or one of the citrus oils to refresh stale air.

Skin creams
● Many essential oils are particularly beneficial to the skin. Add a few drops to a commercial fragrance-free skin cream, or try making some of the basic cosmetic recipes in the previous chapter (see pp. 212–227).

Perfumes
Several essential oils smell beautiful on their own but from the range available you have enormous scope to make your own blends. Mixtures of alcohol and oil are necessary to preserve the scent of essential oils. Perfumes are 15–25 percent essences in pure alcohol. *Parfum de toilette* is 12–15 percent essential oils blended with over 50 percent alcohol and some distilled water.
● See p. 223 for some recommended perfume recipes.

Baths
Aromatic baths using essential oils are highly therapeutic, particularly for muscular aches and pains, skin disorders, circulation problems, tension, fatigue and insomnia.
● Put 5 to 10 drops of oil into a bath of warm water after the water has settled. Mix it around in the water. Relax in the bath for about 10 minutes, with the door and windows closed so you get the full benefit of the aromatic vapours.

Saunas
● Two drops of pine or eucalyptus oil added to a ladle of water or 15 drops to a small bucket make a very pleasant and antiseptic fragrance for inhalation during a sauna.

Inhalants
Steam inhalation is an excellent method of application for everyone except asthmatics. It is particularly effective for treating problems of the respiratory system, such as colds, coughs and sinus, and for relieving tension and headaches. The aroma goes straight to the brain while the therapeutic qualities of the oils breathed in pass from the lungs into the blood stream.
● Put 5 to 10 drops of oil in a bowl containing 1 pint (570 ml) of hot water. Drape a towel over your head if you wish. Inhale the steam for 5 to 10 minutes about 9 in (22.5 cm) above the water. Repeat no more than three times a day.
● Inhalation can also be accomplished by putting 5 to 8 drops of oil on a handkerchief or tissue and taking four deep breaths. A portable treatment when in bed, at work, or while travelling. When the tissue is not in use, place it against the breast bone where it will continue to work.

Compresses
These are excellent for treating local problems. Hot compresses soothe old injuries, sprains, muscular aches and pains, neuralgia, painful periods, cystitis and skin problems.
● Put up to 6 drops of chosen oil in enough hot water to soak a compress (an essential oil remains potent no matter how much it is diluted). Soak the compress and squeeze it until it stops dripping. Apply to the affected area and cover with plastic. Keep on for at least two hours. To help retain the heat, add a pre-warmed towel and then place a blanket over the towel and the patient.
● Use a cold compress (made as above but with cold water and refrigerated for soothing coolness) on recent sprains, bruises or swellings and headaches.

Stress
Bathing in water with a few drops of essential oil added is one of the most effective ways to relieve stress.

Insomnia
To relieve insomnia, try putting a drop of basil, chamomile, clary sage, juniper or lavender onto your pillow at night.

Studying
● When studying into the small hours of the night, add a drop of uplifting essential oil to a page in each book you are using. Try basil to clear your head; rose to lift your spirits; bergamot to bring freshness; cardamom to reduce mental fatigue.

Internal use
It is important to realize the strength and power of essential oils. One teaspoon (5 ml) of some essential oils taken internally could be lethal. For this reason they should only be taken under the direction of an aromatherapy doctor or herbalist trained in the use of essential oils.
● Teas can be flavoured by adding 5 drops of, say, citrus oil to a packet of tea leaves. An alternative is to add one drop to a tea bag and use this to make a whole pot of tea.

A GUIDE TO ESSENTIAL OILS

The oils listed below are commonly available and have many uses. The chart lists each oil's properties; conditions it treats; other oils it blends with, and any special points. Each oil is also described by its "note" (under the name).

In simple terms, this refers to its evaporation rate: top notes evaporate quickly; middle notes are mellow; base notes are lasting (see p. 231 for further explanation).

OIL	PROPERTIES	USE TO TREAT	BLEND WITH	SPECIAL NOTE
Basil top	Uplifting, energizing, antidepressant	Anxiety, concentration, digestion, headaches, respiratory problems	Bergamot, geranium, hyssop, neroli, marjoram, melissa, lavender	1 drop soothes wasp sting. More than 3 drops of oil may irritate some skins
Benzoin base	Penetrating, warming	Stimulates circulation; aids respiration; soothes irritated skin; reduces nervous tension	Cinnamon, coriander, cypress, jasmine, lemon, myrrh, rose, sandalwood	A useful fixative
Bergamot top	Fresh, uplifting, antiseptic	Anxiety, depression; stimulates appetite; aids digestion; soothes lung conditions; oily skin	Chamomile, coriander, cypress, geranium, jasmine, lavender, lemon, neroli, ylang-ylang	Do not use neat on exposed skin; may cause uneven pigmentation. Use only a $\frac{1}{2}$–1% concentration
Black pepper middle	Light, stimulating	Stimulates circulation, digestion; colds, coughs, muscular aches and pains	Cypress, frankincense, sandalwood, spice oils	
Camphor base	Cooling, highly stimulating	Depression, insomnia, shock, digestion, respiratory problems, oily skin, acne	Frankincense, neroli	Apply immediately in cold compress to reduce swelling of bruises and sprains
Cedarwood base	Sedative, antiseptic, insect repellent	Anxiety, cystitis, all lung conditions, acne, dandruff	Bergamot, cypress, jasmine, juniper, neroli, rosemary	Do not use in pregnancy
Chamomile middle	Refreshing, relaxing, pain reliever for dull aches	Depression, insomnia, digestive problems, menstrual problems, all skin conditions	Benzoin, bergamot, geranium, lavender, lemon, marjoram, neroli, rose, ylang-ylang	First choice for children
Cinnamon base	Warming astringent, antiseptic	Exhaustion, digestion, coughs, circulation	Coriander, frankincense, citrus oils	
Clary sage top	Warming, soothing, nerve tonic	Depression, insomnia, sore throats, digestion, menstruation, dry skin, insect bites	Bergamot, cedarwood, citrus oils, cypress, geranium, jasmine, juniper, lavender, sandalwood	Small percentages may induce intoxication; large percentages induce headaches
Clove base	Warming, antiseptic, disinfectant, pain reliever, insect repellent	General debility, neuralgia, respiratory problems, toothache, mouth and skin sores	Basil, citrus and spice oils	A drop on a surface will kill ants. Use in air freshener
Coriander top	Sweet, uplifting	Nervous debility, digestion, rheumatic pain	Bergamot, lemon, neroli, orange, cypress, spice	
Cypress middle	Relaxing, refreshing, astringent	Circulation, influenza, laryngitis, muscular cramps, mature skin	Benzoin, bergamot, clary sage, juniper, lavender, lemon, orange, sandalwood	Useful for menopausal upsets
Eucalyptus top	Stimulating, antiseptic, anti-viral, insect repellent	Diarrhoea, colds and viruses, respiratory problems, aches and pains, cuts and wounds	Benzoin, hyssop, lavender, lemon, lemongrass, melissa, pine, rose	Aids formation of skin tissue. Massage into feet for deep sleep. Good air freshener
Fennel middle	Antitoxic, antispasmodic, diuretic	Digestion, constipation, nausea, oily skin, cellulite; menopause	Geranium, lavender, lemon, rose, sandalwood	Do not give to epileptics or children under 6.
Frankincense base	Warming, relaxing, tonic	Respiratory problems, aging skin, inflammation, wounds	All oils	Considered rejuvenating
Geranium (Pelargonium) middle	Refreshing, relaxing, astringent, insect repellent	Nervous system, digestion, liver and kidney disorders, menstrual problems; normalizes and cleanses skin	All oils	Most used oil in aromatherapy
Ginger base	Stimulating tonic	Digestion, loss of appetite, rheumatic pains, sore throat	Citrus and spice oils	Valuable bath oil to ward off colds
Hyssop middle	Sedative, decongestant	Anxiety, hypertension, normalizes circulation, digestion, respiratory problems, fades bruises	Clary sage, lavender, rosemary, sage, citrus oil	Do not give to epileptics. Can be toxic
Jasmine base	Relaxing, sedative	Depression, uterine pain, respiratory problems; tonic for sensitive skins	All oils	Expensive, but powerful fragrance

A GUIDE TO ESSENTIAL OILS

OIL	PROPERTIES	USE TO TREAT	BLEND WITH	SPECIAL NOTE
Juniper middle	Stimulating tonic, antiseptic, diuretic	Depression, respiratory problems, aching muscles, acne, skin sores, eczema	Bergamot, citrus oils, cypress, geranium, lavender, rosemary, sandalwood	Do not take during pregnancy
Lavender middle	Refreshing, soothing, antiseptic, insect repellent, relieves sharp pain	Insomnia, circulation, indigestion, headaches, infections, muscular pains, cell renewal; benefits all skin types	Most oils, especially citrus, chamomile, clary sage, geranium, pine, rosemary	Excellent first-aid remedy for insect bites and small burns. Low toxicity makes it good for children
Lemon top	Refreshing, invigorating, antiseptic, insect repellent	Circulation, respiratory problems, sore throats, oily skin, broken capillaries	Benzoin, chamomile, eucalyptus, fennel, frankincense, geranium, juniper, neroli, ylang-ylang	Whitens stained teeth; apply neat to insect bites. 2% solution in pure water stops small cuts bleeding
Lemongrass top	Toning, revitalizing, antiseptic	Circulation, digestion, muscle tone, acne, oily skin	Basil, geranium, jasmine, lavender	Excellent for post-diet saggy skin
Marjoram (Sweet) middle	Calming, warming	Tension, insomnia, high blood pressure, digestion, colds, headaches, muscular cramps, respiratory problems	Bergamot, chamomile, cypress, lavender, rosemary	
Melissa middle	Refreshing, antidepressant	Tension, neuralgia, digestion, fevers, painful menstruation, respiratory problems	Geranium, juniper, neroli, ylang-ylang	Good for the elderly
Myrrh base	Antiseptic, healing, anti-inflammatory, tonic	Digestion, loss of appetite, catarrh, bronchitis, skin inflammations	Camphor, lavender, spice oils	
Neroli top	Ambrosial, antiseptic	Anxiety, insomnia, diarrhoea, rejuvenates skin	Most oils	Powerful scent. Expensive. Excellent for skin.
Niaouli top	Antiseptic, disinfectant, soothing	Respiratory problems, sore throats, colds, skin ulcers, rheumatism	Lavender, pine, mint	Used in many pharmaceutical products: toothpastes, cough drops
Patchouli base	Antiseptic, antidepressant, sedative	Anxiety, dry and mature skins	Basil, bergamot, geranium, juniper, lavender, myrrh, neroli, pine, rose	Small quantities are uplifting; larger doses are sedative
Peppermint top	Invigorating, antiseptic, pain reliever	Fatigue, shock, digestion, travel sickness, headaches, toothache, skin irritations	In small quantities with benzoin, black pepper, melissa, marjoram, spice oils	Use low concentration (1%) on inflamed or sensitive skin
Pine middle	Refreshing, antiseptic, disinfectant	Kidney problems, respiratory problems, asthma, sinus problems and flu	Cedarwood, eucalyptus, lavender, rosemary, sage, spice oils	Use in air freshener
Rose base	Relaxing, antidepressant, astringent, antiseptic	Stress, circulation, digestion, headaches; all skins, especially sensitive	Most oils	One of the least toxic oils. Good for children
Rosemary middle	Toning, invigorating, insect repellent	Fatigue, circulation, digestion, headaches, muscular pains, respiratory problems	Basil, cedarwood, frankincense, lavender, lemon, peppermint	Encourages hair growth
Sage top	Soothing, tonic, antiseptic, decongestant	Fatigue, low blood pressure, respiratory problems; clears sluggish skin, firms tissue	Bergamot, hyssop, lemon, lavender, melissa, peppermint, rosemary	Quite toxic. Use in moderation. Do not use if breastfeeding
Sandalwood base	Calming, antiseptic	Fatigue, diarrhoea, nausea, respiratory problems; softens dry skin: mildly astringent for oily skin	Benzoin, black pepper, cypress, frankincense, jasmine, lemon, myrrh, neroli, ylang-ylang	
Tea tree top	Powerful antiseptic, fungicide	Respiratory problems, skin infections, wounds	Lavender, rosemary, citrus and spice oils	Highly disinfectant without being toxic
Thyme top	Stimulant, antiseptic, nerve tonic	Fatigue, depression, circulation, headaches, digestion, colds and respiratory problems, muscular pain	Bergamot, citrus oils, melissa, rosemary	In the presence of infectious diseases it is said to stimulate the production of white blood corpuscles
Ylang-Ylang base	Sedative, antiseptic, antidepressant	Anxiety, insomnia, frustration; regulates circulation	Most oils	Use sparingly. Too much may cause headaches

HERBS FOR HEALTH

Since the beginning of time, people have turned to plants for healing help. It is rather ironic that this form of medicine, the oldest and still the most important in many parts of the world, should in some way be considered alternative, while the relatively new science of synthetic drugs in Western medicine should be called orthodox. What is important is that the best in every system should be valued and that proper attention should be paid to the dangers of any method. For emergencies, disasters and rapid infections, antibiotics, surgery and powerful drugs are vital to save lives; for minor or chronic ailments other forms of healing may have better results. In 1975 a Chief Medical Officer in Britain commented that "the number of admissions to hospital for treatment of adverse reactions to [medical] drugs now exceeds 100,000 a year".

But it must be recognized that plants too are potent drugs. Indeed, their active principles, isolated and synthesized, form the basis of many of today's drugs, from aspirin to morphine. Consequently, accurate dosage is vital: herbs should never be taken in excessive amounts.

Whenever you are in doubt or have a serious or recurring complaint, you should consult a trained herbalist. Most herbal practitioners follow the holistic approach to medicine. Holistic thinking has a way of spreading outward – like waves from a pebble dropped in water. Just as a whole plant is considered as being greater than the sum of its parts, a person's whole lifestyle and physical, mental and spiritual existence are examined before any treatment takes place. A herbalist will consider your diet, your work, general exercise, home-life and environment as well as the overall balance of your body's systems. Therefore what is prescribed for one patient may well differ from what is prescribed for another with the same symptoms.

Common ailments can be treated at home with a range of simple herbal remedies; follow the preparation instructions and advice in this chapter. You can also assist your health by including herbs in your daily diet. In times past it was the tradition to take herbal tonics in the spring to restore the body's vitality after a winter diet lacking in fresh green vegetables. Among the herbs used as tonics were yarrow, dandelion, sage, peppermint and rose hips, which helped to cleanse the system, and other herbs which were thought to strengthen the whole body, toning and invigorating its systems. Mint, for example, was taken for the digestive tract, and hawthorn berries were taken to improve the circulation system.

As research into the active constituents of herbs continues, increasing numbers of ancient treatments and tonics are becoming validated, revalued, and brought back into common use.

A history of herbal healing

For thousands of years early tribes accumulated a useful body of herbal knowledge through a process of trial and error. Women, with the restricted mobility of the child-bearer, assumed the tasks of collecting and administering herbs, so that medicine was almost universally a female vocation in pre-scientific cultures. Early peoples also saw a link between health renewal and a woman's ability to create new life. The healing craft and plant knowledge were handed down from mother to daughter, and the efficiency of this system depended on both the accuracy of their observations and the nurturing qualities of the healer involved. To help their memories, nomadic tribes would select a visual attribute of each herb to remind them of its usage.

Difficulties in describing and remembering plants lessened with the advent of written language and, by 3000 BC, parallel cultures in China, Babylon, Egypt and India had begun to record their knowledge of medicinal plants.

Chinese herbalism

The country with the longest unbroken tradition in herbal medicine is China. By the time he died in 2698 BC, the legendary Emperor Shen Nung had "tasted one hundred herbs". His *Canon of Herbs* deals with 252 plants, describing how to preserve and administer them and many are still in use.

A hundred years later the Yellow Emperor, Huang Ti, formalized medical theory in the *Nei Ching* and displayed a sophisticated understanding of human disease for the time: "In treating illness, it is necessary to examine the entire context, scrutinize the symptoms, observe the emotions and attitudes. If one insists on the presence of ghosts and spirits, one cannot speak of therapeutics." It was an optimistic book, stating that, with the growth of knowledge, all kinds of disease would eventually be curable.

The *Nei Ching* was updated in the sixth century AD and again in the seventh century, when a certain Su Jing had a vision of a more complete herbal, and approached the Tang dynasty for sponsorship. The court responded with the provision of 20 experts and a command to each province to submit records and illustrations of the useful herbs in their area. After two years *A Revised Canon of Herbs* was published, describing the source, collection methods, flavour and therapeutic properties of 844 herbs. More than 800 years before the Western printing press was invented, the Tang government printed and distributed the revised herbal throughout China.

During the Ming dynasty, a world-famous *Compendium of Materia Medica* was compiled by Li Shizhen (1518–1593). From childhood he had always followed his father, collecting herbs and copying prescriptions, and he became aware of the real need for an accurate and comprehensive manual. His *Materia Medica* was completed in 1578 after 27 years of research: a thoroughly practical and scientific manual, listing 1,800 healing substances, mainly herbs, and 11,000 recipes or compounds. This process of updating and revising information has continued to the present day.

From the Far East to the Middle East

Clay tablets from 3000 BC record herbal imports into Babylon, and there is evidence of trade in ginseng between China and Babylon around 2000 BC. The Babylonians had an enormous pharmacopoeia with 1,400 plants; they used poppy as an anaesthetic and fennel as a digestive. The Greek historian, Herodotus, noted that every Babylonian was an amateur physician since it was the custom to lay the sick in the street and solicit advice from anyone passing by.

The first known Egyptian physician was Imhotep (2980–2900 BC), a priest healer who also designed one of the earliest pyramids. He was greatly respected as a skilled and compassionate healer and was eventually deified.

The Ebers papyri of 1550 BC list many herbal remedies and accompanying incantations, and around this time a form of astrology was incorporated into Egyptian medicine. Egyptian physicians worked with around 900 herbs, and, through their embalming skills, had a superior understanding of the human organism.

At about the same time, Indian physicians were developing advanced surgical and diagnostic skills and used hundreds of herbs in their treatments. Like the Chinese, they used all five senses when diagnosing, and developed a keen sensitivity to assessing breathing, pulse and skin odours.

Herbalism in the Ancient World

The Ancient Greeks acquired their knowledge of herbalism from India, Babylon, Egypt and even China. In the thirteenth century BC there lived in Greece a healer named Asclepius, skilled in the use of herbs. He designed a healing system, whereby people would live through a series of experiences intended to transform them by changing old thinking patterns. Many miracles of healing were attributed to Asclepius and his daughter Hygieia. Eventually he was deified and healing temples sprang up across Greece. His system was practised in Greece for several hundred years, and some of his ideas are still relevant in today's health centres.

In the sixth century BC, the philosopher and mathematician, Pythagoras, set up a university to teach advanced knowledge. Herbs, particularly aromatic gardens, played an important part in the healing and restorative regime which preceded higher learning. Herbs were also used in the special high-energy food mixtures created for Pythagoras's long sojourns for contemplation.

Hippocrates (460–377 BC) brought Western medicine into a scientific framework of diagnosis and treatment. He dismissed the idea of disease being punishment from the gods and considered food, occupation and climate important factors in disease. He believed that it was the individual's responsibility to aid self-healing through diet and plant medicines. He gave the medical profession a code of conduct that is still respected by doctors throughout the world.

Around 300 BC in the new cultural centre of Alexandria a famous medical school was established where herbal research was conducted. By 60 AD herbal knowledge had increased to such an extent that the physician Dioscorides was able to assemble a *Materia Medica* of 600 herbs, with their description, preparation and effect, and a new emphasis on botany. This became the standard herbal reference book for 1500 years.

Soon afterwards, in 77 AD, Pliny the Elder, the most quoted writer from Ancient Rome, completed a listing of over 1,000 plants in his *Historia Naturalis*. Though full of curious information, it is not considered accurate.

More accurate was the herbal written by Galen (131–201 AD), a great physician and philosopher who travelled widely making detailed plant observations. His enthusiasm for drugs and exotic compounds marks the beginning of several hundred years of a fashionable leaning towards complex drugs concocted mainly for the wealthy.

The Dark Ages

During the Dark Ages, Persia became the centre of excellence. There the Nestorian Christians (an Eastern Church not affiliated with Rome) established a famous school and hospital where Greek medical manuscripts were translated into Arabic. At about this time Avicenna (980–1037 AD), a gifted physician and scientist credited with inventing the process of distilling essential oils, wrote his *Canon Medicinae*, full of information on disease, remedies and medical philosophies.

In contemporary Europe medical progress was hampered by the authorities of the Christian church: scientific learning was not highly regarded, experiment was discouraged and originality considered a dangerous asset. Most significantly, the Church viewed disease as punishment for sin. However, plant medicine continued to be practised by monks in the monasteries and by "herb women" in the villages.

The Renaissance

With the development in the fifteenth century of the Western printing press began a golden age of herbals. This was the beginning of the Renaissance, a time for re-examining old ideas, attempting to escape the limitations of old dogmas and giving rein to an eagerness for discovery. A new scientific attitude spread through medicine. The results of herbal remedies were observed more accurately, and the more bizarre drugs were dropped. Rather oddly, in this environment of growing reason, there occurred the cruellest witch-hunts in history. Women were forbidden to study, while non-professional healers were pronounced heretics. Because of this, even today some people equate herbalism with superstition, quackery and magic.

Herbalism today

With the ascendancy of science in the nineteenth century came the ability to synthesize plant parts and concentrate doses. Herb usage probably reached an all-time low in the mid-twentieth century. But now, because of a greater concern about the side-effects of drugs, an understanding of ecology and people's desire to take greater responsibility for their own health, herbal medicine is experiencing a remarkable revival. Research into plants such as feverfew, used to treat migraines, rosy periwinkle, which can control leukaemia, and *Rauvolfia serpentina*, which was used in tranquillizers, has highlighted the potential of herbal materials.

Pharmaceutical companies on the one hand recognize the value of herbs and are busy investigating worldwide herbal lore with unprecedented zeal, while on the other hand they wish to maintain their lucrative near-monopoly over medicinal products. Some drug companies have tried to have herbs removed from the healing arena. One tactic has been to concentrate on finding and isolating a single, toxic constituent in a herb. This happened in the case of sage some years ago, but attempts to quash its usage failed after further research found that the other constituents in sage nullified any toxic element.

In order to use herbs safely, we need to find a sensible middle ground. One solution is a proposal on the statute books of Canada. This is to create a new class of "Folk Medicines". Each product would be labelled with botanical names, the plant parts used and the type of preparation. Ingredients would have to meet set standards of purity and concentration, and advertising would not make extravagant claims. Such a system would guarantee the safety of herbal medicines on the market and allow people to continue using these benevolent plants.

Herbal preparations

It is generally agreed that wild herbs or self-sown herbs, plants growing where Nature has decreed, have the most active ingredients, although with home-grown plants, you are more certain of having the species you want when you want them. There is also less risk of mistaking one plant for another. The dangers of inaccurate identification cannot be stressed strongly enough. Some plants are dangerous under any circumstances, others are dangerous if taken inaccurately.

The quality of a herb is most important when it is to be used for healing. Pick perfect leaves, clean and unblemished, at their prime time, when most active constituents are present (see p. 269). Unless stated otherwise, leaves are at their prime just before flowers open; flowers are at their prime just as they open (coinciding with their moment of greatest beauty), fruit as it comes to ripeness, roots in the autumn when goodness has passed from the leaves back into the roots, and bark after spring when sap has risen.

Use secateurs or sharp scissors to remove parts cleanly, causing as little damage as possible to the plant. Do not pack tightly or allow to sweat before drying. Store carefully, label and date. Dried green herbs lose their medicinal potency after six or seven months; roots, seeds and bark after two or three years.

Remedy recipes and dosage

Generally a recipe can use either fresh or dried herb. Fresh herbs are likely to have the higher medicinal value and, the more recently picked, the higher it will be (unless it is a herb that changes chemically as it dries to give the active substance desired, see the Herbal Index). However, because dried herbs are available all year round, recipes are given in amounts of dried herb. On average, for infusions, or teas, and decoctions, one teaspoon (5 ml) of dried herb equals three teaspoons or one tablespoon (15 ml) of fresh.

To make a single dose use 1 tsp (5 ml) of herb to a cup (225 ml) of water. For a day's dosage add 1 oz (25 g) to 1 pint (570 ml) of liquid. For young children, the weak and very elderly the amount of herb (if using potent plants) should be halved.

The usual dosage is 7 fl oz (200 ml) of infusion, or a third of the reduced quantity for a decoction. As a guide, take this three times a day before meals for one or two days for a minor discomfort such as a mild sore throat, for several days for a cold, or for several weeks for chronic problems, such as migraine or constipation. Effectiveness also depends on lifestyle, general diet and fitness. With longterm problems, when conditions seem to be improving gradually, reduce the amount until you no longer need the remedy.

Although herbs do not have the side-effects of drugs, they do affect major organic functions within the body and should not be taken unnecessarily. It is also important not to assume erroneously that, because herbs are "natural", any quantity or any combination can be taken. Herbal guidelines must be followed.

PREPARATION METHODS
Infusion or tea

Follow the quantities given below left for dosage. For a hot infusion, boil water, wait 30 seconds and then sprinkle the herb onto the water to steep, stirring occasionally, for 10 minutes, or until cool, or leave overnight. This method is preferable for leaves and flowers that easily give up their medicinal properties (especially vitamins and volatile ingredients) to the liquid but remember to keep the container covered. Use a china, glass or enamel teapot or lidded pan and use the purest water or bottled mineral water you can obtain. Water with a high lime content (very hard water) can prevent plants from fully releasing their active principles. Strain the infusion into a cup and drink it lukewarm or cool as tea, though take it hot to break up a cold or cough. Drinks can be sweetened with honey or raw brown sugar to make them more palatable; or other herbs such as lemon verbena or spearmint can be added as long as their own therapeutic effect is in sympathy with the desired result (see individual entries in the Herbal Index). Whenever possible, infusions should be made fresh each day and any unused portion kept refrigerated until needed, when it can be reheated in a glass or enamel pan.

A cold infusion is preferable for some plant parts with highly volatile ingredients. The text states when this is the case. Soak double quantities of these in cold water for 8–12 hours in a glass or enamel pan. Strain and drink. Make fresh daily.

Decoction

Follow the quantities given at left for dosage. Place the dried herb in an enamel or glass lidded pan with cold water and slowly bring to the boil. Reduce the heat and simmer down to a quarter of its original volume (10 minutes or longer) and then steep with the lid on for 3 minutes or until cool. This method is used for hard materials such as roots, bark and seeds, which are bruised or crushed beforehand to release their active principles. It is also used for green parts of plants if mineral salts are required. Strain and take with honey or raw brown sugar if preferred. Make fresh daily when possible and keep any unused portion refrigerated. A decoction should keep for up to 3 days in this way.

Powder

Chop large dried plant parts, such as roots, bark or thick stems, into small pieces, then crush these or dried leaves and flowers with a pestle and mortar, or reduce them to powder in a coffee grinder. Powder can be added to drinks or soups, sprinkled on food, or put into gelatine capsules, which are obtainable from a pharmacist.

Pills

It is possible to make your own pills with a domestic press, although it is much easier (and safer) to buy them ready-made by a professional.

Syrup

Syrups are used to mask unpleasantly flavoured herbs, especially for children, and to make cough medicine easier to take. Bring slowly to the boil 1 pint (570 ml) of selected infusion or decoction with 2–4 tbsp (30–60 ml) honey until the mixture turns syrupy. Store in the refrigerator. This won't keep as long as a sugar-based syrup but it is a healthier mixture.

To mix with a tincture, first heat 1 pint (570 ml) water with 4–6 tbsp (60–90 ml) honey and stir until the mixture begins to boil. Remove from the heat. Mix 1 part tincture with 3 parts syrup. Store in the refrigerator.

Tincture

Put 4 oz (110 g) powdered herb or 8 oz (225 g) fresh chopped herb in a container with a tightly fitting lid. Add 1 pint (570 ml) alcohol, which must be at least 60° proof (e.g. brandy or vodka). Neither treated ethyl alcohol nor surgical spirit is suitable. Stand the mixture in a warm place and shake it twice daily for 2 weeks. Strain through double muslin, squeezing out as much liquid as possible, and store in a well-stoppered dark glass jar. Alcohol preparations will keep for a long time. The dosage is usually 5–15 drops, which can be taken directly or added to a cup of hot water. Homeopaths use very dilute tinctures in many of their preparations.

Essential oils

These are the concentrated essences of plants usually extracted by steam distillation. It is possible to obtain minute amounts at home but more sensible to purchase them. It is important to find a source of pure unadulterated essential oils to ensure that an oil contains all of a plant's active principles. Essential oils are excellent for making tinctures, adding to massage oils, ointments and other external applications. Infused or macerated oils are easy to make (see p. 188) and can be used as they are for massage or added to ointments.

Ointments and creams

Prepare and strain a strong decoction or infusion of the herb and add this to a quantity of pure, cold-pressed vegetable oil, such as sunflower. Boil until the liquid has evaporated (bubbles cease to appear) leaving the herbal principles in the oil. Alternatively use an infused oil (see p. 188). To stiffen as a cream, stir in melted beeswax – about 1 oz (25 g) should be enough for half a pint (275 ml). You can make a cream by melting and blending 1 oz (25 g) beeswax, lanolin or cocoa butter with 4 fl oz (110 ml) vegetable or herbal oil, following the method on p. 215. Add 1 oz (25 g) selected herb, simmer gently for 10 minutes, stirring frequently, sift through double muslin into a wide-necked container with a lid, label and date. A drop of tincture of benzoin or myrrh will extend its life. Do not use borax as it can damage broken skin.

Petroleum jelly acts as a non-penetrative base. Put 3½ oz (90 g) petroleum jelly in an enamel pan or bowl over boiling water and melt. Leave to cool, then stir in a few drops of essential oil (say, eucalyptus for nasal relief), pour into a container, label and date.

Hot and cold compresses

A compress is useful for applying a herbal remedy externally to the skin. For a hot compress, soak a clean linen or cotton cloth in a hot decoction or infusion and apply it to the affected part as hot as can be tolerated. Cover the compress with plastic and a folded towel or blanket to maintain the heat. When cooled, either replace with another hot compress or apply a hot-water bottle over the plastic. Prepare a cold compress in the same way but allow it to cool before applying.

Poultice

A poultice is similar to a compress except that plant parts are used rather than liquid extraction. Mash or crush fresh plant parts and either heat in a pan over boiling water or mix with a small amount of boiling water. Apply the pulp directly to the skin, as hot as can be tolerated, holding it in place with a gauze bandage. If using a dried herb, first powder it and make a paste with a little boiling water. If the paste is liable to irritate the skin, apply it between two layers of cloth.

Poultices are generally more active than compresses. They are used to stimulate circulation, soothe aches and pains or draw impurities out through the skin, depending on the herb chosen. Like massage with essential oils, a poultice will introduce the active parts of the herb into the body without stressing or being affected by the digestive tract before reaching their target area.

A-Z of herbal treatments

Here is a list of some common ailments and medical conditions that often respond to treatment with herbs at home. Do not attempt to treat more serious problems yourself and remember that many complaints are caused by incorrect diet, stress and other external factors.

Botanical names are supplied for the less common plants and for those where there may be confusion between species. Consult the Herbal Index for more detailed information. To be sure of getting the desired active principles, use the main species rather than varieties, cultivars or hybrids. You must be able to identify plants with complete confidence – many are easy to mistake for others and are highly poisonous.

It is always advisable to try a small quantity of any remedy before applying the full dosage. If you have an adverse reaction, or if a complaint seems to worsen or continue for a long time, seek professional advice from a qualified medical herbalist. For information on making up the recipes and on dosages, see p. 241.

Abrasions *see* **FIRST AID**

Acne
After washing, rinse the skin with an infusion of chamomile (*Chamaemelum nobile*) which is purifying, yarrow (*Achillea millefolium*) which helps eliminate toxins, catnip (*Nepeta cataria*) which is antiseptic, lavender (*Lavandula sp*) which is calming and antiseptic or thyme (*Thymus vulgaris*) which is a strong germ-killer. Dab spots with neat lemon juice to kill germs, cool inflammation and improve blood circulation. Apply a calendula ointment to reduce inflammation and improve local healing. Consider your diet and cut out sugars, fats and dairy products.

Appetite, lack of
Caraway (*Carum carvi*) and ginseng (*Panax ginseng*) are powerful appetite stimulants, and a standard infusion of either can be drunk half an hour before a meal or whenever desired. Herbalists have had some success with both herbs in treating serious cases of anorexia nervosa. Horehound (*Marrubium vulgare*) tea, 1 cup (225 ml) taken three times a day, will stimulate the appetite after flu.

Arthritis *see* **Rheumatism and arthritis**

Asthma *see* **Coughs**

Bites, insect *see* **FIRST AID**

Boils and sores
To encourage boils to come to a head, apply neat lemon juice or secure over the boil half a warm baked onion (with the centre layer removed to create a small dome). For boils and sores, apply a poultice of antiseptic catnip leaves (*Nepeta cataria*), antiseptic plantain leaves (*Plantago lanceolata*) or pulverized fenugreek seed to reduce inflammation and improve local healing. If there is any inflammation or fungal infection, calendula petal ointment is a safe treatment. If boils recur, seek professional advice.

Breastfeeding
To stimulate the flow of milk, a standard infusion of the leaves and seed of borage (*Borago officinalis*), dill seed, aniseed and fennel seed three times a day can help. A decoction of fenugreek seed is a strong stimulant. Simmer 1½ tsp (8 ml) seed in 1 cup (225 ml) water for 10 minutes and drink three times a day. A tsp (5 ml) aniseed or honey will improve the taste. Another powerful stimulant is found in the flowering top of goat's rue (*Galega officinalis*): increases in milk flow of up to 50 percent have been recorded. Infuse 1 tsp (5 ml) dried leaves in 1 cup (225 ml) boiling water for 10 minutes and drink twice a day.

Bronchitis
For an effective bronchitis compound, combine equal parts of coltsfoot (*Tussilago farfara*), horehound (*Marrubium vulgare*) and aniseed. *See also* **Coughs.**

Bruises *see* **FIRST AID**

Burns, minor *see* **FIRST AID** *and* **Sunburn**

Chilblains and cold limbs
To warm hands and feet, massage gently with warmed macerated oil of honeysuckle flowers (*Lonicera caprifolium*). This will bring an increased flow of blood to the surface skin. For a foot bath to improve the circulation of cold feet and help chilblains, which are caused by poor circulation, use an infusion of 1 tbsp (15 ml) freshly ground mustard seed to 4 pints (2 litres) water. Cayenne seed powder is also a powerful stimulant to the circulatory system and helps blood flow to the extremities. In an ointment it can be used in moderation for unbroken chilblains.

Elder leaf (*Sambucus nigra*) ointment is useful for chilblains. Heat 1 part fresh leaves with 2 parts petroleum jelly until the leaves are crisp. Strain and label for storage.

To improve bad circulation, drink rose hip or horsetail (*Equisetum arvense*) or buckwheat (*Fagopyrum esculentum*) tea daily to strengthen small capillaries. Some spices and strongly flavoured herbs, such as black pepper, cloves, cinnamon, coriander, cumin, freshly grated root ginger, garlic, marjoram, rosemary and thyme, improve circulation. Include them frequently in your diet, especially in the winter months.

Colds and fevers
To protect against colds, eat or take the juice of a raw clove of garlic three times a day. Essential oils are very efficient at destroying harmful bacteria and viruses. They can also be used in steam inhalants or as a room spray (see p. 235).

Rose hip tea, said to be high in vitamin C, can be used to build resistance to colds and other infections. Cayenne powder is also excellent at warding off colds as it strengthens and stimulates the circulatory and digestive system. Infuse ½–1 tsp (3–5 ml) cayenne powder in 1 cup (225 ml) boiling water for 10 minutes. Strain and take 1 tbsp (15 ml) of this mixture topped up with hot water when needed or before each meal.
At the first sign of a cold, take a mixture of elderflower (*Sambucus nigra*), peppermint (*Mentha piperita*) and yarrow (*Achillea millefolium*).

Infuse ½ tsp (3 ml) of each together in 1 cup (225 ml) boiling water for 20 minutes. Strain, add 1 tsp (5 ml) honey and ¼ tsp (2 ml) cayenne pepper. This should decrease the intensity and the discomfort of a cold or flu. If the mixture benefits you, the herbs are worth storing as a dried blend for winter use. Another remedy to take at the earliest-possible moment is 9 small horehound leaves (*Marrubium vulgare*) chopped finely and eaten raw with 1 tbsp (15 ml) honey. Repeat as necessary.

To fight colds and flu, take hot lemon and honey as often as desired as lemon has antibacterial properties. Take frequent hot drinks of elderflower (*Sambucus nigra*), peppermint (*Mentha piperita*) or yarrow (*Achillea millefolium*) tea to promote perspiration and to reduce temperature. Elderflower is also useful for reducing any nasal inflammation from catarrh. If this is accompanied by a penetrating chill, add grated root ginger or cayenne. Black pepper sprinkled over food also has a restorative effect, or you could take an infusion of mustard

seed, ¼ tsp (2 ml) powder infused for 5 minutes in 1 cup (225 ml) boiling water, three times a day, or add 4 pints (2 litres) of mustard infusion to bathwater.

For catarrh and flu, golden rod (*Solidago virgaurea*) is good because it is antiseptic, expels catarrh and soothes inflammation. Infuse 2 tsp (10 ml) dried flowering stalks in 1 cup (225 ml) boiling water for 10 minutes and drink a cup (225 ml) three times a day. Goldenseal root (*Hydrastis canadensis*) is also excellent for its healing and tonic powers on the mucous membranes. Drink an infusion of ½–1 tsp (3–5 ml) of powdered root in 1 cup (225 ml) boiling water three times a day. Do not take this during pregnancy. You can also try a hot infusion of borage (*Borago officinalis*), coltsfoot (*Tussilago farfara*), comfrey (*Symphytum officinale*), or ground ivy (*Glecoma hederacea*) to relieve catarrh.

Relieve stuffiness by inhaling the vapours from a steam bath of chamomile flowers (*Matricaria recutita*) or eucalyptus leaves (*Eucalyptus globulus*) (see also p. 235 for additional inhalation ideas). A

pinch of basil taken as snuff can bring back your sense of smell. When your temperature has returned to normal, drink a warm infusion of clivers (*Galium aparine*) three times a day to continue a mild perspiration action, help prevent gastric disturbance and promote restful sleep. Begin taking vegetable juices and progress to homemade vegetable soup, fresh fruit and salads. Reintroduce heavier foods slowly to avoid overloading the digestive system when it is still vulnerable.

Horehound tea restores an appetite that may need stimulating after flu. If lethargy or depression follow, take lemon balm (*Melissa officinalis*) or vervain (*Verbena officinalis*) tea. If this persists after a few days, seek professional advice.

Colic *see* **CHILDREN'S PROBLEMS**

Constipation

Long-term constipation, or any unusual changes in bowel habits, should be discussed with a medical herbalist or doctor. Roughage in the diet and regular exercise are

---

CHILDREN'S PROBLEMS

Colic
First choice for children is dill water (see p. 45). If you anticipate digestive discomfort, try giving the baby a teaspoonful before she or he feeds. Otherwise give a teaspoonful as required.

Diarrhoea
Always seek the advice of a trained medical practitioner for persistent children's diarrhoea. A standard agrimony (*Agrimonia eupatoria*) infusion is a specific herbal remedy for childhood diarrhoea, as is a decoction of bistort root (*Polygonum bistorta*). Either can be drunk, 1 cup (225 ml) three times a day. An infusion of coriander also eases diarrhoea safely for children. Use 1 tsp (5 ml) bruised seed infused for 5 minutes and drink before meals or three times a day.

Headlice
Maggie Tisserand, in her book *Aromatherapy for Women*, has developed a recipe of essential oils which eliminates lice and leaves the hair lustrous and shining. Combine 25 drops of rosemary oil, 25 drops of lavender oil, 13 drops of geranium (*Pelargonium*) oil and 12 drops of

eucalyptus oil in 3 fl oz (75 ml) vegetable oil. Divide the hair into small sections and saturate each section with the mixture down to the roots. Pile long hair on top of the head ensuring that every bit is oiled. Wrap plastic around the head and behind the ears to stop the oils from evaporating. Make sure that small children cannot move the plastic anywhere near the nose or mouth and restrict breathing. Leave it on for 2 hours. Remove the plastic, add shampoo and rub in well, rinse thoroughly and comb through with a fine nit-comb. Repeat three days later.

Nappy rash
If practicable, expose the baby's bottom to fresh air frequently. A cool compress of calendula or chamomile (*Matricaria recutita*) can be laid on sore areas for short periods. Use a lotion or ointment made with calendula, comfrey (*Symphytum offincinale*) or marsh mallow (*Althaea officinalis*) to soothe the skin and promote rapid healing.

Sleep problems
Chamomile (*Matricaria recutita*) tea is a safe and gentle sedative for children

and traditionally recommended for those having nightmares. Give 1 cup (225 ml) of warm infusion half an hour before bedtime and remember to take the child to the toilet again just before bed. For small babies, put 1 tbsp (15 ml) in a sterilized feeding bottle. For older babies, use up to half a cup (125 ml).

Teething
Chamomile tea calms some fractious children as do homeopathic granules of chamomile (sold as chamomilla). Babies can be given a clean piece of marsh mallow (*Althaea officinalis*) root to chew on. Make sure that the baby cannot choke on the root.

Worms
As garlic kills intestinal parasites, make a garlic ointment and apply it around the anus nightly for two weeks. Pumpkin seeds (*Cucurbita maxima*) are among the most efficient remedies for killing intestinal parasites, including tapeworms, but a routine of fasting, cleansing the bowels and precise dosage must be followed, so it is wise to carry out the treatment under the supervision of a qualified medical herbalist.

important for healthy functioning bowels, while tension and emotional worries can contribute to constipation. Herbs can be used for short-term relief but underlying causes should be addressed.

Syrup of figs is a valuable remedy, taken as required. An infusion of crushed flax seed (*Linum usitatissimum*) has a purgative action which brings relief: drink 1 cup (225 ml) morning and evening.

Liquorice root (*Glycyrrhiza glabra*) is a mild and pleasant laxative. Chew root as desired or make a decoction of 1 tsp (5 ml) root in 1 cup (225 ml) water and take three times a day. Stewed rhubarb in moderate doses is a gentle laxative for children; large doses cause a more powerful reaction. Rose hip tea is also a mild laxative. Use a decoction or infusion with halved hips, but strain through filter paper to remove the seeds and tiny hairs which are an irritant to the body. Drink whenever necessary.

Coughs

To fight bronchial infections, eat raw garlic cloves for their strong antibiotic content. To help dispel fluid and mucus from the lungs and air passages, horehound (*Marrubium vulgare*) is the first choice. Drink a hot standard infusion three times a day. Another important herb in the treatment of lung problems, coughs and colds, and asthma is coltsfoot (*Tussilago farfara*). An infusion of the leaves and flowers will soothe the bronchi, encourage tissue healing and protect the delicate mucous membranes from further irritations.

To ease cough spasms and help expel mucus, make cowslip flower (*Primula veris*) syrup or decoct cowslip root, simmering for 5 minutes, and drink 1 cup (225 ml) three times a day. It can be combined with coltsfoot and aniseed (*Pimpinella anisum*). Aniseed has an expectorant action and can also help make cough mixture more palatable.

For an irritating bronchial cough with a great deal of catarrh, the expectorant, antiseptic action of elecampane root (*Inula helenium*) along with the soothing effect of its mucilage makes it an excellent remedy, especially for children. Infuse 1 tsp (5 ml) shredded root in 1 cup (225 ml) cold water for 9 hours. Drink it hot three times a day. An irritating cough can also be soothed by an infusion of powdered marsh mallow root (*Althaea officinalis*). It combines well with horehound (*Marrubium vulgare*) and liquorice (*Glycyrrhiza glabra*). For dry coughs, combine coltsfoot with horehound and mullein (*Verbascum thapsus*).

To reduce catarrh in the lungs, apply a poultice of freshly ground mustard seed. Mix 4 oz (110 g) seeds with warm water to make a thick paste. Apply the paste between two pieces of gauze with the bottom piece dampened so that is does not stick to the skin. Leave for one minute only. If skin is reddened, massage with an appropriate aromatherapy oil or any vegetable oil. Flax seed can be used with mustard to help reduce lung catarrh. A tea of plantain leaves (*Plantago major*) is a gentle expectorant and the herb is widely cultivated by Russian pharmaceutical companies. A standard infusion of star anise (*Illicium verum*) has expectorant and antibacterial properties. It mixes well with other cough remedies.

Cystitis

Drink a standard infusion of silver birch leaves (*Betula pendula*) against cystitis and other infections of the urinary tract, and to remove excess water from the system. It can be combined with bearberry (*Arctostaphylos uva-ursi*). A decoction of sweet Joe Pye root (*Eupatorium purpureum*), drunk three times a day, is helpful for urinary infections including cystitis. A standard infusion of yarrow (*Achillea millefolium*) is antiseptic to the urinary tract and assists recovery from cystitis.

Cuts see FIRST AID

Depression

A lavender flower infusion, taken three times a day, can be effective in clearing depression especially combined with rosemary (*Rosmarinus officinalis*) or skullcap (*Scutellaria lateriflora*). Rosemary is useful if your depression results from psychological tension or if you are feeling run-down after illness. Drink a standard infusion. It also combines well with skullcap.

Take a standard infusion of vervain (*Verbena officinalis*) to ease depression and melancholy which may follow flu. It also combines well with skullcap.

Diarrhoea

Sudden, painful diarrhoea and chronic diarrhoea need expert medical attention. Other cases are often the body's way of attempting to dump toxic material as fast as possible. Most herbal remedies attempt to assist this action while soothing the bowel and reducing inflammation.

Self-heal (*Prunella vulgaris*) has a gentle action which soothes inflamed mucous membranes. Drink an infusion three times daily. The same dose can be taken of agrimony (*Agrimonia eupatoria*) and coriander seed infusion (*see also* **CHILDREN'S PROBLEMS**).

Digestion

Most flavouring and seasoning herbs stimulate the flow of digestive juices in the stomach and intestine, and this increases the efficiency with which fats are broken down into fatty acids and nutrients are absorbed by the body. Classic herb partnerships reflect this benevolent fact: rosemary helps the digestion of fatty lamb, fennel assists the digestion of oily fish and horseradish aids the digestion of beef.

Many of the aromatic seeds are useful digestives. Take 1 tbsp (15 ml) ground aniseed boiled in 1 cup (225 ml) milk and drink this twice a day to improve the digestive system. Cardamom increases the flow of saliva and adds a pleasing aroma to digestive mixtures. Take 1 cup (225 ml) of infusion half an hour before each meal. Hot peppermint tea can be taken after a meal. A dish of digestive herbs including aniseed, caraway, dill and fennel seed is sometimes offered at the end of an Indian meal and greatly assists the body to digest rich foods.

If there is persistent or severe pain with digestion, consult a medical herbalist or doctor; if there are regular difficulties with indigestion not caused by disease, then rushed eating, an unbalanced diet or tension may be the cause, and it is sensible to consider solutions to these while taking herbs to alleviate the problem (*see also* **Stomach ache**).

Earache

Eardrops made from a weak infusion of goldenseal (Hydrastis canadensis) soothe earache. Mullein (Verbascum thapsus) can be addded to the infusion. Where catarrh of the middle ear is causing tinnitus, an infusion of ground ivy (Glecoma hederacea) flowering stems is helpful.

Eczema, rashes and itchy skin

Make a weak infusion of golden-seal root (Hydrastis canadensis) and use externally as a wash or compress for eczema and itchy skin. Expressed juice of chickweed (Stellaria media) will soothe sores or itchy patches from eczema or psoriasis and will tone and invigorate the skin, while a poultice of crushed flax seed (Linum usitatissimum) brings relief to shingles and psoriasis.

For children's eczema and nervous eczema, nettle (Urtica dioica) is specifically recommended by herbalists. Drink an infusion three times a day.

For weeping eczema, drink an infusion of the flowering tops of heartsease (Viola tricolor) three times a day. It combines well with nettle and red clover (Trifolium pratense).

Comfrey oil (see recipe, p. 131) often brings relief from patches of itchy rough skin and evening prim-rose oil can help.

Fevers see Colds and fevers

Flatulence

Seeds of aniseed, caraway or fennel are all effective at expelling wind but even more so in combination. Infuse crushed mixed seed and drink a cup (225 ml) slowly 30 minutes before each meal.

Many spice seeds help disperse wind; cloves or allspice can be chewed or infused as often as desired. Black pepper sprinkled on food removes wind. Infusions of root ginger, cardomom and coriander have pleasant aromas and relieve griping pains of wind. Star anise (Illicium verum) dispels wind

and is often included with dill and fennel seed in colic preparations for young babies. Take a standard infusion three times a day.

Lemon balm (Melissa officinalis) relieves flatulent spasms, and a dose of $\frac{1}{4}$–$\frac{1}{2}$ tsp (1–3 ml) powdered angelica root (Angelica archangelica) will quickly expel gas from the stomach and bowel with a gentle action that is safe for children.

Haemorrhoids

First choice for mild haemorrhoids is pilewort or lesser celandine (Ranunculus ficaria). It shrinks and soothes the swollen veins around the anus. Drink a standard infusion of the root or apply an ointment made with a strong infusion. For bleeding haemorrhoids, apply an ointment of self-heal (Prunella vulgaris).

An infusion of horse chestnut fruits (Aesculus hippocastanum) drunk three times a day or applied as a compress will tone and strengthen veins and help heal haemorrhoids (see also **Varicose veins**).

FIRST AID

Bruises and sprains

Apply distilled witch hazel (purchased from a chemist) with sterile cottonwool as soon as possible to small bumps and bruises. This will halt the swelling. Comfrey oil or ointment is good for messy scrapes, bruises and sprains. A poultice of comfrey leaves (Symphytum officinale) will reduce bruising and speed healing of sprains and fractures. It's best not used on deep wounds, as comfrey is such a powerful tissue healer that the surface skin may heal before the wound has healed deeper down. Comfrey also encourages good formation of scar tissue.

Both a lotion of St John's wort (Hypericum perforatum) and arnica (Arnica montana) ointment are excellent for sprains and bruises, especially if there is any pain or inflammation of the skin. **Caution:** Do not use arnica where the skin is broken.

An ointment of calendula petals, agrimony (Agrimonia eupatoria) or elder leaves (Sambucus nigra) is soothing and healing for bruises, sprains and other minor wounds.

Burns, minor

Immediately apply the cool inside surface of an aloe vera leaf to reduce pain, speed healing and leave a protective seal against infection. Later,

apply calendula as a cool compress or ointment to soothe and heal (see also **Sunburn**).

Major burns are an emergency: summon professional help at once. Cool the burn with cool (not ice-cold) water while waiting, and give the patient 6 drops Bach Flower Rescue Remedy and reassure him.

Cuts and abrasions

First clean the cut by soaking in witch hazel diluted with 4 parts, water or an antiseptic herbal infusion; elder leaves (Sambucus nigra) are excellent. A speedy alternative is to add 3 drops thyme or rosemary oil or $\frac{1}{2}$ tsp (3 ml) tincture of calendula to 1 cup (225 ml) hand-hot, boiled water. The antiseptic wash can also be gently swabbed on with a series of sterile cottonwool balls. A dose of 4 drops Bach Flower Rescue Remedy has a calming effect, while an infusion of lady's mantle (Alchemilla vulgaris) can be applied as a compress to arrest bleeding.

For slow-healing wounds, apply a compress or poultice of comfrey (Symphytum officinale), self-heal (Prunella vulgaris) or yarrow (Achillea millefolium). Add plantain leaves (Plantago major) for their antibiotic properties. If applying a poultice to an open wound, dip leaves briefly in boiling water to sterilize them.

To continue treatment, a soft ointment of comfrey, calendula or agrimony (Agrimonia eupatoria) is soothing and healing.

Stings and insect bites

Wasp stings are alkaline: apply inside surface of a houseleek leaf (Sempervivum tectorum), onion slices, or dab on vinegar (if possible thyme vinegar). Bee stings and ant bites are acid: apply sodium bicarbonate dissolved in ice-cold water. Remember to remove the bee sting.

Reduce painful swelling with a drop of neat lavender or eucalyptus oil. To soothe lingering irritation, apply a cold compress of tincture of calendula or calendula ointment.

To soothe nettle stings, rub on crushed dock leaves (Rumex obtusifolius).

Travel sickness

Recent research confirms that the best treatment to settle the stomach and help prevent nausea is an infusion of root ginger. Take a bottle of tincture of ginger when travelling, and give 10 drops in half a cup (125 ml) of water for adults or 2–3 drops mixed in a little warm water for children.

Pick large leaves of fresh angelica (Angelica archangelica) and crush them on the journey; the scent allays nausea and refreshes stale air.

Hangover

Lemon in water or in orange juice for extra vitamin C, hot peppermint or wild thyme tea can alleviate the discomfort. A drink of yarrow (*Achillea millefolium*) and elderflower (*Sambucus nigra*) tea will help the body to eliminate toxins.

Hay fever

Sufferers of hay fever and other allergies may benefit from an infusion of golden rod (*Solidago virgaurea*). Take half a cup (125 ml) four times a day. The irritated mucous membranes are relieved and soothed by drinking a warm infusion of hyssop (*Hyssopus officinalis*), lavender (*Lavandula* species), marjoram (*Origanum marjorana*) or thyme (*Thymus vulgaris*).

Apply cold compresses of witch hazel diluted in 4 parts boiled water to soothe the eyes. Hot mullein flower (*Verbascum thapsus*) tea and eyebright (*Euphrasia rostkoviana*) tea will help eliminate excess mucus, and eyebright will reduce redness around the eyes. Drink three times a day. Red and sore eyelids may result from other conditions. If symptoms persist, consult a qualified herbalist.

Headaches and migraines

Herbs may bring relief though they will not remove the cause. Fever-few leaf (*Tanacetum parthenium*) has justifiably become the primary remedy for migraine. A small to medium, fresh or frozen, leaf eaten between slices of bread (it can cause mouth ulcers in very sensitive people) three times a day has been found to reduce the intensity or frequency of 70 percent of migraines (usually in sufferers who gain relief from warmth applied to the head). Its action is cumulative and can take up to six months to show results. Do not take during pregnancy as it can stimulate the uterus. Alternatively take half a cup (125 ml) of leaf tea twice a day to reduce the pain of migraine.

Lavender (*Lavandula* species) is useful for stress-related headaches and combines well with valerian (*Valeriana officinalis*). Drink an infusion of lavender flowers three times a day. A standard infusion of valerian is useful in tension headaches, when it combines well with skullcap (*Scutellaria lateriflora*).

Headlice *see* CHILDREN'S PROBLEMS

High blood pressure

High blood pressure is a serious condition which must be monitored by a qualified medical person. Ripe hawthorn berries (*Crataegus monogyna*) are a gentle yet powerful tonic for the heart and circulation, bringing both low and high blood pressure back to normal when used over a long period. Infuse 2 tsp (10 ml) berries for 20 minutes in 1 cup (225 ml) boiling water and drink three times a day for an extended period. For high blood pressure hawthorn combines well in an infusion with lime blossom (*Tilia cordata*) and yarrow (*Achillea millefolium*). Yarrow reduces high blood pressure by dilating peripheral blood vessels.

Chronic hypertension responds well to 1 cup (225 ml) dandelion leaves (*Taraxacum officinale*) infusion taken three times a day. Garlic is reliable, but it will take four weeks for any drop in blood pressure. Eat raw cloves up to six times a day.

Insomnia

A cup (225 ml) of hop (*Humulus lupulus*) tea taken before retiring to bed is a useful sedative for insomnia except for anyone suffering from depression. It combines well with valerian (*Valeriana officinalis*) which reduces tension and anxiety, and passion flower leaves (*Passiflora incarnata*). Chamomile (*Chamaemelum nobile*) tea and catnip (*Nepeta cataria*) tea are traditional relaxing bedtime drinks that will reduce anxiety and promote restful sleep. Passion flower tea and orange blossom tea can also help insomniacs (*see also* CHILDREN'S PROBLEMS).

Itchy skin *see* Eczema, rashes and itchy skin

Joints, stiff *see* Muscles and joints

Kidney and liver complaints

Dandelion (*Taraxacum officinale*) is the ideal balanced diuretic as it supplies potassium, a substance lost during diuretic action. Decoct 1 tbsp (15 ml) root in 1 cup (225 ml) water and drink three times a day.

Menstrual cycle

The best remedy for the dull headache, irritability, mild depression, fluid retention or breast discomfort experienced by many women just before their period is evening primrose oil. Tests at a London hospital indicated that 85 percent of those in the trial experienced improvement. The herb (*Oenothera biennis*) is easy to grow but extracting the oil from the seed is complex, so purchase capsules from a health shop. Those that also contain a marine oil are particularly recommended. Skullcap (*Scutellaria lateriflora*), chamomile (*Matricaria recutita*) and lime blossom (*Tilia cordata*) are safe teas to soothe and reduce discomfort of PMT (premenstrual tension). Take an infusion three times a day to relieve the symptoms.

For menstrual cramps drink an infusion of chamomile or valerian (*Valeriana officinalis*) three times a day, or half a cup (125 ml) of feverfew (*Tanacetum parthenium*) tea taken twice a day.

For cramps with a feeling of heaviness, a hot infusion of raspberry leaf (*Rubus idaeus*) tea is recommended.

To help reduce period pains and excessive bleeding, try lady's mantle leaves (*Alchemilla vulgaris*), taken in a double-strength infusion three times a day. This also eases changes of the menopause.

To help relieve menopausal symptoms, try dried berries of the chaste tree (*Vitex agnus-castus*), which normalize the activity of sex hormones. They are also of benefit in PMT and help to normalize the body's natural balance after taking contraceptive pills. Infuse 1 tsp (5 ml) berries for 15 minutes; drink 1 cup (225 ml) three times a day. Motherwort (*Leonurus cardiaca*) reduces the discomfort of the menopause. When symptoms include irritability and anxiety, St John's wort (*Hypericum perforatum*) is recommended. Drink a standard infusion of flowering tops three times a day.

Muscles and joints

Essential oil of fennel is one of several oils which, used in a massage oil, will ease muscular pains (see also p. 250). The moist inside surface of fresh silver birch bark (*Betula pendula*) applied over the area will ease painful muscles, while a poultice of mustard seed (see recipe, p. 60) stimulates circulation and relieves muscular and skeletal pain.

An ointment or poultice of wintergreen leaves (*Gaultheria procumbens*) has painkilling and anti-inflammatory properties that are excellent for chronic muscular problems. If you suffer from muscular cramps, a standard infusion of valerian (*Valeriana officinalis*) will bring relief.

Nappy rash *see* CHILDREN'S PROBLEMS

Nausea

Freshly grated ginger or powdered cinammon bark infused on their own or sprinkled in other teas can be taken whenever necessary to relieve nausea and vomiting. Cloves, as a flavouring in food or drunk as an infusion, will allay nausea and vomiting while stimulating the digestive system. Infuse about 10 cloves in 1 cup (225 ml) boiling water for 10 minutes and take as required, *see also* **Pregnancy and childbirth**.

Nervous tension

Unlike tranquillizers, herbs that work to relax nervous tension also counter stress by reviving and toning the central nervous system.

The two finest treatments are skullcap flowering top (*Scutellaria lateriflora*), which is suitable for a wide range of nervous complaints and valerian root (*Valeriana officinalis*), which is suitable for nervous spasms and tremors, phobias, insomnia and restlessness. Fortunately they work well together. Take an infusion individually or in combination. Take 1 cup (225 ml) infusion up to three times a day or half a cup (125 ml) every three hours in times of great stress, but not for long periods of time. A standard infusion of borage leaves (*Borago officinalis*) is a restorative tonic to the adrenal glands, which are increasingly exposed to stress. Borage flowers and leaves in wine have a traditional reputation for bolstering courage. The combination seems to cause a significant rise in blood-adrenalin level, and a wine-glassful (150 ml) will relieve nervous tension during times of stress.

After a hectic day, try drinking a tea of ginseng (*Panax ginseng*), lime blossom (*Tilia cordata*) or lavender (*Lavandula* species) to calm and tone the nervous system. Lime and lavender combine well to combat nervous exhaustion, while lemon balm (*Melissa officinalis*) relieves tension and stressful states with a mild antidepressant action. It combines well with lavender flowers and lime blossom. Take a cup (225 ml) of mixed teas morning, evening and when required.

Wood betony (*Stachys officinalis*) strengthens the central nervous system and is mildly sedative, being especially good for headaches and neuralgia of a nervous origin. Take 1 cup (225 ml) tea three times a day or combine it with skullcap.

For relaxants, try chamomile (*Chamaemelum nobile*) which can be drunk as desired, and cowslip (*Primula veris*), which is a relaxing sedative for stress-related tension. Make an infusion of the petals and drink 1 cup (225 ml) three times a day. It can be combined with lime blossom or skullcap.

To ease tension a standard infusion of St John's wort (*Hypericum perforatum*) has pain-reducing and sedative properties, making it useful for anxiety-related conditions, unless there is also depression. Rosemary on the other hand, is a stimulant to the nervous system and useful for psychological tension which is causing depression.

Pregnancy and childbirth

Herbs with a strong action must be avoided during pregnancy, particularly those that stimulate the uterus, such as goldenseal (*Hydrastis canadensis*).

To prevent morning sickness, first try not to eat "junk" foods, which many herbalists feel contribute to this problem. Include plenty of fresh fruit and vegetables in your diet. Mild herbs that may help include meadowsweet flowering tops (*Filipendula ulmaria*), chamomile flowers (*Matricaria recutita*), lime blossom (*Tilia cordata*) and peppermint (*Mentha piperita*). Drink a standard infusion on rising in the morning, at midday and in the evening. An infusion of powdered cinnamon bark and freshly grated ginger will allay nausea. These can be individually infused or sprinkled

on the previously mentioned leaf and flower teas.

To tone and strengthen the tissue and muscle of the uterus, raspberry leaf (*Rubus idaeus*) tea has a deservedly high reputation. Take an infusion of 2 tsp (10 ml) with 1 cup (225 ml) boiling water and drink freely during the last few months of pregnancy. This will tone the muscles to assist contractions and check bleeding in labour. An infusion of goldenseal root (*Hydrastis canadensis*) stimulates the involuntary muscles and is an excellent aid during labour but must be avoided during pregnancy. Infuse ½–1 tsp (3–5 ml) powdered root in 1 cup (225 ml) water for 10 to 15 minutes; drink three times a day.

In the early stages of labour, a sponge wash with rosewater, lavender water or an infusion of rosemary has a pleasantly relaxing scent and mild antiseptic qualities.

Rash *see* Eczema, rashes and itchy skin

Rheumatism and arthritis

The causes of these ailments are complex, and a qualified herbalist should be consulted to discover which aspects of diet or lifestyle may be contributing to the problem. Devil's claw (*Harpagophytum procumbens*) has been found to be effective in many cases: it appears to detoxify the body and to stimulate the body's immune system. So far, no harmful side-effects have been discovered but it can be nauseous. Decoct ½–1 tsp (3–5 ml) root in 1 cup (225 ml) water and boil for 15 minutes. Drink three times a day for at least a month to assess its effect.

To treat rheumatoid arthritis, try an infusion of celery seed, which helps to counter acid in the blood. Take 1 cup (225 ml) three times a day. It works well combined with dandelion root (*Taraxacum officinale*) or devil's claw.

A standard infusion of valerian (*Valeriana officinalis*) will relieve the pain of rheumatism, and a double-strength infusion of chickweed (*Stellaria media*) steeped for 5 minutes has brought relief to some.

One of the beneficial side-effects noticed by a significant number of patients using feverfew (*Tanacetum parthenium*) to treat migraine was a reduction in their pain from arthrit

Try a dose of 1 leaf in a sandwich three times a day for up to six months (but not during pregnancy).

Essential oils such as rosemary, applied in a massage oil, can bring relief to rheumatic and arthritic pains (see p. 231). Wintergreen (*Gaultheria procumbens*) ointment contains useful painkilling and anti-inflammatory ingredients, arnica (*Arnica montana*) ointment reduces discomfort, and a compress of cayenne pepper infusion eases pain by increasing circulation.

Skin ulcers

The fruit of the fig tree has strong antiseptic and disinfectant properties. Apply a poultice of dried figs to chronic leg ulcers. A poultice of comfrey leaves (*Symphytum officinale*) has given remarkable results in many cases of chronic varicose ulcers and is more beneficial if combined with the soothing properties of marsh mallow (*Althaea officinalis*). Calendula petals, applied either as a compress of the infusion or as an ointment, reduce inflammation and speed healing.

Sores *see* **Boils and sores**

Spots *see* **Acne**

Sprains *see* **FIRST AID**

Stings *see* **FIRST AID**

Stomach ache

Sharp or prolonged pain in the stomach needs a professional medical diagnosis. For those who already know what is causing their ailment, herbs can be helpful as long as the condition is monitored.
To soothe and heal the delicate mucous membranes in the stomach, drink chamomile (*Matricaria recutita*) tea for its anti-inflammatory effect or marsh mallow (*Althaea officinalis*) as desired.
For digestive disorders, slippery elm (*Ulmus rubra*) (purchased as a powder) is both a soothing remedy as well as a wholesome food for those unable to face solid food, and it is safe for children over 12 months. Make a paste with ½–1 tbsp (8–15 ml) powdered bark and a little cold water. Stir in 1 cup (225 ml) of hot milk or water and sweeten with honey if desired.

For stomach cramps caused by indigestion, drink an infusion of antiseptic catnip (*Nepeta cataria*).
For stomach ulcers, chew liquorice root (*Glycyrrhiza glabra*) as desired or take a dose of ¼ tsp (1 ml) powdered root daily (strong doses are laxative). A calendula petal infusion, drunk three times a day, especially combined with marsh mallow root, soothes and aids the healing of stomach ulcers.
For gastric and duodenal ulcers, lime blossom (*Tilia cordata*) tea has useful anti-inflammatory properties and the softening mucilage of comfrey (*Symphytum officinale*) makes it a soothing and healing treatment. Boil 1 tsp (5 ml) dried root in 1 cup (225 ml) water for 10 minutes.
For stomach ulcers and colitis: Half to 1 tsp (3–5 ml) powdered goldenseal root (*Hydrastis canadensis*) infused in 1 cup (225 ml) boiling water for 10 minutes is a powerful tonic for all parts of the digestive tract. *See also* **Digestion.**

Sunburn

Aloe vera leaf juice is cooling and healing for sunburn and minor burns. Apply directly to the area of sunburn. A compress of sorrel (*Rumex acetosa*) also has a cooling effect. Sorrel tea is said to nullify the effects of sunstroke and exhaustion: take one cup (225 ml) three times a day.

A macerated oil of St John's wort (*Hypericum perforatum*) is excellent for minor burns once they have cooled.

Teething *see* CHILDREN'S PROBLEMS

Throat, sore

Purple sage (*Salvia officinalis* 'Purpurea') is an excellent treatment for sore throats. It is antiseptic and healing for inflammation of the mouth, throat and tonsils. Drink half a cup (125 ml) infusion four times a day, and gargle with it as often as required. Do not drink it during pregnancy: it may cause abortion.

The bacterial qualities of lemon, another popular remedy, are increased if you take it in an infusion with a natural antiseptic such as eucalyptus (*Eucalyptus globulus*) and honey. Thyme (*Thymus vulgaris*) is a powerful disinfectant and excellent gargle for sore throats, laryngitis and tonsillitis.

Gargle with a standard tea of fenugreek seed, agrimony (*Agrimonia eupatorium*) or self-heal (*Prunella vulgaris*), or a decoction of bistort root (*Polygonum bistorta*) for relief of sore throats, inflammation of the mouth or tongue and laryngitis, or a cayenne infusion for laryngitis (see recipe, p. 243).

The anti-inflammatory and antiseptic properties of chamomile (*Matricaria recutita*) make it a useful gargle for sore throats and mouth infections such as **gingivitis.** Use a double-strength infusion of the flowers. The menthol in peppermint (*Mentha piperita*) makes it a pleasant antiseptic.
Soothe a sore throat by wrapping round a hot compress of sage (*Salvia officinalis*) or thyme (*Thymus vulgaris*), kept warm and in place with a scarf. Chew liquorice root (*Glycyrrhiza glabra*) as desired.

Toothache

Cloves are a powerful local antiseptic and mild pain reliever. Put a drop of oil of cloves (available from chemists and essential-oil suppliers) on the end of a cotton-wool bud and dab on or near the tooth; alternatively place a clove in the mouth near the tooth for as long as it is effective.

Travel sickness *see* **FIRST AID**

Ulcers, skin, *see* **Skin ulcers**

Ulcers, stomach *see* **Stomach ache**

Varicose veins

Much can be done to prevent varicose veins. Tackle constipation, improve your diet, adding vitamins B, C and E, take more exercise, stop smoking, avoid hot baths and standing for hours.

Take spices that stimulate the circulation, such as ginger and cayenne, and an infusion of herbs that contain rutin, such as buckwheat (*Fagopyrum esculentum*), hawthorn berries (*Crataegus monogyna*) and horse chestnuts (*Aesculus hippocastanum*). Drink no more than three times a day, or use as a compress or lotion.

If your veins are inflamed or ache, a compress of calendula tincture or witch hazel will relieve the pain (*see also* **Haemorrhoids**).

THERAPEUTIC INDEX OF ESSENTIAL OILS

Essential oils are useful supplements for treating minor ailments but for serious conditions, or if there is any uncertainty of diagnosis, be sure to consult a qualified practitioner. Apply the oils through massage, blended with a carrier oil, as described on pp. 230–4, or by one of the methods on p. 235. Do not take internally. Note that oils listed at the beginning of each group (out of alphabetical order) are considered most significant for that treatment. Use the oils in combination to treat your various symptoms. Refer to pp. 236–7 for ideas for blends.

Acne Cajuput, juniper, bergamot ($\frac{1}{2}$% concentration), chamomile, cedarwood, eucalyptus, lavender, lemongrass, sandalwood

Anxiety Jasmine, lavender, marjoram, neroli, basil, bergamot, camphor, chamomile, frankincense, geranium, juniper, melissa, rose, sandalwood

Apathy Jasmine, rosemary

Appetite, loss of Chamomile, bergamot, black pepper, coriander, fennel, ginger, hyssop, myrrh, sage

Arteriosclerosis Lemon, juniper

Arthritis Benzoin, chamomile, cypress, sage, juniper, lemon, thyme

Asthma Hyssop, lavender, pine, rosemary, basil, benzoin, cajuput

Athlete's foot Myrrh, lavender

Backache Chamomile, geranium

Blood pressure, high Clary sage, lavender, lemon, marjoram, melissa

Blood pressure, low Sage, hyssop, rosemary, thyme

Bronchitis, chronic Eucalyptus, hyssop, niaouli, cajuput, lavender

Bruises Hyssop, calendula, fennel

Burns and scalds (seek medical advice) Lavender, chamomile, eucalyptus, geranium, niaouli

Capillaries, broken Chamomile, cypress, rose, lavender, neroli

Catarrh Hyssop, basil, benzoin, black pepper, cedarwood, chamomile, eucalyptus, frankincense, jasmine, lavender, lemon, myrrh, thyme

Cellulite Cypress, fennel, oregano

Chilblains Lavender, lemon, camphor

Circulation, poor Black pepper, juniper, cypress, marjoram, lavender

Colds Lemon, pine, orange, tea tree

Constipation Fennel, marjoram, black pepper, rosemary, camphor

Coughs Cypress, eucalyptus, hyssop, thyme, benzoin, cedarwood

Cramp Basil, cypress, marjoram

Cystitis Pine, benzoin, bergamot, black pepper, cajuput, cedarwood, chamomile

Dandruff Chamomile, cedarwood, juniper, lavender, rosemary

Depression Camphor, chamomile, jasmine, thyme, basil, bergamot, clary sage, cypress, geranium

Diabetes Geranium, juniper

Diarrhoea Lavender, black pepper, chamomile, cinnamon, clove, ginger, juniper, lemon, myrrh, neroli, peppermint, sandalwood

Earache Basil, chamomile, clove, hyssop, lavender, rose

Eczema, dry Chamomile, geranium, hyssop, lavender

Eczema, weeping Bergamot, juniper

Fevers Basil, black pepper, bergamot, camphor, chamomile, eucalyptus, hyssop, melissa, peppermint

Flatulence Coriander, fennel, peppermint

Flu Black pepper, eucalyptus, peppermint, rosemary, cypress

Fluid retention Cypress, eucalyptus, fennel, geranium, juniper, lavender

Food poisoning Black pepper, fennel

Haemorrhoids Cypress, frankincense, juniper, myrrh

Hair loss Lavender, rosemary, sage

Hay fever Chamomile, cypress, hyssop, lavender, lemon, pine, rose

Headache Chamomile, lavender, lemon, marjoram, peppermint, rose, rosemary

Herpes Geranium, lemon, myrrh, chamomile, eucalyptus, lavender

Indigestion Bergamot, chamomile, fennel, peppermint, rosemary, sage

Insect bites Lavender, basil, cinnamon, lemon, melissa, sage, thyme

Insomnia Basil, chamomile, clary sage, juniper, lavender, marjoram, neroli, rose, sandalwood, ylang-ylang

Itching skin Chamomile, cedarwood

Laryngitis Cypress, frankincense, lemon, sage, thyme, sandalwood

Lice Cinnamon, eucalyptus, clove, geranium, lavender, lemongrass

Liver, cirrhosis Juniper, rosemary

Lung disease Eucalyptus, tea tree, thyme, clove, pine

Malaria Eucalyptus, lemon

Menopause Cypress, sage

Menstruation, painful Cypress, peppermint, sage

Mental fatigue Rosemary, basil, peppermint

Mosquito repellent Eucalyptus, clove, geranium, peppermint

Muscular aches Eucalyptus, lavender, rosemary, black pepper

Muscle stiffness Rosemary, thyme

Muscle tone Lavender, lemongrass, rosemary, black pepper

Nausea Peppermint, basil, black pepper, fennel, lavender, rose

Nerves, panic Basil, bergamot, cedarwood, chamomile, geranium, juniper, lavender, marjoram, melissa, neroli, rose, thyme

Neuralgia, facial Chamomile, geranium, eucalyptus, peppermint

Over-exertion Basil, lavender

Premenstrual syndrome Benzoin, cedarwood, chamomile, cypress, frankincense, geranium, juniper

Psoriasis Bergamot, cajuput, lavender

Rheumatism Rosemary, ginger, oregano, pine, thyme

Sedatives Chamomile, lavender, lemon, marjoram, thyme

Shingles Eucalyptus, geranium, peppermint

Shock Camphor, melissa, neroli, peppermint

Sinusitis Basil, eucalyptus, lavender, lemon, niaouli, pine, thyme

Skin, chapped Benzoin, patchouli, chamomile, geranium, rose

Sore throat Tea tree, lemon, bergamot, clary sage, eucalyptus, geranium, ginger, sage, thyme

Spots Juniper, lavender, lemon

Sprains Eucalyptus, lavender

Stress Neroli, cedarwood, juniper

Sweating, offensive Cypress, pine

Tonsillitis Geranium, ginger, lemon

Toothache Clove, black pepper

Travel sickness Peppermint, ginger

Ulcers, skin Tea tree, bergamot, camphor, eucalyptus, frankincense

Ulcers, stomach Chamomile, geranium, lemon, peppermint, rose

Verrucae and warts Lemon

Vomiting Basil, black pepper, chamomile, fennel, lavender, lemon, melissa, peppermint, rose

Wounds (for serious bleeding get help immediately) Lemon on bandage to arrest bleeding; clean with lavender, eucalyptus, chamomile, geranium, hyssop, juniper

Wounds, infected Tea tree, chamomile, eucalyptus, lavender, myrrh, hyssop, thyme

CULTIVATING & HARVESTING HERBS

Herbs must be among the easiest plants to cultivate, being amenable to most conditions and rarely troubled by disease. The following pages provide information on growing herbs from seed and from cuttings; in the garden, in containers and indoors. There are practical ideas for making a variety of traditional herb garden features, notes on making herbal pesticides and fertilizers, and instructions on how to harvest and preserve different plant parts.

Soil preparation

Many herbs can survive on poor, stony ground, but few can cope with water-logged soil. Ideally, they prefer a light, open soil which is well aerated yet able to retain moisture and nutrients. To help them thrive, prepare the soil in early spring before sowing or planting. Dig deeply and create a fine tilth, then rake to a smooth level surface. Allow the soil to settle at least one week before planting seed. Pot-grown plants can be planted almost immediately in prepared soil.

Improving drainage
To increase air spaces and drainage in heavy soils, first dig over in early winter as the presence of frost helps to break down solid clods of earth. In early spring, mix coarse grit, horticultural sand or vermiculite into the top 18 in (45 cm). Add compost to supply a more fibrous texture and nutrients. All these create space for extra oxygen, which means an increase in bacterial activity. This in turn results in more available plant food. They also make the soil more attractive to earthworms, whose presence enriches and lightens any soil.

When planting one of the Mediterranean herbs such as rosemary, sage, thyme, lavender, or savory, incorporate a child's bucket of grit into each cubic foot (30 cm) of planting space to help the drainage.

If soil is very waterlogged, you can improve it for a few years by building a rubble drain. Dig an 18 in–2 ft (45–60 cm) deep ditch angled toward an existing ditch or drainage facility. Half fill with coarse rubble and cover with a 3 in (8 cm) layer of gravel, clinker or ash, replacing the top soil. For a more permanent solution, make the ditch 2 ft 6 in–3 ft (75 cm–1 m) deep with plastic drainage pipes along the bottom leading to a soakaway and proceed as before. Alternatively, if soil is prone to being waterlogged, consider making raised beds (see p. 261).

Eliminating weeds
While preparing the soil for planting, get rid of persistent weeds such as bindweed (*Convolvulus arvensis*), couch grass (*Agropyron repens*) and ground elder (*Aegopodium podagraria*), which can quickly take over a herb bed. Dig up weeds with taproots, taking care not to break off any of the root or it will sprout. Fork out longer straggling roots over a period of about a month. Dig through the soil at weekly intervals. Don't throw uprooted weeds on the compost heap; you'll transplant them.

Enriching soil
A light, free-draining sandy soil does not hold moisture and is usually low in nutrients. Although the Mediterranean herbs can thrive on such a soil, others, such as mint and chives, may benefit from the addition of compost, or a well rotted straw-based manure, to help retain moisture and supply nutrients. These are best worked in after winter rains so most of the nutrients will be available for spring growth. Peat helps to retain moisture but it does not contribute nutrients and may make the soil too acid if used in large quantities.

Most herbs are like vegetables in their preference for a slightly alkaline soil. If your soil is acidic, add a sprinkling of lime, not as a plant food but as a catalyst to help the plants take up the nutrients present. Use the lowest amount recommended. Ashes from wood fires are also beneficial as they contribute lime and potash.

Avoid using artificial fertilizers as these can make growth too lush, which will result in a plant with poor flavour. However, if you know your soil is poor or lacking in minerals, try one of the herbal fertilizers listed on p. 267.

Mulching
Once herbs are established they will benefit from a mulch, a covering of organic matter spread over the soil. The mulch helps to stop the soil drying out and provides nutrients. Applied during the growing season, it boosts lush growth in salad herbs such as sorrel and purslane, and in shade- and moisture-loving herbs such as mint, angelica and sweet cicely. It can also protect plant roots from frosts.

Mulching is usually most beneficial after a heavy rain. Spread light, organic matter over the soil and around plants in a layer up to 3 in (8 cm) deep. The Mediterranean herbs such as rosemary, thyme, sage and lavender may benefit more from a layer of gravel or clinkers if the soil is very moist. Mulching also helps to control weed-growth by blocking out light.

Propagation

Many herbs will grow from seed and readily self-seed once established. A large proportion can also be grown from cuttings and division.

Sowing seed on site

Annual plants of the Umbelliferae family (anise, chervil, dill, coriander and cumin, and the biennial parsley) are best sown on site, where you wish them to grow, as any root disturbance in transplanting can make them run to seed before they have produced a useful crop of leaves. Parsley seed is exceptionally slow to germinate so do be patient.

As a rule, sow seed in mid- to late spring after the soil has been prepared and warmed up. One of the most reliable signs is the emergence of new weed seedlings in the ground. Remove weeds and sow seeds thinly in shallow drills (see below).

If the soil feels heavy and lumpy, spread a layer of fine sand along the drill to give seeds a better start. Barely cover seeds with a fine sprinkling of soil and tap down gently. Water with a fine spray. Mark each row with the name of the herb and date of sowing.

Covering with cloches gives seeds a head start and provides protection from late frosts and hungry wildlife. Lay the cloches in position a few weeks before you sow so the soil warms up.

Thin out seedlings when they have reached a height of 2–4 in (5–10 cm). Water the soil the day before you remove them. Use a trowel or your fingers to lift them from the soil and handle very carefully when replanting. See the Herbal Index or seed packet for planting distances.

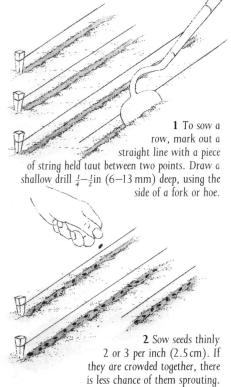

1 To sow a row, mark out a straight line with a piece of string held taut between two points. Draw a shallow drill $\frac{1}{4}-\frac{1}{2}$ in (6–13 mm) deep, using the side of a fork or hoe.

2 Sow seeds thinly 2 or 3 per inch (2.5 cm). If they are crowded together, there is less chance of them sprouting.

Growing seed indoors

It is better to grow expensive, rare or unfamiliar seeds in seed trays indoors, where all conditions can be controlled. Sowing seeds indoors also allows you to start the plants off before the soil has warmed up.

Buy a proprietary loamless seed growing mixture or mix your own with two parts sterilized loam, one part fine peat, one part coarse sand and a dash of fertilizer. Blend well and pass through a $\frac{3}{8}$ in (8 mm) sieve.

A shallow seed tray 2 in (5 cm) deep is the best size for sowing small seeds. Small pots can also be used and are better if you only wish to sow a few seeds. If using deeper containers, fill the lower section with clean drainage material – a layer of gravel, perlite or broken crocks. Add growing mixture to within $\frac{1}{4}$ in (6 mm) of the top. Give the tray or pot a sharp downward tap then press the soil surface gently with a flat board. If the mixture is very dry,

Preparing pots and trays

seeds
growing mixture
drainage material

water and leave it to drain. Sow seeds thinly, mixing fine seeds with sand so they spread out evenly. Sprinkle over a fine layer of potting mixture to hold the seeds in place. Cover larger seed with a layer as deep as the seed.

Water with a fine rose, beginning the flow off the tray and ending off the tray. Label, date and cover, with a layer of glass and a layer of newspaper.

Seeds germinate faster in the warmth of a greenhouse or indoors (preferably

in a warm place such as the airing cupboard) and need to be watched daily. If further watering proves necessary, set the pots in water until the top appears damp.

When sprouting begins, move the trays into the light. Lift the covering at one edge for two days. Then take off the cover but shade the seedlings from bright sun for several days.

Transplanting seedlings

As soon as plants are large enough to handle, thin them out or transplant them to a larger box or a pot to prevent overcrowding. Wait, though, until the first pair of true leaves has formed, after the cotyledons – two seed leaves which are a completely different shape.

Handle young seedlings by a leaf rather than by their stems and take them carefully out of the soil to avoid breaking or bruising their tiny new roots and stems. Make a hole in the soil then insert the seedling. Firm the compost, water it and site the plants in a light location out of direct sunlight. Daily attention is important at this stage as overcrowded seedlings or those not in good light can become weak and leggy within two days. If this happens, repot them at a lower depth, by burying half the elongated stem.

Once seedlings are growing well, remove any feebler ones and leave the strongest to grow on. Transfer to larger pots with potting grade compost (see p. 264) or plant out.

Firm in a seedling after careful transplanting.

HERBS WORTH GROWING FROM SEED		
An enormous number of herbs, common and rare, can be grown from seed but the group listed below		is generally the easiest. If you require only one plant, it is often cheaper and quicker to buy one.
All the annuals		
anise	coriander	orach
basil	cumin	purslane
borage	dill	salad rocket
calendula	mustard	summer savory
chamomile, annual	nasturtium	sweet marjoram
chervil		
Biennials		
angelica	parsley, curled and broad	wild celery (smallage)
caraway	leaf	woad
Perennials		
catnip	lovage	salad burnet
chamomile, flowering	marjoram, French	sorrel
chives	marsh mallow	sweet cicely
fennel, green and bronze	onion, Welsh	thyme, common
feverfew	oregano	winter savory
good King Henry	rue	wormwood
hyssop	sage	

Planting out

All plants hate shocks; they need to get acclimatized to new conditions. Plants propagated indoors should move outdoors gradually. Set them out in a sheltered position during the day, and take them in at night. After several days, leave them out at night as well. Plant out after about a week.

Do not plant out half-hardy plants until you are sure spring frosts are over. Avoid planting out on hot or rainy days. The best days are calm and warm; early evening is often ideal as the soil is warm and the sun low.

Water the soil beforehand, if it isn't already moist. Make a hole the size of the root, insert the plant, handling the root area very carefully; fill the hole with soil and firm the plant in.

OTHER FORMS OF PROPAGATION

Herbs can also be grown easily using vegetative means of propagation: cuttings, dividing and layering. With these methods, you can be more certain of the resulting flower and leaf shapes and colours on the new plant whereas plants grown from seeds are often more variable. These methods of propagation are also beneficial to the parent plants, which might otherwise become overcrowded and straggly.

Propagating from cuttings

There are three main types of stem cuttings which are suitable for herbs: softwood, from new shoots which have not yet hardened; semi-hardwood from new growth when it has started to firm up at the base; and hardwood, from woody shrubs and trees.

Softwood cuttings are taken in late spring from strong new growth, or in late summer after flowering. Semi-hardwood cuttings are usually taken from midsummer to mid-autumn, from shrubby herbs such as rosemary and myrtle. Hardwood cuttings are taken in mid- to late autumn. If you are propagating a variegated or coloured leaf plant, choose the most highly coloured pieces for your cuttings.

Planting cuttings

To plant cuttings in open ground, choose a warm sheltered spot out of direct sunlight. For softwood and semi-hardwood cuttings, a soil temperature of 55–64 °F (13–18 °C) is adequate. Dig in extra sand and peat to create a loose open soil, which will encourage quick root formation. An even easier method is to place a few cuttings under the mother plant, but remember to water them for the first few days and in dry weather. Softwood cuttings soon wilt so plant them out promptly. Spray leaves lightly, and frequently during dry weather.

Planting cuttings in containers gives greater flexibility for positioning and for supplying bottom heat to speed root formation. Insert cuttings to a third of their depth in potting compost or garden soil lightened with sand and peat. Firm in no more than necessary to hold them upright; the looser the soil, the easier it is for roots to grow. Place several cuttings of the same species around the edge of a pot, add three tall sticks and cover with a clear plastic bag to retain moisture and warmth. Open the bag every few days to change the air and prevent mould building up. As soon as cuttings show signs of growth, place them in a sheltered sunny position and provide with some plant nutrients. Ensure that the plants don't get too much strong sunlight early on.

Softwood and semi-hardwood cuttings usually root in about six weeks (four for sages and pelargoniums).

Plant cuttings to one third of their depth in cutting compost.

Plant several cuttings from one species in a pot and cover with a plastic bag, raised so it doesn't contact the leaves.

Hardwood cuttings gradually develop roots over the winter. Transplant the following year to a permanent location.

Most herbs root easily without a hormone rooting compound. If you do use one, shake off any excess as too much can be worse than none at all.

PLANTS FOR CUTTINGS

The following grow well from cuttings taken from a healthy parent plant.

curry plant	rue varieties
hyssop varieties	sage varieties
lavender varieties	santolinas
lemon verbena	tarragon, French
marjorams	thyme varieties
myrtle	winter savory
pelargoniums	wormwood
rosemary varieties	varieties

HOW TO TAKE A CUTTING

Follow the same method for all three types of cutting. For softwood cuttings, take sturdy pieces 2–4 in (5–10 cm) long with plenty of leaves; for semi-hardwood cuttings, take pieces 4–6 in (10–15 cm) long; for hardwood cuttings, take pieces 6–15 in (15–38 cm) long.

Take cuttings from just below a leaf node; the collection of cells at leaf junctions encourages growth. Choose healthy, vigorous shoots without flower buds. Use a sharp knife or secateurs to make a clean cut without ragged edges. If the cutting is torn from the main stem, trim the heel, leaving a neat sliver of the main stem wood, as the greater the cut surface the more the chance of infection.

Strip the lower third of leaves away, taking care not to tear the stem, before planting.

For hardwood cuttings, trim the cuttings just below the lowest bud.

Softwood cutting

Hardwood cutting

Cut shoot below a leaf node, leaving a short length of stem.

Trim off the heel if it is ragged.

Gently remove leaves from the lower third.

Cut off any soft growth from the top of hardwood cuttings.

Plant division

Several herbs benefit from being divided. This method checks their spread and keeps them hardier. Dig up the plant preferably in autumn or early spring when it is dormant. Remove old flower stems and carefully separate the plant into individual sections, each having a growing point and some roots. Replant, nurture and water these sections until the roots have re-established themselves and there are signs of new growth.

Bulbous plants such as chives and everlasting onion are pulled apart in the same manner and replanted.

Divide young plants by hand, ensuring that roots have new growth.

HERBS SUITABLE FOR PLANT DIVISION	
alecost	meadowsweet
bistort	primrose
chives	skirret
cowslip	sorrel
elecampane	sweet Joe Pye
good King Henry	sweet violet
lawn chamomile	tansy
lemon balm	tarragon
lovage	thymes
lungwort	wall germander
marjorams	wormwood

Root sections

This is the easiest form of propagation. Dig up the plant in spring or autumn and take 2–4 in (5–10 cm) pieces of roots, each with growing buds; plant these approximately 1 in (2.5 cm) deep in a pot of compost. Use longer pieces if planting straight into the ground. This method is most suitable for spreading plants with creeping roots: bergamot, dwarf comfrey, mints, soapwort and sweet woodruff.

Root cuttings

A few herbs such as horseradish, comfrey and skirret can be propagated from thick pieces of root cut 2–3 in (5–8 cm) long. Insert the cuttings vertically into potting compost with a $\frac{1}{4}$ in (6 mm) covering of sand (see below).

Cut the root into short pieces and insert in potting compost, just below the surface.

Layering

If cuttings are difficult to root, you can try layering. With this method, you encourage new sections of a plant to root while still attached to the parent plant. This is how many shrubby plants like thyme spread in the wild.

Peg a stem to the ground so its underside is in contact with the soil.

Layer by pegging down a stem against the soil.

Mound layer by covering a plant's woody centre with soil.

Once the new roots seem well developed, separate the new shoot from its parent. If the soil is heavy, add some sand or peat before you start.

Another similar method is **mound layering**, which not only creates new growth but also improves the appearance of old plants, particularly sages and thymes, which can go woody in the centre. In spring, pile soil (mixed with peat and sand when necessary) over the woody centre until only the young shoots show. By late summer, roots will have formed on many of the shoots, and these shoots can be taken from the parent plant and planted in a new location.

Maintaining and creating plant shapes

Herbs are basically wild plants and have vigorous survival instincts to cope with poor or crowded conditions. When herbs are planted in rich garden soil, their growth is exuberant and often needs curtailing.

Controlling growth

Tenacious spreaders, such as the mint family, should have their roots contained in a sunken 14 in (35 cm) pot, black polythene bag with drainage holes or an 18 in (45 cm) deep tube of drainpipe. Bottomless restraining barriers such as a pipe must be at least 18 in (45 cm) deep or the roots will spread back up along the surface. Other vigorous-growing herbs such as soapwort, dwarf comfrey and sweet woodruff need to have spreading roots removed regularly.

For sorrel, lemon balm and the annual salad herbs, remove the flowering stems as soon as they sprout to ensure the production of more succulent leaves. Others, such as good King Henry and marjoram, can be cut back hard just after flowering in time to grow a fresh young crop of leaves before autumn.

Depending on your priorities, you can harvest seed heads or leave them on the plant as winter food for the birds, cutting back hard early in the spring. Other late-flowering stalks can be left on over the winter if their dead leaves provide some wind and frost protection for themselves or their neighbours. Avoid leaving tall or thick stems standing if your soil is very light and the herbs are liable to be rocked about by winter winds. This can create pockets of frost around the stems and lead to rot.

Pruning

Lightly prune aromatic shrubby perennials such as lavender, hyssop, santolinas, southernwood and curry plant by cutting off their dried flower stalks in autumn, then cut them right back the following spring to encourage new growth. In general, cut back to about 9 in (23 cm), or to the previous year's growth, as long as you can see some green shoots below this level. Sage needs more care as stems often refuse to break lower down. You may be better off replacing some sages and lavenders every four or five years.

It is preferable to do a regular gentle pruning each year. Many people leave shrubby herbs two or three years then discover a tangled mass with leggy stems. The solutions are to cut back as far as green can be seen, to propagate cuttings for replacement plants or to dig up the entire plant and replant at a lower level, burying the long stems. Do make sure that the soil is well drained below the new depth or the plant will rot.

Prune shrubby herbs in autumn, cutting back to the previous year's growth.

All aromatic herbs are antiseptic so you can use prunings in several ways: lay wormwood in the vegetable garden as an insect repellent or dry the leaves and hang them indoors to deter moths; infuse thyme and rosemary to make disinfectant waters; burn any of the aromatic herbs on a fire to scent and purify the air.

Picking herbs

The way you pick leaves for use can make a plant grow bushier. Basil, tarragon, marjoram, oregano and the evergreens maintain a bushier shape if the growing tip is pinched out first. Then pick the larger side leaves. In general, do not remove more than a fifth of the total leaves of a herb before allowing the plant time to regrow.

Pinch out the growing tip for better growth.

Mint produces small side leaves if the top is snipped off, but it's better to cut off a whole stem as the plant responds with more succulent growth.

Pick the outer leaves of parsley, sorrel, lovage and salad burnet to encourage continuing growth. If one of these plants produces a strong central stem as a prelude to flowering, remove it straight away. Parsley is a biennial and produces the best leaves in its first season. When replacing a parsley plant, add the old roots to a bouquet garni.

Small sprigs of rosemary, thyme, sage and winter savory can be picked on an aesthetic basis: remove pieces which spoil the look of the herb.

Chives and Welsh onion can be cut down to 1½ in (4 cm) and then allowed to regrow. Less is wasted if you cut a few blades of chives down to 1½ in (4 cm) instead of nipping a layer off the top of the whole plant, as each blade yellows for a further inch or two after being cut.

Winter protection for herbs

Many herbs will not survive a cold winter if left outdoors, but by being brought indoors in pots, annuals can have their lives extended by some months, and less hardy perennials often benefit too (see p. 264 for potting up and pp. 266–7 for growing herbs indoors). At the first sign of crisp autumn air, basil should be brought indoors. Pale, mottled or otherwise unhappy leaves may be signalling the plant's displeasure at cold evenings. Before a heavy frost, pineapple sage (*Salvia elegans*), fringed lavender (*L. dentata*), pelargoniums, balm of Gilead (*Cedronella canariensis*) and Crete dittany (*Origanum dictamnus*) need to be brought indoors. All will reward your effort with aromatic leaves and occasionally with winter blossoms.

In colder climates with longer periods of frost and snow, rosemary, sage, winter savory, curry plant, lavender and the more delicate thymes should be brought indoors to survive the winter. Protect mature plants that winter outside by layering soil, straw or compost around their roots.

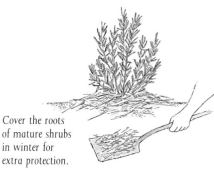

Cover the roots of mature shrubs in winter for extra protection.

If you grow herbs in pots all year (see pp. 264–5), plunged in soil in summer, it's easier to bring them indoors. Trim any roots which may have grown through the base, or pot on if the maximum pot size has not been reached. Try to make the transfer while outdoor and indoor temperatures are similar. If that is not possible, go through an intermediate stage using an unheated greenhouse for a few days, or a cool garage for a few nights, to ease the transition.

Some herbs, such as chives, have an intimate relationship with the seasons and feel strongly that autumn onwards is rest time. Practise a little deception: pot them on in early autumn, water and cut back the growth as necessary. Put them in a warm, humid place, out of direct sun, for a week or two to encourage root growth into the new soil. Then put them into a cooler location for a few weeks, while you still have other chives growing outside. When the other chives die back, bring the potted ones indoors to start their "spring" growth, with additional artificial light if possible.

Much less trouble to bring in is the Welsh onion, which has a larger onion leaf than chives and maintains some green throughout the winter, even outdoors. Chervil and winter purslane do well indoors as they prefer growing at this time of the year, while summer-sown parsley and tarragon will tolerate being moved indoors. Don't bother transplanting whole mint stems; pot 3–4 in (8–10 cm) healthy cuttings with plump leaf buds. Within six weeks you should have fresh new mint leaves available for harvesting.

Enclosures

An important aspect of a traditional herb garden, an enclosure reduces wind damage, raises the overall average temperatures, creates privacy and retains the perfume of aromatic herbs. It can be as permanent or temporary as you require. Upkeep and expenditure vary from type to type.

HEDGING

Once established, this is the easiest form of tall, long-term enclosure, and gives further opportunities for using herbal and aromatic plants around the

Informal hedging

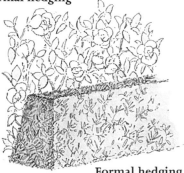

Formal hedging

garden, as many shrubby herbs are evergreen and clip well. Hedging can be neat and formal or soft and wild in effect, depending on the plants you select and how you trim them. However, it cannot be immediate. All hedging plants take some years to reach a good height.

Yew (*Taxus* species) is a classic hedging plant for good reasons. Its dark green leaves are the perfect size and colour as a backdrop to all shades of green, gold, bronze, silver and greys as well as any flower colour, and it clips well. Yew has a reputation for being slow but it rewards good cultivation. Enrich the ground with bonemeal and compost, and water yew plants well in their first season to help speed up their growth. Start with 18 in (45 cm) plants spaced at 2 ft (60 cm) intervals. To shape, prune in midspring and again in late summer. Following this procedure, our yew hedge reached waist-height in three growing seasons and head height in six years.

Box (*Buxus sempervirens*) is another traditional hedging plant. Although quite slow-growing, it has neat, small, glossy leaves which suit being clipped into tight, formal shapes. Plant at 18 in (45 cm) intervals.

Sweetbrier rose (*Rosa eglanteria*) is often associated with herb gardens for the lovely apple scent of its leaves. It is large, untidy and prickly but can be trained into a natural style hedge. Plant at 3 ft (1 m) intervals.

Arbor-vitae, the *Thuja* family of conifers, has aromatic foliage of a pleasant, fruity, almost pineapple scent, and *T. plicata* and *T. occidentalis* are excellent plants for tall hedges. Both appreciate clipping and are tolerant of shade and shallow soils. An annual pruning or pinching back is best in late summer to allow for any new growth to ripen before the first frosts. Plant at 2–3 ft (60cm–1 m) intervals.

The giant fir, *Abies grandis*, makes a good windbreak on all but very exposed sites, but it should not be clipped. Its foliage releases a refreshing orange-grapefruit scent when crushed. Plant at 6–12 ft (2–4 m) intervals.

Low hedging

Low hedging is a feature of many herb gardens. It is used to separate species and beds as well as for ornament, as seen in knot gardens. In order of hardiness, dwarf box (*B.s.* 'Suffruti- cosa'), lavender, santolina and rosemary are the most popular plants for low hedges. When making your choice, it is important to know whether the species will survive the regular winter conditions in your area. Single plants can be replaced in the occasional severe winter but to have a hedge killed just as it reaches full glory can be a heartbreaking experience.

Rosemary can reach a height of 6 ft (2 m) in sheltered areas, though 3 ft (1 m) is more the norm. *Rosmarinus officinalis* 'Miss Jessopp's Upright' provides the least sprawling form. A new form called *R.o.* 'Sawyer's Selection', cultivated at Suffolk Herbs, has reached 8 ft (2.4 m) in four years and appears to have the same degree of hardiness as common rosemary, as well as a vigorous habit.

Next in size are the large lavenders at 3–4 ft (1–1.2 m), Old English lavender

(*L. angustifolia*), with 'Grappenhall' and 'Hidcote giant' the two largest named cultivars. The intermediate sized lavenders include white, pink, blue and purple flowering varieties, so you can grow an interesting hedge with a range of colours and flowering times. Clip the hedge after harvesting the flowers.

Santolina chamaecyparissus creates an intensely silver hedge that will grow about 2 ft (60 cm) high. Clipped regularly, it can make an attractive dense shape though you won't get the little yellow flowers.

Curry plant (*Helichrysum angustifolium*), hyssops in different colours, southernwood, upright wall germander, rue, winter savory, shrubby thymes and the herbaceous chives and wormwood can all be planted and clipped to make good low hedges.

Planting and maintaining a hedge

It's easiest to grow a hedge from purchased container-grown specimens or cuttings, which can be set directly into position. As a rough guide, allow a space of two-thirds the eventual height of the plant between hedging specimens: for a 3 ft (1 m) lavender hedge, set the plants 2 ft (60 cm) apart; for an 18 in (45 cm) rock hyssop hedge, set the plants 12 in (30 cm) apart.

To keep the growth healthy and dense, clip the hedge regularly along the top to encourage bushy side growth. Spread a well-rotted compost around the roots each spring and water well during periods of hot weather, as a thick hedge can prevent the roots from receiving much rain water.

Trim the hedge so that the sides slope a little, making it broader at the base than the top. This will make the hedge grow sturdier and more able to cope with a weighty layer of snow.

KNOT GARDENS

Knot gardens were first recorded in the fifteenth century and are one of the most traditional styles of herb garden planting. This delightful skill of using clipped edging plants to create "ribbons" (and hence "knots") of colour is now enjoying a revival, albeit on a more intimate scale than in the grand

gardens of the past. It is a highly attractive method for separating plants and displaying colour.

Try your hand by marking out a bed not less that 6 ft (2 m) square (it is difficult to achieve any weaving of lines if the outside dimensions are less than this), following the method below. Plan it as a feature on its own or as the centrepiece of your herb garden. Well kept, it will make an entire garden appear mature and cared for.

Choose to plant a square or rectangle, as contained geometric patterns suit this style of planting. Carefully plan out your design on grid paper with the thickness of the hedging correctly drawn. For inspiration, look at knot patterns featured in old herbals or turn to the art of ancient cultures which used geometric designs; Indian, Arabic and Chinese material is a particularly rich source of ideas.

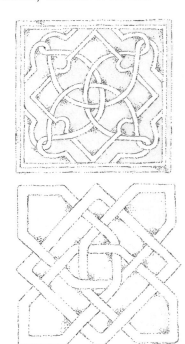

Two ornate knot garden designs based on ideas from a 17th-century gardening book.

The interest in a knot garden comes from contrasting the foliage colours of different evergreen herbs. Choose from light green dwarf box (*Buxus sempervirens* 'Suffruticosa'), rock hyssop (*Hyssopus officinalis* 'Aristata'), the green *Santolina virens*; the dark green of upright wall germander, winter savory or rosemary; the silver of *Santolina chamaecyparissus* 'Nana' and the dwarf lavenders; the willow green of *Santolina* 'Lemon Queen'. In fact, by using just the three santolinas, you can make a highly satisfying pattern, with different colours of foliage and uniform growth and leaf size.

Traditionally, the space between the plants was covered with coloured sand

A reconstruction of an Elizabethan knot garden at the Tudor House Museum, Southampton.

or gravel. but this is difficult to obtain and maintain. Dark peat shows off the coloured plants very well, or as nature always rushes to fill a space, ground-hugging evergreens like creeping thymes can be used. Thymes range in leaf colour from the dark green T. *herba barona* to the light green T. *caespititius*, and the gold variegated varieties. In high summer, their colourful flowers can add an extra dimension to your design.

Making and maintaining a knot garden

Before planting out the herbs, clear the ground of all weeds and cultivate it well, digging in additional coarse sand or grit to ensure good drainage.

After working out your design on grid paper, mark it out with lime, sand or string, using a card template for any small, repeated shapes.

Plant selected perennial evergreen herbs 9 in (23 cm) apart for 9 in (23 cm) high ribbons. Lower, 6 in (15 cm) ribbons do work with dwarf box but any other plants in the ribbon will spend most of the season denuded from being constantly cut back. Plant the corner herbs first to ensure even spacing. With pot-grown plants, the first pruning can begin as soon as they are in the ground. Clip the top and sides so each plant is neat.

Cut back in late spring to encourage new growth. When pruning the shape, give extra flow and movement to the design by emphasizing any crossover of two ribbons by height. If a silver ribbon crosses a green ribbon, clip it to make a gentle hump-back curve, and make the ribbon passing "underneath" curve down as it nears the join.

Make your last cutting in late summer so the plants have some leaf protection during the winter.

An instant knot garden

A light-hearted and inexpensive way of trying out a knot garden or even creating a temporary pattern, perhaps for a special occasion, is to lay out a design with cuttings. Prepare the bed as described above, adding more peat and sand. Select one or two large plants of your chosen ribbon herbs to take cuttings from. Place 6 in (15 cm) cuttings at 4 in (10 cm) intervals to mark out the design. Water daily for the first two weeks and shade with a net curtain on twigs in high summer until rooted. Plant a few extra cuttings on the sidelines to replace any that die.

WALLS

A solid walled garden can give the equivalent in increased warmth to moving 200 miles (320 km) nearer to the equator. It also gives a feeling of privacy and solitude. High walls are expensive and require skilled construction. However, even a small wall provides shelter and a boundary.

When constructing a wall, choose materials that are sympathetic in texture and colour with those of your house and of any other hard surfaces such as a terrace or paths. Use local stone, hollow concrete blocks or bricks. If selecting bricks from a large range, take accurate colour samples of materials from your house and paved areas to check compatibility. If pink is a predominant colour in your garden, take along a few blooms as these often clash with the colours of brick.

Limit yourself to constructing low walls about 2 ft (60 cm) high as shown right. Dry stone walls (those without

mortar), retaining walls and low brick walls, with a double thickness of brick, can all be constructed in this way, so they contain pockets of soil which will accommodate a wide range of herbs. When constructing a double thickness wall, set a good layer of rubble or stones in the centre and then top up with a layer of soil.

Making a stone wall
Dig a shallow trench the proposed width of the wall. Put a layer of rubble or stones in the base of the trench to hold the first layer of stones in position. Start with a broad base about two stones wide, and narrow to a stone's width at the top. Use soil between the stones as mortar and slot in plants as you go. Place long stones across the width of the wall at intervals as extra anchorage.

HERBS FOR WALLS

Any herbs accustomed to rocky hillsides will revel in a sun-facing wall. The following trailing plants are attractive for planting in crevices or on top of a sunny wall:

creeping thymes	low-growing
prostrate winter	artemisias
savory	maiden's pink
rosemary	alpine lady's
catmint	mantle
	prostrate sage

The following evergreen shrubby herbs add colour and height if planted along the top of a wall:

lavender	juniper
hyssop	santolina

Herbs with the word "wall" in their name are obviously well suited to this situation:

wallflowers	wall germander
pellitory-of-the-wall	wall pennywort

Herbs that enjoy dry locations grow well on a wall:

perennial chamomile	houseleek

Moisture often collects along the base of a wall, making a good location on the shady side for:

primroses	mints
violets	meadowsweet
sweet cicely	angelica

FENCES

For those without the time or space to grow a hedge or build a wall, an interesting range of fencing materials is available. These give wind protection and privacy, and provide an instant screen around such utilitarian areas as a compost heap. Select materials such as timber, bamboo, sturdy wattle or trellis, which will harmonize in colour and texture with the natural softness of herbs. Solid panelling gives the greatest privacy but many climbing plants benefit from the extra light and ventilation that open fencing provides.

All fencing needs maintenance and eventually replacing, so choose the best quality materials you can afford. As a rule, the cheaper the material, the shorter its lifespan.

Fencing posts must be solid and secure. If you use a lightweight open fence or trellis, support it with sturdy posts: a trellis is easy to replace but the posts involve much harder work. Concrete posts set into concrete form the most solid support but they are not the most attractive. Timber is more sympathetic but must be treated with a preservative. Remember that if you use creosote you cannot grow plants against it for a season. Timber posts set directly into the earth will rot relatively quickly. When possible, fix timber posts at ground level to a metal collar which is fixed into the earth, or set them in a concrete base partly filled with stone and rubble.

Use low fences to define boundaries and edges between beds. White picket fences are a charming feature of many

Wattle-fencing in the medieval style.

Traditional white picket fencing.

American herb gardens. They show off the plants, look trim and provide a tidy sense of order.

To give a more rustic feel around a small bed, you can renew a medieval tradition by making low-level sections of wattle fencing. These are woven using flexible, green branches of hazel, willow or dogwood approximately $\frac{1}{4}$ in (6 mm) diameter. Select sturdy pieces as verticals $\frac{1}{2}$–$\frac{3}{4}$ in (12–18 mm) in diameter and 12 in (30 cm) long. Push them into the soil at 9 in (23 cm) intervals, leaving 5 in (13 cm) above ground. Then weave the hazel strips between the verticals, pushing each one down firmly as you proceed.

Screens

To provide a visual barrier without heavy shade, create an open screen. Posts with garlands of rope or chain, along which climbing roses, honeysuckle, hops or ivies have been trained, often look effective. The idea can be developed further with a crisscross of

diagonal ropes stretched between posts. Train a climbing plant such as ivy along the ropes and clip in the spaces to keep the "windows" open. For a temporary screen lasting a few seasons, bamboo canes can be inserted at 6–9 in (15–23 cm) intervals, wired together for support and planted with a lightweight climber such as nasturtium, sweet pea, or a climbing bean with attractive flowers or foliage.

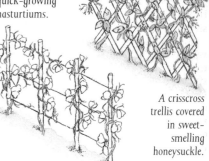

A fence of wire and canes covered in quick-growing nasturtiums.

A crisscross trellis covered in sweet-smelling honeysuckle.

Trellis

Treillage or trellis work, a combination of plant support and screen, is fast developing into an art form of its own. Available in a variety of patterns on different scales, trellis is bought in panels, which come in a range of widths, 6 ft (2 m) high. It is a delightful way of adding lightness and decorative richness to large surfaces such as house walls or flat fences and dark corners. Select climbing plants from the list on p. 259 or grow tall herbaceous herbs

---

PLEACHING TREES

In this technique of training trees, young branches are braided together to form one flat wall of greenery with the lower section left open. All low branches are removed and eventually the trunks assume the stature of pillars. Early versions were a favourite in medieval herbaries, designed to form a green gallery or covered walk around the herb garden. Charming examples can be seen at the Queen's Garden, Kew, London, and National Trust gardens at Sissinghurst, Kent, and Hidcote, Gloucestershire.

Pleached trees create shelter and define areas without causing the claustrophobic feeling a tall hedge can give in a small space. They can frame features, block out tall eyesores, hint at vistas beyond and make a suitable architectural link between two styles of gardening; say between formal beds and an informal herb garden, or a formal herb garden and an informal swimming pool area. If they are grown as a single row, a

parallel hedge planted one path's width away will make a windbreak.

Hornbeam and lime are the two most frequently trained species but willows, privet, whitethorn, sycamore, chestnut and the dogwood *Cornus mas* can all be used. Plan the aspired size and shape carefully, testing out the heights with canes in the garden. Check the vista from every direction and from windows in the house.

Start with young trees which have straight stems. Prepare the ground well, mixing in additional bonemeal and good compost. If you're aiming for a slender wall of greenery, the trees will need a support system of posts and horizontal wires (similar to those used for espalier fruit trees). Plant the trees at 4–8 ft (1.2–2.4 m) intervals and prune as described at right. Each autumn, prune and train until a dense network of twigs is built up. Thereafter just clip the foliage to keep its shape.

1 *Remove any side shoots below the level desired. Remove any branches not growing in the desired direction.*

2 *Prune upright branches or twigs above a set of buds and encourage this new growth along the wires.*

in the screen's shelter. For woody climbers, such as honeysuckle and jasmine, choose more permanent materials because it is difficult to remove damaged trellis or wattle from a tangle of branches. With some ingenuity, pieces can be combined to create structures such as an arbour (see p. 262) or a pergola (see below).

PERGOLAS

A pergola consists of a series of rectangular or curved "arches" joined horizontally and covered with climbing plants to create a semi-covered walkway. It is one of the quickest ways of bringing mystery and interest to a small, bland garden or flat landscape.

A pergola can also be built with vertical supports and horizontal beams extending from the house, creating a successful architectural link between house and garden and a delightful outdoor room. It can mask unsightly views, provide a strong identifiable entrance into the herb garden or be used to emphasize a route.

A traditional pergola makes an airy covered walkway or shelter.

When building a pergola, there is a difficult balance to draw between genuine rural charm and fairy-tale sweetness. Simple structures of metal arches, or rectangular frames of posts and rails are usually the most successful. Plant climbers at each support post. If you are growing climbing roses, try to ensure that no thorns brush against those walking along the path.

To make a double arch, position four stout poles at the required intervals and wire flexible branches, such as green hazel, between them. Add horizontal rails for rigidity.

A double arch makes an effective entrance as shown above. It can also be used at the crossroads of two paths, as in the illustration above opposite. The garden design on p. 31 features a pergola created from espaliered fruit trees.

For structures of timber, hardwood always lasts many years longer than softwood but is considerably more expensive. Treat all wood with a preservative that is safe for plants. For square posts, consider purchasing a metal collar with an extended pointed piece which you hammer into the ground. This supports the post just above ground level and prolongs its life by keeping it out of damp soil.

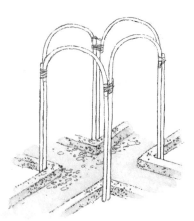

For arches at the crossroads of two paths, omit the side rails and add two extra arches at right angles to the first pair.

To train stems up a post, fix a screw eye or loop at the top and the base, and loosely spiral up a length of plastic wire between the two. As branches grow, tuck them into the wire.

CLIMBING PLANTS FOR THE HERB GARDEN

Roses This list includes only scented and continuous or repeat flowering roses, which have the soft colours and graceful growth of the old-fashioned species.
'Albéric Barbier': yellow buds to creamy white flowers.
'Bloomfield Abundance': miniature pink blooms in profusion, as the name suggests.
'Gloire de Dijon': buff yellow, early flowering. Will grow on a shady wall.
'Guinée': rich velvet scarlet, perfect buds to dry for potpourri.
'New Dawn': silver blush pink; fruity fragrance.
'Zephirine Drouhin': cerise pink.
'Blush Noisette': lilac pink; rich clove scent.
'Cécile Brunner': tiny blush blooms.
'Constance Spry': luminous pink; myrrh fragrance.
'Leverkusen': lemon yellow flowers with lemon fragrance.
'Mme Alfred Carrière': blush white globes, very fragrant and hardy.
'Maigold': bronze yellow; strong fragrance, prickly.

Other scented climbers
Jasmine is easily grown in fertile soils and prefers a sunny position. Its heady fragrance can fill an arbour.
Jasminum officinale: clusters of tiny white fragrant flowers in summer.
J. beesianum: small deep red flowers in late spring.
J. x stephanense: small fragrant pale pink clusters in summer.

Honeysuckle grows well in most soil and enjoys half shade.
Woodbine *Lonicera periclymenum* A traditional cottage garden climber, vigorous and the most fragrant form.
L. japonica repens: flowers, leaves and shoots are flushed purple.

Akebia (*Akebia quinata*): grows 27–36 ft (9–12 m) high and is an unusual and hardy semi-evergreen climber with delicate whorls of leaves. It produces tiny, scented, purple-red flowers in spring and small edible fruits if the summer has been a hot one.
A. trifoliata: 27 ft (9 m) high, a similar elegant climber with dark purple flowers and pale lilac fruit.

Hops are easy to grow in most soils.
Humulus lupulus: 9 to 18 ft (3 to 6 m), large deeply lobed leaves.
H. lupulus 'Aureus' is a golden form with soft yellow leaves. It prefers sun.

Unscented climbers
Ivies *Hedera helix*: There are 29 cultivars with silver, gold, variegated large, tiny or crinkled leaves.

Clematis The prolific small flowered varieties are most sympathetic to the intimate scale of a herb garden:
Clematis macropetala 'Snowbird' has tiny birdlike flowers.
C. montana 'Elizabeth' is scented.

Grapevines Probably the most ancient climber to be planted in gardens, these are vigorous plants with large handsome leaves. Vines are easy to grow but require a long hot summer and skilled attention for a good crop of fruit.
Vitis vinifera 'Apiifolia' has divided leaves.
V. vinifera 'Purpurea' has rich red leaves later turning to wine colour. Stunning next to silver herbs.

Herb lawns

" But those which Perfume the Aire most delightfully, not passed by as the rest, but being Troden upon and Crushed, are Three: That is Burnet, Wilde-Time, and Water-Mints. Therefore, you are to set whole Allies of them, to have the Pleasure, when you walke to tread."

Francis Bacon
An Essay of Gardens (1625)

A fragrant lawn carpet can be laid with several different perennial herbs. It is best to begin with a small area as all herb lawns involve a lot of weeding, although generally they don't need mowing. Start by creating a welcoming mat as you enter the herb garden or a "hearth rug" in front of a garden seat, so swinging legs will gently brush the surface and release a herbal aroma.

Planting a herb lawn
To prepare the ground, weed thoroughly to remove every trace of perennial weeds, then rake the soil to a smooth surface. In a lightly shaded or cool patch, add rich compost to hold moisture, and plant either pungent peppermint-scented pennyroyal at 9 in (23 cm) intervals or the tiny-leaved *Mentha requienii* with its crème-de-menthe scent at 4 in (10 cm) intervals. The watermint suggested by Bacon requires moist soil and would probably leave numerous gaps, but it could be tried with pennyroyal or lawn grass.

If the area is in sun, incorporate a sandy compost and plant Roman or perennial chamomile with its apple-scented leaves at 4 in (10 cm) intervals.

'Treneague' is a non-flowering clone, which is convenient, as it saves having to remove flower heads, but the ordinary Roman chamomile can be started from seed, which is much less expensive. Prepare the soil and then broadcast the seed. Cover with a thin layer of soil and keep moist (not wet). Once seedlings appear and have at least two sets of leaves, thin them out to about 3 in (8 cm) apart. Don't walk on them until they're beginning to bind together. Remove most flower heads as they appear, to ensure leaf vigour, but allow occasional flowers to remain as they form part of the lawn's charm. Avoid having a chamomile lawn bordering on a grass or wild garden area as creeping weeds will soon invade the lawn, and uprooting them will also mean disturbing the shallow-rooted chamomile plants. A surround of stone, brick or paving slabs is ideal.

A popular alternative to a lawn is to plant creeping thymes at 9 in (23 cm) intervals or sow them in groups following the same procedure as for chamomile. Select thymes according to their leaf colour (gold, variegated, grey, light and dark green) or leaf scent (thyme, lemon, pine, caraway) and flower colour (see p. 142). In midsummer, the flowers (white, pink, mauve or cochineal) provide the possibility of a kaleidoscope of colour and scent. Wait until spring before removing flowering stems as they supply some protection to the herb during winter.

Corn mint (*Mentha arvensis*), the farmer's nightmare, tolerates dry

conditions and could be tried on its own or grown with grass. Several mints will grow amid grass if it is not mown low too often, or you can incorporate them into little used paths as an aromatic treat.

The only suggestion of Bacon's I haven't tried is the salad burnet. It is a robust plant with a cucumber scent and could form part of a lawn.

Although all these lawns will take some traffic, they are not suitable for continuous heavy footfalls. Where necessary, paving stones or slices of redwood or elm should be used as stepping stones. Certain areas, often the centre, receive rougher treatment, while lush vigorous plants around the edges continue to flourish. If this is the case, you can always transplant rooted pieces from the outside to the centre.

LAWN HERBS
Chamomile
Chamaemelum nobile 'Treneague': apple-scented, non-flowering variety. Tolerant of dry conditions.
Mints
Corsican mint (*Mentha requienii*): tiny leaves, strong scent. Likes moisture. Pennyroyal (*M. pulegium*): bright green, pungent peppermint scent. Corn mint (*M. arvensis*)
Thymes
All the creeping varieties (*Thymus serpyllum, T. praecox, T. pseudolanuginosus*) are suitable for cultivation in lawns. Prefer dry, sandy soil.

Paths

Access to plants is essential in a herb garden to enable you to pick leaves, flowers and seeds whenever you wish and to ease the task of maintaining the garden. A path can be as narrow as 18 in (45 cm) or as wide as 6 ft (2 m), depending on the size and style of the herb garden and surrounding area.

Grass
A grass path is the simplest form of path, especially if you are cutting your herb garden out of existing lawn. Any of the lawn herbs listed above can also be used. The path must be at least the width of your lawnmower or else have an edging of flat bricks to take the weight of any wheels. Laid end-on between the path and the herb bed, a row of bricks gives space for plants to tumble forward without restricting traffic. In the absence of a hard edge, make a sharp cut 3 in (8 cm) deep down each edge of the path, to stop the

grass spreading into the soil and to create a clear edge for maintenance.

The main drawback of a grass or herb path is that it won't stand a lot of heavy traffic. One way round this is to insert round cuts of timber at intervals as stepping stones – aromatic woods such as cedar are ideal. Alternatively, use pavers or bricks as stepping stones.

A chequerboard pattern of stone slabs interplanted with low-growing plants.

Gravel paths
Gravel or pea shingle is an attractive material for paths. Gravel differs in colour depending on the stone from which it is broken. Use lighter shades

to brighten a dark area and darker shades to heighten distance or space. Gravel paths require regular rolling to maintain a level surface, and regular weeding. You may need to add a layer of gravel occasionally if the path has a lot of traffic. Planks of wood can also be embedded in gravel.

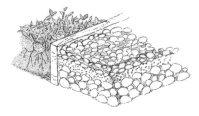

Making a gravel path
First lay a 4 in (10 cm) layer of hardcore, then a thin layer of sand and top with a 2 in (5 cm) layer of gravel. For paths longer than 15 ft (5 m) it is advisable to make a slope so puddles do not form during periods of heavy rain.

Stone and brick paths

Hard surfaces are preferable on well-used paths and for comfortable access in all weather conditions, ease of maintenance and durability.

Whatever material you choose, take care to select colours and textures which harmonize with the soft naturalness of herbs. Paving bricks and concrete brick-sized units are now produced in subtle colours. If selecting reconstructed stone or concrete blocks, look for irregular textures and changes in colour. Any uniform colouring looks bland and lacks depth.

Old bricks are another classic paving material, suitable for almost every site. They are highly versatile for creating patterns. Running in the direction of the path, they make its extent seem longer; placed horizontally or in patterns, they make a path appear wider and shorter. Bricks can be set in many patterns: herringbone, fans, or mixed schemes of horizontally and vertically laid bricks as in the stretcher bond scheme shown below.

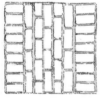 

Stretcher bond   **Diagonal herringbone**

Particularly attractive is a narrow gauge 2⅞ in (72 mm) brick paver, which is especially suitable for the intimate scale of a herb garden. The contemporary paviers require a hardcore of 4 in (10 cm) and a 1 in (2.5 cm) layer of mortar if the path will be in constant use. Otherwise make the path wide enough to fit the brick layout plus edge retainers (see right). You should also aim to make a slight gradient to avoid puddles forming.

Making a brick path

Construct a traditional brick path to add character and permanence to a herb garden. Follow the steps below.

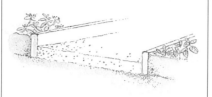

1 *Dig out the whole area to a depth of 4 in (10 cm) and insert metal or timber edging (see below right). Spread a 2 in (5 cm) layer of sharp sand over the base and dampen slightly.*

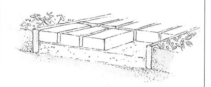

2 *Lay the bricks on top, leaving ⅛–¼ in (2–5 mm) gaps between, and bang them into place using a mallet and board, or a hired plate vibrator.*

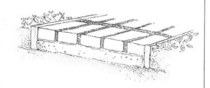

3 *Spread the joints with a mix of fine dry sand and cement (a mix of 1:4) and brush it in. The mixture will gradually absorb moisture from the atmosphere so in time it will secure the bricks in place.*

Concrete paths

Laying your own concrete path is a neglected opportunity for creative endeavour. You can make a highly individual path by adding mosaic-sized pieces of china or glass, seashells, iron work, pebbles, or bricks, or you can even use herb leaves to imprint their shapes on the concrete. Plan your ideas carefully on paper first. Follow these ground rules: to achieve unity there must be constants; either the same material used to create the patterns, or the same pattern repeated with different colours or different materials, or most successful, the same pattern and material repeated with very slight variations. The Chinese use curved tiles laid edge to edge to create many shapes, and then infill the sections with oval, coloured pebbles.

Design the path in sections; a square at a time based on the path's width is easiest. Within each square assemble your chosen materials. Before laying, check that no sharp edges protrude and that colours harmonize. When positioning small pieces such as pebbles, make sure the space between them is less than the size of the pebble. If you are short of pebbles, don't spread them evenly, group them in tight patterns with larger spaces between the groups. Make sure all your materials are ready beforehand; once poured, concrete waits for no-one.

Edge retainers

These help to hold bricks in place.

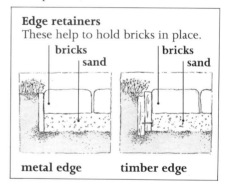

metal edge   **timber edge**

Raised beds

If your soil is poorly drained, and particularly if it's heavy clay, it would be advisable to grow your herbs in raised beds. In these beds the surface of the soil is higher than the surrounding area, thus improving drainage. Often depicted in medieval woodcuts, raised beds also help to define areas, stop trespassing feet and make weeding and harvesting easier. They are accessible for people in wheelchairs.

If drainage is not a problem, you can make a raised bed simply by piling soil higher than the surrounding area, flattening it and giving the area a slight slope on the edges. For more permanence, and better drainage, make a bed

Cross-section of a raised bed

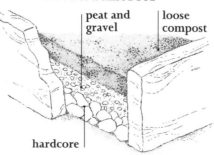

with a layer of hardcore below, a layer of rough peat and gravel above that and a topping of loose compost, all contained by a timber or brick wall.

The best height for a raised bed is between 1 and 3 ft (30 cm–1 m). Any higher and you will need solid foundations for the retaining wall so it can support the weight of the soil. Keep the width under 5 ft (1.5 m) so you can weed and harvest the centre.

For those in a wheelchair, a bed can be raised on concrete supports, like a large sink with drainage holes, and should be at least 6 in (15 cm) deep (deeper if there are strong winds). Most herbs can grow in such a bed, but the moisture-lovers such as mint and sweet cicely will need frequent watering. If possible, confine them to a bed near to the water supply.

Sloping banks

A good way to grow less hardy sun-loving plants, especially if you live in a cool region, is to plant them on a sun-facing bank or slope. Not only does a bank increase the area of growing space available, but it can act as a windbreak or be created as part of a raised bed. It is also a useful device if you have surplus rubble to hide after building work. Arrange the rubble as a base for the bank, keeping the slope at a gradient less than 45°. Cover in topsoil and hold in place with netting pegged into the earth until the plants are established.

The top will drain very quickly so plants in the upper sections should be drought-resistant, whereas the base will receive moisture. If you build a new bank, take particular care in the first two seasons to prevent erosion, either by covering the bank with netting or building a small retaining wall at the base. Thereafter the plant roots should bind the soil together; but on steeper slopes, it's best to have a low wall holding back the soil.

"I know a bank whereon the wild
thyme blows,
Where oxlips and the nodding
violet grows."

Shakespeare's choice of plants would make a colourful and sweet-smelling bank. The herbs listed on p. 257 for growing on a wall will enjoy the situation of a sunny bank. Marjorams, mugwort, alexanders, cowslips, cala-mint, Jacob's ladder, columbine and horehound are particularly suited.

Spreading herbs suitable for banks include dwarf comfrey, lady's bedstraw, bugles and lamiums, and in a shady area, sweet woodruff, periwinkle, bugles (the darker-leaved forms) and the wild or alpine strawberry.

For a damp bank such as the side of a ditch, the Tibetan cowslip (*Primula florindae*) is a spectacular addition, with its giant honey-scented flowers, which appear in midsummer.

Seats

Often considered as an afterthought and sometimes not at all, a seat is most important in developing a relationship with herbs. For every gardener, there are always more jobs than hours in the day but with practice, the art of sitting and watching can be cultivated along-side the art of gardening.

Choose the site for your seat with care. Select a sheltered location with the most attractive vista according to the time of day you are most likely to use the seat and whether you want to catch the sun early or late in the day.

Choosing a seat
The colour and character of stone or reconstituted stone looks very attractive with the silver, grey and muted flower colours of many herbs; try, too, to choose a stone that is compatible with the style of your house. Stone seats are beautiful but rather uncomfortable for any length of time. Keep cushions handy for summer use.

Classic timber garden seats in hardwood are still firm favourites. Teak weathers to a silver grey and will last 70 years or a lifetime. There are also many interesting pieces of garden furniture available in wood made by a new generation of designers. Remember to renew preservative treatment on wood from time to time.

For further pleasure, plant sweet-smelling mints, lemon balm and pelargoniums around the seat, or site them in pots nearby.

ARBOURS
A seat encourages one to take time to contemplate the delights of a herb garden, and the experience is bettered by a seat in a protective enclosure of aromatic plants called an arbour. You can buy metal or timber frames or construct a simple arch over a seat by fixing four stout timber poles into the ground and binding two flexible branches, such as green hazel, to form two arches. Add two crosspieces at shoulder height for extra rigidity.

Another simple but rectangular form can be made with four 3 × 3 in (8 × 8 cm) supporting corner posts and trellis sides, back and top. Choose the sturdiest trellis (usually with square rather than diagonal panels) and secure it to the posts. Although trellis is a lightweight material, I have found that the right angles of the structure provide sufficient rigidity. Climbing plants bind it together further, but you need substantial corner posts to prevent the whole structure leaning.

Check the sizes of materials available and plan the shape accordingly. For example, if panels are available 8 ft (2.5 m) high in 3 ft (1 m) and 4 ft (1.25 m) widths, you could make each side 3 × 8 ft (1 × 2.5 m), use two panels 4 × 8 ft (1.25 × 2.5 m) for the back and a 3 × 8 ft (1 × 2.5 m) piece for the top, with a 5–6 ft (1.7–2 m) seat inside. An extra vertical support would be needed where the back panels join. A 6 ft (2 m) height and width and 2 ft (60 cm) depth will just work, but more care is needed to stop plants infringing the seat area. For an even less expensive enclosure, use horticultural plastic netting and train climbing plants over it.

Check the list of climbing plants on p. 259 and select a mixture to give

---

MAKING A HERB BENCH

Attractive to look at and pleasant to sit on, a herb bench is a cross between a wall, a seat and a lawn. It's easy to make a comfortable solid bench as a brick box planted with scented thymes or chamomile.

Dig out the base to a depth of 14 in (35 cm). Put in a 4 in (10 cm) layer of hardcore and a 2 in (5 cm) layer of sand. This leaves space for two layers of brick up to ground level. Five layers of brick above ground make a comfortable seat height with a further two layers as arm and back rests. Set the bricks with mortar, leaving some drainage holes, to ensure the seat is solid and safe. Instead of having a row of bricks along the top at the front, which would be uncomfort-able to sit on, use an equal thickness of treated wood.

Fill with rubble to 6 in (15 cm) below the seat and then infill with good compost. Plant perennial chamomile 6 in (15 cm) or thyme at 9 in (23 cm) intervals. Alternatively, put 6 in (15 cm) wide slats across the top at 3 in (8 cm) intervals and plant herbs between them. To help maintain the herbs, add a thin layer of compost each spring to replace soil and to provide a surface for new runners.

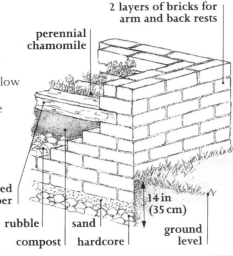

2 layers of bricks for arm and back rests

perennial chamomile

treated timber

rubble

compost

sand

hardcore

14 in (35 cm)

ground level

fragrance over a long season and if possible, fruits to nibble. Choose one or two with evergreen leaves for the garden in winter and look for a contrast of leaf shapes and sizes so you can enjoy the special magic of looking up to see sparkling sunlight filtered through large and decorative leaves.

The frequent advice to plant climbers 6 ft (2 m) apart is necessary only if you wish to have a 6 ft (2 m) run of wall displaying a single plant. If you are happy for climbers to mingle, they can be planted as close together as 2–3 ft (60 cm–1 m). Alternatively, a single vigorous climber such as honeysuckle can cover an entire arbour in just a few seasons.

Arbours can also be shaped out of hedges. In the 1st century AD, Pliny the Elder commented on the Romans' invention of the *romora tonsilis*, the clipped arbour. In this practice, one enormous Mediterranean cypress was clipped into a protective shelter open at the front with a seat inside. The idea can be transferred successfully to a yew hedge in colder climates.

A fragrant arbour in the author's garden.

Focal points

Being a place of contemplation, a herb garden often incorporates a focal point. Traditionally, this is positioned as a centrepiece or set at the end of a path to draw people along its length. It may take the form of a piece of topiary such as a ball bay (see below). Or it may be associated with the wildlife which is drawn to herb gardens – a beehive, or a feeding table or water area for birds. A wide shallow bowl or a pond is appealing as the water reflects the sky, and can be used to float flowers in. An attractively planted urn or other large container also draws the eye. A sundial has long been a favourite centrepiece, often inscribed with philosophical meditations such as Plato's advice that turning from the shadow to the sun is the mind's supreme activity. Statues of St Fiacre, the patron saint of gardeners, or Kwan Yin, the Chinese goddess of mercy, are both classical, tall, slender shapes with pleasing proportions. Representations of the mythical piper, Pan, are also enjoyable and light-hearted garden sculptures.

TOPIARY

Many of the evergreen herbs are suitable for this ancient form of sculpture. It is a way to bring order and architecture to a garden, an enjoyable contrast to the voluptuous disorder of many herbs. The Mediterranean cypress (*C. sempervirens*) has long been popular for making into shaped forms, as have the hardier yew and box. Bay, santolina, savory, sweet myrtle and upright germander can all be shaped, as can rosemary, which was much clipped as hedging in Shakespeare's time.

A good eye is needed for judging shapes, especially where curves are involved. Simple geometric shapes like the sphere and cone are most successful, although a little eccentricity can make a garden memorable.

For small-leaved plants like dwarf box, start clipping them once they have reached the desired height. To maintain a topiary shape or a formal geometric hedge, two clippings a year are needed: one in late spring or early summer, after new shoots have formed, and a second in late summer, allowing time for subsequent new shoots to ripen before winter frosts. This keeps the plant clothed in fresh new shoots for most of the year.

TRAINED SHAPES

Medieval gardeners used several ingenious ways of training climbing plants into ornamental shapes, some based on designs originally developed to support grapevines. One form often seen in medieval illumination is that of a tiered structure with one central pole supporting three or four circular wire trays. Sometimes these "estrades" had climbing plants trained into the tiers (see right) and sometimes the trays were used to hold pots of plants hung with decorative coloured balls.

You can make a simpler version of this idea with just one circular wire frame fixed atop a central pole. Train a quick-growing climber round this shape by allowing two of its stems to twist up the central pole, cutting back any side shoots, and twist its branches into the wire frame so it eventually forms a disc of foliage.

A stunning focal point can be created within two years using a tripod or single vertical post as support for a vigorous climber such as scented honeysuckle, grapevine, golden hop, decorative ivies or *Akebia quinata*.

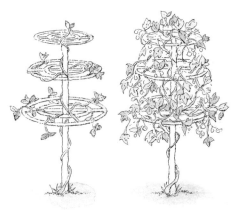

A three-tiered "estrade" with hops trained up it becomes an eye-catching shape in a few seasons.

MAKING A BAY TREE BALL

Plan the shape you want on paper, especially if the bay is to be container grown, so the proportions of sphere, stem height and container are right. Generally, the taller the stem, the bigger the sphere should be.

1 *Grow the tree 6 in (15 cm) higher than the desired finished height. Then clip back the tip, remove the side shoots below where you want the ball to begin and trim the side shoots in the sphere down to two or three leaves.*

2 *When the side shoots have formed four or five leaves, clip back again to two or three, and repeat with all shoots until you have a ball shape. Thereafter prune with secateurs in early and late summer to maintain its appearance.*

Growing herbs in containers

Most herbs are willing to grow in pots, so town-dwellers with a balcony, roof garden or outdoor windowsill can enjoy them. Herbs in containers look pleasing in groups and benefit from the microclimate that grouping creates. The flexibility of containers means they can be repositioned to catch the sun; rearranged to make a focal point or used to fill seasonal gaps. The plants are easy to monitor.

Before planting out containers on a balcony or roof garden, check the strength of the structure, as the combination of soil and water can be very heavy. Wind factor and drainage must also be taken into consideration. Small containers can easily be blown away, and soft-leaved herbs soon spoil with strong winds.

Potting up

All containers need drainage holes and all, except for hanging baskets, need a layer of gravel, perlite or broken crocks in the bottom to prevent waterlogging (for choice of containers and different pot sizes see opposite). Fill containers with a good potting mixture. This can be either peat based or soil based. Peat-based mixtures tend to be very light when allowed to dry out. (If this happens, submerge the pot in water to just below rim level and soak for several hours.) A soil-based mixture is more suitable for large plants.

A traditional potting compound can be made using seven parts loam, three parts peat and two parts grit or sharp sand, with some well-rotted compost or comfrey leaves (mixed with the peat the previous season so they have had time to decompose and have their nutrients absorbed). Sun-loving Mediterranean herbs benefit from a larger proportion of grit or horticultural sand in the mixture, say six parts loam and three parts sand. Do not use builder's sand as it has a rounded surface and makes drainage worse.

Most gardening books recommend the use of sterilized loam in potting mixtures. However, the sterilizing process is time-consuming. I use organically enriched garden loam unsterilized in my potting compound, and although it gives me weed seedlings to contend with, in 10 years I have never experienced any soil-borne diseases. This may be because I keep any mixture loose and open, not stored in plastic, which would assist fungal spores to develop, and because herbs contribute to a healthy soil (see p. 267).

To provide the alkalinity herbs prefer, mix agricultural lime with the potting compost each year – a teaspoon (5 ml) of lime for a $4\frac{1}{2}$ in (11.5 cm) pot. A layer of charcoal granules near the bottom of the soil, about a tablespoon (15 ml) to a $4\frac{1}{2}$ in (11.5 cm) pot, helps to keep the soil sweet by absorbing any waste products.

General care

Pots can be moved outdoors or plunged into soil in spring or early summer. Introduce plants to sunlight gradually. Clip or pick leaves often to encourage bushy new growth. In cold climates bring plants indoors, as described on p. 255, as soon as there is any danger of frost. For information on watering and feeding, see p. 266–7.

Potting on

When the roots of a herb are protruding through the base of a pot, it is time to pot it on, to transplant it into a bigger pot. Usually the next size up is appropriate. Use the same soil mix.

The best time for potting on is in the spring. Avoid transferring at the end of the growing season or when the plant is dormant as no new roots will grow to anchor the plant into the new soil.

Carefully remove the plant from the original pot, then clear any weeds or moss from the soil's surface, line the new pot with drainage material and a

large spoonful of granulated charcoal. Add a little of the soil and check to see the plant will sit at the same level. Then loosen the roots, put in the herb, fill with soil, firm gently and water well.

Carefully remove the plant with its soil. Set it in the next size pot at the same level.

Eventually, when the maximum pot size has been reached, remove the top layer of soil each spring and replace with a fresh mixture spiced with a slow-release fertilizer (see p. 267).

Newly potted herbs will not require fertilizing for at least a month or six weeks because of the nutrients already present in the fresh soil.

Perennial herbs should be potted on in stages until they are in $4\frac{1}{2}$–6 in (11.5–15 cm) pots for good bushy specimens of smaller varieties and 8–10 in (20–25 cm) pots for larger herbs. In general, the larger the pot, the better the crop. All the smaller herbs can be grown in pots (see p. 252 for instructions on growing seed indoors), but annuals grown for their seed may bolt because of the confined root space.

Taprooted herbs such as borage, parsley and dill do better in deep pots. For lovage and fennel, it is best to put three seedlings in a 6 in (15 cm) pot and use the leaves when the plants are young. After one restricted season they often make a desperate attempt to set seed and neglect to produce further succulent leaves. Alternatively, put three seedlings into a 12 in (30 cm) pot for two years of growth.

CHOOSING CONTAINERS

Containers come in all shapes and sizes and in a wide range of materials. For individual herbs, pots are probably the most practical and useful. Plastic pots are reasonably priced, easy to clean and store, and lightweight. This last property makes it possible to judge the moisture content of the soil just by lifting the pot. If your plans include pots spending anytime outdoors, ensure that the plastic will not crack in cold spells.

Clay pots

Unglazed clay pots have greater aesthetic appeal and allow excess water to evaporate through their

fabric. Check the moisture content of the soil by sharply rapping the pot with your knuckles: a dull thud means the soil is too wet, a hollow ring means it is too dry. Soil in clay pots dries out more quickly than in plastic pots, so you will have to water more often. New clay pots should be soaked in water for 24 hours before use.

Understanding pot sizes

Traditional round pots are listed by a number, which is their diameter and roughly their height. So the 3 in (8 cm) pot in which many herbs are sold is 3 in (8 cm) across the rim and $3\frac{1}{2}$ in (9 cm) from the top of the rim

to the base. Vigorous herbs quickly outgrow this size so check when you buy a herb in such a pot as it may already need potting on. If roots appear through the bottom, or the herb seems overcrowded, move it on to the next size up. Suprisingly a 4 in (10 cm) pot holds double the soil volume of a 3 in (8 cm) pot, and a $4\frac{1}{2}$ in (11.5 cm) pot holds three times that of a 3 in (8 cm) pot.

New square pots are stamped as 6 k, 8 k, 10 k, etc. and although this is said to refer to the volume of the pot, the number is the same as the width across the top in centimetres.

PLANTING UP A LARGE CONTAINER

Always set a large container in position before filling it with soil and planting. Once filled, you will not be able to move it. Alternatively, keep it on a base with castors, so you can reposition it with ease. Fill some of the centre depth with lightweight rubble or perlite to save compost and weight, and fill with a soil-based potting mixture to within 1 in (2.5 cm) of the rim. Plant up with herbs which enjoy the same growing conditions, say parsley, chives and buckler leaf sorrel for a culinary collection set near the kitchen door.

Insert long, open-ended tubes to help water reach the lower depths of tall containers.

Contained planting schemes

Grow more of the plants you use most often. Use a 12 in (30 cm) pot for sun-loving seedlings of sweet basil, lemon basil and sweet marjoram. Chervil, coriander and parsley could share a pot as they all prefer a bright position without constant direct sun, and like the environment to be a little cooler and wetter than the first group.

Several varieties of mint can be grown in one pot as they enjoy moderately wet soil and all tend to spread their roots. Angelica does not take kindly to being in a small pot, but planted in a cool location in a large container, a splendid tropical-looking specimen can be grown. Angelica and mint make excellent bed-fellows. When the angelica has reached the conclusion of its three-year life cycle, it would also be time to replant the mint.

Bay, rosemary, santolina, sweet myrtle, box, lemon verbena, sage and lavender make fine single specimens in 9½–12 in (24–30 cm) pots, and the first five also lend themselves to topiary. These herbs might benefit from a carpet of aromatic herbs to keep the soil shaded and restrict evaporation – scented thymes in sunny spots; perennial apple-scented chamomile in dappled light or the tiny peppermint, *Mentha requienii*, in a cool location.

Unusual containers

An old rectangular sink at least 5 in (13 cm) deep and set on bricks to allow for drainage makes a convenient and attractive miniature herb bed. Large strawberry pots, troughs and wooden boxes and half barrels also make good containers.

Sink

Chimney pot

HANGING BASKETS

A hanging basket is an ideal way to bring height into a patio or balcony, though it also demands some careful attention: herbs are vigorous plants to grow in a confined space. If they are too cramped or watered irregularly, they will soon drop their lower leaves and give a sad, spiky appearance.

Hang the basket on a well-secured, strong bracket. Ensure that it is set clear of the wall and that there is no danger of it falling. A planted-up basket can be heavy. Take care not to position hanging baskets between tall buildings where powerful wind tunnels often exist, causing damage to delicate herbs.

Baskets may need watering two or three times a day in high summer so you need to consider ways of watering conveniently. Small long-necked watering cans are ideal, or use a hose pipe to avoid lifting a heavy can.

HERBS FOR A HANGING BASKET

Select plants sympathetic to the shape of the container: plants whose leaves appear to grow in layers or horizontal mounds, or herbs with graceful arching or trailing branches. Avoid upright plants unless they are surrounded by others to soften the outline. The following are all attractive.

In a sunny location: different creeping thymes such as lemon-scented, caraway-scented thyme, pine-scented creeping thyme.
catmint (*Nepeta mussinii*)
ivies
prostrate winter savory
prostrate rosemary
prostrate sage
lady's mantle

For the shady side of a hanging basket: pennyroyal, variegated mints with ginger mint, periwinkle.

With so many trailing and horizontal herbs to choose from, it's easy to tuck in a parsley out of direct sunlight, or a clump of chives to provide a complete mini herb garden in a basket.

MAKING A HANGING BASKET

Follow the procedure below to plant up a hanging basket. Make a rough plan of the arrangement you want and check that you have enough room for all the plants.

3 *Place trailing herbs around the outer rim and plant two or three in the outside of the basket through the moss and the holes in the plastic lining. Put taller herbs in the centre.*

1 *To plant up a hanging basket, balance it on a bucket. If it is a wire basket, line with sphagnum moss, then black plastic punctured with drainage holes.*

2 *Half fill with a moisture-retentive compost. Loosen the soil of any pot-grown plants you wish to add and blend it into the new compost mixture.*

4 *Top up with compost and water well. Drain before hanging in position.*

WINDOW BOXES

Given a sunny aspect and proper attention to watering and pruning, a useful selection of herbs can be grown in a window box. Particularly appropriate for such a location are many of the culinary and aromatic herbs, arranged for convenience and so their fragrance will waft indoors.

Before you plant up a window box, check local byelaws and tenancy contracts in case window boxes are prohibited, and make sure the windowsill is sound and strong enough to take the weight. Whatever fixing you use, it must remain secure as a falling window box could prove fatal to a pedestrian below. For extra

security and peace of mind, attach the box to the wall with a chain or strap. When positioning the window box, consider where water will drain: use a removable drip tray if possible.

Choosing a window box

Plastic troughs are light and easy to maintain but wood is visually more pleasing. For timber, choose treated hardwood such as oak or elm, or marine plywood. Raise the base slightly on wedges to allow the bottom to dry out occasionally and give space for a drip tray. Clay window boxes are available at many garden centres and complement the foliage of many herbs. They are often supplied with raised supports. However, they may crack or flake in a cold winter.

FILLING A WINDOW BOX

Position the box and cover the first 1 in (2.5 cm) with broken crocks or other drainage material. Some growers recommend adding a sheet of heavy plastic punctured with drainage slits to help retain moisture and stop the soil being washed away. In a wooden box, if the plastic comes up the sides as well, it will extend the life of the timber.

In colder climates where the herbs are to be left outside during frosts, a layer of polystyrene will give the roots some protection from rapid freezing and thawing. Another solution is to keep perennial herbs in individual clay pots, which allow moisture to permeate through, and then plant these in a trough of moist peat compost, for extra insulation. Plant any annuals in the peat.

When filling a plastic box, add a thin layer of charcoal granules to keep the soil sweet. Then add a soil- or peat-based compost.

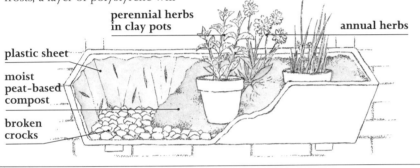

perennial herbs in clay pots
annual herbs
plastic sheet
moist peat-based compost
broken crocks

HERBS FOR A WINDOW BOX

With a small space you will want to make every herb count. For culinary usefulness, grow parsley, chives, a small rosemary and a golden creeping lemon thyme, and basil if the position is sheltered. A calendula adds cheerful colour and flower petals for salads and rice dishes. A nasturtium provides trailing leaves and colourful flowers which you can add to salads. If your position is hot and dry, try the saffron crocus (*Crocus sativus*) for its valuable crop.

Growing herbs indoors

Sun-loving herbs need at least six hours of sun a day to thrive, which is why many do not do well indoors. With inadequate light, plants become thin and elongated, producing smaller leaves and a poorer aroma. When selecting a location for herbs indoors, keep in mind that the reflective properties of glass can reduce light by 30 to 50 percent. Consider also the outside environment; a large white wall or glass surface facing a window can act as a mirror reflecting back much of the light; conversely an apparently sunny window can have its light reduced because of deep eaves or a wall. An interior white wall and glossy surfaces also make more light available. Turn herbs a little each day so all parts receive the same amount of sun, or consider artificial lighting as a supplementary source.

Basil requires the sunniest position and tolerates dry air. Thyme, sage, marjoram, pelargoniums and dwarf lavender also enjoy direct sun. Dill, savory and chives like full sun but a cooler temperature. Rosemary likes a bright situation (this can be reflected

light) but prefers a cooler atmosphere of 60 °F (15 °C) to produce its flowers. Coriander, salad burnet and parsley also prefer this combination.

Tarragon and lemon balm take full sun but tolerate light shade. Mint and chervil enjoy some sun but not the hot midday sun, and both like a moist, cool soil. Lemon verbena and bay prefer filtered sun with rich soil in a cool spot.

TEMPERATURE

Most herbs prefer a pleasantly warm temperature of 60–70 °F (15–21 °C) with a 10 °F (5 °C) drop at night. Herbs will tolerate from 45–75 °F (7–24 °C) but do not thrive at the lower temperatures.

Draughts affect growth and survival. A door opened in cold weather causes a sharp drop in temperature, an open fire draws in a large amount of the air from any cracks or openings, creating draughts in a straight line to the fire, and single-glazed windows allow enormous temperature drops in the sill area during the night. Every sharp temperature drop is a stressful shock to a herb and weakens its constitution, so attempt to position herbs where there

will be a minimum of shocks.

Although herbs do not like draughts, they do like some fresh air each day. This removes stale air, hinders airborne diseases and helps to disperse possible oil or gas fumes from heating systems.

WATERING

Potted herbs indoors and out are more vulnerable than plants in the open ground and more dependent on your care. Pots outside dry out very quickly, not just from the top but from every direction. During hot weather check the soil each day. In autumn water only when the soil is dry, particularly the aromatic herbs such as thyme and rosemary. Seedlings usually need daily watering. Herbs with large soft leaves, in hot sun, in active growth or in small pots also need frequent watering.

Plants prefer a substantial watering when dry to a little water more frequently, as sometimes the bottom area of soil does not receive moisture. It is best to use tepid water and apply it in the morning, so excess moisture evaporates during the day. If uncertain about the need to water, wait another day, then water. For accurate guidance with indoor plants, small stick gauges are available which change colour as the moisture level changes. Simply push them into the soil.

Do not overwater. Air is an important requirement for root hairs, and if vital air pockets in the soil are eliminated by waterlogging, a perfect environment is created for rootrot fungus to thrive.

If a pot with a peat-based mixture has dried out and become very light, this will create a gap between the pot and soil. Plunge the pot in water for 15 minutes or more to just below the rim of the pot. This allows the water to permeate the peat. If poured in, it will run down between the pot and the soil. Peat particles have a natural waterproof coating which helps retain moisture when it is wet but actually prevents water being absorbed if it has dried out. Many modern mixtures have a wetting agent added to counteract this.

Moisture in the atmosphere is also important to most herbs. Grouping plants together helps create a humid environment, as does a layer of sphagnum moss on the soil's surface; you can also place the pots on trays of moist pebbles, vermiculite or perlite. A quick spray of tepid water with a mist atomizer all around the plants is useful in hot weather, especially for herbs with soft leaves such as basil.

Ensure that all containers are adequately drained. Indoors they require a drip tray or outer container where excess water can collect. A large tray containing clean gravel is best as this holds the herbs above excess water, and can double as a humidifier.

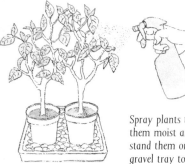

Spray plants to keep them moist and stand them on a gravel tray to drain.

FEEDING

Herbs that are regularly harvested need feeding with a weak liquid fertilizer every two weeks in spring and summer, reduced to a monthly feed as the growth-rate slows. Do not feed plants during the winter and never use more fertilizer than the manufacturer's instructions recommend.

Leaf blemishes

Pale yellow leaves or yellow spotting, as frequently seen on the outside leaves of parsley, fennel and overcrowded seedlings, are an indication that

fertilizer is needed. Other signs are lower leaves dropping early and weak growth with susceptibility to disease.

Signs of over-fertilization are brown patches or scorched edges to leaves and possibly malformed leaves. A blanket of green moss, liverworts or slime means an excess of nitrogen. This usually occurs in winter when plants are dormant and it is less likely to develop in dry interiors.

Types of fertilizer

Liquid fertilizers properly dissolved in water are reliable and can be applied from above or below. Slow-release fertilizer tablets and sticks are available to push into the soil, but they can create spots of concentrated fertilizer. For indoor use, there are also mats impregnated with nutrients, which feed the plant through base watering.

If you buy larger evergreen herbs in pots, you may notice little white globules, smaller than peas, mixed with the soil. These are slow-release fertilizer pellets, which provide feed for a whole growing season.

Herbal fertilizers

You can grow and make your own herbal fertilizers from a surprising number of herbs. One comfrey plant in a small barrel or a 12 in (30 cm) pot will provide four crops a year. Comfrey fertilizer (see recipe on p.131) supplies the three primary fertilizing ingredients: nitrogen, phosphorus and abundant potash, as well as several trace elements and minerals.

To make up a standard fertilizer, follow this basic recipe: pour 2 pints (1 litre) of boiling water over a good handful of fresh herb or 2 tablespoons (30 ml) dried herb, cover and allow to infuse for at least 10 minutes. Strain before using.
Select from the following:
Coltsfoot (*Tussilago farfara*) for sulphur and potassium.
Couch grass (*Agropyron repens*) although a weed, is rich in minerals, potassium and silica.
Dandelion (*Taraxacum officinale*) supplies copper.
Dill (*Anethum graveolens*) is rich in minerals, potassium, sulphur and sodium.
Fat hen (*Chenopodium album*) contains iron and other minerals.
Fenugreek (*Trigonella foenum-graecum*) The sprouted seed heads are rich in nitrates and calcium.
Horsetail (*Equisetum hyemale*) is high in silica.
Nettle (*Urtica dioica*) is a treasure house of iron, nitrogen, and several minerals and trace elements. Make a fermented brew following the comfrey recipe on p.131, steeping the nettles for 3 weeks.
Sunflower (*Helianthus annuus*) The ash of sunflower stalks is high in potash.

Tansy (*Tanacetum vulgare*) is rich in potassium and other minerals.
Tea leaves contain nitrogen, phosphoric acid, manganese and potash. These are locked in the tannin but released by brewing.
Yarrow (*Achillea millefolium*) provides copper and is a good general fertilizer.

ARTIFICIAL LIGHTING

Special fluorescent lights are available which supply the radiation required by plants for photosynthesis. These will improve the growth of herbs indoors, particularly where there is little natural light. Alternatively, you can combine two domestic fluorescent lights, one "cool white" and one "warm white", for a similar effect.

Use available daylight first and top up with fluorescent lights in the evening to achieve the optimum 15 hours a day for good seed germination and maximum plant growth. These lights should be sited 6–9 in (15–23 cm) above small herbs and 12–16 in (30–45 cm) above larger herbs. If the lights are too close, the leaves will be scorched; if too far away, the plants will grow tall and spindly.

CARE AND CLEANING

If your water has a high lime content which manifests itself as a white deposit on the soil's surface, scrape it off periodically and top up with fresh compost. To remove lime from the surface of bay leaves, wipe gently with a clean damp cloth. You could use a water-filter jug for lime-free water.

A mist spray of water on the leaves of all indoor herbs helps to keep any dust from clogging their pores. An occasional wipe is necessary if you have any larger leaved plants in the kitchen, where a fine film of grease builds up and acts as a magnet for dust. As a rule, the kitchen is not a good place to grow herbs because of the temperature variations and cooking fumes. Use a pipe cleaner or brush to dust woolly-leaved herbs, as shown below.

Remove any dead or damaged leaves and faded flowers rather than have them rot on the parent plant.

Use a small, soft paintbrush to clean woolly-leaved plants such as clary sage.

Keeping herbs healthy

Routine plant care, common sense and observation are the main requirements for maintaining healthy plants. Herbs are mainly disease-free but overcrowding in pots or too much water can weaken plants and make them more vulnerable, so look first for physical conditions which might require attention.

PESTS: PREVENTION AND CURE

Whenever you buy or are given a new plant, check to make sure it has no small creatures lurking under leaves or in the leaf axils. A good prevention is to plunge each plant into a bucket of mild washing-up solution. Hold your hand over the soil area, or cover with plastic or card, invert the plant and swish it around gently as shown below.

Dip new plants in a mild solution of washing-up liquid to remove insects.

Organic insecticides

If you do have problems with insects, try to combat them with an organic or herbal insecticide. Unlike ordinary garden chemicals, these are non-persistent, remaining active for generally no more than a day. Derris is a vegetable insecticide taken from the roots of *Derris elliptica*, a tropical legume. It is available ready to mix from organic suppliers and comes with full instructions. Use against biting and sucking insects: red spider mite, wasps, cabbage caterpillars, raspberry and flea beetles, sawfly larvae and aphids. It is not selective and is harmful to cold-blooded creatures like toads, tortoises and fish so keep it away from ponds. It breaks down quickly once exposed to air and sunlight and is harmless to humans, dogs, cats and birds. Spray on a windless day, and preferably in the late evening, to avoid harming helpful insects such as bees and butterflies.

Several herbs have insecticide properties which can be sprayed onto troubled leaves. Use the formula for chamomile in the box below unless indicated otherwise, adding a teaspoon (5 ml) of washing-up liquid or soft soap flakes to help the mixture stick to the leaves.

Elder leaves for aphids: take 8 oz (225 g) of leaves, simmer in 2 pints (1 litre) of water for 30 minutes, stir well, strain and cool. Separately, dissolve a teaspoon (5 ml) of soap flakes or washing-up liquid in 1 pint (570 ml) cold water. Mix with the elder water.

Rhubarb leaves for aphids. Follow the above recipe, using roughly cut rhubarb leaves.

Basil leaves for aphids.

Garlic cloves for aphids: use two crushed cloves of garlic for each pint (570 ml) of water.

Costmary leaves as a general insecticide.

Great fleabane (*Inula conyza*) **leaves and roots** make a strong insecticide.

Wormwood leaves protect against larger pests such as caterpillars, moths and flea beetles as well as aphids. Make this decoction at half strength and use only on mature plants because of its toxic properties.

Pyrethrum, dried and powdered flower heads This well-known natural insecticide has a rapid paralyzing effect on insects. It decomposes rapidly, especially in bright sunlight. It is sometimes found in commercial products mixed with other insecticides, or you can make up your own insecticide following the recipe on p. 67. Use against all common sucking insect pests; it's also effective against bedbugs, mosquitoes, cockroaches and the domestic fly. Wear gloves when processing the flower heads as prolonged contact can cause allergic conditions in some people.

For scale insects on sweet bay or citrus plants, scrub the leaves with a strong washing-up solution and a soft nail brush, or wipe with methylated spirits, dislodging persistent scales with your fingernail.

Remove scale insects from bay by scrubbing the leaves with a strong detergent solution, as described above.

DISEASES: PREVENTION AND CURE

Avoid using harmful chemicals on edible herbs. To help fight ailments, spray plants with one of these brews.

Chamomile flowers help prevent damping off mould in seedlings. Pour 2 pints (1 litre) of boiling water over a handful of fresh or 2 tbsp (30 ml) of dried herbs. Cover with a lid and steep for 10 minutes, then strain, cool and use at once.

Couch grass rhizome tea sprayed onto leaves helps to prevent mildew and fungus diseases. Prepare and use as for chamomile flowers.

Horsetail (*Equisetum hyemale*) is useful against mildew, rust and other fungus diseases. Use only half a handful of fresh horsetail or $\frac{1}{2}$ tablespoon (8 ml) dried to 2 pints (1 litre) water. Boil for 20 minutes, covered, and stand for 24 hours before straining and using.

COMPANION PLANTING

Many gardeners have observed how certain herbs benefit the growth of nearby plants: garlic and chives under roses deter greenfly, nasturtium repels woolly aphids from apple trees and a nearby chamomile can act as a tonic to an ailing plant.

Science is beginning to discover how some plants communicate and assist others through their root secretions. Some tagetes secrete chemicals which kill ground elder and bindweed, reduce couch grass and stop eelworm from recognizing their host plant. Many aromatic leaves such as wormwood, hyssop and savory repel or mislead insects pests. Others such as tagetes, calendula, nasturtiums, poppies and fat hen attract hoverflies, whose larvae feed on aphids. Refer to entries in the Herbal Index for further information.

Plant dill and tagetes among cabbages to divert pests.

Harvesting herbs

Fresh leaves can be picked for immediate use at any time during the growing season (see below). Evergreen herbs such as thyme can be picked throughout the year, although new growth should be given the chance to harden before winter sets in. For all herbs there is an optimum time when their leaves, flowers, seeds or roots should be harvested for storage, as described below. See the Herbal Index for details on individual plants.

Place cut plants, leaves and flowers gently in a flat-bottomed basket, trug or wooden box. Do not put them in a sack or bag or they'll be crushed, bruised and start to sweat. In this condition, they are not worth preserving.

If collecting from the wild, be certain of identification: it is easy to confuse plants, and some are highly poisonous. Also check the legality as most countries have some protected species, and do not collect too much from any one plant. Do not pick any parts that grow where car fumes or chemical sprays may have affected the plant. Ensure that herbs in your own garden have not been sprayed with chemical pesticides or herbicides.

Ideally, harvest only one species at a time. Sort and clean these before gathering parts from other plants.

Leaves

Collect in the morning after the dew has evaporated. As the day warms up and photosynthesis gets underway, various organic components start moving around the plant system. Essential oils are concentrated in the leaves, ready to give off their protective cooling and antiseptic essence in the midday heat. To obtain the maximum potency and flavour, the leaves must be picked after some warmth has drawn up the oils but before any has escaped in the heat.

Leaves are most tender and sweet when the plant is young, up to flowering time. From this point on the plant's priorities change and the energy goes into reproduction.

Pick the succulent leaves of sorrel, bistort, good King Henry, angelica, and all the salad herbs, when young. This type of leaf is not generally suited to drying and should either be frozen in a cooked dish or preserved in oil or vinegar (see p. 188).

Treat all leaves gently, taking care not to bruise or crush them. Pick only healthy whole leaves without blemish, yellowing or insect damage.

Leaves of aromatic evergreens (rosemary, sage, thyme, savory) can be picked throughout the year but for maximum flavour collect them just before flowering. Leaves of basil, mint, marjorams and lovage hold their pungent flavours well throughout the summer but they will be sweeter if picked before flowering. Later in the season, if mints have depleted the soil of plant food, the leaves begin to acquire a hint of turpentine.

With tall plants like marsh mallow, collect only the top growth.

Use secateurs to collect whole stems of mints and small-leaved herbs such as thyme and marjoram as this makes drying a more convenient process.

Whole plant

The best time to harvest a whole plant is just before the flowers open. If you want the green parts only, cut back annuals 3 in (8 cm) above the ground but take no more than a third from perennials.

Flowers

Flowers are best collected at midday in dry weather. Pick them just as they open fully, their moment of greatest beauty. Snip lavender flower stalks whole and pick other flowers by hand, if possible without touching the petals. Treat all flowers with great care. Avoid damaged and wilted flowers, particularly if you wish to crystallize them. Once picked, keep flowers loose in open containers as they bruise easily and soon begin to sweat.

Seeds and fruit

Pick seed on a warm dry day when it is fully ripe but before it has been dispersed. It should be buff, brown or black, with no green remaining, and it should be hard with paper dry pods. Shake small seed into a paper bag or cut the flower head on its stalk and hang it over a tray to catch the seed. Keep all seed separate, label and date.

Remember to collect the seed of annuals and any others required for propagation, as well as culinary seeds such as fennel, dill, coriander, lovage and caraway.

Pick fruit when ripe but before it becomes soft. Berries and hops can be collected on their stalks and forked off when they are half dried.

Roots and rhizomes

Harvest roots in autumn when plant parts above ground are beginning to wither and die. This is also the time when the greatest concentration of therapeutic compounds is stored in the roots. Dig up annuals when their growing cycle has been completed at the end of the year. Gather up perennial roots in their second or third year of growth, when the active components should have developed. Ginseng is believed to require seven years for maturity, though researchers are trying to find cultivars which develop faster.

Carefully dig up the whole root, taking care not to bruise or cut the sections. Separate off the amount required and replant the remainder.

Most roots such as horseradish and comfrey can be scrubbed clean and have their fibrous hairs removed but others, such as valerian, should not be scrubbed as their precious constituents are contained in the epidermal (surface) cells.

In Britain it is illegal to dig up roots from any land other than one's own without the owner's permission.

Bark

Bark peels off readily in damp weather and should be collected from young branches or trunks, preferably on trees already cut down. Trees can be killed if too much bark is taken, especially in a circle round the trunk.

Preserving and storing herbs

Most herbs wilt soon after cutting. Putting them in a jar of water out of the sun helps for an hour or so, but to keep picked herbs such as parsley fresh for a few days, or to revive wilted cut herbs, place them in a plastic bag filled with air and tightly secured. Store in the refrigerator and they should remain in good condition for several days.

Many herbs keep their flavour well when dried, and some even seem to improve with drying. However, suc-cessful preserving requires care and specific conditions. For information, refer to entries in the Herbal Index.

DRYING HERBS

As soon as a leaf or flower is separated from the plant, metabolic changes begin. Individual cells start to die as their supply of moisture and nutrients ceases. Enzymes which previously helped to create active constituents now begin to break down these substances. With this decomposition, the medicinal values and flavour are reduced on a sliding scale. The sooner drying begins and the quicker the system, the better the quality and colour of the dried herb will be. The speed is limited however as moisture must be removed gradually from a plant. Drying leaves in the oven is not satisfactory as the water evaporates too quickly and essential oils are lost. Microwave ovens do speed up the process considerably without affecting the flavour of herbs but they may destroy some of the therapeutic properties in the process.

Keep herbs quite separate when drying to avoid any confusion or tainting, especially if they are to be used medicinally. Do not introduce fresh plant parts into an area where drying is in process.

Drying leaves

Wipe off any soil or grit and avoid washing leaves unless absolutely necessary. Keep the leaves out of sunlight as this extracts and evaporates essential oils.

Choose a warm, dry, dark situation with adequate ventilation – an airing cupboard, warm loft or outhouse for example. A drying temperature of 90 °F (32 °C) is ideal for the first 24 hours with a reduced temperature of 75–80 °F (24–26 °C) thereafter. Leaves which are not unduly thick will take about four days at these temperatures. Allow one to two weeks in cooler temperatures.

Hang stems of leaves such as sage, rosemary, savory and thyme in small bunches, tied with string. Do not pack stems too tightly together as air needs to circulate through and around the bunch. About 10 stems at a time should be the maximum. Hang bunches stem upwards. If you're hanging them anywhere dusty, place loose paper bags over them with the bottom end open.

When drying small quantities, spread the leaves thinly on muslin, cheesecloth, or brown paper punctured with fine holes. Stretch the material over a frame or wire cooling rack so air can circulate freely.

When drying is completed, the leaves should be paper dry and fragile, but not so dry that they powder on contact. Avoid drying strongly flavoured herbs such as lovage close to others as their flavour may spread.

Storing dried leaves

Once dried, remove leaves from stems. Keep them whole so they retain their scent and goodness for as long as possible; break them up only if you have to fit them into jars. Crush them just before using.

Leaves should be stored in dark glass, airtight bottles away from sunlight, moisture and dust. Plastic and metal containers are not suitable as they may affect the chemistry of a herb.

Label bottles with the name and the date. If you notice any condensation on the glass, the leaves were not dried enough before storage. Remove them immediately and dry them further.

Some herbs are hygroscopic when dried – they absorb moisture from the air. This can reactivate their enzymes enough to cause chemical deterioration so they should not be stored for too

long. Marsh mallow and lady's mantle leaves behave this way.

Check dried leaves periodically for moisture, moulds and insects and discard them promptly if you discover anything. Most herbs deteriorate after a year, by which time you can replace them with a new harvest. Put excess sweet-smelling dried leaves into potpourri, herb bags or on an open fire. Use the pungent herbs to sprinkle over seed trays to discourage mice or put them on the compost heap.

Drying flowers

Dry flowers in the same way as leaves. When dried correctly they should retain their colour. Delicate flowers such as borage and sweet violets must be spread out carefully so they maintain their shape. Allow one to three weeks drying time depending on the thickness of the petals. Store flat if possible. For calendula, remove the dried petals to store. Keep chamomile, lavender and smaller headed flowers intact.

Drying seed and fruit

After removing the seed heads of annual and culinary herbs such as fennel and dill, hang them to dry over a box or sheet of paper, or with a paper bag or piece of fine muslin tied lightly over the head to collect seeds as they fall. Dry sunflower heads whole and separate the seeds for storage when they become loose.

Seeds dry very quickly in an airy, dry, warm environment, usually within two weeks, and should be labelled and stored in dark airtight jars. Seed required for sowing should be kept in a cool, dark place, free of frost.

Berries and fruits such as rosehips take longer to dry and can be placed in an airing cupboard to speed up the process. Fleshy fruits need frequent turning until they are dry.

Drying roots

All roots should be clean with fibrous parts removed before drying. Cut large thick roots in half lengthways and then into small pieces to facilitate drying. Roots require higher temperatures – 120 °F (50 °C), even up to 140 °F (60 °C). You can dry them in the oven, turning them regularly, until they are fragile and break easily. Peel the roots of marsh mallow and the rhizomes of liquorice before drying.

Once dried, store roots in dark, airtight containers. Roots of parsley and angelica re-absorb moisture from the air. Discard if they become soft.

Drying bark

Bark may need washing to remove insects and moss, then dry out in a dry, warm, airy, dark place as flat as possible. Store in airtight jars.

FREEZING HERBS

Freezing retains colour and flavour as well as most of the nutritive value of fresh young leaves. This is now the most popular way to preserve culinary herbs because it is convenient and fast (though it is reported that it is not suitable for those herbs required for therapeutic use). It is also a far more satisfactory method of preserving the more delicate culinary herb leaves such as fennel, salad burnet, chervil, parsley, basil, tarragon, sweet cicely and chives.

Some people recommend blanching first, which may be necessary for long term storage and for large leaves. Rinse when necessary and shake dry beforehand.

The easiest way to freeze herbs is simply to pack them into plastic bags and label, either singly or in mixtures such as bouquet garni. Store small packets in larger rigid containers in the freezer to avoid the possibility of them being lost or damaged. Alternatively, put finely chopped leaves into ice-cube trays and top up with water. One average cube holds one tablespoon (15 ml) of chopped herb and one tablespoon (15 ml) of water – a convenient quantity for cooking. If the water is not required in a recipe, the ice cube can be placed in a sieve over a bowl and allowed to thaw.

Flowers and leaves such as borage or mint are particularly attractive frozen individually in ice cubes for drinks.

OTHER METHODS OF PRESERVING

The flavour of herbs can be preserved in herb vinegars and oils, as described on p. 188. This is an excellent method for well-flavoured culinary herbs, and the resulting liquid makes an interesting addition to dressings, pickles and marinades. Use the same technique to make aromatic herbal or floral vinegars and oils, for perfume, medicinal and cosmetic purposes.

There are numerous alternative techniques for preserving culinary herbs: in pickles, jellies, sugar and alcohol, as described on pp. 188–193.

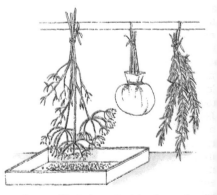

A selection of herbs being dried for their seeds and their leaves.

A catalogue of herbs

In every country there are herbs employed by local people for seasoning, medicine or household uses which may be unknown to others. As these practices come to notice, some are investigated and brought to wider attention. This gives the subject of herbs frequent new surprises and is part of its continuing appeal.

One such example is the oil found in the jojoba plant which has the same properties as the oil of the sperm whale and should mean a reduction in the killing of these huge creatures. Jojoba grows on semi-arid land and could be cultivated as a cash crop on the desert margins.

This catalogue includes a selection of useful herbs, including trees and shrubs, and some lesser known herbs which were popular in the past. It also includes spices, that unique group of plants which compelled explorers to discover new lands. *Do not try remedies without seeking medical advice, particularly if you are pregnant or undergoing any medical treatment.*

Spices

Capsicum annuum
Sweet pepper/Chili pepper
Solanaceae

Description Annual or biennial grown commercially in the tropics and subtropics. Grows 1–3 ft (30 cm–1 m) high with oval, pointed leaves and white flowers in summer. Fleshy, edible fruit with furrowed sides varies in colour (yellow, brown, purple, bright red) when mature. When unripe it is green but still edible.
Cultivation Grow under glass in a sunny position in rich soil. Avoid extremes in temperature. Sow in spring.
Uses Eat fruit in salads, as a vegetable or add to casseroles and stews. Fresh or dried fruit is used as a stimulant and digestive. Sprinkle ½ tsp (2.5 ml), finely chopped, in ½ cup (125 ml) of boiling water or hot milk at the first sign of a chill. The dried fruit of *C. tetragonum* is crushed as paprika pepper. It has a sweet mild flavour, which is free of the hot pungency of chili. It should be brilliant red; if brown it is probably stale. Paprika is high in vitamin C and should be used generously in stews and meat dishes.

Capsicum frutescens
Tabasco pepper/Cayenne
Solanaceae

Description Perennial shrub in the tropics and subtropics; annual elsewhere. Grows 2–6 ft (60 cm–2 m) tall. Woody stem, elliptical leaves and star-like, white flowers with yellow centres, appearing in summer. Small, leathery, oblong pods, containing numerous pungent seeds, develop in various shades of red and yellow.
Cultivation Grow under glass in a sunny position. Sow in spring.
Uses Pulverize seed and use the hot spice discreetly. Pods contain vitamin C and magnesium. They stimulate blood circulation and the digestive system and help to ward off colds. Use to relieve colic, flatulence, stomach pains and cramp. Infuse weakly as a throat gargle.

Cinnamomum zeylanicum
Cinnamon
Lauraceae

Description Tropical evergreen tree. Reaches 20–30 ft (6–9 m) tall with thick, smooth, pale bark, leathery, oval, green leaves with paler undersides and small, white flowers. Bark, leaves and oval, bluish fruit are fragrant.
Cultivation Grows best in pure sand in a sheltered place with constant rain, heat and even temperature. Propagate by seed, cuttings or division of roots.
Uses Dried inner bark of the branches employed as a spice in teas, cooked fruit, pickling liquids, honey, punches and mulled red wine. Ground spice added to sweet baked puddings, cooked fruit and some meat and fish dishes. Coarsely ground seed used in potpourri and seed oil in perfumery. Bark used medicinally as an antiseptic, astringent and stimulant; will relieve nausea, flatulence and diarrhoea.

Crocus sativus
Saffron
Iridaceae

Description Bulbous perennial. Reaches 12–18 in (30–45 cm) high. Numerous, narrow, grass-like, grey-green leaves; funnel-shaped, rich purple flowers appear in autumn. Each flower has three stamens which protrude out of the flower, a feature which distinguishes it from the poisonous *Colchicum autumnale*.
Cultivation Grows in any rich, well-drained soil in a sunny, sheltered site. It requires a long hot summer to produce flowers. Break off outer corms and replant in late summer.
Uses Most delicately flavoured spice; use stigmas to flavour and colour rice, meat and fish dishes, soups, breads, cakes and biscuits. In herb liqueurs, it flavours and stimulates the appetite. Saffron's strong yellow dye is water-soluble. Use to tint hair and to scent perfumes. Stigmas aid digestion, reduce fevers and cramp. Formerly considered an aphrodisiac.

Cuminum cyminum
Cumin
Umbelliferae

Description Tender annual. Grows 6–12 in (15–30 cm) tall. Leaves are slightly fragrant and thread-like; white or pinkish flowers appear in summer and are followed by aromatic seeds. These are similar in appearance to caraway seeds, except they are bristly.
Cultivation Grows in light, well-drained soil in sheltered, sunny site. Sow in late spring in warm situation.
Uses Powerfully flavoured seeds, whole or ground, are added to many Middle Eastern and Indian dishes, especially to lamb, curries and yogurt. Also used for pickling and flavouring liqueurs and cordials. The seed oil is employed in perfumery and in veterinary medicine. Thought to relieve flatulence, colic, indigestion and diarrhoea.

Curcuma domestica
Turmeric
Zingiberaceae

Description Tender perennial. Grows to 2 ft (60 cm) high. Large, fragrant, ovoid roots, with deep orange flesh, send up large lance-shaped leaves in tufts. Clusters of pale yellow flowers in dense spikes appear from late spring to midsummer.
Cultivation Grows in rich loamy soil in humid conditions. Take root cuttings in autumn.
Uses Dried root has bitter, gingery flavour when soaked in water or alcohol. It also provides a culinary and medicinal colouring agent and will dye cloth a rich yellow. Soak unglazed white paper in a tincture and then dry for a yellow paper. Root may relieve catarrh and some blood problems and, used externally, heal bruising.

Elettaria cardamomum
Cardamom
Zingiberaceae

Description Tender perennial from the tropics. Reaches 6–10 ft (1.8–3 m) high. Leaves are lance-shaped and dark green, with paler, silky undersides; creeping roots are large and fleshy. Small yellow flowers spread along the ground during mid- to late spring, followed by green, three-celled pods containing dark red-brown seeds.
Cultivation Grows in rich, moist soil in shade. Sow seed or divide rhizomes.
Uses Whole seeds used to flavour marinades, liqueurs, punches, mulled wines and pickling liquids. Add ground seeds as a spice to fruit salads, curries, cakes, breads, biscuits and coffee. Chew seeds to freshen breath. Use in potpourri and in perfumes. Helpful for flatulence, indigestion and headaches.

Illicium verum
Star anise
Magnoliaceae

Description Tender evergreen tree. Grows 15–30 ft (4.5–9 m) high with aromatic, white bark, aromatic, glossy, elliptical leaves and whitish, yellow or purple flowers surrounded by many narrow petals. These are followed by star-shaped, grey-brown fruits.
Cultivation Grows in well-drained soil in sunny, sheltered sites. Propagate by seed or stem cuttings.
Uses Seed oil provides important substitute for aniseed as a flavouring agent. Seed employed as a spice. Add to drinks. Seed promotes digestion and appetite, and relieves flatulence, coughs, bronchitis and rheumatism.

Myristica fragrans
Nutmeg and Mace
Myristicaceae

Description Bushy, tender, evergreen tree. Reaches 25 ft (7.5 m) tall with smooth, grey-brown bark and aromatic, leathery, elliptical, glossy, dark green leaves. Yellow flowers are followed by globular red or yellow fruits, containing an aromatic, ovoid, brown kernel (nutmeg) surrounded by a red membrane (mace).
Cultivation Grows in humus-rich loam in a heated greenhouse with high humidity and ambient temperature. Take hardwood cuttings in autumn.
Uses Dried kernel provides very strong, bitter flavour; add freshly grated to sweet and savoury dishes, especially to milk and cheese dishes. Used to flavour mead, milk drinks, liqueurs and cordials. Add to potpourri. In very small quantities, nutmeg will improve appetites and digestion. It can be mildly hallucinogenic.

Note: *Use nutmeg very sparingly.*

Pimenta dioica
Allspice
Myrtaceae

Description Aromatic tender evergreen tree. Grows 40 ft (12 m) tall. Leaves are leathery, glossy and oblong, in pairs along stem; small, white clusters appear from summer to early autumn, followed by fleshy, purplish-black sweet fruits.
Cultivation In temperate climates, allspice is grown as a non-flowering ornamental in the greenhouse. Take cuttings or layer the stem.
Uses Dried, unripe fruit employed mainly as a spice and as a condiment; add to curries, rice, puddings, pickling liquids and mulled wines. Use to perfume soaps and notepaper. Grind seed and sprinkle over potpourri. Oil from fruit relieves colic and flatulence. Boil crushed fruit and apply on cloth to treat rheumatism and neuralgia.

Piper nigrum
Black pepper
Piperaceae

Description Tender perennial climbing shrub from the tropics. Grows to 20 ft (6 m) or more. Strong, woody, twining stems bear broad, oval, glossy dark green leaves with prominent veins. White flower clusters appear in summer, followed by aromatic, globular, wrinkled, red fruits.
Cultivation Grows in high humidity in shade. Needs supporting. Propagate by softwood cuttings.
Uses Dried unripe fruit used as a spice and a condiment; add freshly ground to all savoury foods. It kills bacteria so employ as a food preservative. Use as a diuretic, stimulant, digestive and anti-flatulence remedy. Good for constipation, nausea, vertigo and arthritis.

Syzygium aromaticum (Eugenia aromatica)
Clove
Myrtaceae

Description Tender evergreen tree from the tropics. Reaches 30 ft (9 m) or higher with large leathery, oval, glossy leaves in pairs. Bell-shaped, red flowers appear for two separate periods during growing season. Pink flower buds turn reddish-brown after drying.
Cultivation Well-drained, acidic soil in shade. Protect from wind.
Uses For a spicy flavour, add whole, dried, unopened flower buds, known as cloves, to curries, stewed fruit, marinades, pickling liquids, mulled wine; grind cloves for breads, biscuits, cakes. Use in pomanders and potpourri. Chew as a breath freshener. Infuse as a tea to relieve nausea. Drop clove oil into a tooth cavity to stop toothache. Apply externally to ease neuralgia and rheumatism.

Vanilla planifolia
Vanilla
Orchidaceae

Description Tender tropical climber. Grows 30–50 ft (9–15 m) tall. Long, leathery, fleshy, oval leaves grow on stout stems. Yellow or orange flowers appear after third year of planting and are followed by long aromatic pods.
Cultivation Grows in high humidity under shade, on poles or tree trunks. Propagate by stem cuttings.
Uses Dried, cured fruit pods, known as vanilla beans, principally used as culinary and commercial flavourings and as a pharmaceutical colouring agent. It was used by the Mexican Aztecs to flavour chocolate. Also used in cosmetics, especially perfumes. Add to potpourri. Sprinkle powdered beans over notepaper for an attractive scent.

Zingiber officinale
Ginger
Zingiberaceae

Description Tender creeping perennial from the tropics. Grows 3–4 ft (1–1.2 m) high. Thick, aromatic, fibrous, knotty, buff-coloured tuberous roots produce erect, annual stems bearing long, narrow to lance-shaped leaves. Sterile, fragrant, white flowers with purple streaks appear rarely.
Cultivation Grows in rich, well-drained loam in light shade. Propagate by root cuttings
Uses Fresh ginger root peeled and sliced, or grated, can be added to stews, sauces and oriental dishes. Use ground root in gingerbread, cakes, biscuits, mulled wine, liqueurs and cordials. Preserve young green roots in syrup. Apply fresh root externally as a "rouge" as it stimulates circulation. Infuse root as a tea to cleanse the body's systems, ease a cold and to bring warmth on cold days. Chew root to soothe a sore throat. Recent research confirms that an infusion is excellent to settle the stomach and prevent nausea when travelling.

Trees and shrubs

Buxus sempervirens
Box
Buxaceae

Description Slow-growing hardy evergreen tree. Grows 15–20 ft (4.5–6 m) high. The rugged, grey bark surrounds yellow, hard timber. Dense branches bear leathery, glossy, oval, dark green leaves with paler undersides. Small pale yellow flowers appear from midspring. B.s. 'Suffruticosa' is a dwarf form for edging.
Cultivation Prefers alkaline soil. Take stem cuttings in spring.
Uses Whole plant, when close clipped, makes an excellent edging to a formal herb garden. The timber is very durable.

Camellia thea
Tea
Theaceae

Description Tender evergreen shrub. Grows 7–8 ft (2.1–2.4 m) high under cultivation; up to 30 ft (9 m) in the wild. Rough, grey branches bear toothed, elliptical, dark green leaves; white flowers appear in spring and are followed by flat, rounded fruits.
Cultivation Requires deep acid soil in equable temperature and high humidity. Propagate by seed.
Uses Dried green leaves yield "green tea" which is the primary drink in China and has medicinal virtues listed 5,000 years ago. It aids digestion of oily foods and is thought to normalize metabolism. To make black tea, the leaves are fermented which increases the tannin, caffeine and stimulant properties. Drink in moderation.

Citrus limon
Lemon
Rutaceae

Description Tender, subtropical, evergreen tree. Grows 10–20 ft (3–6 m) high with grey bark, elliptical leaves; clusters of white flowers, with pink outsides, appear at all seasons and are followed by sour-tasting, bright yellow fruits, indented with oil glands.
Cultivation Prefers a light, well-drained fertile soil in a site protected from wind. Propagate by seed.
Uses Fruit, juice and peel, which are rich in vitamins and minerals, are widely used in cooking, sweets and drinks, and as an antioxidant. Add to potpourri, herb pillows, soaps and perfumes. Has many household uses: cleans brass, silver, marble and rust stains. Use as an astringent and skin tonic. Bleaching properties may remove nicotine stains from nails and teeth, fade freckles and condition blonde hair. Juice soothes colds, coughs, sore throats, headaches, rheumatism and fevers. Use as an antiseptic to neutralize bacteria.

Eucalyptus globulus
Eucalyptus
Myrtaceae

Description Evergreen tree whose young leaves are susceptible to frosts. Grows to 300 ft (90 m) or more. Bark is peeling and papery; leaves when mature, are leathery, lance-shaped, bluish-green and covered with oil-bearing glands. Small, petal-less, white flowers appear in summer.
Cultivation Grows in a wide variety of soils and conditions. Sow in spring.
Uses Leaves provide an effective flea repellent. Timber is used as an exterior building material. Leaves are included in dry potpourris. Volatile, greenish-yellow oil from mature leaves useful for catarrh, sore throats, bronchitis, indigestion, fevers and as an inhalant, antiseptic, deodorant and stimulant. Apply diluted externally for burns, wounds and ulcers.

Note: *In large doses, eucalyptus is toxic.*

Gaultheria procumbens
Wintergreen
Ericaceae

Description Hardy evergreen shrub. Grows up to 5–6 inches high. Its creeping stems produce stiff branches. Leaves are strongly aromatic, leathery, glossy and oval; drooping, bell-shaped white flowers, which appear in mid- to late summer, are followed by fleshy bright red berries.
Cultivation Grows in acidic soils in light shade. Sow seed, take stem cuttings or layer in spring or autumn.
Uses Leaves contain magnesium and potassium and painkilling ingredients in an oil readily absorbed by the skin. Diluted oil can be applied externally for rheumatism, inflammation and skin diseases. Infuse leaves as a tea and as a gargle for headaches and sore throats.

Ginkgo biloba
Maidenhair tree
Ginkgoaceae

Description Very slow-growing hardy tree that has a fossil record dating back some 200 million years. Grows 30–50 ft (9–15 m) tall. The trunk is light brown with corky fissures. The leaves are fan-shaped and bright green, turning yellow in autumn. Flowers are rare and on separate trees: male flowers small, green catkins; female ones small, globular and green, followed by small, plum-shaped foul-smelling fruits.
Cultivation Grows in any fertile, well-drained soil in sun or light shade. Propagate by stem cuttings in spring.
Uses Inner bark yields a pale brown dye. Roasted or pan-fried seed are pleasant to eat and relieve hangovers. In China, the seeds and leaves are used for coughs and asthma.

Hamamelis virginiana
Witch hazel
Hamamelidaceae

Description Hardy tree. Grows 8–10 ft (2.4–3 m) high with brown bark and toothed, elliptical leaves with hairy undersides. Scented, yellow flowers, with strap-like petals, appear late autumn.
Cultivation Grows in moist, lime-free soil in sun or light shade. Propagate by layering in autumn.
Uses Forked branches formerly used as water divining rods. Apply distilled extract from young flower-bearing twigs (available commercially as witch hazel) externally for bruises, sprains, varicose veins, haemorrhoids, insect bites and to stop bleeding. Used as an astringent cosmetic.

Note: *A tincture from the bark or leaves may disfigure skin.*

Ilex aquifolium
Holly
Aquifoliaceae

Description Hardy evergreen tree. Reaches 30 ft (9 m) in height. Green branches bear leathery, glossy, wavy edged, prickly, oval, dark green leaves. Small fragrant, white flowers appear in clusters in early and midsummer and are followed by globular, red or yellow fruits. Some trees are hermaphrodite, others require a male tree nearby for successful pollination.
Cultivation Grows preferably in humus-rich, moist, well-drained soils in light shade. Sow seed in spring.
Uses Whole plant makes a decorative garden plant and is excellent for hedging. Timber used for engraving and for walking sticks. Burn green branches as firewood. Infuse leaves as a tea for coughs, colds, catarrh, influenza, fevers and rheumatism.

Morus nigra
Black mulberry
Moraceae

Description Hardy tree. Grows to 30 ft (9 m). Bushy, with thick, toothed, heart-shaped leaves and unisexual green catkins in clusters, which appear in late spring and early summer. They are followed by oblong, purplish-red fruits.
Cultivation Grows on well-drained, loamy soil in a warm position; protect from cold winds and frosts. Sow in spring. Take stem cuttings in early spring. Layer in autumn.
Uses Fruit is rich in vitamin C and grape sugar; eat raw or cooked and make into wines and jams. Leaves used for silkworm rearing (until replaced by white mulberry) and diabetes. Fruit provides a laxative, a convalescent syrup, and colouring and flavouring for other medications. White mulberry (M. *alba*) has similar properties.

Myrica gale
Sweet gale/Bog myrtle
Myricaceae
Description Bushy deciduous shrub, 4–5 ft (1.2–1.5 m) tall, with fragrant wood and leaves when bruised. Toothed, glossy, lance-shaped leaves have slightly hairy, paler undersides and a few shining oil glands. Catkins of brown or yellow-green unisexual flowers appear in late spring and early summer, followed by small, flattened, fruit catkins, which contain wax.
Cultivation Grows in damp, acidic soil in shade. Take stem cuttings, divide root or transplant suckers in spring or early autumn.
Uses Dried leaves and fruits used as a spice in soups and stews. Leaves provide a flavouring for beer and, when dried, will perfume linen. Roots and bark yield a yellow woollen dye. Fruits used to make an insecticide and aromatic candles. Infuse leaves as a tea for stomach disorders.

Phyllostachys nigra
Bamboo
Gramineae
Description Hardy evergreen perennial. Grows 26 ft (8 m) high in clumps. Stems, which are dense, woody and resilient, change from green to brown-black at maturity. Leaves are long, narrow and pointed. Bamboo seldom flowers.
Cultivation Grows on moist soil in sun or light shade, protected from cold winds. Propagate by plant or rhizome division in late winter or early spring.
Uses Young shoots are edible in spring. Stem provides materials for garden stakes, building, basketwork and musical instruments. Detoxifies the body and is diuretic. Roots soothe high fevers and fretfulness in infants.

Populus balsamifera
Balsam poplar
Salicaceae
Description Hardy aromatic tree. Grows 100 ft (30 m) high. Highly aromatic, sticky, resinous leaf buds during winter develop into toothed, heart-shaped, dark green leaves with hairy white undersides. Drooping, yellow catkins appear in spring.
Cultivation Grows in any conditions and soils. Propagate from suckers or 12″ (30 cm) cuttings in autumn.
Uses Add buds to potpourri. Oil in leaf buds is used to give a resinous balsamic fragrance to many articles. In a tincture, leaf buds relieve coughs, laryngitis, bronchitis, stomach and kidney complaints, and rheumatism. Use also as an antiseptic, stimulant, tonic and diuretic. Apply as ointment for cuts, bruises and general pain relief.

Prunus dulcis
Almond
Rosaceae
Description A somewhat frost-sensitive tree. Grows 30 ft (9 m) tall with finely toothed pointed oval leaves. Pink or white flowers in late spring precede ovoid light green fruits containing two nuts.
Cultivation Grow in well-drained soil in full sun, protected from cold winds. To propagate, bud onto stock in spring.
Uses Nuts used in cakes, sweets, savoury dishes, confectionery and liqueurs. Use ground nuts to make marzipan. Hard pale red timber provides tool handles, veneers and ornaments. Oil is valued for perfumes, skin creams, facial masks and is the most popular carrier oil in aromatherapy massage. It is a soothing oil for sunburn, cough medicine and a laxative.

Quercus robur
Oak
Fagaceae
Description Hardy tree, grows to 110 ft (33 m) with lobed oval leaves, long male catkins and small green-yellow flowers in spring. Autumn brings oblong cupped fruits (acorns) and sometimes oak galls – ball-like growths produced by larvae.
Cultivation Grows in any soil in any situation. Sow seed or graft in autumn.
Uses Roast acorns for a coffee substitute. Strong durable timber is used to build ships, buildings, furniture and weapons, as fuel and to smoke ham. Bark yields tannin for leather, twine and various dyes. Galls yield black ink (see p. 202). A decoction of unblemished bark collected in late spring is an effective astringent to take internally for diarrhoea, haemorrhoids, varicose veins, a gargle for sore throats or applied directly to bleeding gums or piles. Use in a lotion for cuts, burns and haemorrhoids.

Rubus fruticosus
Bramble
Rosaceae
Description Perennial shrub. Reaches 10 ft (3 m) tall with thorny biennial stems and toothed leaves. Pink or white flowers appear from summer and are followed by blackberries.
Cultivation Grows in most situations. Tip layer in summer, sow in autumn.
Uses Fruits are high in vitamin C; eat raw or cooked in puddings, jams, jellies, wine and vinegar. Organic acids in fruit are useful in face masks. Roots provide orange dye. Infuse leaves and shoots in bath water to revive skin. Decoct leaves as a tonic, gargle, or poultice for skin ulcers.

Simmondsia chinensis
Jojoba
Buxaceae
Description Tender woody evergreen shrub. Grows 2–8 ft (60 cm–2.4 m) high with hairy young stems and lance-shaped grey-green leaves. In spring there are clusters of cup-shaped, greenish male flowers or single bell-shaped female ones which develop ovoid one-seeded capsules. Seeds contain a scentless, clear waxy oil.
Cultivation Grow in well-drained, dry soil in full sun. Propagate by seed.
Uses The seed oil is the only known plant equivalent to sperm whale oil. Used as a diet oil as it passes largely unutilized through the digestive tract. Use in soaps, shampoos, hair tonics and skin creams. Add to furniture polish or car wax, or use as a lubricant for high-speed machinery. Seed makes excellent basic fodder for cattle.

Taxus baccata
Yew
Taxaceae
Description Hardy evergreen tree. Grows to 50 ft (15 m). Flaking reddish-brown bark and long, narrow, glossy, dark green needles with paler undersides. Yellow male flowers appear in spring, as do female ones, which are small and green. These develop into bell-shaped, red or yellow fruits.
Cultivation Grows best on alkaline soil; tolerates shade. Sow seed or take heeled cuttings in early autumn.
Uses Orange-brown timber is water-resistant and hard; use for furniture, archery bows and as firewood. A homeopathic tincture made from leaves and berries is used medicinally.

Note: *All parts of yew are poisonous, including the seed (but not its fleshy covering).*

Vitex agnus-castus
Chaste tree/Monk's pepper
Verbenaceae
Description Hardy tree or shrub. Reaches up to 20 ft (6 m). Leaflets are aromatic, long, oval and dark green; clusters of fragrant, lilac-blue flowers, in long, erect spikes, appear in autumn and are followed by small, spherical fruits containing aromatic seeds.
Cultivation Grows in full sun on light, well-drained, acidic soil, protected by a wall. Sow seed in spring. Layer in spring or summer. Take cuttings in early autumn.
Uses Ground seed used as a peppery condiment. Stems are woven in basketwork. Dried fruits contain hormonal constituents which normalize pituitary gland functions and relieve menopausal changes. They have a reputation as an anaphrodisiac for men, hence the name Monk's pepper.

Other herbs

Acorus calamus
Sweet flag
Araceae

Description A perennial marsh plant from temperate regions with a knobbly aromatic rhizome. The iris-like leaves reach 3 ft (1 m) with tiny green flowers appearing in mid-summer on a curved protruding spike half way up the stalk.
Cultivation Grow in a sunny position in shallow water or rich, marshy soil. Plant pieces of rhizome with small roots attached in spring or autumn.
Uses The whole plant has a rich cinnamon-spicy fragrance. Dry leaves and two-year old rhizome for potpourri and sweet bags. The root was formerly a popular strewing herb and used to flavour meat dishes.

Agastache foeniculum (A. anethiodora)
Anise hyssop
Labiatae

Description Hardy perennial. Grows 2–3 ft (60 cm–1 m). Oval, pointed leaves, with whitish undersides have an aniseed scent. Long spikes of purple-blue flowers appear in late summer.
Cultivation Grows in rich, moist soil in a sunny site. Propagate in spring by seed or divide creeping root.
Uses Use dried leaves as a seasoning or infuse as a tea. An excellent bee herb.

Anchusa officinalis
Alkanet/Bugloss
Boraginaceae

Description Biennial or perennial. Grows to 12 in (30 cm). Similar to borage with rough leaves, thick tap root and small bright blue flowers in early summer.
Cultivation Tolerates any soil. Sow in spring; divide in autumn.
Uses Add flowers and young leaves to salads. Decoct root for blood cleanser and expectorant for coughs. Root gives a strong red dye in alcohol or oil. Once used as face rouge. Valuable bee plant.

Arnica montana
Arnica
Compositae

Description Hardy perennial, growing 1–2 ft (20–60 cm) tall. Oval, hairy leaves form rosettes and large, scented, yellow flowers appear all summer.
Cultivation Plant in sandy, acidic soil, rich in humus, in a sunny position. Divide creeping rhizomes in spring. Sow in spring; slow to germinate.
Uses A good bee plant. Leaves and roots smoked in herbal tobaccos. Use a tincture of flowers for sprains, wounds and bruises, relief from rheumatic pain and on chilblains when skin not broken. Add to a relaxing footbath.

Note: *Potentially toxic if taken internally.*

Bellis perennis
Lawn daisy
Compositae

Description Hardy perennial. Grows 3–6 in (8–15 cm) tall with flat rosettes of finely hairy, serrated leaves. Single or double, white or pink flowers with golden centres bloom from spring through to autumn.
Cultivation Easy to grow on fertile soil in sun or part shade. Divide in spring or sow in spring or late summer.
Uses Add young leaves and petals to salads; add flowers to potpourri. Good nectar plant for bees and butterflies. Infuse flowers for a spring tonic bath to revive dull skin or drink for enteritis, diarrhoea or as an expectorant for coughs and colds. Crushed fresh leaves or a decoction helps to heal wounds and bruises.

Calaminta grandiflora
Calamint
Labiatae

Description Hardy perennial. Reaches a height of 12 in (30 cm). Its square, hairy, woody stems arise from creeping rootstalk. Dense whorls of bluish flowers, appearing from midsummer until early autumn, are borne beside each pair of mint-scented toothed, oval leaves.
Cultivation Prefers chalky soil in dry woodlands and wasteground. Sow in spring. Take stem cuttings in spring. Divide root in late spring or autumn.
Uses Calamint contains camphor-like essential oils. Infuse dried leaves as a tea for flatulent colic and as an invigorating tonic. Leaves also produce peppermint-flavoured tisane. Use fresh in a poultice for bruises. Take as a syrup or decoction for coughs.

Carthamus tinctorius
Safflower
Compositae

Description An annual that is not related to saffron, although the flowers are used similarly; grows 2–3 ft (60 cm–1 m) tall. Prickly oval leaves grow along its stiff whitish stem, which branches near the top and terminates with an orange-yellow flower in summer. It has white, shiny fruits.
Cultivation Sow in spring.
Uses Seed is rich in linoleic acid, an essential fatty acid, so excellent for culinary purposes, to lower blood cholesterol and help prevent heart disease. Flowers yield yellow and red dyes, which when mixed with powdered talc form "rouge". Add flowers to potpourri. Infuse flowers as a laxative, diuretic, and perspiration inducer, and to alleviate skin diseases.

Note: *Do not take large amounts during pregnancy.*

Cymbopogon citratus
Lemongrass
Gramineae

Description Tender perennial grass from the tropics. Grows 6 ft (1.8 m) tall. Densely tufted with fragrant, very long, thin, pointed leaves with prominent mid-veins. Greenish flowers, with reddish tinge, appear in nodding clusters in summer.
Cultivation Grow in moist soil in full sun in the greenhouse, minimum temperature of 55 °F (13 °C). Propagate by division.
Uses Chop tender stalks into salads. Infuse leaves as a herbal tea. Use oil to clean oily skin and as a relaxant in bathwater. Add to perfumes and soaps.

Dictamnus albus
White dittany/Burning bush
Rutaceae

Description This hardy perennial with a penetrating orange-like scent exudes so much inflammable vapour in heat or dry, cloudy weather that it can sometimes be ignited. Grows 2 ft (60 cm) high with round, hairy stems and fragrant, toothed, oval leaflets; all parts are covered with glandular dots. Long spikes of large, red, white, blue or striped flowers appear in summer.
Cultivation Grows in well-drained, alkaline soil in sunny gardens and warm places such as sheltered woodlands. Sow in late summer in situ.
Uses Dry leaves for potpourri. Infuse leaves as a herbal tea. Distilled water used as a cosmetic. Leaves and flowers produce tincture for rheumatic pains. In the past leaves were infused for nervous complaints. Decoction of rootstalk was used for fever and stomach cramps, and, combined with seeds, for kidney and bladder stones. One constituent, dictamine, is toxic in strong doses. Avoid during pregnancy.

Echium vulgare
Viper's bugloss
Boraginaceae

Description Biennial, closely related to borage. Grows 2–3 ft (60 cm–1 m) tall with oblong prickly leaves and stem, often spotted with red. Pink buds open into blue-violet flowers from early summer to early autumn.
Cultivation Easily grown in dry or stony, chalky or sandy soils, especially near the sea. Sow in late summer in situ. Self-seeds profusely.
Uses Add flowers to salads, make into a cordial and crystallize them. Infuse lower leaves to produce sweating in fevers; also to relieve headaches, colds, nervous complaints and inflammatory pain. Seeds used to be decocted and mixed in wine, to "comfort the heart and drive away melancholy".

Equisetum arvense
Horsetail/Bottlebrush
Equisetaceae
Description A resilient perennial, practically unchanged in form since prehistoric times. Grows up to 18 in (45 cm) tall with whorls of small green branches around larger central stems. *E. hyemale* grows to 5 ft (1.5 m).
Cultivation Grows in dry, stony soil. Spreads easily by creeping rhizomes and air-borne spores.
Uses Whole plant yields a yellow ochre dye. Stems have a high silica content and can be used to scour metal and polish pewter and fine woodwork. They contain vitamins and minerals and make a strength-giving tea which enriches the blood and hardens fingernails. A decoction is also astringent when applied externally. A poultice helps to heal wounds and ulcers.

Eryngium maritimum
Sea holly
Umbelliferae
Description Hardy perennial forming a semi-spherical bush, 1–3 ft (30 cm–1 m) high. Leaves are very stiff, fleshy, prickly and blue-green edged with white. Tiny, thistle-like, metallic-blue flowers appear in mid- to late summer. The edible root is extremely long, brittle, fleshy and white.
Cultivation Well-drained sandy soil in full sun near the sea. Sow seed and divide roots in autumn.
Uses Crystallize roots as an aphrodisiac and nerve tonic. Boil young flowering shoots and serve like asparagus. Leaves are also edible. Use powdered root in a poultice to aid tissue regeneration. Drink root decoction as a tonic, diuretic and for cystitis, urethritis and inflamed prostate gland.

Euphrasia officinalis
Eyebright
Scrophulariaceae
Description Annual. Grows 2–8 in (5–20 cm) high with deeply cut, hairy, toothed, oval leaves and square, branched stems. Numerous small, white flowers with purple and yellow spots or stripes appear from mid-summer to late autumn.
Cultivation Difficult to grow as it is semiparasitic on certain grass species. Sow in spring on chalky soil.
Uses Infuse whole plant or crush fresh stem and use strained juice to relieve eye inflammations, eye strain and other eye ailments; also for hay fever, colds, coughs and sore throats. *E. rostkoviana* is the most useful species for eye treatments. Apply externally as an eye compress and in a poultice to aid wound healing.

Note: *Seek medical advice before treating eyes.*

Galega officinalis
Goat's rue
Leguminosae
Description Hardy perennial. Reaches 3 ft (1 m) high. Bushy with smooth, hollow, branched stem, lance-shaped, bright green leaflets and pea-like, purplish-blue or white flowers from midsummer to midautumn, followed by long, erect, red-brown pods. The plant produces a disagreeable odour when bruised.
Cultivation Grows in deep, moist soil in a sunny position. Sow in spring. Divide roots in spring or autumn.
Uses Fresh juice clots milk and may be used in cheesemaking. Infuse dried flowering tops to stimulate the flow of milk in nursing mothers and animals. Pulverize the dried herb as a diuretic; also to reduce fevers. The seeds apparently lower blood sugar levels and may assist diabetics. Use only under strict medical supervision.

Galium verum
Lady's bedstraw
Rubiaceae
Description Hardy perennial; grows 1–3 ft (30 cm–1 m) tall. Delicate whorls of thread-like leaves on square stems. Dense clusters of tiny honey-scented yellow flowers appear all summer.
Cultivation Thrives in deeply dug, well-drained manured loam in sun or part shade. Divide underground runners or sow seed in spring or autumn. Seed needs stratification; graze between sandpaper.
Uses Strong decoctions of whole plant curdle milk when boiled for cheesemaking, while flowers give cheese a golden colour. Dried leaves contain coumarin and smell of new-mown hay. Add leaves and flowers to potpourri and herb pillows. Used in the past to stuff mattresses. Roots and lower stems yield red dye, flowers give yellow dye.

Genista tinctoria
Dyer's greenweed
Leguminosae
Description Hardy deciduous shrub. Grows 1–3 ft (30 cm–1 m) tall. Leaves are small oblong glossy dark green; yellow pea-flowers appear in midsummer, followed by long, narrow seed pods in autumn.
Cultivation Grows on dryish, sandy soils. Sow in spring. Take cuttings in late summer.
Uses Flowers yield a yellowish-green dye. Formerly used as a diuretic but now considered poisonous.

Glycyrrhiza glabra
Liquorice
Leguminosae
Description Hardy herbaceous perennial. Grows 2–5 ft (60 cm–1.5 m) tall with long, narrow, dark green leaflets. Its taproot has several long branches, which are wrinkled and brown, with yellow flesh. Yellow or purplish flowers appear in summer, followed by reddish-brown pods.
Cultivation Grows readily in deep, moist, rich, sandy loam. Divide roots in autumn or spring.
Uses Root flavours beers, confectionery, tobaccos and snuffs. Root pulp is incorporated in mushroom compost. Root contains glycyrrhizin, a substance many times sweeter than sugar. Infuse as a refreshing tea and as a remedy for coughs and chest complaints. Strong decoction makes a laxative for children and may reduce fever.

Hydrastis canadensis
Goldenseal
Ranunculaceae
Description Hardy herbaceous perennial. Grows 6–12 in (15–30 cm) tall with hairy stems, toothed, lobed leaves and thick, knotted, yellow rootstalk. Greenish-white flowers (without petals) appear in late spring and early summer, followed by raspberry-like, inedible fruits.
Cultivation Grows in well-drained, moist, rich soil in partially shaded sites. Divide rootstock in early autumn.
Uses Root yields a yellow-orange dye. Take a few drops of tincture to relieve constipation or add them to distilled water to make a lotion for skin ulcers. Use as a weak infusion for conjunctivitis and as an antiseptic mouthwash.

Hypericum perforatum
St John's wort
Hypericaceae
Description Fragrant, hardy, shrubby perennial. Grows 1–3 ft (30 cm–1 m) tall. Leaves are pale green, oblong and covered with tiny perforations – the oil glands. Lemon-scented yellow flowers appear in summer and early autumn.
Cultivation Tolerates most soils in sun and light shade. Propagate from runners at base in autumn or seed.
Uses Leaves make an interesting salad herb. Flowers yield a yellow woollen dye with alum, or violet-red silk dye with alcohol. Infused flower oil helps healing of bruises, wounds, varicose veins, ulcers and sunburn. Flowers have been infused as a pain-reducing sedative tea for anaemia, rheumatism, headaches and nervous conditions. Now considered unsafe by some.

Indigofera tinctoria
Indigo
Leguminosae

Description Perennial semi-tropical shrub. Pairs of oval leaves grow along its stems and clusters of small purplish flowers appear in summer.

Cultivation Must be grown in a greenhouse in temperate climates. Sow seed and take cuttings in spring.

Uses Famed for its rich blue dye since ancient times. Demand for it has not ceased since it was first introduced to the West three centuries ago, although its production as a colourfast blue dye agent involves surprisingly complex procedures such as fermentation.

Iris florentina
Orris root
Iridaceae

Description Hardy perennial. Reaches 2–3 ft (60 cm–1 m) high. Its stout rhizomatous roots are scented of violets and its leaves are sword-shaped. Large white flowers tinged with pale lavender and with a yellow beard appear in early to midsummer.

Cultivation Grows in deep, rich, well-drained soil in a sunny position. Divide roots in late spring or early autumn.

Uses Roots provide bitter flavouring for certain liqueurs. Powdered root imparts a refreshing scent to linen; also used as a base for dry shampoos, tooth powders and face packs as well as perfumery. Powdered root used as a fixative in potpourri. The root is a powerful purgative and now considered too strong to use medicinally. Dried root used to be used for coughs, hoarseness, bronchitis, colic and congestion in the liver. It also used to be chewed for disagreeable breath.

Lawsonia inermis
Henna
Lythraceae

Description Perennial tropical shrub. Can grow up to 10 ft (3 m) high. Bushy with narrow, grey-green leaves and small, sweet-scented pink or cream flowers, which give way to clusters of blue-black berries.

Cultivation Requires dry, well-drained soil and a tropical climate.

Uses Dried leaves produce a strong red dye and have been used for centuries in the East to colour hair, skin and nails. Dried leaves also have astringent properties. Apply in a cold compress to soothe fevers, headaches, stings, aching joints and skin irritations.

Leonurus cardiaca
Motherwort
Labiatae

Description Hardy perennial with pungent odour and bitter taste. Reaches 3–5 ft (1–1.5 m) tall. Thick, grooved, hairy, square stems bear hairy, lobed, toothed, dark green leaves with paler undersides. Whorls of pale pink to red-purple flowers appear from midsummer to midautumn.

Cultivation Grows on well-drained, light, limy soil in full sun. Sow in spring. Divide roots in late spring or midautumn. Self-seeds freely.

Uses Whole plant yields a dark green woollen dye and is also slightly astringent. Infusion of dried plant eases false labour pains and is a relaxing tonic for menopausal changes. Also can be used as a heart tonic and to lower blood pressure.

Linum usitatissimum
Flax
Linaceae

Description Hardy annual. Grows 1–4 ft (30 cm–1.2 m) tall with narrow, hairy, sword-shaped leaves and red, white or blue flowers appearing in early to late summer. These are followed by spherical capsules with shiny, light brown seeds high in oils with linoleic acid.

Cultivation Grows in dryish, well-drained soil in an open sunny position. Sow in spring or early summer.

Uses These go back to the earliest times. Seed and unripe capsules provide food when roasted. Seed oil (linseed) is important in paint and varnish manufacture. Stems can be used to make paper and cloth. Seeds provide a setting lotion for hair and, when eaten whole, a laxative. Drink seed infusion for all pulmonary infections and use as a poultice for boils and inflammations.

Lupinus polyphyllus
Lupin
Leguminosae

Description Herbaceous perennial. Grows 2½–4 ft (75 cm–1.2 m) high with whorls of long, narrow leaves and pea-shaped, deep blue, purple, pink, white or yellow flowers. These appear in late spring and early summer and are followed by flattened, spherical, white seeds in long pods.

Cultivation Grows in light, sandy soil in sun or light shade. Sow in spring.

Uses Bruise seeds as a facial steam, or make into skin lotion, to cleanse oily skin. The plant may have a role in absorbing radiation and has been planted around the nuclear disaster area of Chernobyl in Russia.

Note: *The raw seed of some species is toxic when eaten.*

Onobrychis viciifolia
Sainfoin
Leguminosae

Description Attractive bushy perennial. Grows 4 in–2½ ft (10–75 cm) high. Leaflets are narrow and in pairs, and cone-shaped spikes of pink flowers, streaked with red, appear from late spring to late summer. This is likely to be the Anglo-Saxon herb "Atterlothe", the last unidentified plant of the Nine Sacred Herbs listed in the eleventh-century herbal, the *Lacnunga*. The Archeological Unit of Bury St Edmunds in England translated the word as "cock spur grass" and Culpeper's herbal of 1645 listed a "cock's head fitch" as *Onobrychis*.

Cultivation Grows in dry, well-drained soil. Scratch seeds, then sow in situ in spring or early autumn.

Uses Makes good honey as its pollen is attractive to bees. Use as a fodder plant.

Panax quinquefolius
American ginseng
Araliaceae

Description Hardy perennial. Grows 1–1½ ft (30–45 cm) tall with finely toothed, oval leaflets and aromatic, fleshy, spindle-shaped, pale yellow to brown root. Small yellow or pink flowers appear in late summer and are followed by bright red berries.

Cultivation Grows in cool humus-rich soil in shade. Sow seed in early spring in a heated greenhouse. Transplant outside. Harvest after 3–9 years.

Uses Infuse dried root as a tonic drink for increased mental and physical vigour, against depression caused by exhaustion, or external stress, as an appetite and digestive stimulant, and for relief from nausea. It is helpful for coughs and chest disorders. Oriental ginseng (*P. pseudoginseng*) has similar uses.

Polygonum bistorta
Bistort/Snakeweed
Polygonaceae

Description Hardy perennial. Reaches up to 3 ft (1 m) high. Leaves are broad oval and blue-green with heart-shaped base; knobbly, twisted blackish-brown roots have red flesh. Pink flowers, in dense spikes, appear late spring.

Cultivation Grows in moist soil in sun or shade. Divide creeping rootstock in spring or early autumn; can be invasive.

Uses Young raw leaves are pleasant to eat. Root can be used to tan leather. Pulverize dried root and use as a very astringent tea for both internal and external bleeding, diarrhoea and as an enema. Decoct root as a mouth wash for ulcers and as a remedy for coughs, sore throats and dysentery. Applied direct to a wound, the root powder helps to stop bleeding.

Reseda luteola
Weld
Resedaceae

Description Hardy biennial. Grows 2–5 ft (60 cm–1.5 m) high with rosettes of long, wavy-edged leaves in its first season; graceful, curved spikes of small yellow-green flowers appear during summer of second season.
Cultivation Grows in fertile, well-drained alkaline soil in full sun. Sow seed in late summer. Seed stays fertile for many years.
Uses Whole flowering plant yields a strong, clear yellow dye for woollens and silks. Once mixed with woad to create "Saxon green".

Rubia tinctorum
Madder
Rubiaceae

Description Hardy perennial climber with prickly, weak stems. Grows 2–3 ft (60 cm–1 m) high with whorls of large, rough, prickly-edged, lance-shaped leaves; root is thick, fleshy and reddish-brown. Small yellow-green flowers appear from early summer to early autumn, followed by spherical, black fruits.
Cultivation Grows in well-drained soil in full sun or light shade. Sow seed in spring or autumn in well dug loam. Divide creeping root.
Uses Root and leaves of this traditional dye plant yield pink, red (alizerin crimson) and brown dyes, depending on the mordant used, for cloth and leather. Leaves can be used as metal scourers. Powdered root may heal urinary disorders and prevent stone formation. Leafy stems, when infused, may relieve constipation.

Scutellaria lateriflora
Skullcap
Labiatae

Description Hardy perennial. Reaches 1–3 ft (30 cm–1 m) tall. Branching stems bear oval, toothed leaves and small pretty blue flowers appear along the stem during summer. Roots are fibrous and yellow.
Cultivation Grows in ordinary, well-drained soil in sun or light shade. Sow under gentle heat in late winter. Divide roots in early spring.
Uses Whole plant very effective as a soothing, antispasmodic tonic and remedy for hysteria and hydrophobia. Infuse powdered herb as a tea for premenstrual tension, rheumatism, neuralgia and severe hiccups.

Sesamum indicum
Sesame
Pedaliaceae

Description Strong-smelling, tender annual, native to the tropics. Reaches 3 ft (1 m) high with lance-shaped leaves; drooping, purple to white flowers are followed by long capsules containing numerous flat, white or yellowish seeds.
Cultivation Prefers sandy loam in a sunny position. Propagate by seed.
Uses Seeds provide excellent source of protein, niacin, phosphorus, sulphur and carbohydrates, and have a sweet, nutty flavour; sprinkle over breads, biscuits, vegetables and casseroles. Sesame seed paste (tahini) is mixed into spreads, sauces, casseroles and pâtés. Seeds will also relieve constipation, haemorrhoids and genito-urinary infections.

Stachys officinalis
Betony
Labiatae

Description Hardy perennial. Reaches up to 2 ft (60 cm) tall. Hairy, square stems bear aromatic, slightly hairy, round-lobed leaves; dense spikes of pink or purple flowers appear from mid- to late summer.
Cultivation Grows in ordinary soil in sun or shade; prefers some humus. Sow seed in spring. Divide roots in spring or autumn.
Uses Try dried leaves as a tea substitute. Fresh plant yields yellow dye and hair rinse to highlight golden tones in grey hair. Leaves now chiefly employed in herbal smoking mixtures and snuffs; in poultices, and also in homeopathic tinctures for diarrhoea. Whole plant has aromatic, astringent and blood-purifying properties. Infuse as a sedative and antispasmodic for migraines and indigestion.

Stellaria media
Chickweed
Caryophyllaceae

Description Vigorous creeping annual, 4–12 in (10–30 cm) long. Succulent, oval leaves grow on very straggly, brittle, much branched stems that are hairy on only one side. Small, star-like, white flowers appear from early spring until midwinter.
Cultivation Easy to grow in any soil in any position, but prefers moist places. Sow in spring. Self-seeds readily.
Uses Leaves contain vitamin C and phosphorus and are delicious eaten raw in salads or boiled as a vegetable. Fresh leaves in a poultice relieve inflammation and ulcers. Decoct whole plant to treat constipation, piles and sores. Apply in an ointment to heal eczema, psoriasis and other irritating skin diseases.

Taraxacum officinale
Dandelion
Compositae

Description Very common hardy perennial weed. Grows 2–12 in (5–30 cm) high. Long, milky taproot and stem bear oblong, toothed leaves in flat rosettes. Golden flowers appear from spring to midautumn and are followed by globular clusters of tufted seeds.
Cultivation Grows in most soils in open sunny positions. Sow in spring to early autumn. Self-seeds profusely.
Uses Leaves, which are high in vitamins A and C, niacin and various minerals, and roots can be eaten raw in salads. Grind dried and roasted root as a coffee substitute. Root yields a magenta woollen dye. Latex in the leaves is a rich emollient for facial steams, cleansing milks and moisturizers for all skins. Add to bathwater as a tonic. Decoct flowers as a cosmetic wash. Root increases bile production and is an effective diuretic; also good for rheumatism, gout, eczema, constipation and insomnia.

Tussilago farfara
Coltsfoot
Compositae

Description Hardy perennial. Reaches 3–12 in (8–30 cm) high with small, white, spreading roots and toothed, dark green leaves with grey undersides; small yellow flowers appear in spring.
Cultivation Grows readily in most soils; can be invasive. Sow in spring. Take root cuttings in spring and autumn. Divide plant in autumn.
Uses Eat fresh leaves in a salad; dried ones are included in herbal tobaccos. All parts of coltsfoot contain a mucilage which is good for coughs and bronchitis. Decoct leaves for colds, flu and asthma.

Urtica dioica
Nettle
Urticaceae

Description Perennial with separate male and female plants. Grows up to 4 ft (1.2 m) high. Leaves are toothed, pointed and oval; they sting when touched. Bristly, square stems also bear minute, greenish flowers from early summer to early autumn.
Cultivation Grows readily on any soil. Sow in spring. Divide roots in spring.
Uses Young nettles are rich in vitamins and minerals; eat in a salad, boil as a vegetable, or drink as a herbal tea. Use to make nettle beer. Whole plant yields a greenish-yellow woollen dye. Nettle fibres spun into rope and made into cloth and paper. Astringent young leaves used in facial steams, bath mixtures and hair preparations. Infuse or decoct herb as a digestive, diuretic, astringent.

Glossary

acid A term applied to soil with a pH content of less than 6.5 and which contains no free lime.

alkaline A term applied to soil with a pH content of more than 7.3. Some herbs actively prefer an acid soil, but most will thrive in alkaline soil.

annual A plant that is grown from seed, flowers then dies all in one growing season.

astringent A substance that contracts living tissue. An astringent cosmetic preparation tightens the skin.

axil The angle between the upper side of a leaf stalk and its stem.

biennial Taking two growing seasons to complete a life-cycle. A biennial plant produces stems and leaves during the first growing season, flowers and seeds during the second, after which time it dies.

bract A small, modified leaf at the base of a flower.

compress A piece of linen or cloth soaked in a herbal infusion or decoction and applied externally.

cordial A warming and reviving drink. The term is also applied to a medicine that stimulates the heart.

coumarin A compound present in certain plants which, if taken in large amounts, can cause haemorrhage. It gives the plant the smell of new mown hay after it has been dried.

crown The base of a herbaceous perennial plant from which the roots and shoots grow.

cultivar A cultivated variety of plant, rather than one that occurs naturally in the wild.

cutting A leaf, bud or part of the stem or root removed from a plant to form the basis of a new plant.

deadhead To remove withered flowers, usually to prevent seeding.

deciduous A plant, especially a tree or shrub, that sheds its leaves at the end of the growing season.

decoction A herbal dose obtained by boiling or simmering a certain weight of herb in a certain quantity of liquid for a given length of time. A standard decoction is made with 1 oz (25 g) of herb to 1 pint (570 ml) water. To make a mild decoction, halve the quantity of herb; for a strong decoction, double the quantity.

distillation The process of separating components of a liquid with different boiling points by heating the liquid until it becomes a vapour and then condensing the vapour and collecting the ensuing liquid.

diuretic A substance that promotes the flow of urine.

effleurage A light sweeping stroke used in massage.

emetic A substance that causes vomiting.

emollient A softening substance.

enfleurage The extraction of perfumes from flowers by the use of fats.

evergreen A plant that bears living foliage all year round.

expectorant A substance that encourages phlegm to be coughed up from the lungs.

genus The botanical name for a group of closely related plants.

half hardy May not survive cold frosts. Some half-hardy plants can be grown outdoors only during the summer. Others, particularly some shrubs, will successfully overwinter outdoors in sheltered positions in regions where the climate is mild.

hardy Capable of surviving the winter outdoors without protection.

herbaceous Usually refers to perennial plants whose stems are not woody and which die down at the end of each growing season.

infusion A herbal dose obtained by pouring a certain quantity of boiling liquid over a certain weight of herb and leaving it to steep for a given length of time. For a standard infusion use 1 oz (25 g) dried herb to 1 pint (570 ml) water. To make a mild infusion, use half the amount of herb; for a strong infusion, use double the amount.

maceration The extraction of a drug from a herb by steeping it in a solvent.

mucilage A gelatinous substance which occurs naturally in some herbs and is used to soothe and treat inflammation of the skin.

mulch A soil covering laid down to protect plant roots.

narcotic A substance which in small doses deadens pain but in large doses can damage the nervous system and lead to unconsciousness and even death.

nervine A substance or remedy used to treat nervous disorders.

perennial Living from year to year. The stems and leaves of a perennial plant die down in the winter, and new shoots appear each spring. The term is usually applied to herbaceous plants.

pH scale A system devised for measuring the acid-alkaline content of soils. Numbers below 7 denote acidity; higher numbers show alkalinity.

poultice Crushed herb or plant extracts heated and applied to bruised or inflamed skin.

propagate To increase and reproduce plants.

prostrate Growing flat over the surface of the soil.

purgative A strong laxative taken to empty the bowels.

rhizome A horizontally creeping, swollen underground stem that stores food and from which roots and shoots are produced.

rootstock The crown and root system of herbaceous perennials and suckering shrubs. The term is also used to describe a vigorous plant onto which another plant is grafted.

runner A stem that spreads along the soil surface, rooting wherever it comes in contact with moist soil to form a new plant.

salve A soothing ointment.

self-seed A term applied to plants that drop their seed around them, from which new plants will grow, sometimes with poorer and more varied flowers.

shrub A perennial whose branched stems are woody.

species A classification applied to a plant or plants within a genus. Grown from seed, species remain consistently true to type.

stamen The pollen-bearing part of a flower.

subshrub A low-growing shrub whose base is woody but whose stems are soft.

sucker A shoot which grows up from below ground level.

tincture A solution of extracts of medicinal plants obtained by steeping the plants in alcohol or in a solution of alcohol and water.

topiary The clipping of evergreen trees and shrubs into geometric and fanciful shapes.

tuber A swollen root or underground stem in which food is stored.

umbel A flat-topped mass of small flowerheads on stalks that radiate out from a central point.

variegated A term used to describe leaves that have markings in a secondary colour.

variety A term applied originally only to a naturally occurring variation of a species, but now often used also to describe a cultivar.

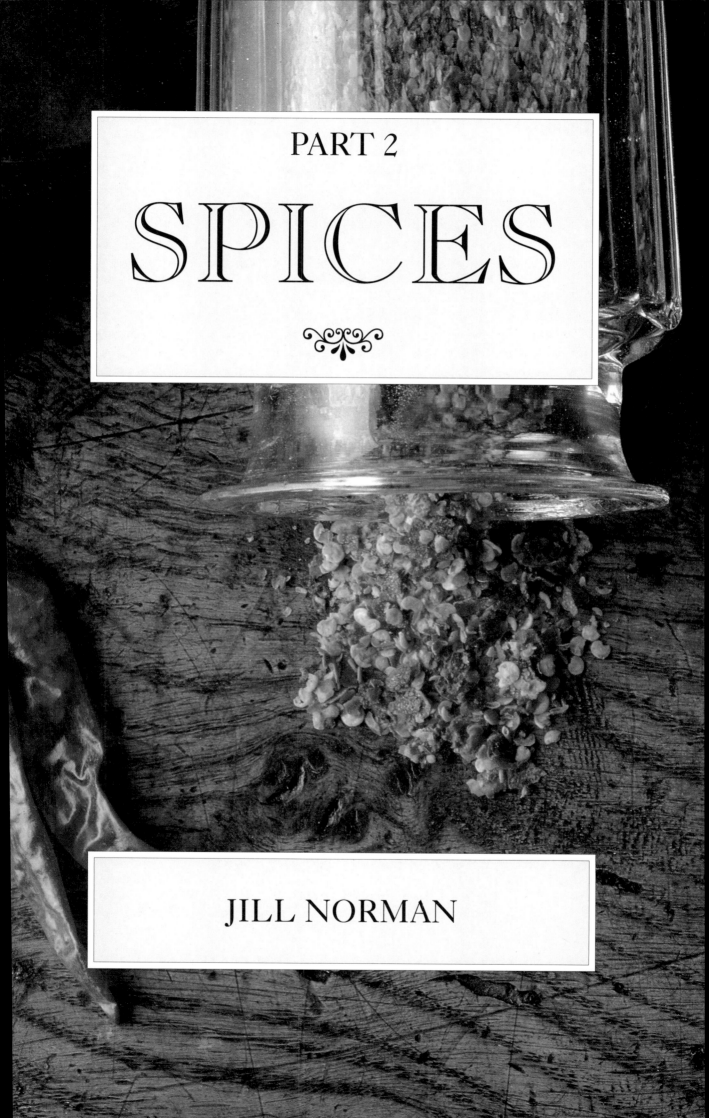

PART 2

SPICES

JILL NORMAN

Introduction

" Ah, que j'aime t'ouvrir cher tiroir aux épices,
Souffle d'Orient gratis, voyage inespéré,
Colombo et Ceylon aux magiques caprices,
A défaut de vous voir, je puis vous respirer."

Roger Lecuyer

What is a spice?

Defined in the *Oxford English Dictionary* as "one or other of various strongly flavoured or aromatic substances of vegetable origin, obtained from tropical plants, commonly used as condiments", spices are aromatic dried roots, bark, buds, seeds, berries and other fruits. The word "spice" derives from the Latin word *species*, meaning specific kind, and later, goods or merchandise.

Most of the important spice plants - cinnamon, pepper, ginger, cloves, nutmeg - are native to the Asian tropics; allspice, vanilla and chillies come from the West Indies and Central America; the Mediterranean basin has produced many of the aromatic seeds - coriander, fenugreek, fennel, poppy, mustard; the colder regions have contributed caraway, dill and juniper.

What makes a spice spicy?

Spices acquire their characteristic odour from volatile constituents in the plant material. These aroma constituents are extracted in steam and are present in the essential oil (a term derived from the word "quintessence" - the embodiment of the specific aroma and flavour) distilled from the plant. The volatile oils are largely responsible for a spice's characteristic flavour, although the pungent principle - the hot sensation produced in the mouth by constituents of spices such as pepper, chillies or ginger - also contributes to flavour. Four specific tastes can be detected in different parts of the mouth - sweet, sour, salty and bitter; pungency can be recognized in taste too, but the rest of the complex flavours of any food or drink are identified through smell.

Our vocabulary for describing smell and taste is extremely poor; they are usually described only in terms of other smells and tastes. "Aromatic" and "pungent" are the two adjectives most used about spices, but in a discussion of several spices, aroma and pungency need to be more accurately defined to make comparisons possible. For example, one group of spices has a distinct anise note: dill, fennel, anise, caraway, cumin and star anise. All are members of the same family except star anise. The anise element in dill is mild and subtle; in fennel it is more clear and distinct; anise itself has a sweetish taste with a note of liquorice; in caraway the anise flavour is more subdued again, although the overall effect is warm and slightly bitter; cumin is the most forceful of the group, its anise tones combine with other constituents to give an acrid, intense character. Star anise often has a more pronounced anise aroma than any of the others; it has sweet and bitter tones and is very liquorice-like. Only a tasting comparison will fix the subtle differences in flavour and aroma levels.

The changing role of spices

Spices were once one of the most expensive items in household accounts and were usually kept locked up in the drawers or compartments of special spice cupboards or boxes. In ancient times they were significant as medicines, preservatives and perfumes. Cassia, ginger and pepper were imported by the Greeks; anise, coriander seeds, saffron and poppy seeds were grown locally, as were thyme, mint and marjoram. Dioscorides' De Materia Medica, written in the first century AD, was the earliest Western herbal to describe these plants and remedies based upon them. The Romans were the first to use great quantities of spices in cooking, where they were employed in the same generous manner as they were strewn or burned in houses to drive out noxious smells.

Spices were also popular in the new Islamic empire of Mohammed which reached great cultural heights while western Europe went through the Dark Ages. The court of the Caliphs of Baghdad was renowned for science and medicine, art and poetry, and for its sumptuous banquets. The cooks sought to achieve a harmony of flavours, sweet and sour, aromatic and pungent, using many spices and flavourings from the Orient and Middle East such as galangal, cloves, cardamom, nutmeg, cinnamon, pepper, asafoetida, ginger, saffron and rose water.

The widespread use of spices for cooking did not come to Europe until the late Middle Ages. At the end of the 14th century a Parisian housewife could buy spiced sauces from professional saucemakers: "a quart of cameline for the dinner and for the supper two quarts of mustard" were required for a wedding feast, according to Le Ménagier de Paris (1393). Made with cinnamon, ginger, cloves, grains of paradise, mace, long pepper, and bread soaked in vinegar, cameline was the most popular sauce of the time. Heavily spiced food remained the norm for the banquets of the rich until the 17th century. Meat and fish were sauced with cinnamon, pepper, cloves, nutmeg, ginger, galangal and saffron throughout Europe. Most dishes were liberally dosed with sugar, sometimes vinegar too, creating a sweet-sour taste. The Germans also used caraway, cumin and lovage seeds; the Italians, fennel.

By the 17th century spices were cheaper and more widely available so they were used with less ostentation by the rich. In baking and sweet dishes they were still important: custards were spiced with nutmeg and cinnamon; saffron cake and seedcake recipes were common. Some of the medieval spices - grains of paradise, cubebs, zedoary - disappeared, but new aromatics arrived from the Americas: allspice, capsicums and vanilla. At the end of the 18th century liquid pickles were on sale as bottled sauces in England. Spices, garlic and fruits were put in casks with vinegar and soy sauce and left to macerate for up to two years. Households and commercial producers had their individual formulae. Among the earliest successful commercial sauces were Lazenby's anchovy essence and Harvey's sauce. Tabasco sauce from Louisiana appeared later in the mid-19th century when Edward McIlhenny, a banker during the Civil War, turned to making sauces.

Today spices are an accepted part of our daily lives. We can choose from a wider selection of spices than we have ever known; try dozens of sauces and essences from all over the world; buy our spices whole or ground, plain or blended as barbecue mix or more dubious-sounding confections such as chicken seasoning, Season-All or Bon Appétit. The increasing choice implies a much deserved revival of interest in spices. Experiment with their flavours and discover their different qualities. Let your palate be the judge of the role spices play in your cooking today.

Jill Norman

1
The spice trade past & present

Spices have been used for thousands of years throughout Asia, Arabia and the Mediterranean region. Once valued as highly as gold, they were much sought after in the West and the quest for spices influenced the course of history dramatically. Countries vied to win control over their production, navigators set sail to discover new sea routes to the East, which eventually allowed small nations to build large empires. Although the days of warring over spices are now over, spices still play a significant role in the economies of many countries.

The origins of the spice trade

THE PEOPLES OF the Mediterranean traded for spices from the earliest times. The Egyptians used herbs and spices for embalming, for body ointments and anointing oils, and to fumigate their homes. The Ebers papyrus, a medical document of about 1550 BC, records that anise, caraway, cassia, cardamom, mustard, sesame, fenugreek, saffron and other aromatics were all used by the Egyptians. Frankincense, a resin from trees that grow in the Arabian peninsula, myrrh from East Africa, spices and precious stones from the Far East were taken overland by donkey and later by camel caravans along the Incense Route. This trail led from Hadhramaut in South Arabia along the Arabian coast, then north via Mecca to Egypt and Syria.

Spices are frequently mentioned in the Bible as a valuable commodity; the Queen of Sheba rushed to present Solomon with gold, jewels and spices when through an alliance with his Phoenician neighbours their ships entered the Red Sea, threatening the trade routes she controlled (*Kings* I:10 and *Chronicles* II:9), and Joseph was sold by his brothers to merchants from Gilead travelling to Egypt "with their camels bearing spicery and balm and myrrh" (*Genesis* 37:25). For centuries Arabs acted as middlemen in the trade with the Orient and Africa south of the Sahara. They were in an excellent location, and to preserve their monopoly they kept secret from their Mediterranean customers the provenance of their wares. Alarming tales about the location of spices were put about to discourage the spice buyers from trying to determine the true source of supply and dealing direct.

The Phoenicians distributed spices around the Mediterranean until Tyre, their great commercial centre, fell to Alexander the Great in 332 BC. In the same year he founded Alexandria, the city that was to become the meeting place for merchants from East and West. Several routes were used by the Greeks to bring spices from the East. The oldest sea route was probably that from the Malabar coast of India, up the Persian Gulf and then either via the Tigris and Euphrates valleys to Babylon and Antioch, or round the coast of Arabia and up the Red Sea.

Fig. 6.

Pepper *The spice that inspired the search for new routes to the East and changed the course of history.*

Camel caravan *For centuries spices were transported across Asia from China to Europe along ancient caravan trails such as the Silk Road.*

The spice trade in Roman times

The Romans started sailing to India from Egypt in the first century AD; it was a hazardous business and the voyage took two years, until the middle of the century when Hippalus, a Greek merchant sailor, discovered the monsoon winds. Ships sailed to India with the southwest monsoons from April to October and returned with the northeast monsoons blowing from October to April. The journey now took less than a year; the Romans brought back fabulous cargoes and rapidly became extravagant users of spices for perfume, cosmetics, medicine and cooking.

At about the same time the overland route from China, the Silk Road, came into use. Starting from the Chinese city of Chang'an (Xian) it led west, skirting the Himalayas, then on across Persia and the Fertile Crescent to the Mediterranean, or down the Indus valley to the coast, or sometimes north via the Aral and Caspian seas to the Black Sea and Byzantium. The routes varied according to political stability and the taxes levied on caravans, but by the second century the Han emperors extended their control of central Asia far enough to police the roads, and merchants then travelled regularly and in relative safety, carrying silks, jewels, cassia, cumin and ginger to Rome. These land and sea routes continued in use for centuries; indeed the monsoons governed all sea transport to and from India until steamships were introduced.

Pepper was the most popular Oriental spice in Rome, followed by ginger and turmeric. Most of the recipes in Apicius' *De Re Coquinaria* - "On Cookery" written in the first century AD - included an extensive range of spices to aid digestion, to preserve food and to enhance its flavour. As the Roman empire extended across the Alps the inhabitants of northern Europe acquired the taste for spices too. By the time the Goths laid siege to the city in AD 408 they knew well the value of pepper, silks, gold and silver, and the Romans handed over a huge tribute to prevent the sacking of their city. Rome's fall two years later virtually marked the end of the western empire. Constantinople became the capital of the eastern empire and trade routes developed around the growing city. At about this time too, cloves and nutmegs found their way to the West, probably taken first to India by Indonesian merchants.

Constantinople *Once the eastern capital of the Roman empire, the city of Constantinople was the centre for spice trading between East and West.*

The Middle Ages

The flow of goods from East to West dwindled and by the time the Arabs conquered Alexandria in AD 641 it had virtually stopped altogether. The seventh century saw the rise of Islam and by the middle of the eighth century the Arab empire spread from Spain to the borders of China. For 400 years very few spices reached Europe; there was little direct trade between the Muslim Arabs and Christian Europe. In the political and commercial chaos of the Dark Ages which resulted from the barbarian invasions, Europe had nothing to offer in exchange for goods from Asia. The few spices that did arrive were found only in the great houses and palaces and in monasteries and cathedral priories.

Towards the end of his reign Charlemagne decreed that certain herbs and temperate spices, some 70-odd in all, were to be cultivated on all the imperial estates. Monastery gardens were the other places where herbs and spices were grown; the plan of St Gall, made at about the same time, shows a physic garden with beds for cumin, fenugreek, fennel, lovage, mint, rosemary, rue and sage, and a kitchen garden which included celery, coriander, dill, nigella, garlic and poppy.

Monastery accounts give some idea of the spices used in Britain in the Middle Ages; at Norwich cathedral priory in the years 1346 to 1350, purchases of fennel, ginger, galangal, saffron, garlic, pepper, cloves and cubebs were recorded. About 100 years later accounts from Canterbury show expenditure on cloves, mace and saffron. Pepper and other spices were often used as part payment for rents too; mustard is shown as being part of the revenue for lands owned by St Germain-des-Prés in Paris in the 14th century. Spices were taxed at every opportunity; in the tenth century the Statutes of Ethelred required Easterlings (merchants from the Hanseatic towns) to pay 10 lb of pepper as part of a tribute to allow them to trade in London. In 1305 a toll was created to pay for repairs to London Bridge; anise, liquorice and cubebs were among the items taxed. The counts of Provence levied taxes on pepper, ginger, cubebs, cloves, saffron, cumin and sugar from the towns in their domain.

The early European spice trade centres

Trade with the East was reopened by the Crusades in the 11th century. For 200 years there was a stream of Crusaders and pilgrims to the Holy Land where they developed a taste for the foods of that warm climate. Venice and Genoa became principal suppliers to the Crusaders and set up trading concessions in the Near East. Wool, clothing, iron and lumber were exchanged for dates, figs, lemons, oranges, almonds and Oriental spices - pepper, nutmeg and mace, cinnamon, cloves and cardamom. Although spices were still expensive, their use was not restricted to the very wealthy or privileged now, but spread to the middle class. However, the trade was not as easy and natural as it is sometimes made out to be; there were many transactions to be negotiated. A consignment of spices passed through a chain of hands from leaving Aleppo or Alexandria before it reached Lyons or Nürnberg or Bruges. Prices, and sometimes adulteration - although severe penalties were imposed for this crime - increased on each occasion. The Italian city states grew enormously in prosperity and the bitter rivalry between them lasted until Venice defeated Genoa in 1380 and thereafter controlled trade with the Orient for more than 100 years. The Republic enjoyed an unprecedented boom in trade; the demand from Europe for spices, silks and precious stones could probably not have been satisfied had the Indians and Chinese not wanted large quantities of gold, silver, coral, saffron and wool in return.

New routes East and the rise of Portugal

The first steps towards the discovery of new routes to the East were taken in 1418 when Prince Henry (the Navigator) of Portugal set up a navigational school at Sagres in southwest Portugal. He sent out expeditions down the west coast of Africa, hoping to find a route to the East. During his lifetime the Portuguese did not succeed in getting there, but they brought back valuable cargoes from tropical Africa, including grains of paradise.

In May 1498, after a voyage of ten months, the Portuguese explorer Vasco da Gama reached Calicut, the most important port on the west coast of India. After a stay of several months he returned to Portugal with a cargo of spices and jewels, and the news that the ruler was willing to trade with Manuel I. In 1500 Cabral followed with a larger fleet - discovered and took possession of Brazil for Portugal on the way - and a year later returned with a cargo of pepper and other spices. The Venetian monopoly was broken; prices fluctuated wildly; in 1504 Manuel declared a fixed price for pepper and in 1506 made the Lisbon spice trade a crown monopoly.

Cardamom *Carried to Europe along the ancient caravan routes, cardamom was used medicinally and as a flavouring for centuries in the East.*

Vasco da Gama *The Portuguese explorer who discovered the sea route to India via the Cape of Good Hope.*

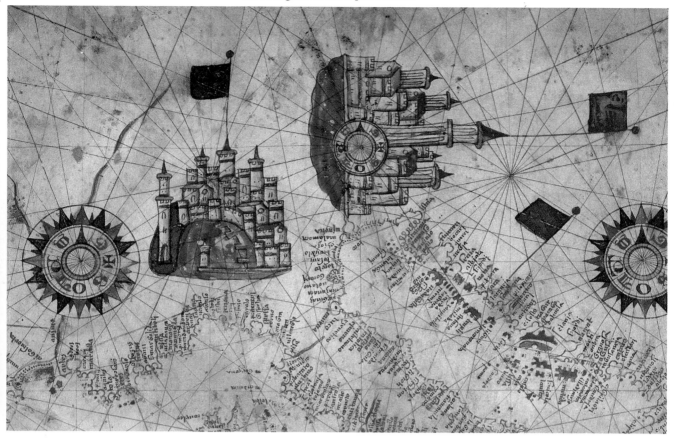

Control of the Spice Islands

By 1510, after battles with the Arabs who for centuries had controlled trade in the Indian Ocean, the Portuguese were established at Goa and on the island of Ceylon. Here they rapidly exploited the cinnamon forests, enslaved the workers and built up a lucrative trade monopoly that was to last well into the 17th century. They moved further east and settled in the trading town of Malacca at the southern end of the Malay peninsula, close to the Spice Islands (the Moluccas) where their cargoes of spices, silks and porcelain were assembled. In due course they moved in to occupy some of the islands too, building fortresses, signing treaties with the local rulers, and oppressing the natives. When the remnants of Magellan's fleet, sailing westwards round the globe under the auspices of the Spanish crown, arrived in the Moluccas in 1522, this set up a struggle between the two powers in the islands until they were united under a common (Spanish) crown in 1580.

The Portuguese were concerned about territorial acquisitions, and to some extent about spreading Catholicism, as well as about trade. Their style of trading was still of the old order; officials were required to provide an annual revenue for the crown, but were also permitted to trade on their own account. The crown tried to restrict local trading by fixing prices and forcing buyers to hand over a percentage of the goods purchased. Not surprisingly the state ended up with the poorer quality merchandise and found the arrangement very difficult to police. Private Portuguese trade flourished and local Asian trade patterns continued.

Trade was based largely on barter. For example, on Banda, the group of Moluccan islands where nutmeg trees grew, the inhabitants were accustomed to exchanging their spices for food and clothing, neither of which they produced themselves. They maintained the relative values of mace and nutmeg by selling mace seven times more expensively than nutmeg (the approximate ratio of production).

The Portuguese shipped spices to Lisbon, but for the first 60-odd years of the 16th century it was the Dutch who controlled shipping and trade in northern Europe, making handsome profits in their turn from the sale of spices. Then in 1568 Philip II of Spain moved into the Netherlands and war broke out. After 15 years the Dutch managed to dislodge the Spaniards from the northern, Calvinist provinces, but not from the Catholic south.

Genoa and Venice *During the Middle Ages these rival city states became extremely wealthy and powerful. Eventually Venice won control of trade with the Orient.*

Nutmeg and mace *Introduced to Europe by the Crusaders, these prized spices did not become readily available until the sea routes to the Spice Islands were discovered.*

Although the defeat of the armada in 1588 reduced Spain's sea power, Philip II was still able to deny the Dutch access to Lisbon for trade. They started to sail down the African coast and with information gathered from "spies" in Lisbon and from Jan van Linschoten, who returned after nine years in Goa with information about the spices, trading methods and Portuguese fortifications in the region, they planned their first voyage to Asia.

The rise of the Dutch East India Company

A group of Amsterdam merchants financed an expedition to the Indies in 1595. In many ways it was a catastrophic voyage; after two and a half years 89 men returned from a company of 248, brawling and arguing, but the

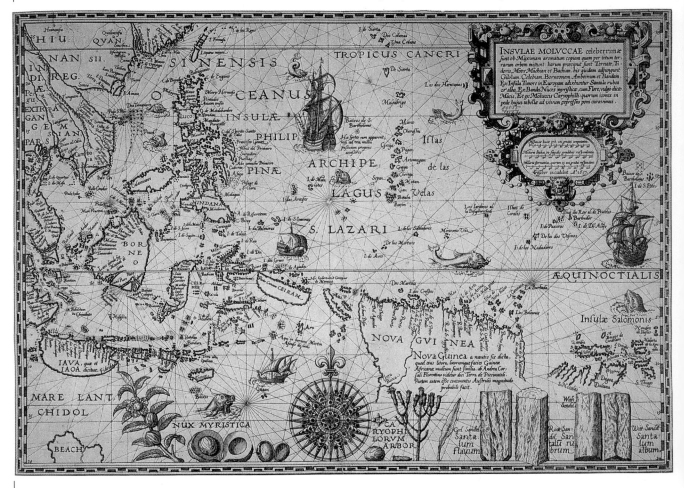

The Moluccas Also known as the Spice Islands, these were the main source of cloves, nutmeg and mace and the subject of much fighting between the Portuguese, the Dutch and the English in the 16th and 17th centuries.

merchants among them did have 245 bags of pepper, 45 tons of nutmeg and 30 bales of mace. This started a rush eastwards, with competing groups of merchants sending out expeditions. In 1602 the *Vereenigde Oost-Indische Compagnie* (United East India Company) was formed to put a stop to internal competition. Given sweeping powers, including the right to carry on the war with Spain in the Indies (at the company's expense), the VOC was the unwitting beginning of the Dutch colonial empire and also gave the Dutch the monopoly of the spice trade.

Portuguese superiority over the Asians was based on their naval and military strength; the Dutch soon proved themselves superior to the Portuguese in these fields as well. Their concerns were war and a monopoly on trade. Native rulers enlisted the help of the Dutch to rid them of the Portuguese, little realizing the consequences. In the first half of the 17th century the Dutch dislodged the Portuguese from Ceylon, the Moluccas and Banda, blockaded Malacca and established their main base at Batavia (Djakarta) on the island of Java. They tried to make contracts with native princes to buy at prices fixed by the company, paying in silver reals (Spanish coins) rather than allowing the barter system to continue, and obliging the natives to buy poor quality food and cloth at inflated prices from the company warehouses. They tried to stop all other trade, even by acts of

piracy, to prevent Chinese and other traders selling spices to the Portuguese or the English. To control production the Dutch had nutmeg and clove trees uprooted and permitted plantings only on certain islands; native resistance met with near extermination and replacement by Dutch colonists, yet the output of spices increased. In 1622 the clove crop of Amboina and Ceram was twice world consumption, and even the colonists in Banda had to be asked to grow food crops instead of nutmegs because production was too great. To maintain prices in Europe huge quantities of spices were burned in the streets of Amsterdam.

The cost of this pursuit of monopoly was so immense that it is questionable whether the spice trade was profitable. By the 18th century spices were definitely on the deficit side of the company ledger. The man who masterminded the growth of the VOC was Jan Coen, a young book-keeper who sailed to the Indies in 1607, rose to become director-general of the VOC, then governor-general of the Indies, all within ten years. Virtually single-handed he created the Dutch empire, whose wealth was built on cloves, mace, nutmeg and Sumatran pepper.

English intervention in the spice trade

While the Dutch were displacing the Portuguese in the East, the English were also thinking seriously about trading voyages rather than piracy. In 1600 Elizabeth I granted a charter to an English company, but each expedition had to be financed separately, so that by 1609 the English had managed only to fit out 14 ships for five voyages - the Dutch usually sent a fleet of about this size every two years. In 1609 James I granted a new charter which gave the East India Company the monopoly of English trade with the East. A period of constant harassment between the Dutch and the English followed. In 1619 the new Dutch Republic signed a treaty with England which said that they should join forces and divide the spoils of the Indies, especially the Moluccas. For helping to fight the Spaniards and Portuguese, the English were to get one third of the Moluccan trade. The English were not strong enough to sustain the agreement; Coen sabotaged it and the English moved out of the Spice Islands to Macassar. They still managed to trade, though, sending back cloves regularly over the next 60 years in spite of punitive Dutch expeditions in the Spice Islands. However, by 1682 the English had been driven back west of the Indonesian archipelago.

The Dutch monopoly was not to last for ever; about 1770 Pierre Poivre, a botanist who was administrator of the Ile de France (Mauritius), smuggled clove and nutmeg trees out of the Spice Islands and cultivated them successfully. New plantings were made in other French tropical colonies - the Seychelles, Réunion and Cayenne, and later in Zanzibar and the West Indies. In 1795 the English planted clove trees on Penang. By the 19th century no European country had a monopoly on any spice and prices started to fall.

A caravel The fastest and most sea-worthy vessels in the 15th and 16th centuries, caravels played a significant role in the discovery of new routes to the East and West.

Spices from the West

Six years before Vasco da Gama reached the East, Columbus made landfall on the Caribbean island of Hispaniola and subsequently on the mainland of America. He made four voyages westwards, still looking for the fabled riches of China; instead he brought back tobacco, yams, kidney beans, many new fruits and nuts, and the chilli pepper. Some years later the allspice berry, recorded on the second voyage, became popular in Europe. In 1519 Hernan Cortés led his troops on the conquest of Mexico, eventually bringing back to Spain not only great wealth in gold and silver but also vanilla, chocolate, turkey, maize, tomatoes and potatoes. The Spaniards planted ginger in their New World colonies, capsicums in the Mediterranean region and in the East.

Trading in the Moluccas This was based largely on barter.

American entry into the spice trade

The United States entered the spice trade towards the end of the 18th century. Ships from Salem, New London, New Bedford, and Boston sailed for the East carrying tobacco, foodstuffs and even ice to trade for tea, coffee, textiles and spices - particularly pepper, ginger, cloves, cassia and cinnamon. Pepper from Sumatra and from Malabar was by far the most important import, in quantity and in value.

The decline of the New England ports in the 19th century gave New York the lead in importing spices, a position it still holds, with almost 60 percent by value of US spice imports in 1988. Baltimore and San Francisco come second and third with 11 and 6 percent respectively.

Drying chillies *Trays of chillies drying in the sun in rural China.*

The spice trade today

The United States is now the largest importer of spices in the world, followed by West Germany, Japan and France. Singapore is the largest entrepot for spices, notably pepper, vanilla, cinnamon, cloves, anise, coriander and cumin. Hong Kong is a significant entrepot too, especially for ginger, chillies and cassia from China.

In 1986 the international trade in spices was estimated at 350,000 to 370,000 tons in volume and valued at more than US $1,000 million annually. Japan, West Germany and Saudi Arabia are growth areas; the American market is declining somewhat, with imports of black pepper, mustard and sesame - the three largest items - down quite substantially from 1987 to 1988, partly because smaller crops have resulted in higher prices. However, US imports of spice oleoresins (aromatic extracts) continue to rise.

Pepper is the most important spice imported in most markets, in terms of both volume and value. Next in importance are the capsicum spices - paprika, chilli and cayenne pepper. Cardamom accounts for a large share of the spice imports in the Middle East and North Africa (where it is used to flavour coffee) and in Sweden and Finland (where it is used in baking). Indonesia produces large quantities of cloves but also uses substantial amounts for its kretek cigarette industry. However, it is now almost self-sufficient, which has led to a significant drop in prices and severe export problems for Madagascar and Tanzania as stocks of unsold cloves rise. Cassia, cinnamon, nutmeg and mace figure prominently in the imports of West European countries and the United States; Mexico and Brazil also buy

Vanilla *As it is one of the three most expensive spices, a large proportion of vanilla flavouring on the market is synthetic - as much as 90 percent in the United States.*

substantial amounts of cassia; allspice is bought in large quantities by the USSR and the countries of eastern Europe. Ginger and turmeric sell in significant volume worldwide, as do aromatic seeds like coriander, anise, caraway and cumin - but the value of the seeds is low. Demand for anise, star anise and juniper comes mostly from distilleries for the production of anise-flavoured drinks and gin. Saffron, cardamom and vanilla remain the three most expensive spices; consumer demand for "natural" flavourings has given a small boost to the vanilla market, but synthetic vanillin still accounts for a very large percentage of vanilla flavouring.

Ninety percent of the international trade in spices is in whole spices; paprika is the only spice sold ground in significant amounts, and curry powder the only blend that has any commercial importance internationally. The producing countries invariably ship in bulk and spices are packed for the retail market by the importers. The remainder of the trade is made up of essential oils and oleoresins. The latter are finding a growing market with industrial food manufacturers who prefer them to natural spices because of ease of handling and storage, freedom from bacteria and consistency in quality. Oleoresins are highly concentrated and have to be diluted in alcohol or another solvent, or blended with a dry ingredient before they can be incorporated in a food product. India, Sri Lanka and Indonesia have flourishing oleoresin-producing plants, as do most industrialized countries.

Cloves Indonesia produces large quantities of cloves and is now almost self-sufficient in supplies for its kretek cigarette industry.

Exporting countries

India leads the export league in spices (principally pepper, cardamom, chillies, ginger, turmeric, cumin and other seeds, curry powder) followed by Indonesia (pepper, nutmeg and mace, cassia, ginger, cardamom, vanilla), Brazil (pepper, cloves, ginger), the Malagasy Republic - Madagascar (vanilla, cloves) and Malaysia (pepper, ginger). More than 80 percent of spice exports are from developing countries, and production and export are an important element of the agricultural economy; the incomes of thousands of peasant farmers are supplemented by growing spices as a secondary cash crop. Yet even an export value of more than US $1,000 million annually represents only half a percent of the value of exports of all agricultural and fishery products, and is much lower than the value of exports of staple crops such as sugar or coffee. Nevertheless spice exports make a healthy contribution to foreign exchange earnings.

In an effort to reduce fluctuations in earnings from spices the producer countries are trying to set up more efficient trading operations and marketing programmes, to match supply to demand more carefully, and to increase the value of their crops by trying to meet the health regulations and quality controls of importing countries more adequately. The International Pepper Community has existed for many years and successfully pooled information on disease control, processing, marketing and price stabilization, but other individual spices have not benefited from such international support. Now the International Spice Group, set up in 1983 with members from importing and exporting countries, aims to provide the forum where the concerns of both buyers and sellers can be considered.

Spice stall in Morocco A colourful display of assorted spices including paprika, peppercorns, cumin and cinnamon.

2

Spice index

A comprehensive photographic index of both common and lesser-known spices from ginger and cinnamon to screwpine leaves and grains of paradise, arranged alphabetically by botanical name. Each entry covers the origins and history of the spice, its cultivation, distribution, and culinary and traditional uses throughout the world. The index shows the different forms in which the spices are available – fresh, dried, whole, ground – evaluating their relative merits. It describes the aroma and taste of each spice and gives helpful suggestions for using spices to flavour foods.

Grains of paradise

The plant has pink or yellow showy, trumpet-shaped flowers.

T HE MOST INTERESTING OF the spices related to cardamom, now fallen into obscurity, grains of paradise have a hot peppery taste and replaced true pepper when its price was high. Indigenous to the coast of West Africa along the Gulf of Guinea, from Sierra Leone to the Congo, grains of paradise are also known as Guinea pepper or Guinea grains, and Melegueta pepper. In the 14th and 15th centuries, production of the spice was so important that the coast became known as the Grain or Melegueta Coast. From here it was taken across the Sahara and shipped to Europe from Tripoli; later Portuguese traders took it to Europe directly from the African coast.

Today, grains of paradise feature almost exclusively in West African cookery. They are not easy to obtain but can occasionally be bought from suppliers of herbal medicines. A mixture of pepper and a little ginger has been used as a substitute.

Seeds These are a red-brown, chestnut colour and have the form of a tiny blunt pyramid. Between 60 and 100 seeds are enclosed in the red-brown fruit of the plant.

Ground The seeds are white inside and grind down to a fine aromatic powder.

Tunisian five spices
Grains of paradise are one of the ingredients in this North African spice blend (p.385).

Mulled wine spice mix
In the past, grains of paradise were popular ingredients in spice blends for mulling wine.

CULTIVATION
Distribution Cultivated in Ghana, Guinea, the Ivory Coast and Sierra Leone; most exports today are from Ghana.

Appearance & growth Grains of paradise are the seeds of a perennial reed-like plant that grows to a height of 2m (6ft).

Harvesting The seeds are removed from the bitter white pulp of the ripe fruit and allowed to dry before use.

Aroma & taste The grains taste pungently hot and peppery, without the camphor element that some cardamoms have; their odour is similar but fainter.

USES
Culinary In the past, grains of paradise were used to spice wine and beer. A popular tonic in the 17th century, especially in hot sack, today grains of paradise are little used in Western cooking. They are a valued seasoning in West Africa and

to the north in the Magreb, where they are one of the components of ras el hanout (pp.372–73). Grains of paradise are excellent in mulled wine, in braised lamb dishes, and with potatoes and aubergines.

Medicinal Used in West African herbal remedies, grains of paradise relieve flatulence and also have stimulant and diuretic effects. The seeds are an ingredient in a number of veterinary medicines.

Dill

The name dill comes from old Norse *dilla* meaning "to lull". Dill water was believed to have a soothing effect on the digestive system and was given to babies to relieve hiccups and colic. Grown for both its seeds and its leaves, dill has been known since antiquity. In medieval times, it was considered a magic herb to be used against witchcraft, and as an ingredient in love potions, while it was popular in the kitchen as a condiment. It was cultivated in England from the 16th century but was not introduced into the United States on a commercial scale until the 19th century. It is now grown in a number of countries, mostly in the northern hemisphere.

Anethum sowa, Indian dill, resembles the European plant, but the seeds are longer and narrower, the ridges are paler, and they taste slightly different.

The plant has thin, feathery leaves and clusters of tiny seeds.

Whole Mid-brown with a lighter tan rim, the seeds are curved, oval, and flattish, with five ribs, two of which form a broader rim. The seeds are extremely light; 10,000 seeds weigh about 25g (1oz).

Ground Crush whole seeds as required.

Dill weed The leaves are aromatic, adding a hint of anise to salads, vinegars, pickles and fish dishes.

Seed head The aromatic, tiny yellow flowers turn to seeds in late summer.

Essential oil Used in commercial food flavourings.

CULTIVATION

Distribution Native to southern Russia and the Mediterranean region; the main producers of dill today are Poland, Russia, Scandinavia, Turkey and the UK.

Appearance & growth Dill is a hardy annual that grows up to 1m (3ft) tall and produces clusters of small yellow flowers in the summer. It likes a sandy soil and good sunlight.

Harvesting To obtain good dill weed, the plant is cut before flowering. For seeds, the fruits are left to mature on the plant. Harvesting of the fruits begins when they turn yellow-brown, and is usually carried out when the dew is on the plants. The seeds are threshed, then dried.

Aroma & taste The aroma faintly resembles that of caraway, but is not as pronounced. Its taste is warm, pungent and slightly sharp. It lingers in the mouth for some time if the seeds are chewed on their own - quite a good way of eliminating less agreeable tastes.

USES

Culinary Pickled cucumbers, or dill pickles, have been favourites on both sides of the Atlantic for many years. In Scandinavia, both the leaves and seeds are much used in breads, with potatoes and with seafood. In Poland and Russia, dill is added to soups and stews, and the French use the seeds in cakes and pastries.

Medicinal In addition to its use in the relief of digestive problems, dill has been taken by nursing mothers to stimulate milk.

Celery

In summer, clusters of pale yellow flowers are succeeded by green seeds.

THE CELERY PLANT known to us today was developed from wild celery, or smallage, a common European plant found on marshy ground, especially near the sea. Smallage was used in ancient times as a medicine. To our palates it would have a very bitter taste, but it was popular with the Romans as a flavouring. To them it also signified ill-fortune and death, and smallage leaves were used to make wreaths.

In the 17th century, Italian gardeners bred out the bitterness of smallage and today, garden celery is grown for its stalks, leaves, seeds, essential oil, and in the case of one variety, celeriac, for its root. Celery seeds enhance or introduce a celery flavour to dishes but are not always easy to obtain. Celery salt is more available, but it soon develops a stale taste.

Seeds *The tiny seeds are 1-1.5mm long and very light - approximately 75,000 seeds weigh 50g (2oz). They are mid- to dark brown, with five lighter ridges. Stalk ends are sometimes still attached.*

Ground *Good in drinks such as Bloody Mary, but for most purposes the tiny seeds can be used.*

Leaves *These can also be bought dried and are used to flavour soups and casseroles.*

Celery salt *A salt-based seasoning flavoured with the essential oil.*

Essential oil
Provides a savoury flavour.

Celery stalks *Eaten on their own, with salad, or braised as a vegetable.*

CULTIVATION
Distribution Native to southern Europe, celery is grown today from Scandinavia to North Africa, in North America and northern India.

Appearance & growth Celery is a member of the parsley family that grows to 1.2m (4ft). It thrives in a moist, cool climate in sandy loam. It has branched, fleshy, ridged leaf stalks, and dark green leaves.

Harvesting In its first year of growth, celery is harvested as a vegetable. From the second year, the seed heads are dried and the seeds are beaten from them.

Aroma & taste The seeds have a pronounced, celery-like smell. They taste warm and rather bitter, with a hint of nutmeg and parsley.

USES
Culinary Celery seeds are used in the food industry: in pickles, tomato ketchup, and tomato juice. In domestic cooking they are not as widely used as they might be. The Scandinavians and Russians add them to sauces and soups, and the seeds give a pleasant warmth to dressings for winter vegetable salads. Try the seeds with fish, in egg dishes, in stews, and sprinkled over bread.

Medicinal Until the 19th century, the essential oil was recommended as a cure for rheumatism. Celery is believed to be a tonic for asthma and herbalists use it to treat liver diseases, bronchitis, fever and flatulence. Celery seed tea is said to promote rest and sleep.

Mustard

Known for thousands of years, mustard has always had manifold uses. Its English name comes from the Latin *mustum ardens* "burning must" because the ground seeds were mixed with grape must (unfermented grape juice). In the first century AD the Roman writer Pliny noted that mustard "has so pungent a flavour that it burns like fire". He also listed 40 remedies based on mustard.

In medieval Europe, mustard was the one spice ordinary people could afford to flavour their bland, monotonous diet. At the end of the 15th century, the Portuguese navigator, Vasco da Gama, took mustard on his voyage to the East; when the exotic spices he returned with became more widely accessible in Europe, mustard declined in popularity.

Mustard plants bear smooth or hairy seed pods, depending on the variety.

White mustard The pale, sandy-brown or yellow seeds of the white form are larger than black, brown or Oriental seeds. They are much less pungent, but have excellent preservative qualities.

Oriental seeds A form of Brassica juncea, *used by the Japanese in cooking and as a condiment.*

Brown mustard In large-scale farming, brown mustard has replaced black. Black and brown seeds look very similar, but brown seeds are less pungent. The names black and brown are often interchanged.

Black mustard Now grown only in peasant economies.

Crushed Yellow seeds, which have been ground just enough to crack them.

Powder Finely ground mustard seeds are used in many smooth blended mustards.

Essential oil This is highly caustic.

CULTIVATION

Distribution Black mustard is native to southern Europe and temperate western Asia. Brown mustard is native to India. White mustard has long been naturalized in much of Europe and North America. It is grown in most temperate countries.

Appearance & growth All the mustards are annuals and produce small yellow flowers. White mustard is hardy, grows to about 80cm (2¹/₂ft) and flourishes in heavy sandy loam. Black mustard is taller and grows best in rich soil. Brown

mustard is closely related but is smaller with paler flowers.

Harvesting Mustard pods must be harvested before they burst, but when fully ripe. They are stacked in sheaves to dry, then threshed.

Aroma & taste If you chew a brown mustard seed, the taste is slightly bitter, then hot and aromatic; white mustard seeds have an initial sickly sweetness, followed by mild heat; black seeds have a strong, pungent flavour. Unlike other spices, the seeds have virtually no smell.

USES

Culinary White seeds are used as a pickling spice. Brown seeds are an important flavouring in southern India. Before they are added to a dish, they are usually heated in hot oil to bring out their nutty flavour.

Medicinal Less widely used today than in the past, mustard induces vomiting, and is considered a diuretic and stimulant. In traditional medicine, mustard plasters are a common treatment for arthritis and rheumatism. **Caution:** mustard plasters can irritate sensitive skins.

Blended mustards

THERE ARE TWO basic types of prepared mustard: those that are smooth and those that contain whole seeds. They may be flavoured with herbs, chillies, peppercorns, citrus fruits, soft berry fruits, champagne or sherry. They can be mild or fiery, lightly aromatic or pungent and eye-watering.

Initially mustard was prepared at home; the seeds were pounded in a mortar and mixed with vinegar. and sometimes with honey and other spices. Then sauce and vinegar makers started to prepare mustards. By the 14th century Dijon was firmly established as a mustard-producing centre, well supported by the gourmand Dukes of Burgundy.

Bordeaux mustard
The other principal type made in France. It has a darker colour, a hint of sweetness and is often flavoured with herbs such as tarragon. It has a mild, less well-defined taste than Dijon.

English mustard *Made by mixing mustard powder with water, and leaving it to stand for ten minutes so the flavour develops.*

Dijon mustard *Legally, this can be made anywhere in the world; the name refers to a style of mustard that is pale, smooth and clean tasting, made with brown mustard seeds, water, white wine, salt and spices. The city remains the mustard capital of France, producing about 80 percent of the country's output. Since 1937 Dijon mustard has been an appellation contrôlée.*

American mustard *The essential accompaniment to the hot dog and hamburger, American mustard is bright yellow and has a mild, clean taste. It is usually made from white mustard. Americans are also fond of sweet mustards that go well with ham.*

German mustard
This is sweetish, often flavoured with herbs and spices, and well suited to German sausages. Düsseldorf is the main mustard town of Germany.

Small mustard workshops were established, where black or brown seeds were crushed between huge, round stones, and then mixed with grape juice to make a paste. In the 17th century, a French mustard-maker, Bornibus, discovered a method of pressing mustard into tablets; these were manufactured in Dijon.
In the 1720s, a process of grinding mustard to a fine dry powder was developed. This caught on because it could be kept indefinitely. Early in the 19th century Jeremiah Colman started producing a high-quality mustard flour, which is still popular in England today.

Champsac mustard
An aromatic dark brown smooth mustard, flavoured with fennel seeds.

Herb mustard *This smooth, mild French mustard is lightly flavoured with mixed herbs.*

Beaujolais mustard
A fruity bilberry-coloured blend of coarse-ground mustard seeds and red wine.

Champagne mustard *A smooth, pale mustard, blended with champagne. Its mild flavour complements spicy foods.*

Red mustard *Made from whole mustard seeds and chillies, this pungent mustard goes well with bland foods.*

Wholegrain mustard
Whole mustard seeds give a crunchy texture to this hot English mustard.

Honey mustard
Made from coarse-ground mustard seeds, honey, raw sugar, vinegar and spices, this mustard has a sweet flavour.

Chillies

C. frutescens

C. annuum

Mtext{EMBERS OF THE} capsicum family, chillies and sweet peppers come in all shapes, sizes and colours, ranging from tiny, pointed, explosively hot birdseye chillies, to large, fleshy peppers with a mild flavour. Indigenous to Central and South America and the West Indies, they had been cultivated there for thousands of years before the Spanish conquest, which eventually introduced them to the rest of the world. Columbus wrote in the Caribbean island of Hispaniola that *axi* (an Indian name for capsicum) was stronger than pepper and that people would not eat without it. On Columbus's second voyage in 1495, de Cuneo wrote: "In those islands there are also bushes like rose bushes, which make a fruit as long as cinnamon, full of small grains as biting as pepper; those Caribs and the Indians eat that fruit like we eat apples".

In 1569 the celebrated doctor Nicolas Monardes wrote at length about chillies and their successful adoption in Spain in his book on plants of the New World. Echoing him, the 17th century herbalist, John Parkinson, noted that in Spain and Italy chillies were: "set in pots about the windowes of their houses". He also listed 20 types of capsicum, describing them as olive-shaped, heart-shaped, spear-like, cherry-shaped, and "broad and crumpled".

Today there are probably 200 different types of chilli grown in all parts of the tropics. They are used ripe, when they may be red, orange, yellow or purple, and unripe, when they are green. When buying fresh chillies, make sure they are crisp and unwrinkled. Ripe chillies are available dried, crushed, flaked and ground, and form the basis of many products (p.304). With pepper, ginger and turmeric, capsicums are the most widely cultivated spice crops today.

Jalapeño

Ancho

Serrano

Cascabel

Chile seco

Mexican chillies *Small, pungent, fresh green chillies are widely used in Mexican cooking. Serrano, jalapeño and poblano are the main green chillies of Mexico. The most common dried chillies are ancho, pasilla, guajillo, chipotle and cascabel.*

CULTIVATION

Distribution India has long been the largest producer of chillies and is a major exporter, along with Mexico, China, Japan, Indonesia and Thailand. All these countries are also great consumers of chillies. Sri Lanka, Malaysia and the United States are the main importers.

Appearance & growth Chillies are grown in the tropics from sea level to altitudes of 2,000m (6,600ft). Sweet peppers and chillies will grow in warm temperate zones too, but are susceptible to frost, and so are cultivated from seed in nurseries and transplanted later. C. *annuum* and C. *frutescens* are believed to come from one original species, so the two types are frequently confused. The C. *annuum* plant usually grows to 30cm-1m (1-3ft) high. Most sweet peppers, as well as some of the hot varieties, come into this group. C. *frutescens* is a perennial plant, which grows up to 2m (6ft); this species includes most of the small, pungent forms of chilli.

Harvesting Green chillies are picked three months after planting; other varieties, such as cayenne, are left longer to ripen. The harvest usually lasts three months. After picking, the chillies are either dried in the sun or artificially. Most chillies are grown annually as they become smaller and less pungent after the first year.

Aroma & taste Chillies have little aroma, but they vary in taste, from mild to fiery hot. Generally, the large, round, fleshy varieties are milder than the small, thin-skinned, pointed types. Capsaicin, the pungent principle that gives chillies their kick, is present in the seeds,

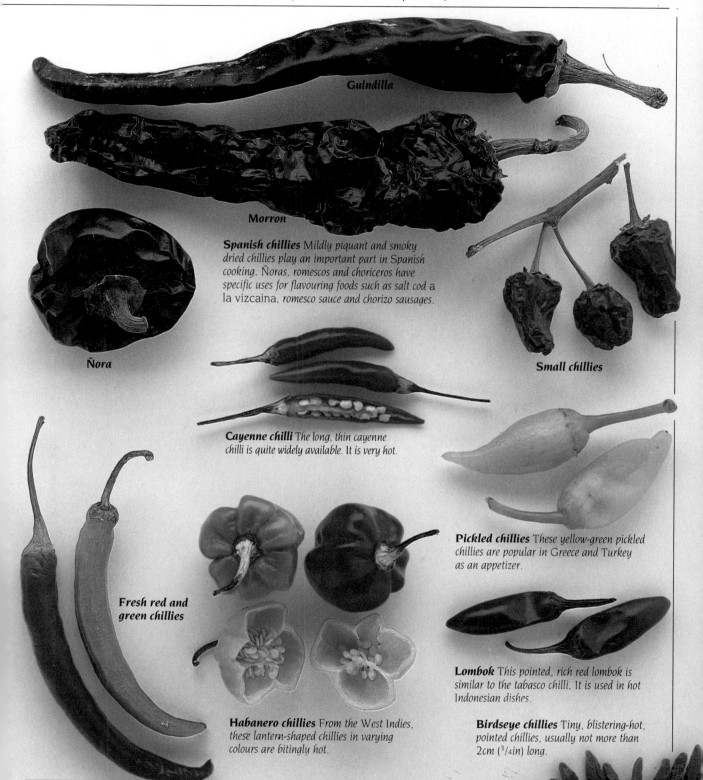

Guindilla

Morron

Spanish chillies Mildly piquant and smoky dried chillies play an important part in Spanish cooking. Ñoras, romescos and choriceros have specific uses for flavouring foods such as salt cod a la vizcaina, *romesco sauce and chorizo sausages.*

Ñora

Small chillies

Cayenne chilli The long, thin cayenne chilli is quite widely available. It is very hot.

Pickled chillies These yellow-green pickled chillies are popular in Greece and Turkey as an appetizer.

Fresh red and green chillies

Lombok This pointed, rich red lombok is similar to the tabasco chilli. It is used in hot Indonesian dishes.

Habanero chillies From the West Indies, these lantern-shaped chillies in varying colours are bitingly hot.

Birdseye chillies Tiny, blistering-hot, pointed chillies, usually not more than 2cm (³/₄in) long.

veins and skin in varying amounts, depending on the species and the state of ripeness. Try removing the seeds and the veins to reduce fire.

USES
Culinary In the tropics, chillies enhance the bland flavour of the staple foods: rice in India and Southeast Asia, beans and corn in Mexico, and cassava in South America. They provide the heat in curry powders, are used in pickling spice, in pepper sauces, chilli oils and essences. Chilli extracts are even used in ginger beer and other

drinks. **Caution:** When handling chillies, wash your hands well and avoid touching your eyes, and any sensitive areas or cuts (pp.430–31).

Medicinal Fresh capsicums are rich in vitamin C; they help in the digestion of starchy foods and may be taken as a tonic. **Caution:** In large doses, chillies may cause stomach and intestinal burns. Even when taken in small quantities, chillies can burn: soothe a sore mouth with plain rice, bread or beans. Do not drink: it will make the burning worse.

Chilli products

Cayenne This very pungent, finely ground spice is made from a blend of small, ripe chillies of various origins.

Chilli flakes Made from dried, crushed chillies and used commercially in sausages, pickles, and sauces for pizza and pasta.

Paprika A red powder, with a sweet or lightly pungent flavour and a faint bitter aftertaste. Essential for goulash, paprikash and many other Hungarian and Balkan dishes, it is also widely used in Spain.

Chilli powder The red powder is made from dried, ground chillies; the darker is an American invention, designed to flavour many southwest American and Mexican dishes. Ground chilli is mixed with other herbs and spices. Not all such mixtures are very pungent.

Red pepper A Turkish condiment, red pepper is prepared from moderately pungent capsicums of Turkey and southern America. The deeper the colour, the better the quality. When roasted to enhance the flavour, the colour darkens, as shown above right.

Chilli paste Often available in Oriental shops, this forms the basis of many fiery sauces.

Tabasco sauce This world-famous hot sauce is made from red chillies and vinegar.

Chilli oil Dried red chillies and vegetable oil have been heated together to make this pungent Chinese chilli oil.

Pepper sauce A golden, hot pepper sauce from the West Indies, where chilli sauces are served as a condiment with dishes.

Sambal In Indonesia, spicy hot pepper relishes, or sambals, are served in small dishes as an accompaniment to food.

Red-hot sauce Ginger adds a sweetish flavour to this biting chilli sauce from Malaysia.

Caraway

A MEMBER OF THE SAME aromatic family as parsley, caraway has been used since antiquity and cultivated in Europe since medieval times. The first-century epicure, Apicius, suggests flavouring vegetables with caraway, and describes a fish sauce containing caraway, oregano, mint, honey, oil, vinegar and wine. Medieval cooks added caraway to soups and to bean and cabbage dishes, and it was traditionally served with roast apples. Early recipes combine garlic, coriander and pepper with caraway. In the 17th century the herbalist John Parkinson notes in *Paradisi in sole* that "the seed is much used to be put among baked fruit, or into bread, cakes, &c to give them a rellish". He also tells us that seeds coated with sugar (comfits) were served with fruit as a digestive.

Caraway is frequently confused with cumin, particularly in Oriental cookery books, in which cumin is usually intended.

Caraway has feathery leaves and clusters of tiny whitish-green flowers.

Seeds About 4-7mm long, the curved seeds are tapered at the ends. The hard, brown seed shells have five lighter-coloured ridges.

Ground Although caraway is mostly used whole, it can be bought ground. It is easy to grind or pound your own at home.

Essential oil This has all the aromatic properties of the seeds, but in a more intense form. A few drops diluted in a teaspoon of water can help relieve flatulent indigestion.

Bread and cheese Rye breads and cheeses from countries such as Germany and Holland are often flavoured with whole caraway seeds.

CULTIVATION

Distribution Caraway is native to Asia and northern and central Europe. Holland is the world's major producer of the seed, followed by Germany, Poland, Morocco, parts of Scandinavia and the Soviet Union. It is also grown in the United States and Canada.

Appearance & growth A hardy biennial that grows to about 80cm (2¹/₂ft) high. Seeds appear throughout the summer. Caraway grows best in a rich light clay soil.

Harvesting The stems are cut once the fruit ripens. The seeds are then threshed and dried.

Aroma & taste Caraway has a pungent aroma which, like its flavour, is warm and slightly bitter. When combined with fruits and vegetables, caraway seems to add a hint of lemon.

USES

Culinary Popular in central European and Jewish cooking, caraway is used to flavour breads, sausages, sauerkraut, cabbage, soups and cheeses. In Alsace, local Munster cheese is traditionally served with a small dish of caraway seeds. Elsewhere in France, the seeds are also used to spice *pain d'épices*. The liqueur *kümmel* is flavoured with caraway.

Medicinal Said to relieve flatulent indigestion, colic and bronchitis.

Other uses The essential oil is used to flavour mouthwashes, gargles, perfumes and soap.

305

Cassia

ONE OF THE OLDEST of spices, cassia is native to Assam and northern Burma. It is recorded in a Chinese herbal in 2700 BC and in the Bible as one of the spices with which Moses was commanded to anoint the tabernacle (*Exodus* 30: 23-25). Arab and Phoenician traders took it to Europe in classical times.

The dried bark of a tree in the laurel family, cassia is sometimes known as Chinese cinnamon. Cassia and cinnamon, another member of the laurel family, are used interchangeably in many countries, and in the United States cassia is often sold simply as cinnamon. Although they are closely related, cassia is thicker and coarser and its taste is less delicate. In Britain, the two spices are differentiated. Cassia is used widely in America but is in less demand than cinnamon in Europe.

The tree has large shiny leaves and small, pale yellow flowers.

Bark *Available as flat, short pieces because it breaks easily. The outer layer of grey bark may be removed before cassia is dried. The inner bark is red-brown and easy to distinguish from that of cinnamon (opposite), which is finer and lighter in colour.*

Ground *The bark is so hard it is usually ground commercially. The more pungent the smell, the better its quality.*

Essential oil *Popular as a flavouring in processed food, it is also sometimes used in inhalations to ease head colds.*

Infusing cassia *When cassia or cassia buds are used as flavourings, they can be placed in an infuser for easier removal.*

Cassia buds *The dried unripe fruits of the cassia tree are used in pickles in the Far East. Their flavour is musky, sweet, and similar to cinnamon.*

CULTIVATION

Distribution Cassia is grown in China, Vietnam, Indonesia and Central America, as well as Burma.

Appearance & growth A tropical evergreen that grows to about 3m (10ft) in height. The bark is rough and greyish-brown outside and smoother, reddish-brown within.

Harvesting This starts in the rainy season when the bark lifts easily. The bark is stripped from the tree, then dried on mats or wire netting. As it dries, it curls into quills which are graded according to length, aroma and colour.

Aroma & taste Cassia has a more intense and less fragrant aroma than cinnamon. The taste is slightly sweet, with a bitter, astringent edge.

USES

Culinary Cassia seems better suited to savoury dishes rather than sweet. It is an essential spice in Chinese cuisine: ground, it is one of the constituents of five-spice powder (pp.348–49). It is frequently added whole to flavour braised dishes and spiced sauces. In India the spice can be found in curries and pilafs; in Germany and Russia, it is in demand to flavour chocolate. In many countries it is popular with stewed fruits, especially apple. Try it with grains such as couscous and pearl barley, and with split peas and lentils.

Medicinal Cassia is used as a tonic and a treatment for diarrhoea, nausea and flatulence.

Other uses Can be crushed and added to spicy pot-pourri blends.

Cinnamon

ONE OF THE FIRST spices sought in the explorations of the 15th and 16th centuries, true cinnamon is indigenous to Sri Lanka. Like cassia, it is the dried bark of a tree of the laurel family. There are references to it in the Bible and to its use in ancient Egypt, but it seems likely that cinnamon was confused with cassia, as it is not recorded in Sri Lanka until the 13th century.

The Portuguese occupied Sri Lanka for the spice until driven out by the Dutch in 1636. The Dutch began the cultivation of cinnamon, previously gathered in the wild, and kept prices high by burning excess supplies in Holland. Their monopoly of the trade ended in 1796 when the English East India Company took control. The trade became more competitive from the 1770s, however, when plants were taken to Java, India and the Seychelles.

The tree has shiny leaves, yellowish-white flowers, and dark blue berries.

Quills Cinnamon quills are assembled using the longest and best pieces of bark on the outside. They are rolled by hand to press the outside edges together, then rolled daily until properly dry, when they become tan in colour and are smooth, thin and brittle.

Quillings Broken quills are called quillings. Often these smaller pieces are rolled inside larger quills.

Ground It is possible to distinguish ground cinnamon from cassia by its tan colour, which is paler than the red-brown of cassia.

Essential oil Used widely in food processing and in the soft drinks industry. In aromatherapy, cinnamon oil is taken as an inhalation for colds and flu.

CULTIVATION

Distribution Native to Sri Lanka, also grown in India, Brazil, Indonesia, the West Indies, and Indian Ocean islands. The largest producer is Sri Lanka, followed by the Seychelles. Cinnamon from Sri Lanka is regarded as the best quality.

Appearance & growth The evergreen cinnamon tree grows to 10m (33ft) in the wild, but it is cropped to smaller, dense trees to ease harvesting. It thrives in a tropical maritime climate at a low altitude, and likes sandy soil.

Harvesting This is carried out in the rainy seasons: in Sri Lanka, between May and June, and October and November. The first harvest yields thick inferior bark. The quality improves with successive cropping and the finest bark comes from the thin shoots at the centre of the plant. Quills are assembled then dried in the shade as direct sunlight warps them.

Aroma & taste The agreeably sweet, woody aroma is quite delicate yet intense. The taste is well-defined, fragrant and warm.

USES

Culinary Suited to both sweet and savoury dishes, cinnamon is particularly good with lamb in Moroccan *tagines* and Iranian *khoraks*; in rice dishes; in fruit compotes (especially pear); in chocolate desserts, cakes and drinks; in spice breads; and as cinnamon toast. Cinnamon was once commonly used to flavour ale and wine, and it is still a good spice for mulled wine.

Other uses The spice is widely used in making incense, pomanders and pot-pourris (pp.424–27).

Coriander

The upper leaves are thin and feathery; the lower, broader and flat.

INDIGENOUS TO THE Mediterranean region, coriander is now cultivated worldwide. Its culinary and medical use has been documented for over 3,000 years: it is named in the Ebers papyrus of 1550 BC, in Sanskrit literature, and in the Bible: "Manna was like coriander seed, white" (*Exodus* 16:31). Hippocrates, the Greek "father of medicine", used coriander as a drug, and the Romans spread the use of the spice through Europe. It was one of the earliest spice plants to reach America and was grown in Massachusetts before 1670.

The fresh leaves of the plant are the ubiquitous green herb of southern Asia and South America, and the fruit is the spice, which has a completely different smell, taste and character. In most producing countries there is a large domestic demand for both herb and spice.

Whole (Moroccan) *More commonly available than the Indian variety, the seeds are spherical, ribbed, and 3-4mm in diameter.*

Ground (Moroccan) *Whole seeds are brittle and easy to grind to a fine powder at home.*

Leaf *A popular flavouring herb and garnish in Middle Eastern and Asian cuisines.*

Whole (Indian) *This has a sweeter flavour than Moroccan.*

Ground (Indian) *In India, coriander is usually dry roasted before grinding to enhance its flavour.*

Essential oil *Considered to be a digestive stimulant.*

CULTIVATION

Distribution Production is often small scale. India, Iran, the Middle East, the Soviet Union, the United States, and Central and South America all grow substantial crops.

Appearance & growth An annual, coriander grows from 30-80cm (1-2½ft) tall and bears small clusters of tiny white or pink flowers. The plant grows best in sunny situations.

Harvesting The seeds are picked when fully ripe; the plants are cut with the dew to avoid the seed pods splitting, then dried, threshed and sieved. The spice is stored in sacks.

Aroma & taste The leaves and unripe fruits have a strong, fetid smell. The ripe fruits have a sweet, spicy-woody aroma with a peppery, balsamic note; their taste is mild, sweet, and slightly burning, with a clear hint of orange peel.

USES

Culinary Coriander is used in both savoury and sweet dishes. It is an essential ingredient in curry powder. In the Middle East, it is popular in minced meat dishes, sausages and stews; in Europe and America it serves as a pickling spice and is used in baking. The classic French vegetable dishes *à la grecque* are flavoured with coriander. The essential oil flavours chocolate, as well as liqueurs and other drinks.

Medicinal The spice and the essential oil are used in pharmaceutical preparations for migraine and indigestion.

Other uses The essential oil is used in incense and perfumery.

Saffron

T HE MOST EXPENSIVE SPICE in the world, saffron costs ten times as much as vanilla, and 50 times as much as cardamom. The fact that the dried, thread-like stigmas of the saffron crocus are so light - over 20,000 produce only 125g (4oz) - and have to be hand-picked, accounts for their high cost.

Saffron was probably first cultivated in Asia Minor. It was used by all the ancient civilizations of the eastern Mediterranean, by the Egyptians and the Romans, in foods and wines, as a dye, in perfumes and as a drug.

By the seventh century, the plant was known in China, where it was in demand as a drug and a perfume. Three centuries later it was grown in Spain, probably taken there by the Arabs; in the 11th century it reached France and Germany; and England in the 14th century. Throughout this period, saffron was treated as a commodity of great commercial value, and severe penalties, even death, awaited anyone who adulterated it.

The blue-violet, lily-shaped flowers appear in autumn.

Threads *The stigmas are vibrant red-orange, or sometimes yellow, and wiry, about 2.5cm (1in) long. The deeper the colour, the better the quality. They are extremely light.*

Ground *Mix ground saffron well with other ingredients to distribute its flavour evenly. It is preferable to buy threads, as ground saffron may be adulterated.*

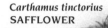

Carthamus tinctorius
SAFFLOWER

Often known as bastard saffron, safflower is cultivated in China, India, the Middle East and Mexico. Unscrupulous merchants often try to sell it as saffron. Its colour is less vibrant and more regularly orange than that of saffron; the price is a fraction of saffron's cost. Safflower will colour food but not flavour it.

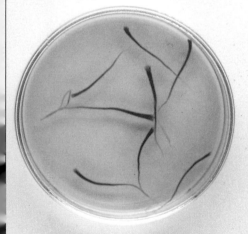

Infused *For even colouring, soak the stigmas briefly in a little hot water and add both saffron and water to the dish.*

Dye *For centuries saffron was used to colour cloth.*

Saffron bun
A mildly spiced traditional teacake (*see also* Saffron Bread, *p.415*).

CULTIVATION

Distribution Spain, Greece, France, Turkey, Iran, Morocco and Kashmir are the main producers. The best saffron is said to come from La Mancha in Spain.

Appearance & growth The saffron crocus is a perennial bulb that is planted in mid- to late summer. It grows to a height of 15cm (6in) and thrives in a sunny position in well-drained sandy soil.

Harvesting The flowers are picked once the petals open, which is usually in autumn. The stigmas are then hand-picked and dried.

Aroma & taste It has a distinctive, tenacious aroma and a penetrating, bitter, but highly aromatic, taste. A small amount will flavour a large dish and colour it a brilliant gold.

USES

Culinary Saffron is used less widely today than in the past, when it was added to sauces, soups and dishes for Lent. In Spain, it is a key ingredient in fish and rice dishes such as *zarzuela* and *paella*. It is used in France with fish, notably in *bouillabaisse*, and in Italy in *risotto*. It has long been used in England to make saffron cakes. Liqueurs, such as chartreuse, contain saffron.

Medicinal Prescribed in India for urinary and digestive problems. Research has revealed it to be rich in vitamin B2 and riboflavin.

Cumin's flowers are
white or pale pink.

Cumin

An essential spice, cumin gives a distinctive warm flavour to an enormous range of savoury dishes in India, North Africa, the Middle East, Mexico and America. In the past it was used widely in baking, particularly in central and eastern Europe, but it is little used in European food today.

Cumin is often confused linguistically with caraway. In French, caraway was often referred to as *cumin des prés*, and inaccurate translations from Indian languages have confused *jeera*, which usually means cumin, with *shia jeera*, or caraway, which is little used in India. Black cumin (*kala jeera*) is a rare variety of cumin found in Kashmir, Pakistan and Iran. Sometimes called black caraway, it is used mostly in north Indian and Moghul cooking. It should not be confused with nigella (p.324), which has also been known by the same name.

Seeds *Oval and 5-6mm long, with longitudinal ridges and a few little bristles. They are usually light brown, but may be greenish or greyish.*

Essential oil *Added to flowery scents of the violet, lily of the valley and hyacinth type.*

Black cumin *The seeds of this variety are smaller and have a sweeter smell.*

Ground *The combination of ground cumin and coriander leaves accounts for the characteristic smell of much Indian food.*

Curry powder *Cumin is one of the main constituents of curry powders (pp.356–57).*

Ground black cumin *The taste of black cumin falls between that of cumin and caraway; its smell resembles that of a haystack.*

CULTIVATION

Distribution Native to the Nile valley, but cultivation soon spread throughout North Africa and Asia Minor, and from there to Iran, India, Indonesia and China. From North Africa, cumin was taken to Spain and then to the Americas.

Appearance & growth An annual and a hot-climate plant, cumin grows to a height of about 30cm (1ft) and tends to sprawl.

Harvesting The stalks are cut when the seeds begin to turn yellow, then

they are threshed and the seeds dried in the sun.

Aroma & taste The smell of cumin is quite pronounced: strong and heavy, with acrid or warm depths. Cumin seeds taste slightly bitter, sharp and warm, and their pungent flavour persists for some time.

USES

Culinary In India, cumin is generally dry roasted before use to bring out its flavour. Essential in mixtures such as garam masala (pp.360–61) and panch phoron (pp.358–59), it is

also found in pickles, relishes and salads. In North Africa, it is an ingredient of ras el hanout (pp.372–73) and flavours *merguez* sausages and many couscous dishes. In the Arab countries further east and in Turkey, ground cumin is frequently added to minced meat dishes and to vegetables. In Spain it is combined with cinnamon and saffron in stews, and in Texas it is used in chilli con carne.

Medicinal Taken in India as a remedy for diarrhoea, flatulence and indigestion.

Turmeric

A MEMBER OF THE ginger family, turmeric is used throughout southern Asia for its musky flavour and attractive golden colour. On his travels in China, Marco Polo noted that turmeric was "a fruit that resembles saffron; though it is actually nothing of the sort, it is quite as good as saffron for practical purposes". He unwittingly set the tone for a major use of the spice in the West, where it frequently serves as a cheap substitute for saffron.

Turmeric is traded whole, and ground in the consuming country. It is available fresh in some Asian shops in the West.

Used for centuries in the East as a medicine and a dye, turmeric is also thought to have magical properties: on many islands in the Pacific, it is carried or worn as a protective charm to ward off evil spirits.

The plant bears large leaves and clusters of flowers in spikes.

Ground *Mostly used and sold in this form. Turmeric's colour indicates its quality: the deeper the pigmentation, the better the spice.*

Fresh *The rhizome, or underground root, has a rough, segmented, light-brown skin. Inside it has bright orange flesh. It consists of a thick part and several stubby "fingers". These yield the best-quality turmeric.*

Dried *Turmeric is dried for export, during which time it loses about 75 percent of its original weight.*

Turmeric dye *A strong, golden-yellow.*

CULTIVATION

Distribution India is the main producer. Turmeric is also cultivated in Indonesia, China, Bangladesh, South America and the Caribbean.

Appearance & growth A robust perennial that grows to a height of 1m (3ft), turmeric is usually propagated from "fingers", or small sections, of rhizome from the last year's growth. The rhizomes grow best in a hot, moist climate.

Harvesting The whole clump of the rhizome is lifted carefully to prevent any damage, and the fingers are broken off from the larger rhizomes. The turmeric is boiled or steamed, then dried. The outer skin is removed and the rough brown fingers become orange-yellow and waxy to the touch.

Aroma & taste Lightly aromatic, turmeric smells peppery and fresh with a hint of oranges and ginger. It tastes pungent, bitter and musky.

USES

Culinary Essential in curry powder, turmeric is also an important flavouring for many south Asian dishes. Indian vegetarian cooking relies heavily on it, especially in bean and lentil dishes, and in the West, turmeric is used commercially in sauces and in processed foods. It is often added to mustard blends.

Medicinal In Asia, turmeric is taken as a tonic and as a remedy for liver problems. Added to ointments, it is applied to treat skin diseases.

Other uses Turmeric is a traditional textile dye. In paste form, it is applied as a beauty mask in India.

311

Zedoary

A HIGHLY AROMATIC SPECIES related to turmeric, zedoary is native to India and Indonesia. During the sixth century it was brought to Europe by Arab traders and had some success in medicine and as a source of perfume, reaching the height of its popularity in the Middle Ages. In T'ang China, powdered zedoary or saffron and camphor were spread on paths where the emperor was about to walk.

The plant's large, fleshy yellow rhizome, or underground stem, is the source of the spice; it is sliced and dried, and used in Southeast Asian cooking. The rhizome also yields a light yellow essential oil. Medicinally, zedoary has similar properties to ginger, and it is used as a digestive aid in the East. Zedoary is almost unknown in the West; ginger can be used as a substitute.

The plant bears large leaves, red or green bracts and yellow flowers.

Ground *Use as you would ground ginger, but remember that the taste of zedoary is somewhat bitter.*

Slices
Greyish-brown in colour, the hard, dry slices of rhizome are about 2-4cm (³/₄-1¹/₂ in) in diameter. They have a rough, slightly hairy texture.

Swedish bitters *A herbal tonic, which contains zedoary extract.*

Perfume *Zedoary is used in Indian perfumery.*

CULTIVATION
Distribution Zedoary is grown throughout Southeast Asia in sub-tropical wet forest zones. It figures little in export trade.

Appearance & growth There are two kinds of zedoary, C. *zerumbet*, which is long, and C. *zedoaria*, which is round and stubby. The plant is propagated from small sections of rhizome, which are planted out in raked soil at the beginning of the monsoon. It grows to about 1m (3ft) high and takes two years to reach full development.

Harvesting Resembles that of turmeric (p.311). The rhizomes are then cut in slices and dried.

Aroma & taste The aroma is musky and agreeable, with a hint of camphor; it slightly resembles rosemary. The flavour is pungent and resembles that of ginger, but is not as bitter.

USES
Culinary In producing countries, zedoary is used as a spice in the preparation of condiments and in dishes in which turmeric or dried

ginger might be used. It goes well with chicken and lamb in south Indian and Indonesian dishes. The young shoots of the plant are eaten in Indonesia, where the leaves are also used to flavour fish.

Medicinal A stimulant, zedoary is also rich in starch and is given to babies and invalids in India. It is combined with pepper, cinnamon and honey and used to treat colds.

Lemon grass

A TALL, TROPICAL GRASS with a bulbous base and a clear smell and taste of lemon, this handsome plant is found throughout Southeast Asia. The base and lower shoots of the plant are used in Southeast Asian cooking, and give a fresh, elusively aromatic taste to many Thai, Malay and Indonesian dishes. In the West, fresh lemon grass is available in some supermarkets, and Oriental shops keep the dried and powdered variety, as well as the fresh, often under the Indonesian name *sereh*. In Holland, look for lemon grass in Indonesian shops, where very fresh, long stalks are sold. It is fairly easy to grow as a houseplant: choose a stalk that has some bits of root, and put it in a pot of water; the roots will develop quite quickly. Once it is established, plant it in a large pot as it soon spreads.

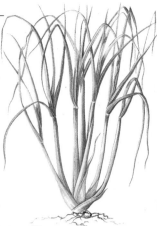

Narrow, fibrous, pale green leaves grow from the bulbous base.

Fresh *The fleshy, fibrous stalk is slightly longer than a spring onion; cut it in small pieces and add directly to the dish.*

Dried strips Dried lemon grass, processed into thin curly strips like lemon peel.

Dried leaves These are hard and fibrous and have little flavour.

Powder Add the powder straight to the dish; use sparingly.

CULTIVATION

Distribution Native to tropical Asia; also cultivated in Africa, South America, Australia, Florida and California.

Appearance & growth A perennial tufted grass, lemon grass grows in dense clumps and thrives in a hot, sunny climate with some rainfall. It is better suited to sandy soil, which produces a higher content of the essential oil.

Harvesting The plants are harvested every three to four months.

Aroma & taste Distinctly lemon-like; lemon grass contains citral, also present in lemon peel, which is used in the production of artificial lemon flavours. Dried lemon grass doesn't have the clean, refreshing taste of the fresh variety. If you can't find lemon grass, use lemon balm or lemon peel as a substitute.

USES

Culinary A common ingredient in Southeast Asian cooking, lemon grass is often used whole or sliced in a clear soup, or is pounded to a paste with other ingredients and

added to a stew. Lemon grass remains fibrous after cooking, so avoid chewing it. It combines well with garlic, shallots and chillies, and with fresh coriander to flavour fish, shellfish, chicken and pork.

Medicinal In the past, lemon grass was prescribed to relieve flatulence and as a sedative.

Other uses The essential oil, extracted by steam distillation, is used in perfumery.

Cardamom

The stems produce short flower stalks that bear small oval fruits after flowering.

CARDAMOM IS ONE of the most ancient spices in the world and one of the most highly valued: it is the third most expensive spice after saffron and vanilla. The seeds were prized in India long before the birth of Christ. Gradually, the spice reached Europe along the caravan routes and in ancient Greece and Rome it was an ingredient in perfumes, although it was valued too for its digestive properties and as a breath freshener. In India it is called the queen of spices, second only to pepper, the king, in economic importance.

Cardamom is also held in high regard in Bedouin culture. Tradition has it that before guests are served with cardamom coffee, the cardamom to be used is displayed. Its appearance is significant: plump, blemish-free pods imply esteem and respect for the guests.

Green cardamoms Considered the best, these oval-shaped fruits are 5-10mm (^{1}/4-^{1}/2in) long. Each pod contains 12 to 20 dark brown or black highly aromatic seeds.

White cardamoms Thought to be more aesthetically appealing by some, these are simply bleached green cardamoms.

Brown cardamoms Not true cardamom, these pods are about 2.5cm (1in) long, and coarser in texture and flavour. They contain 40-50 hard, brown seeds.

Seeds Dark, often sticky, with a lemony, fresh flavour.

Seeds Black to light brown, with a sharp, breath-freshening taste.

Seeds Dark, sticky and hard, with a distinctly camphorous, almost antiseptic, taste.

CULTIVATION

Distribution Cardamom grows wild in the rainforests of southern India and Sri Lanka at altitudes between 750 and 1,500m (2,500-5,000ft). It is now cultivated quite widely in Guatemala, Tanzania and Vietnam, as well as in its native habitat.

The green pods from Kerala, southern India, set the standards of quality and also price levels. International trade is in whole pods: whole green - fruits in which the colour has been preserved; whole bleached - bleached with sulphur dioxide when the colour has faded; whole straw colour - mature fruits dried in the sun; husked pods - usually when the capsule has split. India exports greens and a few bleached; Guatemala and Sri Lanka greens only. Tanzania exports sun-dried pods.

Appearance & growth A large perennial bush of the ginger family that grows to 2-5m (6-15ft) high.

Harvesting The first small harvest occurs three years after planting and

Related to true cardamom are plants of the Amomum and Aframomum genus. The seeds of many of these are marketed as cheap cardamom substitutes. *Amomum subulatum*, greater Indian or Nepal cardamom, is a native of the eastern Himalayas; a perennial plant growing up to 2m (6ft), with somewhat triangular-shaped fruits that are ribbed, and deep red when ripe, dark brown or black when dried. *Amomum globosum*, round Chinese cardamom, is also dark brown and rather hairy. It is often on sale in Chinese shops. Thailand trades in local Amomum species within Southeast Asia, which is also where most of the Javanese winged cardamom is used. *Aframomum korarima* from Ethiopia is another variety that is sold as a cheap substitute for green cardamom. The flavour of these other cardamoms is distinctly camphorous.

Ground cardamom *Easy to adulterate, so it is better to grind your own powder as required.*

Essential oil *An ingredient in perfumes, and in liqueurs and bitters.*

Garam masala *Essential in Indian cookery, cardamom is one of the main ingredients in this mixture (pp.360–61).*

Cardamom-flavoured coffee *A popular drink in Middle Eastern countries.*

thereafter the plants bear for 10-15 years. The fruits ripen at intervals from September to December and are harvested every few weeks just before they ripen. If left to ripen on the plant they split open. After picking, the capsules are dried on open platforms in the sun, or on large plantations, in special drying rooms. The dried pods are hard, and the best are greenish in colour.

Aroma & taste The aroma of cardamom is mellow. Initially the taste has a penetrating note of camphor; it is sharply bitter and

strong, and lingers quite long in the mouth if you chew a few seeds, but is warming and agreeable.

USES
Culinary Cardamom can enhance both sweet and savoury tastes. The pods themselves are inedible: all the flavour is held in the small, but very hard, seeds. In India, cardamom is one of the main components of garam masala and curry powders. It is also used in sweetmeats, pastries, puddings and ice creams. The Arabs put a few pods in the spouts of their coffee pots to give the drink a

distinctive taste. In Europe, the Scandinavians are the biggest importers of cardamom for flavouring their spiced cakes, pastries and breads.

Medicinal Tincture of cardamom is considered a useful medicine for flatulence and stomach disorders. Chewing a few seeds cleanses the breath, particularly of excessive garlic. Together with betel leaves and areca nuts, cardamom forms part of the betel quid that Indians like to chew as a mouth freshener and digestive aid.

Cloves

Clove buds form in clusters at the ends of branches.

ONE OF THE MOST important spices of commerce, cloves are the unopened flower buds of a small evergreen tree, native to the Moluccas, or Spice Islands, which today form part of Indonesia.

The earliest references to cloves are in ancient Chinese literature. Courtiers and officers of state were required to have a few cloves in their mouths when addressing the Emperor to keep their breath sweet. By the second century AD, cloves were part of the caravan trade to Alexandria, and their use slowly spread through Europe. By the 16th century, the Portuguese controlled the trade until driven from the Moluccas by the Dutch in 1605. They restricted the cultivation of clove trees to one island, and it was not until 1770 that the French smuggled seedlings to Mauritius and Bourbon. From there, plantations were eventually established on Zanzibar (now part of Tanzania) and in Madagascar, today's largest exporters.

Clove infuser Used to add the flavour of cloves to foods without their texture.

Whole Look for cloves that are a bright, reddish-brown colour on the stem and lighter on the crown. They should be rough to the touch and snap cleanly. Good cloves will exude a small amount of oil if pressed with the fingernail.

Clove pomander An orange stuck with cloves is a traditional way to scent clothes (p.425).

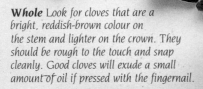

Ground One of the ingredients of the Indian spice mix garam masala (pp.360–61).

Essential oil An antiseptic and analgesic, diluted oil of cloves can be used as a mouthwash or gargle. Rubbed on to the gums, it relieves toothache.

CULTIVATION

Distribution Indonesia produces the largest crop of cloves, followed by Madagascar (the Malagasy Republic), Tanzania, Sri Lanka, Malaysia and Grenada.

Appearance & growth Restricted to a height of 12-15m (40-50ft), clove trees take 20 years to reach full bearing, and then continue to bear fruit for about 50 years. They thrive in a tropical maritime environment.

Harvesting Harvested twice a year, from mid- to late summer and again in midwinter, cloves are picked when the buds reach full size but before the petals open. The buds are then dried over several days in the sun; they lose two-thirds of their weight and turn dark brown.

Aroma & taste Cloves have an assertive, dark aroma that is warm and rich. Tasted on its own, a clove is bitingly sharp, hot and bitter, and it leaves a lasting numb sensation in

the mouth. Its effect is tempered by cooking and by other ingredients.

USES

Culinary Cloves go well with sweet or savoury foods and are used, for example, by Americans to stud a baked ham, and by the Germans in spiced breads.

Other uses Indonesian cigarettes are made with two parts tobacco to one part cloves. The essence is a food preservative.

Asafoetida

The whole plant emits asafoetida's distinctive smell.

A LITTLE-KNOWN SPICE outside India, asafoetida is a dried, resin-like substance obtained from the rhizomes of several species of *ferula*, or giant fennel. Its name derives from the Persian *aza*, resin, and the Latin *fetida*, which means stinking and describes this spice's most obvious attribute. Native to south-western Asia, asafoetida seems to have been much prized in Roman cooking. Called *silphium*, *laser* or *laserpitium*, it was imported from Persia and Armenia and the juice of both stem and root was used. It was a costly spice: the Roman epicure Apicius describes how to make an ounce piece last indefinitely by storing it in a jar with about 20 pine nuts. To flavour food, a few of the pine nuts were crushed and added to the dish. The nuts taken from the jar were then replaced.

Block Fresh asafoetida is pale in colour, some types darken eventually to a deep brown. A lump of asafoetida will keep its potency for several years.

To grind Break off small pieces and grind with an absorbent powder, such as rice flour.

Compound Often sold in Indian stores in this form, as granules or as a powder.

Granules
Store asafoetida in an airtight container to prevent its smell from dominating.

Powder
In Indian and Arab cuisines, a tiny amount enhances the flavour of dishes.

CULTIVATION

Distribution Ferula flourishes in the dry regions of Iran, Afghanistan, India and Pakistan.

Appearance & growth Ferula are smelly plants that grow to some 2-4m (6-12ft), depending on the species. They have soft-centred stems, finely toothed leaves, and produce clusters of yellow flowers.

Harvesting In spring, just before flowering, the stalks are cut to the root and a milky liquid exudes which dries to form asafoetida - a solid gum-like mass. The gum is scraped off and further cuts are made until the root dries up, which usually occurs after about three months.

Aroma & taste Powdered asafoetida has a strong, unpleasant smell, reminiscent of pickled garlic, which is caused by sulphur compounds in the volatile oil. The taste is bitter and acrid and decidedly nasty when sampled alone. However, when asafoetida is fried briefly in hot oil, the nastiness disappears and the oil takes on an onion taste.

USES

Culinary In western and southern India, asafoetida flavours pulses and vegetable dishes, pickles and sauces. A piece of asafoetida may be rubbed on a grill before cooking meat. It should always be used sparingly. In Iran, the centre of the stalks and the leaves are eaten as a vegetable.

Medicinal Asafoetida is said to have antispasmodic properties. It has been used in the past to treat hysteria and was sometimes taken as a sedative. In India it is prescribed to treat flatulence and bronchitis.

Fennel

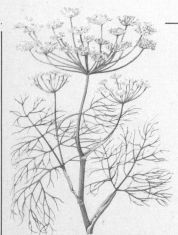

A graceful perennial with feathery leaves and small yellow flowers.

T HE ROMANS VALUED fennel's shoots as a vegetable and added the seeds to sauces for meats. The historian Pliny believed that strengthening eyesight was one of fennel's medicinal virtues, a belief endorsed by later herbalists.

Fennel has long been used in India and China, where the seeds were taken as a remedy for scorpion and snake bites, a use that spread to Europe. Our ancestors hung fennel over the door in the belief that it would guard them against witchcraft, and blocked the keyhole at night with ground fennel seeds to sleep undisturbed.

In 1418, when the Portuguese discovered Madeira, the fragrant smell of wild fennel led them to call the place where they landed Funchal, from *funcho*, the Portuguese word for fennel.

Seeds *Green to yellow-brown, the seeds are 5-10mm ($^1/_4$ -$^1/_2$in) long, oblong, elliptical, straight or slightly curved, with prominent lighter ridges. They sometimes have a short piece of stalk attached.*

Essential oil *The seeds contain a high proportion of anethole, which is used in making pastis and other anise-based drinks.*

Ground *Grind the seeds to a fine powder as required.*

Seed head *Seeds form in clusters after the flowers have died away.*

CULTIVATION

Distribution Indigenous to the Mediterranean region but naturalized in many temperate countries, fennel is cultivated for export in Germany, Italy, France, Russia, the Middle East and India.

Appearance & growth The bright green stalks reach 1.5-2m (5-6ft) in height. The plant will grow in most conditions, although it prefers a sunny, sheltered spot.

Harvesting The seed heads are harvested just before the seeds

ripen. To dry the seed heads, cover them with a paper bag and hang them indoors by the stems.

Aroma & taste The whole plant is aromatic and the seeds smell like anise. The taste is similar, too: warm and fragrant, but not as sweet, with a slight note of camphor.

USES

Culinary The Italians cook fennel with roast pork and add it to the excellent salami from Florence called *finocchiona*. In Iraq it is ground with nigella to flavour bread. The

Indians use fennel seeds in vegetarian cooking, in breath-freshening *paans*, and candied to chew as a digestive aid at the end of a meal. In Europe, fennel is a traditional seasoning for fish, and it flavours pickles for cucumbers, sauerkraut and herring.

Medicinal An important medicinal plant in the past. The herbalist Culpeper noted that the seeds were used in medicines for shortness of breath and for wheezing. Fennel was also believed to help cure stomach complaints and toothache.

Star anise

ONE OF THE FEW spices used in Chinese cookery, star anise is native to southern China and Vietnam. A very pretty spice, it is the fruit of a small evergreen tree of the magnolia family. The shape of ripe star anise is that of an irregular, eight-pointed star. Its Chinese name means eight points.

The use of star anise has never spread much beyond its native region, although wherever the Chinese have settled, they have taken the spice with them. Old recipes reveal that star anise was used in the West in the 17th century, in fruit syrups and jams, and in recent years the spice has been rediscovered by Western chefs, and is often added to fish stews.

The tree bears shiny leaves and small, yellow, multi-petalled flowers.

Ground *The whole fruits are best ground in a mortar or electric grinder as required.*

Whole *When dried, star anise is hard and reddish brown. Each point of the star contains a glossy, brittle, brown seed.*

Seeds *These are less aromatic than the rest of the fruit.*

Chinese five-spice powder *The flavour of star anise dominates this mixture, which also contains fagara, cassia or cinnamon, cloves and fennel seeds (pp.348–49).*

Broken fruit *The fruit is generally used whole, or broken into pieces.*

CULTIVATION

Distribution Southern China and Vietnam.

Appearance & growth The tree grows to a height of about 8m (26ft) and bears small yellow flowers. The flowers are followed by fruits in the sixth year, and the tree continues to bear fruit for up to 100 years. As the fruit ripens, it opens out into a star shape with eight points, each of which is hollow and contains a seed.

Harvesting The fruits are picked before they ripen, then sun-dried.

Aroma & taste Although not related to anise and fennel, star anise has a similar smell and taste. It is more pungently liquorice-like and has a distinct sweet note.

USES

Culinary The Chinese often add star anise to poultry and pork dishes; it is also a key ingredient in five-spice powder. The Vietnamese use the spice in their beef soup, *pho*. It is an ideal flavouring for roast chicken, and goes well with braised fish, with scallops, and in clear soups. Try it with leeks and pumpkin.

The essential oil contains anethole, the principle aromatic constituent, also found in anise. It flavours liqueurs such as pastis and anisette, and is also used in chewing gum and confectionery.

Medicinal Star anise is used in the East to relieve colic and rheumatism and to flavour cough medicines. The spice is chewed whole to sweeten the breath.

Other uses The essential oil is used in soap making and in perfumery.

Juniper

Juniper is probably best known for the distinctive flavouring it gives to gin and other spirits and cordials. The berries come from a prickly evergreen shrub that grows throughout much of the northern hemisphere. Although one of the few temperate-climate spices that can be gathered in the wild or bought quite cheaply, juniper is largely ignored in the kitchens of English-speaking countries. The Scandinavians add juniper berries to marinades for pickled beef or elk, and to red wine marinades for roast pork. In northern France, the berries are used in venison dishes and pâtés; and, in Alsace and Germany, with sauerkraut. Crushed berries can be mixed with salt and garlic and rubbed on to game birds before roasting. Combined with allspice and pepper, juniper is used for spicing beef.

The green berries take two or three years to ripen, turning blue-black.

Berries *These are about the size of a small pea. When freshly picked, they have a green-blue bloom which tends to disappear after drying. Berries grown in warmer latitudes have more flavour.*

Crushed berries *The purple-black, smooth berries are quite soft and easily crushed to show their brown pulp and seeds.*

Plant *The shrub has sharp needle-like leaves, grouped in threes.*

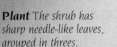

Gin *The name derives from genever, Dutch for juniper.*

Essential oil *Said to aid digestion and circulation.*

CULTIVATION

Distribution The plant grows wild throughout Europe and in America; most berries grown for commerce come from eastern Europe.

Appearance & growth Juniper is a coniferous shrub of the cypress family. After pollination, a pulpy covering forms round the seeds to produce berries, on female bushes.

Harvesting The ripe berries are gathered in the autumn and dried at a temperature below 35°C (95°F) to stop the essential oil evaporating.

Aroma & taste The pleasant aroma is bitter-sweet and unmistakably like gin. The berries taste sweet with a hint of pine and turpentine. They produce a slight burning sensation in the mouth.

USES

Culinary Juniper blends well with garlic; with aromatic herbs such as marjoram and rosemary; and with wine, beer, brandy and, especially, gin. Use it in marinades and sauces for pork and game; in brines and dry-salting mixtures; and in pâtés. Juniper marries well with veal and braised beef dishes and has a natural affinity with cabbage.

Medicinal Described by herbalists as a diuretic and an anti-inflammatory. **Caution:** Avoid juniper in pregnancy and if you have a kidney disorder.

Other uses The berries and roots yield purple and brown dyes. In the past, the leaves and berries were burned to purify the air, and the berries were applied to treat snakebites. The highly aromatic essential oil is added to some insecticides and perfumes.

Galangal

T HERE ARE TWO MAIN TYPES of galangal: lesser and greater. Members of the
ginger family, lesser galangal is native to southern China and greater to
Indonesia. *Kempferia galangal* (p.340) is a similar rhizome, or underground stem,
used medicinally in China. In Indonesia, lesser galangal is called *kencur* and greater
galangal is known as *laos*. The latter is also known as *khaa* in Thailand and *lengkuas*
in Malaysia, and may be sold under any of these names in Oriental shops.

Galangal was known in ancient Egypt where it was used as a fumigant. It
reached Europe in the Middle Ages and was valued both as a medicine and a
spice. Its use declined, however, and today galangal is rarely found outside
Southeast Asia, except in Oriental communities. In England, the word *galingale*
was formerly used for both galangal and the roots of the plant *Cyperus longus*.

*Greater galangal has sword-like
leaves and flowers with pink veins.*

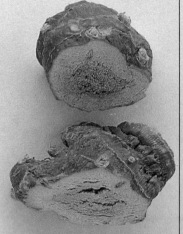

Greater galangal *The larger of
the two rhizomes, greater galangal
usually has an orange-red skin but
sometimes paler varieties are found.*

Fresh slices
Pleasantly aromatic.

Dried rhizome pieces
*These are tougher and
woodier than dried ginger.*

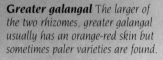

Dried slices *Sold ready-sliced; use in soups and stews, but remove
before serving, as they are unpleasant and woody to chew on.*

Ground *Half a teaspoon of powder is
equivalent to about one small slice of root.*

CULTIVATION

Distribution Both plants are today
cultivated commercially in India and
Southeast Asia.

Appearance & growth Lesser
galangal reaches 1m (3ft) tall and
has long, narrow leaves and small
white, red-streaked flowers. Greater
galangal, as its name suggests, is a
larger plant that grows up to 2m
(6ft). The rhizomes of both plants
are knobbly and ginger-like.

Harvesting For both species, the
rhizome is lifted, cleaned and

processed in a similar way to ginger
and turmeric.

Aroma & taste Lesser galangal has
the more pungent aroma of the two
galangals and has a hint of
eucalyptus; its piquant taste is akin
to cardamom and ginger. The
flavour of greater galangal is like a
mixture of ginger and pepper, with a
sour, lemon-like note.

USES

Culinary Throughout Malaysia and
Indonesia, both types of galangals
are used fresh in curries and stews.

Greater galangal is an essential
component of Thai curry pastes
(pp.354–55), and in Thai cooking is
a much preferred spice to ginger.
Lesser galangal is used in the
manufacture of some bitters and
liqueurs, and to flavour beers in
Scandinavia and Russia.

Medicinal In Asian medicine,
galangal is used to treat catarrh and
respiratory problems. A drink made
from grated galangal and lime juice
is taken as a tonic in Southeast Asia.
In the past, galangal was a treatment
for flatulent indigestion.

Nutmeg & mace

Myristica fragrans is unique among spice plants as it produces two distinct spices: nutmeg and mace. It is a spreading evergreen tree, native to the Banda islands in the Moluccas, or Spice Islands. Nutmeg is the kernel of the seed; mace is the lacy growth, known as the aril, which surrounds the seed.

In the sixth century, nutmeg and mace formed part of the caravan trade to Alexandria. About the same time, nutmeg was being used in China as a medicine for digestive disorders. The Indians and Arabs valued the spice as a treatment for digestive, liver and skin complaints, and both nutmeg and mace were held to be aphrodisiacs.

The pale fruit resembles an apricot. It splits when ripe to reveal its seed.

The spices were probably brought to Europe by the Crusaders. They were used as fumigants and only became popular in the kitchen after the

Nutmeg fruit *Mace is the lacy covering or aril that surrounds the seed. The nutmeg lies within the shell of the seed.*

Nutmeg *Oval in shape, with a grey-brown, wrinkled exterior. The inside is hard and lighter in colour.*

Nutmeg grater
·*Traditional graters have a compartment for storing nutmegs.*

Ground nutmeg
Best ground as required as it soon loses its flavour.

CULTIVATION

Distribution Mace and nutmeg are native to the Moluccas, but are also cultivated in Sri Lanka, Malaysia, and the West Indies.

Appearance & growth The nutmeg tree is an evergreen that grows to 12m (40ft) or more in height. It has dark green oval leaves and small pale yellow flowers. Trees start to bear fruit in the seventh or eighth year, and continue to bear for up to 40 years. They are best suited to a tropical maritime climate, and thrive in the rich volcanic soil of the Moluccas and the fertile loam of Grenada. Plantations are usually below 750m (2,500ft), and the trees are sheltered from high winds.

Harvesting The fruit ripens six to nine months after flowering, and is usually gathered when it falls to the ground. The outer husk is stripped off and the mace is removed, pressed flat and dried on mats. This process may take as little as two to four hours, during which time the mace retains its scarlet colour. Once the mace has been removed, the seeds are dried on trays for four to six weeks until the nutmegs rattle in their outer shell. They are cracked open and the nutmegs removed, then graded according to size and quality. "Defectives", "shrivelled" and "bwp" (broken, wormy, punky) nutmegs are sorted out from the rest, which are graded by size as 80s or 100s, and so on, according to the number in the pound.

Aroma & taste Mace and nutmeg are similar in aroma and taste, but mace is more refined. The aroma is rich, fresh and warm. The taste is warm

Portuguese developed the trade in the Spice Islands in the 16th century. Nutmeg became important as both a medicine and a spice, and by the late 16th century, it seemed to be the cure for just about everything. By the 18th century, people carried their own nutmegs, together with small, ornamental graters of silver, wood or bone, to flavour food and drinks such as hot ale, mulled wine, or possets (curdled milk drinks).

Control of the nutmeg and mace trade passed from the Portuguese to the Dutch and eventually, towards the end of the 18th century, to the English. The English planted nutmeg trees in Penang, Sri Lanka and Sumatra, and in the following century, trees were taken to Grenada in the West Indies, where almost a third of the world's nutmeg is produced today.

Mace *The scarlet aril turns red-orange or orange-yellow by the time it reaches the market, depending on its source.*

Mace blades *Indonesian blades tend to be orange-red; those from Grenada are generally orange-yellow.*

Essential oil of nutmeg *Used in creams designed to relieve rheumatism.*

Ground mace *When ground, mace keeps its flavour longer than some ground spices.*

Coarse ground mace *The blades are hard to grind to a fine powder with a pestle and mortar - use a coffee grinder.*

and highly aromatic - sweetish in nutmeg and more bitter in mace.

USES
Culinary In Southeast Asia, China and India, both spices are used sparingly. In India they are found mostly in Moghul dishes. The Arabs have long added nutmeg to mutton and lamb, but the Europeans have used nutmeg and mace most extensively in both sweet and savoury dishes. Nutmeg is a standard seasoning in many Dutch recipes, and graters resembling pepper mills are a common

household item there. The Dutch add nutmeg to mashed potato, white cabbage, cauliflower and vegetable purées; to macaroni; to meat stews; and to fruit puddings. The Italians enjoy nutmeg with mixed vegetable dishes, and veal, and in fillings and sauces for pasta.

Nutmeg is widely used in honey cakes, rich fruit cake, fruit desserts, and fruit punch. It goes well in stews and meat pies, and in most egg and cheese dishes, as does mace.

Mace gives a lift to bechamel and onion sauce, clear soups, shellfish stock, potted meat, cheese soufflés

and cream-cheese desserts. In Indonesia, the flesh of the fruit is used to make a sweetmeat.

Medicinal More common in Oriental than in Western medicine, nutmeg is used to relieve bronchial disorders, rheumatism and flatulence. In large quantities it may cause drowsiness, hallucinations and euphoria, and an excess can be fatal.

Other uses Nutmeg is used in perfumery, soaps and shampoos.

Nigella

The plant has ragged, grey-green leaves and delicate, five-petalled flowers.

NIGELLA IS THE botanical name for the plant we know as "love-in-a-mist", which is cultivated in gardens for its delicate blue flowers and feathery foliage. The species of nigella grown for its small black seeds is a close relative, but less decorative in appearance. Until the 17th century, nigella was more popular in Europe. The herbalist Gerard describes the seeds as "... of a blackish colour, very like unto onion seed, in taste sharpe, and of an excellent sweet savour". They were used in sweet waters and powders, and ground seeds were wrapped in a piece of cloth and gently heated in the belief that they helped to restore the sense of smell.

In India, where nigella seeds are commonly used as a flavouring, there is much confusion about their name. In the north of the country, where nigella grows wild, they are called *kala jeera*, or black cumin. Real black cumin (p.310) is also known as *kala jeera* as well as *shahi jeera*, or royal cumin. In much of India, nigella seeds are known as *kalonji* (black onion seeds).

Seeds *These are a deep, dull black, 2-3mm long and angular. They have five prominent spikes.*

Ground *Use a coffee grinder to grind the seeds to a powder.*

Nan *Bread baked in the clay tandoor ovens of northern India, nan is flavoured with nigella.*

Panch phoron *Nigella features in many Indian spice mixtures including panch phoron (pp.358–59), curry blends and masalas.*

CULTIVATION

Distribution Native to western Asia, southern Europe and the Middle East, nigella is most widely cultivated in India.

Appearance & growth A hardy annual raised from seed, the plant grows to 60cm (2ft).

Harvesting The seed capsules are gathered as they ripen but before they burst. They are then dried and crushed so that the seeds can be removed easily.

Aroma & taste The aroma of nigella is not strong. The taste is nutty and acrid, like a cross between poppy seeds and pepper; it is reminiscent of oregano.

USES

Culinary In India, nigella is used whole to spice vegetables and pulses, usually after it has been dry roasted to heighten its aroma and flavour. It is an ingredient of several spice mixes and is sprinkled on breads. It is also used to season bread in the Middle East and in Turkey. Nigella is a spice to experiment with; it complements the spices coriander and allspice, and the herbs savory and thyme.

Other uses It is believed to be an insect repellant.

Poppy

THE OPIUM POPPY is a plant of great antiquity. Its botanical name translates as sleep-inducing poppy, and refers to the plant's narcotic properties, as opium, which oozes from the unripe seed pods if they are cut, contains compounds from which morphine and codeine are extracted. These are not present in the ripe seeds. The plant has been cultivated for opium and its seeds from earliest times. A Cretan statue of a poppy goddess of about 1400 BC shows the seed pods cut to extract the opium, just as they are today. A mix of roasted white poppy seeds and honey was popular with wealthier Romans.

By the time of Mohammed (AD 572-632) opium was known for its medicinal and narcotic properties in Arabia and Asia. It was used to relieve cholera, malaria and dysentery, but increasingly as a habit-forming drug in India and China. The great demand for opium made fortunes, legal and illegal.

As the flower dies back, it reveals a bulbous seed capsule.

Creamy-yellow seeds Common in India, these kidney-shaped seeds are about 1mm long. A thousand seeds weigh only 0.5g.

Brown seeds In Turkey, these seeds are mixed with grape syrup and nuts to form a dessert.

Blue-grey seeds Slate-blue seeds are most common in Europe. Like the other varieties of seeds, they are hard and clean looking.

Ground seeds Crush the seeds in a pestle and mortar or grind in a coffee grinder. In India, white ground seeds act as a thickening agent in sauces.

Paste Roasted seeds are ground to a paste to form the basis of many Turkish dishes.

Seed head
The brownish-green seed capsules vary greatly in shape and size, but all have a ribbed outer casing, crowned with a stigma. Inside, there are several chambers containing hundreds of tiny seeds.

CULTIVATION

Distribution Native from the eastern Mediterranean to central Asia; India, China, Iran, Turkey, France, Holland and Canada are the main producers.

Appearance & growth A tall annual raised from seed, the plant bears pale white to violet flowers.

Harvesting When the seed heads turn yellow-brown, the plants are usually harvested mechanically, then stacked like corn stooks, or the capsules are cut off and dried.

Aroma & taste Poppy seeds have a slight but pleasantly nutty aroma, and a similar but more pronounced taste, with an underlying sweet note. They have no narcotic properties.

USES

Culinary In Western and Middle Eastern cooking, poppy seeds are mainly sprinkled on breads and cakes, or crushed with honey or sugar to make pastry fillings. In Turkey they are made into halva or desserts; in India the seeds are usually ground with other spices and used to thicken and flavour sauces for meat and fish. Try adding poppy seeds to dressings for noodles or rice, or to garnish vegetables. Roast first to strengthen their flavour.

Other uses The seeds are an important source of oil. The odourless oil from the first cold-pressing of the seeds has a light almond-like taste and is a good salad oil. Oil from later hot-pressings is used in soap and ointments and, after bleaching, in the manufacture of artists' paints.

Allspice

A TROPICAL SPICE, grown mainly in Jamaica, the reddish-brown allspice berry was introduced to Europe by Columbus and his fellow explorers, who found it growing in the Caribbean islands and mistakenly thought it was pepper, hence its Spanish name, *pimienta* (pepper). Later anglicized as pimento, allspice subsequently became known as Jamaica pepper.

When the English conquered Jamaica in 1655, they acquired an established trade based on substantial plantations; wild fruits were no longer part of its commerce. Jamaican exports increased more than 20·fold between 1755 and the end of the 19th century. Although colonists planted trees elsewhere in the tropics, they did not thrive, and allspice is the only important spice that still comes almost exclusively from the New World.

The berries turn from green when unripe, to purple-brown when ripe.

Whole *The red-brown berries are about the size of a small pea and have a somewhat rough surface. Most of the flavour is in the outer shell rather than in the seeds inside.*

Ground *It is preferable to buy allspice whole and grind it as needed.*

Essential oil *A common ingredient in men's spice-based perfumes.*

Pimento dram *A rum-based drink flavoured with allspice, similar to the Clove Cordial recipe (p.421).*

Pickling spice *Allspice is an essential ingredient in this traditional mixture used for pickling fruit and vegetables (pp.378–79).*

Spiced tea mix *Blend with tea and other spices for a warming drink (p.421).*

CULTIVATION

Distribution Native to the West Indies and Central and South America; the best allspice comes from Jamaica.

Appearance & growth An evergreen, the allspice tree grows to about 9m (29ft) in height. It has dark green, glossy leaves and clusters of small white flowers in the summer. The trees begin to bear fruit when six to seven years old and can continue to bear for up to 100 years. A ratio of ten female trees to one male is the ideal for a good crop.

Harvesting The berries are picked when mature but still green, because they lose their aroma as they ripen. In Jamaica, cultivated berries are hand-picked, dried artificially or on concrete platforms for five to ten days, then winnowed and graded by size. As they dry, the berries turn a red-brown shade.

Aroma & taste Allspice has a pleasantly fragrant aroma and the name reflects the pungent taste, which resembles a peppery compound of cloves, cinnamon and nutmeg or mace.

USES

Culinary Allspice is primarily used in the food industry: in ketchups, pickles, sausages, and in meat canning. It gives a gentle, warm flavour to cakes, jams and fruit pies. In Jamaica the spice is widely used in soups, stews and curries.

Medicinal The essential oil flavours a number of medicines. Allspice gives limited relief for intestinal and digestive disorders.

Other uses For centuries allspice has been included in pot-pourris (p.425).

Anise

K NOWN AS ANISE or aniseed, this spice is related botanically to caraway, cumin, dill and fennel. The aromatic, oval seeds are one of the oldest-known spices. Now grown in many parts of the world, anise is native to the Middle East and the islands of the eastern Mediterranean. The Romans introduced its seed to Tuscany. In the Middle Ages, cultivation of anise spread throughout Europe. It was used in England by the 14th century and grown in many kitchen gardens by the middle of the 16th century. The seed reached the New World with early colonists, where the Shakers grew it as a medicinal crop.

Anise has always been popular as a digestive. In ancient Rome, anise-spiced cakes were sometimes served after a rich meal to aid digestion. Aniseed was also taken as a digestive in the Middle Ages, in the form of comfits (seeds coated with sugar). Today, anise seeds are chewed whole in India to aid digestion and to sweeten the breath.

The plant has bright green feathery leaves and tufts of white flowers.

Seeds *These vary in colour from green-grey to yellow-brown. Oval in shape with ten lighter-coloured ridges, the seeds often have bits of stalk attached.*

Ground anise *Like many other spices, aniseed quickly loses its flavour and aroma when ground. Buy in small quantities and grind as needed.*

Essential oil *Sometimes used instead of liquorice root to give foods a liquorice flavour. Most of the oil distilled for medicinal purposes comes from Russia.*

Anise sweets *The flavour of anise is popular in sweets and confectionery.*

Pernod *A wide range of drinks and liqueurs is prepared with aniseed.*

CULTIVATION

Distribution The spice is cultivated commercially in the southern republics of the USSR, in Turkey, Spain, France, Germany and India.

Appearance & growth An elegant annual, anise grows to a height of 30-40cm (12-15in) and is easily grown from seed in a light rich soil.

Harvesting The plants are pulled up just before the fruit ripens, and piled up to dry. Then they are threshed

and the seeds are dried on trays in light shade outdoors or in moderate heat indoors.

Aroma & taste Both smell and taste are slightly sweet and distinctly liquorice-like.

USES

Culinary In Europe, anise is widely used as a cake and biscuit spice, and in the Middle East and India it is added to soups, stews and sometimes breads. Around the

Mediterranean, the oil from the seeds is much in demand for the manufacture of anise-flavoured aperitifs and liqueurs.

Medicinal Anise is considered a mild expectorant and added to cough mixes and lozenges. It is also used to mask the taste of bitter drugs.

Other uses In India, anise water is used as a cologne.

Pepper & long pepper

T HE SPICE MOST WIDELY USED in the West, and once so highly valued that it was traded ounce for ounce for gold, pepper is native to the monsoon forests of the Malabar coast in southwest India. Black pepper is the unripe fruit of the vine P*iper nigrum*. White, green and pink peppercorns are berries from the same vine, picked at different stages of maturity. P*iper longum*, or long pepper, is a related plant known in Sanskrit as *pippali*, from which our name pepper derives.

Long pepper spread throughout southern Asia before black pepper and was probably the first variety of pepper to reach the Mediterranean. In the fourth century BC, the Greek philosopher Theophrastus described both long and black pepper, and by the first century AD, the Roman historian Pliny reported that long pepper was worth almost four times as much as black. In AD 176, the Romans imposed customs duty on long and white pepper, but black was exempt. Pepper spread from Rome into the Empire, and by the time the Goths laid siege to the city in AD 408, they demanded 3,000 lb of pepper, as well as gold and silver, as their tribute.

For centuries, pepper was negotiable as currency in the East and the West. The Chinese called pepper "fagara of the Westerners" and regarded it as an exotic substitute for their own pepper-like spice. During the Middle Ages, pepper was sometimes used to pay rents, dowries and taxes, and was so expensive that the English took to using a herb substitute to flavour their food. The demand for pepper provided the main impetus for the discovery by the explorer Vasco da Gama of a sea route to the East.

The flowers are replaced by clusters of green berries, which turn red as they ripen.

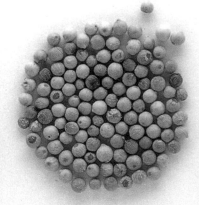

Black peppercorns *Green fruits are picked and piled in heaps to ferment for a few days, then sun-dried; they shrivel and turn hard and black. The peppercorns are more wrinkled than the other types.*

White peppercorns *Ripe berries are soaked in water, the outer skin is rubbed off, and the grey inner peppercorns are dried until they turn creamy-white.*

Fresh *These strings of fresh green berries are sometimes available in supermarkets in the West. Add a few whole berries to duck dishes and to cream and butter sauces.*

Ground black pepper *The aroma of pepper disappears quickly, so it is best to grind peppercorns as needed.*

Ground white pepper *Specks of white pepper are more attractive in creamy sauces than black.*

Pepper mill *For everyday kitchen use, try mixing black and white peppercorns in a pepper mill.*

Ground green pepper
*Seldom available commercially;
prepare at home.*

Green peppercorns Immature pepper,
these are preserved by freeze-drying or
packing in brine or vinegar.

Peppers in brine Rinse the
berries and add either whole
or crushed to the dish.

Ground schinus molle

Schinus molle These berries are often sold
as pink peppercorns. They have a brittle
outer shell enclosing a small seed and taste
aromatic, rather than pungent.

Essential oil Most commercial
pepper oil is produced in the West
from imported black pepper. It is
used in perfumery and flavourings.

Ground mixed pepper

Mixed peppercorns

Long pepper About 2.5cm (1in) long,
resembling small, stiff, grey-black catkins.

CULTIVATION
Distribution India, Malaysia
(Sarawak) and Indonesia (Sumatra)
are the main producers, closely
followed by Brazil. Long pepper
grows wild from the foothills of the
Himalayas to southern India.

Appearance & growth Pepper is a
perennial vine with dark green
leaves and spikes of white flowers.
The vine takes seven to eight years
to reach full maturity, and continues
to bear fruit for 15-20 years. It is
trained up posts or the trees grown
for shade in coffee plantations. Long
pepper, also a tropical vine, has
similar leaves and flowers.

Harvesting The berries of *piper nigrum*
are harvested over 2-3 months in
the spring and summer. Peppercorns - dried berries - are graded by
size: the larger the berry, the better
the quality. Long pepper berries are
gathered when green, then dried in
the sun.

Aroma & taste Pepper has a warm,
woody smell that is fresh, pungent
and agreeably aromatic. White
pepper tastes hotter and less subtle
than black; green pepper is not as
hot and has a clean, fresh taste.
Long pepper resembles black in
taste, but is slightly less pungent,
with a hint of sweetness.

USES
Culinary Pepper is neither sweet nor
savoury, just pungent, and can
therefore be used in both types of
dish. It is so popular that it has given
its name to a wide range of dishes.
  Use peppercorns whole to flavour
stocks and cooking liquids; crush
them coarsely when adding to dry-
spice mixtures or marinades.
  Long pepper is always used whole
and is seldom found outside the Far
East, where it is used as a cooking
spice and in pickles and preserves.

Medicinal Pepper is said to help
relieve flatulence and to have
diuretic properties.

Cubeb

NATIVE TO JAVA and other Indonesian islands, cubebs are the unripe fruits of a plant belonging to the pepper family. They are also known as tailed pepper because of their appearance. The herbalist John Parkinson describes them as "small berries somewhat sweete, no bigger than pepper cornes but more rugged or crested not so blacke nor solid ... and having each a small short stalke at them like a taile".

Used in ancient China as a medicine, cubebs reached the West through Arab traders and were valued as a medicine and a spice. They remained in quite common use until the end of the 17th century. In his *Theatrum Botanicum* of 1640, Parkinson reports that the sale of cubebs was forbidden by the king of Portugal in order to promote the sale of black pepper. By the 19th century, cubebs were virtually unobtainable. Today, medical herbalists are the most likely source of the spice.

The fruits, which are the spice, grow in clusters.

Berries *Dark brown in colour, the tailed berries have a wrinkled, leathery skin. They can be up to 6mm in diameter.*

Split berries *When split open, some of the berries have a small dark or white seed; others are hollow.*

Ground cubeb *The powdered spice can be used instead of ground pepper.*

Essential oil *An ingredient in some throat lozenges.*

Ras el hanout *One of the spice mixtures in which whole cubebs are used.*

CULTIVATION

Distribution Although cultivated commercially in parts of Indonesia and in Sri Lanka, often in coffee plantations, most cubebs are gathered from the wild.

Appearance & growth The cubeb plant is a perennial climber with smooth, pointed leaves and small, white flowers that grow in spikes.

Harvesting The fruits are gathered before they ripen, when still green.

They are then dried in the sun to a deep brown-black.

Aroma & taste Cubebs have a warm, turpentine-like aroma. The taste is aromatic - Parkinson called it hot and glowing - but it is also somewhat bitter. It is closer to allspice than to pepper.

USES

Culinary Today, cubebs are still used in spice mixtures such as ras el hanout (pp.372–73) and in Indonesian

cuisine. They can be added to any dish in place of allspice and are particularly suited to meat and vegetable dishes.

Medicinal Cubebs have been used as a medicine since antiquity and are still valued in the East. They help clear phlegm and are an ingredient in preparations for respiratory complaints. Cubebs also have antiseptic properties.

Sumac

The leaves turn a shade of red in autumn.

THE DECORATIVE SUMAC BUSH grows wild throughout the Middle East and bears spikes of tart, red berries. These are dried to a deep brick colour and used, whole or ground, in the cooking of the region. They give a fruity, sour note to a dish and are used in a similar way to lemon juice or vinegar in the West. Sumac is especially popular in Lebanon, where most homes have a constant supply.

The Romans used sumac as a souring agent before lemons were available in Europe. North American Indians used the red berries of a related shrub, *Rhus glabra*, to make a sour drink. A little-known spice in the West, sumac can be bought from some Middle Eastern shops, where it is usually sold as a deep purple-red coarse powder.

Berries These vary in colour from brick to brown- or purple-red, depending on the area they come from.

Seeds Small brown seeds from the centre of the berries.

Soaked berries If the berries are used whole in recipes, they are cracked and soaked in water for 20 minutes, then pressed well to extract all the juice, which is used as part of the cooking liquid.

Ground In an airtight jar, ground sumac will keep its flavour for several months.

Zahtar A Middle Eastern spice blend of ground sumac, roasted sesame seeds and powdered dried thyme (p.372).

CULTIVATION

Distribution Sumac grows wild in Sicily, and on the high plateau lands running from Turkey eastwards to the Caspian Sea and through the Arab lands to the south.

Appearance & growth The spice comes from a bush, which grows to about 3m (10ft) on sparsely wooded uplands. The plant bears white flowers, which are followed by clusters of small red berries. It thrives on rocky mountains: the higher it grows, the better the fruit.

Harvesting The berries are picked just before they ripen fully. They are dried before use. In early autumn huge piles of drying sumac stalks with strings of tightly clustered berries can be seen in the villages of Anatolia in Turkey.

Aroma & taste Sumac has little aroma, but its taste is pleasantly sour and astringent, without being sharp.

USES

Culinary Widely used in the Middle East: the Lebanese and Syrians sprinkle sumac on fish; the Iraqis and Turks add it to salads; and the Iranians and Georgians season kebabs with it. Sumac goes well with lentils, in a stuffing for chicken, with raw onions and mixed with yogurt.

Medicinal In Middle Eastern countries, sumac is made into a sour drink that is given to relieve mild stomach disorders.

Other uses The bark and leaves of the tree are used as a dye and for dressing leather.

Sesame

The plant has variable, hairy leaves and white or pink flowers.

BELIEVED TO BE the oldest plant grown for its oil, sesame has long been cultivated in Africa and Asia. The seeds contain about 50 percent fixed oil, which is excellent for cooking and does not turn rancid in heat. Sesame probably originated from Africa, though claims have been made for Iran, India and Indonesia. It has been used in China for around 2,000 years, yet, because it is not native, it is still called "foreign hemp". Sesame is one of the medicinal plants listed in the Ebers papyrus (*c*.1550 BC), and excavations in eastern Turkey have found evidence of oil being extracted from the seeds dating back to 900-700 BC. On his travels, Marco Polo noted that the Persians used sesame oil for cooking because they had no olive oil. Sesame reached the New World in the 17th and 18th centuries with African slaves, who called it *benne*.

Brown seeds Oval in shape, these beige, unhulled seeds have a characteristic nutty flavour.

Creamy white seeds These small flat seeds are the most common. They are quite shiny and slippery and not very hard.

Black seeds These are popular in Chinese and Japanese cooking.

"Western" oil A polyunsaturated oil, used in margarines and as a cooking oil.

Halva Probably the best-known sweetmeat made with sesame.

Oriental oil Made from toasted sesame seeds, Oriental oil is a seasoning oil with a deep brown colour and rich, nutty flavour and aroma. It is usually added to dishes just before serving.

Tahina This paste, made from the ground seeds, is used in the Middle East and eastern Mediterranean for dressings, to flavour vegetables and fruit dishes, and as a salad, mixed with garlic and lemon juice, and sometimes ground nuts.

CULTIVATION

Distribution The main producers are China, India, Mexico, Guatemala, and the southwest United States.

Appearance & growth An annual grown from seed, the plant reaches 1-1.5m (3-5ft). The colour of the seeds depends on the variety.

Harvesting The lower pods on the plant ripen first, so harvesting begins when the higher pods are still green. The plants are cut, then threshed, dried and cleaned.

Aroma & taste Sesame seeds have no essential oil, so they are not aromatic. The taste is mild, sweet and nutty, particularly after roasting. Black seeds have a stronger, more earthy taste than the lighter ones.

USES

Culinary In Western and Middle Eastern cooking, sesame seeds are used rather like poppy seeds to decorate and flavour breads, cakes and confectionery, such as halva. The Chinese coat foods with sesame before cooking to give them a crunchy texture; sesame prawn balls

and toast are popular Chinese appetizers. In Japan, the seeds are toasted and sprinkled on rice and other dishes, and are used in dressings for salads and vegetables. Oriental sesame paste is used in dressings for noodles, rice and vegetables.

Medicinal The seeds and their oil are slightly laxative.

Other uses Sesame oil is used in the manufacture of soap and cosmetics; in India it is traditionally rubbed on the body as an anointing oil.

Tamarind

THE DARK BROWN, bean-shaped pod of the tamarind tree has been cultivated in India for centuries, hence its other name, Indian date. Popular with the Arabs in the Middle Ages, it was probably introduced to Europe by the Crusaders. In Tudor times tamarind was known in England for its thirst-quenching properties. In the 17th century it was taken by the Spaniards to the West Indies, where it is cultivated today.

Tamarind is generally sold in sticky brown-and-white blocks of partly dried, broken pods and pulp, or as a concentrate. Whole pods can sometimes be bought in Indian shops. It is used as a souring agent in India and Southeast Asia, much as lemon and lime juice are used in the Middle East and the West. Tamarind is particularly good with fish and poultry dishes.

The fruits are curved pods, which turn dark brown when ripe.

Block A fibrous mass. To make tamarind water, soak a small piece of the block in 300ml (¹/₂pt) of hot water for about ten minutes, and squeeze out the sour brown juice with your fingers. Strain afterwards.

Slices Dried pieces of tamarind; soak in water to extract the flavour.

Pods *The brown pods have a brittle shell and grow up to 10cm (4in) long. Inside is a fleshy pulp, which can contain as many as ten seeds.*

Sugar-coated balls *These have a mild flavour and virtually no smell. Soak in a little water before use.*

Concentrate *A thick, dark paste with a smell resembling molasses and a distinct sharp, acidic taste.*

CULTIVATION
Distribution Thought to be native to East Africa and perhaps southern Asia, the tamarind tree grows wild throughout India, and is cultivated widely in the tropics.

Appearance & growth An evergreen, the tamarind tree bears pale green oval leaves and small clusters of yellow flowers with red veins. Trees are grown from seed or cuttings, and need little attention.

Harvesting The pods may be picked when immature, but usually they are fully ripe and cracked, revealing the red-brown pulp.

Aroma & taste Tamarind has a slightly sweet aroma and a pleasantly sour, fruity flavour.

USES
Culinary In India tamarind is used in curries; *sambhars* (spiced lentil and vegetable stews); *rasams* (highly seasoned lentil soups) and chutneys. In Thailand it makes hot and sour soups; in the West Indies, cooling drinks are made from tamarind syrup. In Jamaica the sweetly acidic fruit is used in rice dishes and stews and to make desserts. Pectin is extracted from the fruit for use in jam and jelly making. In the West, tamarind is imported for condiments such as Worcestershire sauce.

Medicinal Tamarind is a mild laxative, and is used in India as a traditional treatment for dysentery and bowel disorders. Rich in vitamins, tamarind is reputed to be good for the liver and kidneys.

Other uses The leaves of the tree yield red and yellow dyes.

Ajowan

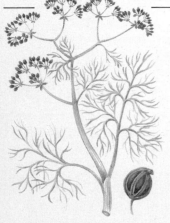

The plant resembles wild parsley.

AJOWAN IS CULTIVATED primarily for its essential oil, the main ingredient of which is thymol, a germicide and antiseptic. Native to southern India, ajowan is an annual related to caraway and cumin, although its taste is quite different, having a close affinity to thyme. Sometimes called lovage, ajwain or carom in Indian recipes, ajowan is a popular spice throughout India, particularly in savoury dishes and snacks, although it is probably used as much for medicinal purposes as for cooking. Ajowan seeds are found in most Indian households, where they are taken to relieve indigestion and flatulence, which may partly explain why they are often cooked with pulses. Ajowan goes well with fish, and the seeds are sometimes added to curries. In the West the spice is available from Indian grocery shops.

Seeds *The curved and ridged oval seeds look similar to celery seeds, but their colour varies from light brown to purple-red.*

Ground *Once crushed, the seeds are highly aromatic. Thyme or lovage can be used as substitutes in recipes.*

Paratha Ajowan *seeds are often added to Indian breads.*

Bombay mix *A popular Indian snack of mixed nuts, pulses and crisp sticks flavoured with ajowan and other spices.*

CULTIVATION

Distribution India is the main supplier of ajowan, but it is also grown in Afghanistan, Pakistan, Iran and Egypt.

Appearance & growth An annual that grows to 30-60cm (1-2ft) in height, ajowan thrives in well-drained soil in a sunny location.

Harvesting Once the seeds have ripened, they are dried and then threshed. The seeds fall off easily if bunches of ajowan are hung upside down in a dry atmosphere, an effective process with most spices in the same family as parsley.

Aroma & taste Until crushed, the seeds have little aroma, but even pressing them lightly in the palm of the hand releases a crude smell of thyme. The taste is hot, bitter and stinging on the tongue if they are sampled alone, but cooked with other ingredients ajowan adds a more subdued flavour of thyme.

USES

Culinary Ajowan seems to have a natural affinity with starchy foods and in southwestern Asia it is widely used in breads and savoury pastries, with root vegetables and with pulses. Many pickles include ajowan. If substituting it for thyme, use less ajowan since it has a much stronger flavour.

Medicinal Besides its use to control flatulence and indigestion, ajowan is prescribed for colic, diarrhoea and other bowel disorders, and in the treatment of asthma. The essential oil is an important antiseptic used, among other things, in mouthwashes and toothpastes.

Fenugreek

A MEDICINAL HERB and popular flavouring since antiquity, fenugreek is native to the eastern Mediterranean. The plant's Latin name, *foenum-graecum*, means Greek hay; *trigonella* refers to the triangular shape of its pale yellow flowers. The Egyptians made a paste from the seeds, which they applied to the body to reduce fever, and fenugreek was one of the spices used in fumigation and embalming. For the Romans, fenugreek was important as cattle fodder; 1,000 years later it was one of the plants grown throughout Europe in the imperial gardens of Charlemagne.

Fenugreek restores nitrogen to the soil and is still used today in the East as cattle fodder. It provides a good source of protein, vitamins and minerals, and is particularly useful in a vegetarian diet.

The whole plant emits a spicy odour when touched.

Seeds *The seeds are yellow-brown with a deep furrow running diagonally across one side. They are smooth and hard, rather like tiny pebbles, about 3-5mm long.*

Crushed *Lightly roast the seeds before crushing to bring out their flavour.*

Ground *It is best to grind fenugreek at home since commercial powder is often bitter and pungent.*

Sprouted *The seeds can be sprouted like mustard and cress to make an excellent salad green.*

Dried leaves *In India and parts of the Middle East, the leaves (methi) are cooked, often in combination with starchy root vegetables. They have a bitter taste and strong aroma.*

Çemen *In Turkey and Armenia, ground fenugreek, red pepper and garlic are blended to coat pastırma, the delicious dried meat of the region.*

CULTIVATION

Distribution Widely grown around the Mediterranean, and in India, Pakistan, Morocco, France and Argentina.

Appearance & growth Fenugreek is a robust annual that grows to 60cm (2ft) in height and thrives in mild climates with low rainfall. Its narrow, beaked seed pods are 10-12cm (4-5in) long, and each contains 10-20 seeds.

Harvesting When the seeds are ripe, the plants are pulled up and dried.

The seeds are then threshed and dried further.

Aroma & taste The strong, aromatic smell of fenugreek is similar to that of celery or lovage, and dominates commercial curry powder.

Uncooked fenugreek tastes bitter, astringent and very disagreeable; it is often lightly dry roasted before use to mellow the flavour.

USES

Culinary Fenugreek is combined with other spices in many Indian dishes and pickles. It is an ingredient of sambhar powder (pp.358–59) as well as curry powder (pp.356–57). In Egypt and Ethiopia, fenugreek is used in bread; it is also a constituent of Ethiopian Berbere (pp.368–69).

Medicinal Fenugreek is an important source of diosgenin, which is used in the synthesis of sex hormones and oral contraceptives.

Other uses Formerly used as a yellow dye.

Vanilla

The vine bears large waxy yellow-green flowers and long narrow pods with small seeds.

USED FOR CENTURIES as a flavouring by the Aztec Indians in Mexico, vanilla was offered as a tribute to the Aztec emperor by his subject tribes. In 1520 one of the Spanish *conquistadores*, Bernal Diaz, recorded that ground vanilla was added to the chocolate drink served to the emperor Montezuma.

The Spaniards imported the fruit and gave it its name: vanilla is the diminutive of *vaina*, meaning pod. By the second half of the 16th century, vanilla was being used to flavour chocolate in Europe, but Mexico kept a monopoly on its production until 1841, when a method of artificially fertilizing the plant by hand was developed, enabling it to be grown elsewhere.

Real vanilla is expensive, so cheap imitations are commonplace. Artificial vanillin was first produced in 1874, and this inferior synthetic, which flavours many commercial products, now meets about 90 percent of world demand.

Vanilla pods *These are dark brown, narrow, long, somewhat wrinkled, waxy and supple. The best pods are coated with white crystals of a natural substance called vanillin, which gives them their characteristic flavour and aroma.*

Inferior pod *Lighter or red-brown in colour, poor-quality pods are hard and dry and lack aroma. Vanillin frosting is not hard to fake, so inferior pods are sometimes "upgraded".*

Split pod *Inside, the pods contain numerous tiny black seeds embedded in dark aromatic oil.*

Pod in alcohol *Vanilla extract and essence are prepared by macerating beans in alcohol; essence usually has added syrup.*

Vanilla essence *This is very concentrated, so use it sparingly. Vanilla extract has a milder flavour; add this half a teaspoonful at a time.*

Vanilla sugar *Keep a vanilla pod in a jar of sugar; it flavours beautifully and lasts for years.*

CULTIVATION

Distribution Native to Central America. Mexico, Puerto Rico, Madagascar and Réunion are the main producers and exporters. Despite the wide use of synthetic vanilla, the natural vanilla market is buoyant and vanilla provides an important source of revenue. The United States, France and Germany are the main importers.

Appearance & growth The fleshy vanilla vine grows in tropical lowland forests and climbs trees to a height of 10-15m (33-50ft); when cultivated

it is trained to a convenient height for pollinating and harvesting.

Harvesting The pods are picked unripe and there is a lengthy and complicated curing process, which helps to explain vanilla's high cost.

Aroma & taste A rich, mellow, perfumed tobacco-like aroma is matched by a mellow, fragrant, sweet taste. Synthetic vanilla has a more obvious, heavy aroma and a rather disagreeable aftertaste. Compare the two and you won't use synthetic again.

USES

Culinary Ice cream, custards, puddings, cakes and chocolate rely on vanilla for their flavour. Much of the flavouring used is synthetic, although vanilla pods are now easier to buy than they used to be, and on the Continent natural vanilla has always been important. It is well worth buying the whole pods: they can be used many times over, and even after soaking in milk or a sauce, just wash, dry and store.

Other uses A concentrated form is used in perfumery.

Fagara / Sichuan pepper

CALLED BY MANY NAMES - anise pepper, Sichuan pepper, Chinese pepper, flower pepper (from its Cantonese name *fahjiu*) - the spice is not in any way related to our familiar black and white pepper. Many kinds of fagara have been used in cooking and in medicine in China, India and Japan for centuries. The Sichuan variety is regarded as the best.

Fagara is the red-brown dried berry of the Chinese variety of the small prickly ash tree. With cassia and ginger, it is one of the oldest established spices in China. In ancient times fagara was used to flavour wines and foods offered to the gods; it is said that the eighth-century emperor Te Tsung took fagara and curds in his tea, and the poet Han-shan of the same period wrote about "roast duck tinctured with fagara and salt". Fagara became a standard table condiment in China and at one time it was fashionable to give sachets of the spice as a gift to friends.

The Chinese prickly ash is covered in sharp spikes.

Whole The red-brown berries are about 4-5mm long, and have a rough, prickly exterior. They are hollow and split open and sometimes have bits of stalk still attached.

Seeds Discard any loose black seeds, or seeds in the centre of the berries; they are very bitter.

To grind Crush the berries in a mortar, or grind in a coffee grinder. For a finer powder, sieve the ground spice to remove the husks.

Seasoned salt From a recipe in Asian Ingredients by Bruce Cost. It is made by roasting two tablespoons fagara, three tablespoons sea salt and one teaspoon white peppercorns in a dry pan until the fagara smokes, then grinding all to a coarse powder.

Xanthoxylum piperitum SANSHO

Also confusingly called Japanese pepper, sansho is closely related to fagara. The berry of the Japanese variety of the prickly ash is dried and ground to an aromatic, tangy, coarse powder. One of the few spices used in Japanese cooking, sansho is used principally to counter the taste of fatty foods; the Japanese sprinkle it on food, much as we do pepper.

CULTIVATION

Distribution This variety of the prickly ash grows wild throughout China, flourishing on hill slopes.

Appearance & growth A feathery-leaved deciduous tree or shrub, which has stout, sharp prickles and bears small red berries.

Harvesting The berries are harvested in autumn and dried in the sun until they split open.

Aroma & taste The berries have a pronounced spicy-woody aroma, and a numbing, rather than a sharp or bitter, taste.

USES

Culinary Fagara is an excellent seasoning for poultry and meat, and in China it is used to flavour dishes such as Sichuan crispy duck and Pang Pang chicken, a peppery dish served chilled with cucumber and spring onions. The ground berries are an essential ingredient in

Chinese five-spice powder (pp.348–49). For more flavour, dry roast the berries in a heavy pan to release their aromatic oils before using whole, crushed or ground. Fagara will smoke as it gets hot, so keep the heat low and discard any berries that have blackened.

Medicinal In medieval Chinese medicine, the berries and their seeds were widely used; one variety of fagara was taken as a cure for dysentery.

Ginger

O NE OF THE OLDEST and most important spices, ginger has been cultivated in tropical Asia for over 3,000 years. It was widely used in ancient India and China, although it is uncertain in which of these countries ginger originates. It was one of the first spices to reach the Mediterranean, probably traded by the Phoenicians, and was known in ancient Egypt, Greece and Rome. The first-century Roman epicure, Apicius, recommends it in sauces for meat and chicken, with dried peas and lentils, and in aromatic salt. By the ninth century ginger was so widespread throughout Europe that it was set out on the table as salt and pepper are today.

Long, slender stalks and leaves grow from the creeping root.

The rhizomes are easy to transport, so ginger was the first Oriental spice to be widely introduced elsewhere. The Arabs took it to East Africa in the 13th century; the Portuguese to West Africa and the Spaniards to the West Indies early in the 16th century. Today it grows almost everywhere in tropical regions.

Ginger is known for its ability to warm people. In his *Theatrum Botanicum* of 1640, the herbalist John Parkinson wrote: "The properties of ginger are to warme a cold stomacke, and to helpe digestion". Ginger spiced up the English language too: "to ginger up" means to liven up. The term "ginger" is applied to people with red hair because of their alleged hot temperament.

Fresh ginger *The fresh rhizome is knobbly, off-white or buff-coloured, and often branched. It should feel firm and the pale yellow flesh should not be too fibrous. Fresh ginger is also known as green ginger.*

Dried ginger *The dried and cracked roots are sometimes called races. These are sold in pieces and are best bruised before using.*

Preserved ginger
Tender pieces of ginger in syrup, often called stem ginger. It is exported from China, Hong Kong and Australia. In the past, it was sold in pottery or china jars.

Ground ginger
This is widely used in European baking, in breads, biscuits, cakes and confectionery, as well as in Oriental spice blends.

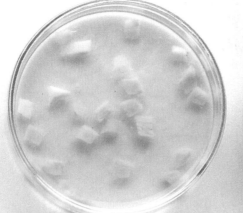

Ginger oil *This flavours wines, beers and cordials. It is also given to relieve flatulence and indigestion.*

Ginger tea *Made by infusing dried or fresh root in boiling water for five minutes; excellent for clearing head colds.*

Ginger wine *A popular and warming drink in cold weather.*

Pickled ginger *Wafer-thin slices of pickled ginger - pink sushoga or red beni-shoga - are served with Japanese dishes, especially sushi.*

Crystallized ginger *Pieces of ginger are candied, dried, and rolled in sugar.*

Gingerbread man *Gingerbread has been popular since the Middle Ages.*

CULTIVATION

Distribution A native of the tropical forests of Southeast Asia, ginger is now widely grown in the West Indies, Hawaii, Africa and northern Australia. China and India are the biggest producers, but Jamaican ginger is said to be the best.

Appearance & growth The ginger plant grows up to 1m (3ft) tall on partly shaded slopes. It has narrow pointed leaves and small yellow, purple-lipped flowers resembling irises. The hard, knobbly rhizome is about 2cm (³/₄in) in diameter.

Harvesting Rhizomes for use fresh or preserved can be dug up five to six months after planting, while still tender. For fresh ginger, the rhizomes are washed, and dried for a day or two. They can then be stored for several months in a controlled atmosphere. Ginger to be preserved is soaked in brine for a few days, then cold water. After this, it is boiled in water, then syrup.

Ginger intended for use dried is usually prepared from rhizomes harvested eight to ten months after planting. By this time, the rhizomes have become more fibrous and pungent. They are peeled or soaked in boiling water before drying.

Aroma & taste Ginger has a warm aroma with a fresh woody note and sweet, rich undertones. Its flavour is hot and slightly biting.

USES

Culinary China and most other Asian countries use fresh ginger, often with garlic. Both fresh and dried are common in India. In Arab and Western cooking ginger is mostly used dried, but fresh is now more widely available, and its use is increasing.

Ginger has numerous applications in sweet and savoury cooking. It is an essential ingredient of curry powder and other spice blends, and is found in gingerbread, biscuits, cakes, puddings, pickles and many Asian vegetable dishes. Ginger beer and wine are popular drinks and in the past, ginger was added to wine.

Medicinal The Greek physician Dioscorides recommended ginger for the stomach and as an antidote to poisons. It is still widely used in Asian medicine as a digestive aid. Ginger tea is a warming drink thought to improve the circulation. It also eases travel sickness, as does crystallized ginger.

Citrus hystrix
Kaffir lime

T HE SMALL KAFFIR LIME TREE grows in Southeast Asia. The rind of the fruit and the leaves are used in Thai and Indonesian cooking, and in the West can be bought fresh or dried from Oriental shops. The leaves have a clean, floral aroma, rather like lemon verbena, and give a distinctive taste to chicken and fish dishes. Lemon grass, lemon or ordinary lime peel can if necessary be used as a substitute, but the flavour will not be the same.

Fruit *Pear-shaped, bumpy and wrinkled. The bitter rind is used in cooking.*

Leaves *The leaves have an unusual double form - as if two leaves have grown end to end.*

Dried leaves *A less fragrant substitute if fresh leaves are not available.*

Languas officinarum / Alpinia officinarum
Lesser galangal

Kaempferia galanga
Kempferia galangal

L ESSER GALANGAL is widely used in Southeast Asian cooking (p.321). Another form of galangal, kempferia galangal, is generally found dried and sliced in the West. It has a refreshing but strong taste, and should therefore be used sparingly.

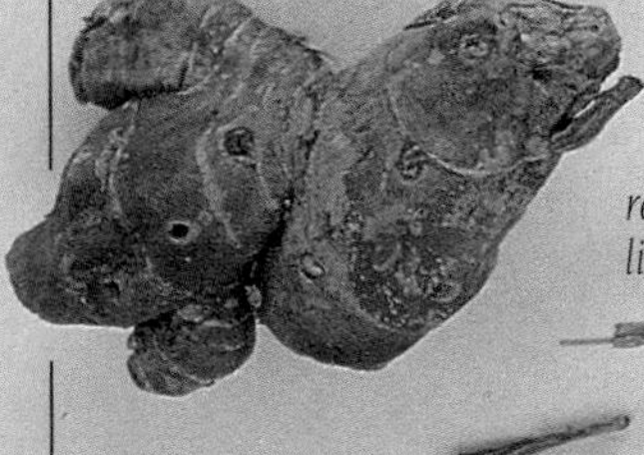

Lesser galangal
A small rhizome with a reddish-brown skin and lighter-coloured interior.

Kempferia galangal *The rhizome resembles a cluster of fingers.*

Mangifera indica
Mango powder (A*mchoor*)

NATIVE TO INDIA, mango is one of the most popular tropical fruits, prized for its use in chutneys and pickles. The spice *amchoor* is made from tart, unripe mangoes, which are sliced and sun-dried, then ground to a powder and used as a souring agent. It is most commonly used in northern Indian vegetarian cooking, and gives a tangy, sour taste to stir-fried vegetables, stuffings for breads and pastries, and soups. In the West, the powder can be bought in most Indian shops.

Powder
The sand-coloured lumpy powder has little smell, but a sharp, acidic taste, similar to lemon or lime.

Slices *Unripe mangoes, sliced and dried to a light brown.*

Murraya koenigii
Curry leaf

CURRY LEAVES COME from a small ornamental tree that grows wild in the foothills of the Himalayas and in southern India and Sri Lanka. It is cultivated in many Indian gardens. The small leaves of this plant are used extensively in Indian cooking, particularly in vegetarian dishes. They give off a distinct curry-like odour when bruised.

Dried leaves *These have virtually no flavour - a handful of dried leaves is needed to give anything like the flavour and aroma of a stalk of fresh leaves.*

Fresh leaves *The small mid-green leaves are usually attached to the stalk. Add the whole stalk to the dish and remove before serving.*

Pandanus odoratissimus
Screwpine

THE SCREWPINE TREE grows in the tropical swamps of southern Asia, and bears narrow, shiny, sword-like leaves. These are used as a flavouring in Malay, Thai and Indonesian cooking, particularly in rice dishes and puddings. In the West, the leaves can be bought fresh from Oriental shops; store them in the refrigerator - they will keep for a week or two. Dried leaves are sold cut into short lengths; their flavour is less fragrant than that of the fresh.

   Screwpine flowers yield an essence, sold as kewra water or essence, which is used in India to flavour meat and poultry dishes and pilafs.

Dried leaves Add directly to the dish.

Fresh leaves The long, thin leaves are added directly to the dish or are sometimes cooked first in a syrup, which is then strained off and added to the dish. They colour food green.

Kewra water This has a delicate floral, rose-like perfume and flavour.

Prunus mahaleb
Mahlab

THE SMALL, beige-coloured oval kernels of the black cherry tree are dried and ground to flavour breads and pastries in Turkey and the Middle East. They are quite soft, and have a nutty chewiness and a bitter, rather sour, taste when sampled on their own. The kernels are not easily available in the West, but can be bought from some Middle Eastern shops. It is best to buy mahlab whole and grind as needed.

Whole   **Ground**

Punica granatum
Pomegranate

NATIVE TO SOUTHWEST ASIA, but now grown throughout the tropics and sub-tropics, the small deciduous pomegranate tree bears glossy leaves, brilliant orange-red flowers and large beige- to red-skinned fruits. These may be sweet, sweet-sour or sour, depending on the variety, but all have rather astringent juice. The seeds of the sour pomegranate are sun-dried and used as a garnish. They have a slightly sour smell and a distinctive, but subtle, sweet-sour taste. In north India, under the name *anardana*, they are ground and used as a souring agent in chutneys and curries, in fillings for breads and savoury pastries, and with braised vegetables and pulses.

Dried seeds
These look rather like red-black raisins.

Fruit
The skin is tough and inedible, but the numerous seeds inside are embedded in white, pink or red juicy flesh.

Raw seeds *In the Middle East, Turkey and Iran, these are sprinkled as a garnish on salads, pastes such as hummus or tahina and on desserts.*

Wasabia japonica
Wasabi

THIS PLANT, the "mountain hollyhock", grows only in Japan on the marshy edge of cold mountain streams. It is otherwise known as Japanese horseradish, probably because of its edible root, fierce aroma and biting, cleansing taste, although it is not related to the Western horseradish plant.

In Japan, the brownish-green skin of the root is removed, and the pale green flesh is grated finely.

Wasabi accompanies most raw fish dishes. *Sashimi* plates always have a tiny mound of grated wasabi or wasabi paste, which is mixed to taste with a soy dipping sauce. *Sushi* has a dab of wasabi paste spread between the rice and fish. Fresh wasabi is seldom available outside Japan but small tins of powder or tubes of paste can be bought in the West.

Powder *Mix wasabi powder with an equal quantity of tepid water and leave for ten minutes to develop its flavour.*

Paste *The pale green paste loses its potency more quickly than the powder.*

3

Spice mixtures

Spice blends are used extensively in many parts of the world to add a distinctive flavour to a dish. They vary in complexity and texture: some are pastes based on fresh ingredients such as chillies, others are dried mixtures of whole or ground spices. In this chapter, instructions are given for making a range of spice blends, from Asian mixtures, such as fiery Indonesian sambals and Indian garam masalas, to blends from Africa and the Middle East, and the West. The recipes can be adapted to suit your taste and the dish by varying the proportions and combinations of ingredients.

Far Eastern spice blends

Japan

Moving east to west across Asia, spice blends increase in number and complexity. In Japan, spices are used mostly as condiments for sprinkling over dishes. China has a few more spice mixtures, but the most varied and extensive range of blends is to be found in Indonesia and Thailand.

JAPAN

The Japanese use many aromatic ingredients in their cooking, although few are spices. Those most commonly used are wasabi and sansho, which are exclusive to Japanese cuisine, chillies, mustard, ginger and sesame. All are used with moderation.

SHICHIMI TOGARASHI

This popular Japanese spice mixture translates as seven-flavour or seven-spice mix. It is used in the kitchen and as a table condiment to flavour soups, noodles and grilled meats. Proportions can be varied. The aroma is of the dried tangerine peel, with a hint of iodine from the laver; the taste is somewhat dominated by the chilli, but not overwhelmingly; and the texture is gritty. Sometimes rape seeds are substituted for the poppy seeds.

2 tsp white sesame seeds
3 tsp sansho
1 tsp small pieces of dried laver (a seaweed, called *nori* in Japan)
3 tsp flakes of dried tangerine peel
3 tsp chilli powder (togarashi)
1 tsp black sesame seeds
1 tsp poppy seeds

METHOD
Grind the white sesame seeds and sansho coarsely. Add the laver and dried tangerine peel and grind again briefly. Stir in the remaining spices and blend well. In an airtight container, the mixture will keep for 3-4 months.

GOMASIO

Goma is the Japanese name for sesame. This mixture is used as a condiment to sprinkle on rice, raw vegetables and salads. It is good on boiled potatoes, too.

5 tsp black sesame seeds
2 tsp coarse salt

METHOD
Lightly roast the sesame seeds in a dry frying pan over a medium heat for a minute or two, stirring frequently. Allow to cool, then grind them together with the salt. In an airtight jar, the blend will keep for 3-4 months.

SHICHIMI TOGARASHI

Chilli powder

Dried tangerine peel

Poppy seeds

Shichimi togarashi

GOMASIO

Black sesame seeds

Coarse salt

Gomasio

Sansho

Dried laver

White sesame seeds

Black sesame seeds

China

CHINA

The Chinese use some spice mixtures, to flavour meats and poultry and in marinades. The best-known spice blend is five-spice powder, but Chinese supermarkets also stock large bags, labelled mixed spices, which contain cassia, star anise, cardamom, dried ginger, fagara, liquorice root and cassia buds. This mixture is used in a technique common throughout China called flavour-potting, where meat is steeped in a rich spiced sauce; the sauce permeates the meat and the meat enriches the sauce. The blend has a predominantly woody smell of cassia combined with anise.

FIVE-SPICE POWDER

This mixture is used throughout southern China and Vietnam to season roast meat and poultry, and to flavour marinades. Besides the five basic ingredients, it can consist of up to two of the following spices: cardamom, dried ginger and liquorice root. The powder varies in colour, from tan to gingery-brown to amber. Star anise dominates the aroma and taste.

I tbsp star anise
I tbsp fagara
½ tbsp cassia or cinnamon
I tbsp fennel seeds
½ tbsp cloves

METHOD
Grind all the ingredients together and use sparingly. Stored in an airtight container, five-spice powder will keep for 3-4 months.

SPICED SALT

This salt is served in small bowls and used as a dip for raw or deep-fried vegetables, roast meat and poultry.

4 tbsp coarse salt
2 tbsp fagara

METHOD
Dry roast the salt and fagara in a heavy frying pan over a medium heat until the fagara darkens. Cool, then grind and store in an airtight container for up to 4 months.

FIVE-SPICE POWDER

Fagara

Cardamoms

Fennel seeds

SPICED SALT

Fagara

Coarse salt

Spiced salt

Star anise

Cloves

Dried ginger

Five-spice powder

Cassia

Liquorice root

INDONESIA

Indonesian cooking is richly spiced with ginger, turmeric; galangal, lemon grass, aromatic leaves and herbs, but above all with chillies. In addition to the spicing used in the preparation of a dish, Indonesians make a range of relishes, based on chillies, called sambals. These are served in small dishes on the table. Some are fiercely hot because the chilli seeds have been left in; all are highly aromatic. The Indonesians use a chilli called lombok, similar to Tabasco, when making sambals but other small red chillies can be substituted. Take great care when handling chillies as they can burn (pp.430–31). More sambal recipes appear on p.384.

Indonesia

SAMBAL OELEK

Jars of sambal can be bought in many Oriental shops and in some delicatessens, but it is quite easy to make your own, especially with a food processor. This is the most basic sambal. To make other sambals, ingredients such as trassi or blachan, a firm paste made of rotted prawns (pp.430–31), and candlenuts are added to the mix.

| 250 g (8 oz) fresh red chillies |
| 1 tsp salt |
| 1 tsp soft brown sugar |

METHOD
Heat a heavy frying pan and put in the chillies after 2-3 minutes. Dry roast over a medium heat for a few minutes. Cool, then chop finely and pound to a paste with the salt and sugar. The chilli seeds may be taken out, or left in if you want a really fiery relish. The sambal will keep for a week or so in a jar in the refrigerator.

SAMBAL BADJAK

SAMBAL OELEK

Salt

Chillies

Brown sugar

Candlenuts

Fresh red chillies

Sambal oelek

Oil

SAMBAL BADJAK

10 fresh red chillies

2 onions

5 cloves garlic

a small piece of trassi (pp.430–31)

5 candlenuts

5–10 ml (1–2 tsp) tamarind concentrate or 30–45 ml (2–3 tbsp) tamarind water (p.333)

½ tsp ground galangal

45 ml (3 tbsp) oil

1 tsp salt

1 tsp soft brown sugar

2 kaffir lime leaves

250 ml (8 fl oz) thick coconut milk, made from 125 g (4 oz) creamed coconut dissolved in 250 ml (8 fl oz) hot water

METHOD
Pound or process the chillies, onions, garlic, trassi and candlenuts to a smooth paste with the tamarind and galangal. Heat the oil and fry the paste for a few minutes, then add the remaining ingredients and cook gently for 15-20 minutes, until the mixture thickens. Cool, and store in a jar in the refrigerator.

Garlic

Trassi

Ground galangal

Tamarind concentrate

Onion

Kaffir lime leaves

Sambal badjak

Creamed coconut

THAILAND

Thailand has the same affection for chillies as Indonesia, and uses them with garlic, coriander, lemon grass and tamarind. Sauces called Nam prik, made with chillies (*prik*), shallots, garlic and trassi (pp.430–31), are the local equivalent of sambals. They are made quickly, with no hard and fast rules: the sauces vary from region to region and cook to cook. Nam prik is eaten with vegetables, rice and fish. More nam prik recipes appear on p.384.

Thailand

ROASTED NAM PRIK

5 cloves garlic, unpeeled

5 shallots, unpeeled

5 fresh red chillies

a small piece of trassi

1 tbsp soft brown sugar

5 ml (1 tsp) tamarind concentrate

2 tbsp peanuts

METHOD
Put the unpeeled garlic and shallots over a barbecue or in a heavy cast-iron frying pan and grill or dry fry until the skins are dark brown and the insides soft. Dry fry the chillies and the trassi wrapped in foil, until the trassi darkens and the chillies soften. Peel the garlic and shallots, chop the chillies, removing the seeds, and pound or process everything to a paste. Store for about a week in a jar in the refrigerator.

ROASTED NAM PRIK

Tamarind concentrate

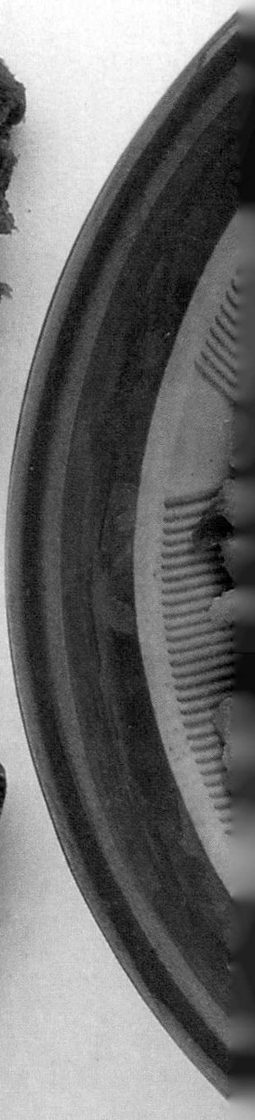

NAM PRIK for raw vegetables

4 dried red chillies

6 dried prawns

a small piece of trassi

2 cloves garlic

30 ml (2 tbsp) fish sauce (see *Simple Thai Fish Soup*, p.388)

1 tbsp soft brown sugar

juice of one lime

METHOD
Remove the seeds from the chillies and chop. Pound or process them with the dried prawns. Heat the trassi (see pp.430–31). Crumble it and pound with the garlic, then combine all the ingredients except the lime juice and process. Add the lime juice, a little at a time, so that the sauce remains fairly thick. Store in the refrigerator.

Trassi

Dried shrimps

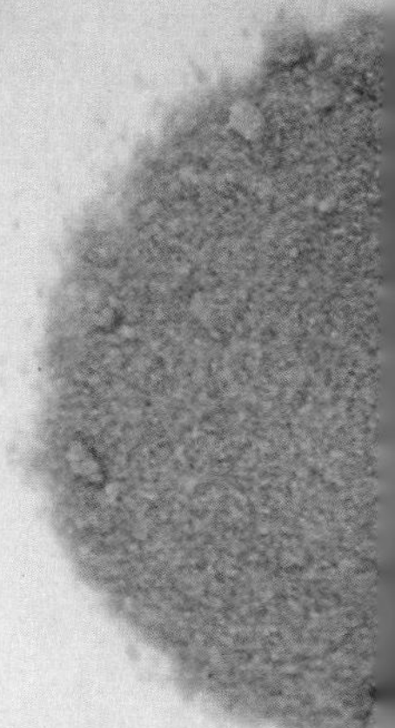

Brown sugar

Peanuts

Shallots

Garlic

Roasted nam prik

Fresh red chillies

Thai curry pastes

Curries are an important element in the Thai menu. They are flavoured with ferociously hot pastes made of spices and either red, green or yellow chillies, according to the ingredients used. As in India, the spice mix is prepared when needed and is not usually stored, but these pastes will keep for about a month in the refrigerator.

RED CURRY PASTE

This is used for beef and other robust dishes.

3 shallots
3 cloves garlic
2 stalks lemon grass
1 tbsp coriander seeds
1 tsp cumin seeds
1 tsp black peppercorns
10 dried red chillies
1 tbsp chopped coriander root
1 tbsp ground galangal
2 tsp grated lime peel
a small piece of trassi (pp.430–31)
salt to taste

METHOD
Chop the shallots, garlic and lemon grass. Heat a heavy frying pan and add the coriander and cumin seeds after 2-3 minutes. Dry roast until they darken, shaking the pan to prevent burning. Allow to cool, then grind to a powder with the peppercorns. Remove the seeds from the chillies and chop. Pound or process all the ingredients to a smooth paste.

VARIATION
◆ For GREEN CURRY PASTE, follow the recipe for Red curry paste, using **fresh green chillies** instead of dried red and adding 2 tbsp **chopped coriander leaves**.

Black peppercorns

Dried red chillies

Cumin seeds

Fresh green chillies

Coriander leaves

Coriander seeds

Trassi

Garlic

Shallots

RED CURRY PASTE

Grated lime peel

Salt

Ground galangal

Chopped coriander root

Lemon grass

Indian spice mixtures

South India and Sri Lanka

The blending of spices is the essence of Indian cookery; to become a good Indian cook you must first become a good *masalchi* (spice blender). The word masala means a mixture of spices, but also refers to the aromatic composition of a dish. The Western notion of having a single masala or curry powder gives little real idea of Indian cooking since there are hundreds of masalas – from different regions, for different foods, and prepared to the taste of different cooks – imparting a distinctive flavour to each dish. The most common ground blends are garam masalas, used in northern cooking, and hotter masalas or curry powders from the south. They are usually made up as required, but will keep for 3-4 months in an airtight jar.

Curry powders

In the hotter southern blends, chillies, mustard seeds, fenugreek seeds, ground turmeric and fresh curry leaves are standard ingredients. More curry mixtures appear on pp.384–85.

BASIC CURRY POWDER

This medium-hot curry blend can be used in any dish that calls for curry powder.

6 dried red chillies
25 g (1 oz) coriander seeds
2 tsp cumin seeds
½ tsp mustard seeds
1 tsp black peppercorns
1 tsp fenugreek seeds
10 fresh curry leaves
½ tsp ground ginger
1 tbsp ground turmeric

METHOD
Remove the seeds from the chillies. Dry roast the whole spices over a medium heat until they darken, stirring or shaking the pan frequently to prevent burning. Leave to cool, then grind to a powder. Dry roast the curry leaves in the pan for a few minutes, then grind and add them to the mixture with the ginger and turmeric, blending well.

VARIATION
◆ To make AROMATIC CURRY POWDER, add 1 tsp **ground cinnamon** and ¼ tsp **ground cloves** with the ginger and turmeric, and use only 2 or 3 **chillies**.

Fenugreek seeds

Black peppercorns

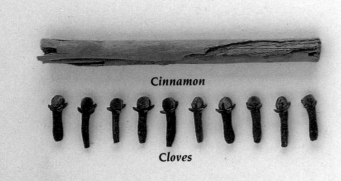

Cinnamon

Cloves

Dried red chillies

Cumin
seeds

Ground turmeric

Mustard
seeds

Ground ginger

Coriander
seeds

Basic curry powder

Fresh curry leaves

SAMBHAR POWDER

This hottish powder is widely used in southern Indian Brahmin cooking, which is vegetarian, to flavour pulses, braised and stewed vegetables, and sauces. The dal in the blend give it a nutty taste, and also serve as a thickening agent.

10 dried red chillies
25 g (1 oz) coriander seeds
20 g (³/₄ oz) cumin seeds
15 g (¹/₂ oz) black peppercorns
1 tsp mustard seeds
15 g (¹/₂ oz) fenugreek seeds
¹/₄ tsp ground asafoetida
1 tbsp ground turmeric
15 ml (1 tbsp) oil
25 g (1 oz) yellow split peas (*channa dal*)
25 g (1 oz) white gram beans (*urad dal*)

METHOD
Remove the seeds from the chillies. Heat a heavy frying pan and dry roast the whole spices over a medium heat for about 5 minutes. When the seeds stop spattering, add the asafoetida and turmeric and stir for a minute longer. Remove the mixture to a dry bowl, add the oil to the pan and fry the split peas and gram beans until they darken, stirring frequently to prevent burning. Add them to the bowl of spices, mix well and grind when cool. Stored in an airtight container, the powder will keep for 3-4 months.

BENGALI PANCH PHORON

This mix of whole spices comes from Bengal in the east of India, where it is used to flavour pulses and vegetable dishes. It may be put into hot oil to perfume it before other ingredients are added, or it is used to spice the ghee that is poured over a dish of lentils as it is served.

1 tbsp cumin seeds
1 tbsp fennel seeds
1 tbsp mustard seeds
1 tbsp nigella seeds
1 tbsp fenugreek seeds

METHOD
Mix all the spices together. Stored in an airtight jar, the blend will keep for 3-4 months.

SAMBHAR POWDER

White gram beans

Yellow split peas

Oil

Sambhar powder

BENGALI PANCH PHORON

Fenugreek seeds

Nigella seeds

Cumin seeds

Mustard seeds

Fennel seeds

Panch phoron

Black peppercorns

Fenugreek seeds

Cumin seeds

Mustard seeds

Coriander seeds

Dried red chillies

Ground turmeric

Ground asafoetida

Garam masala

Garam masala is the principal spice blend of north Indian cookery, and there are almost as many versions as there are cooks. A masala may be a simple blend of two or three spices and herbs; or it may contain a dozen or more. Some masalas, based on pepper and cloves, are quite fiery; others, using mace, cinnamon and cardamom, are aromatic.

Garam masala is always used sparingly. The spices are usually dry roasted, and may be added to the dish, whole or ground, at different stages during cooking. For pilafs, biriyanis and some meat dishes, the use of whole spices is traditional. For some grand Moghul dishes, dried rose petals are added to the basic mixture. More masalas appear on pp.362–63 and p.384.

North India

BASIC GARAM MASALA

Black peppercorns

Bay leaves

BASIC GARAM MASALA

This is a version of the most common type of garam masala used throughout Uttar Pradesh and the Punjab, which goes well with onion-based sauces for meats and poultry. It is a spicy, pungent blend. Change the proportions to suit your taste and the dish.

2 cinnamon sticks
3 bay leaves
40 g (1 1/2 oz) cumin seeds
25 g (1 oz) coriander seeds
20 g (3/4 oz) green or black cardamom seeds
20 g (3/4 oz) black peppercorns
15 g (1/2 oz) cloves
15 g (1/2 oz) ground mace

METHOD
Break the cinnamon sticks into pieces. Crumble the bay leaves. Heat a heavy frying pan and after 2-3 minutes put in the whole spices. Dry roast over a medium heat until the colour darkens, stirring or shaking the pan frequently to prevent burning. Leave to cool, then grind and blend with the mace. In an airtight container, the mixture will keep for 3-4 months.

Ground mace

VARIATIONS
◆ To make a mild and subtle MOGHUL MASALA, use only **green cardamoms, cinnamon, black peppercorns, mace** and a few **cloves**.

◆ For a hot GUJERATI MASALA, add **sesame seeds, fennel seeds, ajowan seeds** and **chillies**.

◆ For a mildish KASHMIRI MASALA, use **black cumin seeds, green cardamoms, black peppercorns, cloves, cinnamon, mace,** and add a little **grated nutmeg**.

◆ For a hot PARSI DHANSAK MASALA, add **fenugreek seeds, mustard seeds, chillies** and **ground turmeric**, and double the amount of **coriander seeds**.

Coriander seeds

Basic
garam
masala

Green cardamoms

Cumin seeds

Cloves

Cinnamon

CHAT MASALA

A fresh-tasting, sourish preparation used with fruit and vegetable salads. If you are unable to find the black salt (pp.430–31), simply increase the amount of coarse salt.

1 tsp cumin seeds

1 tsp black peppercorns

$^1/_2$ tsp ajowan seeds

1 tsp dried pomegranate seeds

1 tsp black salt

1 tsp coarse salt

a good pinch of crushed dried mint leaves

$^1/_4$ tsp ground asafoetida

2 tsp mango powder

$^1/_2$ tsp cayenne

$^1/_2$ tsp ground ginger

METHOD

Grind the whole spices and salt to a powder, then mix in the mint, asafoetida, mango powder, cayenne and ginger. The blend will keep for 3-4 months stored in an airtight container.

CHAT MASALA

Crushed dried mint leaves

Ground ginger

Ajowan seeds

Ground asafoetida

Cayenne

Black salt

Mango powder

Dried pomegranate seeds

Cumin seeds

GREEN MASALA

Excellent with fish or chicken.

a small piece of fresh ginger
1-2 cloves garlic
4-6 fresh green chillies
a small bunch of fresh coriander

METHOD
Peel and chop the ginger and garlic; remove the seeds from the chillies and slice. Remove the coriander stalks. Pound or blend all the ingredients to a paste with a little water.

Black peppercorns

Chat masala

Coarse salt

GREEN MASALA

Fresh ginger

Green masala

Fresh green chillies

Coriander leaves

Garlic

Other curry blends

SRI LANKAN CURRY POWDER

In Sri Lanka, spices are roasted to a deep brown before grinding; this gives much Sri Lankan food a "darker" taste than Indian dishes.

25 g (1 oz) coriander seeds
15 g (¹/₂ oz) cumin seeds
1 tbsp fennel seeds
1 tsp fenugreek seeds
a small piece of cinnamon
6 green cardamoms
6 cloves
6 fresh curry leaves
1 tsp cayenne

METHOD
Dry roast the whole spices in a heavy frying pan over a medium heat until they turn dark brown, stirring frequently to prevent burning. Leave to cool, then combine with the curry leaves and cayenne and grind to a powder. Stored in an airtight container, the blend will keep for 3-4 months.

POUDRE DE COLOMBO

Colombo is a type of curry found in the Caribbean islands of Martinique and Guadeloupe. Although called a powder, this recipe, based on one in *The Best of Caribbean Cooking* by Elisabeth Lambert Ortiz, is in fact a paste.

3 cloves garlic
2 fresh hot red chillies
¹/₈ tsp ground turmeric
1 tsp ground coriander
1 tsp ground mustard

METHOD
Peel and crush the garlic; remove the seeds from the chillies and mash. Combine all the ingredients and mix to a paste. Store in the refrigerator for up to 6 weeks.

SRI LANKAN CURRY POWDER

Fennel seeds

Coriander seeds

Sri Lankan curry powder

Cloves

Green cardamoms

POUDRE DE COLOMBO

Garlic

Fresh red chillies

Ground mustard

Ground turmeric

Ground coriander

Poudre de Colombo

Fenugreek seeds

Cayenne

Cumin seeds

Cinnamon

Fresh curry leaves

African & Middle Eastern spice blends

BAHARAT

Arabian Gulf

Around the Arabian Gulf, highly spiced food is still common; recipes from the region call for complex spice blends, often with chillies. Enthusiasm for rich spicing passes to North Africa, to Ethiopia and the countries of the Magreb (Morocco, Algeria and Tunisia), where food is spiced with pepper, cubebs, cumin, caraway, cinnamon and cassia, ginger and saffron. Chillies and mild peppers are common too, but not all the food is ferociously hot; many Moroccan dishes are quite delicate and subtle in their flavouring. Further south, in both East and West Africa, chillies are the dominant flavouring. Elsewhere in the Middle East, subtle spicing prevails in the Arab countries, Iran and Turkey.

Green cardamoms

Black peppercorns

BAHARAT

A fiery preparation from the Gulf States, used to spice meats and vegetables. The recipe comes from *Cooking with Chillies* by Meg Jump.

¹/₂ nutmeg, grated
1 tbsp black peppercorns
1 tbsp coriander seeds
1 tbsp cumin seeds
1 tbsp cloves
a small piece of cinnamon
seeds from 6 green cardamoms
2 tbsp paprika
1 tsp ground chilli

METHOD
Grind all the ingredients together. The mixture will keep for 3-4 months stored in an airtight jar.

Ground chilli

ZHUG

ZHUG

In Yemen, this is the traditional spice mix, a combination of garlic and peppers, and whatever spices the cook chooses. Use as a table condiment.

2 small mild red peppers
2-3 fresh red chillies
a handful of coriander leaves
1¹/₂ tbsp ground coriander
6 cloves garlic
seeds from 6 green cardamoms
5-10 ml (1-2 tsp) lemon juice

METHOD
Finely chop the red peppers and chillies, removing the seeds. Chop the coriander leaves. Blend or pound all the ingredients to a paste, and store in a jar in the refrigerator for up to 2 weeks.

Ground coriander

Garlic

Green cardamoms

Baharat

Grated nutmeg

Cloves

Cinnamon

Coriander seeds

Cumin seeds

Paprika

Coriander leaves

Lemon

Mild red peppers

Zhug   Fresh red chillies

367

Ethiopia

ETHIOPIAN BERBERE

Berbere is rather like Indian masala (pp.360–63) ~ a complex blend of spices made to suit the dish and to the taste of the cook. Chillies, ginger and cloves are the staples; other spices vary, and some are not found outside the region. Berbere is used in traditional Ethiopian stews, called wats, and in coatings for foods to be fried. Another Ethiopian recipe appears on p.385.

10 dried red chillies
¹/₂ tsp coriander seeds
5 cloves
seeds from 6 green cardamoms
¹/₄ tsp ajowan seeds
8 allspice berries
¹/₂ tsp black peppercorns
¹/₂ tsp fenugreek seeds
a small piece of cinnamon
¹/₂ tsp ground ginger

METHOD
Heat a heavy frying pan and put in the chillies and other whole spices after 2-3 minutes. Dry roast over a medium heat until they darken, stirring frequently to prevent burning. Leave the spices to cool, then remove the seeds from the chillies and crumble them. Grind everything, including the ginger, to a fine powder, and store in an airtight container for up to 4 months.

Ground ginger

Allspice

Green cardamoms

Cloves

BERBERE

Coriander seeds

Dried red chillies

Black peppercorns

Berbere

Fenugreek seeds

Ajowan seeds

Cinnamon

Tunisia

TABIL

This mixture is specific to Tunisia. Tabil means coriander, but generally refers to this blend of ingredients.

| 1 tbsp coriander seeds |
| 1 ¹/₂ tsp caraway seeds |
| 2 cloves garlic |
| 1 tsp dried crushed chilli |

METHOD
Pound all the ingredients in a mortar, then dry in a preheated oven at 100°C, 200°F, gas ¹/₄ for about half an hour. When quite dry, grind to a fine powder and keep in an airtight jar for up to 4 months.

TABIL

Coriander seeds

HARISSA

This fiery Tunisian chilli sauce, also found in Algeria and Morocco, is used in cooking, particularly in the vegetable or meat *tagines* (stews) that accompany couscous; and as a table condiment, rather like Indonesian sambals (pp.350–51). The sauce can be bought ready-made in small cans, but it is easy to make at home and keeps for up to 6 weeks in the refrigerator. Another Tunisian recipe appears on p.385.

| 50 g (2 oz) dried red chillies |
| 2 cloves garlic |
| salt |
| 1 tsp caraway seeds |
| 1 ¹/₂ tsp ground cumin |
| 2 tsp coriander seeds |
| 1 tsp crushed dried mint leaves |
| olive oil |

METHOD
Remove the seeds and tear the chillies into pieces. Soak them in warm water until they soften (about 20 minutes). Drain, and pound or process. Crush the garlic with a little salt. Pound or blend all the ingredients to a paste, then stir in 15-30 ml (1-2 tbsp) of olive oil. Transfer to a jar, cover with a layer of olive oil, and refrigerate.

HARISSA

Olive oil

Dried red chillies

Dried crushed chilli

Garlic

Caraway seeds

Tabil

Caraway seeds

Crushed dried mint leaves

Ground cumin

Harissa

Salt

Coriander seeds

Garlic

RAS EL HANOUT

North Africa

This renowned traditional Moroccan blend of 20 or more spices never fails to intrigue foreigners. *Ras el hanout* means "head of the shop", presumably because the owner mixes the blend to his own taste and to the requirements, including spending power, of the customer. The blends vary from one region to another; those from the bazaar in Fez seem to be the most complex. All contain some aphrodisiacs ~ *cantharides* (the shiny green Spanish fly), ash berries and monk's pepper ~ as well as spices and dried flowers. Ras el hanout is always sold whole and ground as required. It is considered warming, and is used with game; in rice and couscous stuffings; in lamb *tagines* (stews), such as M*rouziya* (p.396); and in a sweetmeat of almonds, honey, butter and hashish called *el majoun*.

ZAHTAR

An aromatic mixture from North Africa, which is also found in Turkey and Jordan. It is sprinkled on meatballs or vegetables, and used as a dip. It can be mixed to a paste with olive oil and spread on bread before baking. See also the recipe for Dukka (p.385).

50 g (2 oz) sesame seeds
25 g (1 oz) ground sumac
25 g (1 oz) powdered dried thyme

METHOD
Dry roast the sesame seeds over a medium heat for a few minutes, stirring frequently. Allow to cool, then mix with the sumac and thyme. Stored in an airtight jar, the blend will keep for 3-4 months.

ZAHTAR

Zahtar

Dried thyme

Sesame seeds

Ground sumac

RAS EL HANOUT

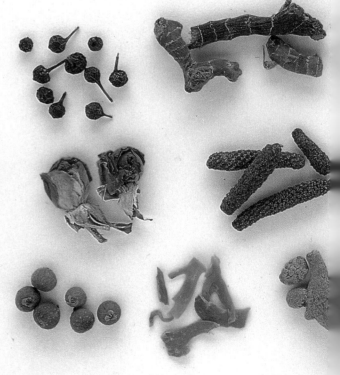

A *typical blend* This could include: *cardamom, mace, galangal, long pepper, cubebs, nutmeg, allspice, cinnamon, cloves, ginger, rose buds, lavender flowers, Spanish fly, ash berries, grains of paradise, black pepper, chufa nuts, turmeric, cassia, nigella, monk's pepper, belladonna and orris root.*

Ras el hanout

Early European spice mixtures

Europe: Italy

Spice mixtures have been used as long as spices themselves. The cooks in great medieval households had their blends of *poudre blanche* and *poudre forte*, which were usually "pointed" (sharpened and dampened) with vinegar before being added to other ingredients. Ginger seems to have been the predominating flavour, with lesser amounts of cinnamon, cloves, pepper, saffron and grains of paradise. In the 13th and 14th centuries huge quantities of powdered sugar were mixed with the spices; presumably sugar and spice went together as an indication of wealth. By the 16th century the sugar had almost disappeared; there was more variety in spice blends for different dishes. At this time, Italy led the way in cooking, and Ruperto de Nola, cook to the king of Naples, gives one of the earliest recipes for an unsweetened mixture, which he calls *Salsa comun*. This consists of: "3 parts cinnamon; 2 parts cloves; 1 part ginger; 1 part pepper with a little ground coriander and a little saffron, if wished".

SCAPPI'S SPICE MIX

Bartolomeo Scappi, the cook to Pope Pius V, specifies this blend of ingredients in his *Opera dell'Arte del Cucinare*, one of the most influential early Italian cookery books.

24 cinnamon sticks
25 g (1 oz) cloves
15 g (¹/₂ oz) dried ginger
15 g (¹/₂ oz) grated nutmeg
7.5 g (¹/₄ oz) grains of paradise
7.5 g (¹/₄ oz) saffron
15 g (¹/₂ oz) soft brown sugar

METHOD
Break the cinnamon sticks into pieces, and grind all the ingredients to a fine powder. Stored in an airtight jar, the mixture will keep for 3-4 months.

SCAPPI'S SPICE MIX

Cinnamon

Dried ginger

Brown sugar

Grains of paradise

Cloves

Grated nutmeg

Saffron

Scappi's spice mix

Later European spice mixtures

Europe: France

In the 17th century the use of large amounts of spices started to diminish; spices were more plentiful and cheaper, and although used by more people generally, were used less to exhibit status. Cookery books no longer give spice mixtures among the basic recipes at the start; the spicing needed is included in the individual recipes. In the 19th century there are more suggestions for mixed spices: Carême, the great French chef, proposes three parts peppercorns to one part of cloves, nutmeg, cinnamon, dried thyme and bayleaf, combined; and a small amount of ginger and mace. Anne Cobbett's "kitchen pepper" in the early 19th-century manual *The English Housekeeper* requires "an equal quantity of finely ground or pounded ginger, nutmeg, black pepper and allspice, cinnamon and cloves".

Today spice blends are used less widely in Europe than in the past. In France, *quatre-épices* is the most popular. In Britain, pudding spice and pickling spice are traditional mixes, still used today.

QUATRE-EPICES

The standard French "four-spice" blend is based on pepper. It is commonly used in charcuterie and in dishes that need long simmering, such as stews. Sometimes cinnamon or allspice is used in the blend.

5 tsp black peppercorns
2 tsp grated nutmeg
1 tsp cloves
1 tsp dried ginger

METHOD
Grind all the ingredients to a fine powder. In an airtight container, the mixture will keep for 3-4 months.

MELANGE CLASSIQUE

More recent French mixtures combine aromatic herbs and spices. This *mélange classique* comes from the chef's handbook *Manuel du Restaurateur*.

5 dried bay leaves
2 tsp dried thyme
1 tsp dried marjoram
1 tsp dried rosemary
2 tsp grated nutmeg
2 tsp cloves
1 tsp cayenne
1¹/₂ tsp white peppercorns
1¹/₂ tsp coriander seeds

METHOD
Crumble the bay leaves. Grind the ingredients to a fine powder and store in an airtight jar for up to 4 months.

Cloves

Quatre-épices

Dried ginger

Black peppercorns

Grated nutmeg

QUATRE-EPICES

Mélange classique

Cloves

White peppercorns

MELANGE CLASSIQUE

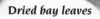

Dried bay leaves

Dried thyme

Coriander seeds

Dried rosemary

Grated nutmeg

Cayenne

Dried marjoram

PICKLING SPICE

An English mixture of whole spices, used for chutneys, pickled fruits and vegetables, and to spice vinegar. The spices can either be tied in a small muslin bag and removed after pickling, or added straight to the vinegar, depending on the type of pickle.

Spice merchants have their own versions; here are two given in *Law's Grocer's Manual* (1950 edition). To make manageable domestic amounts, substitute 25 g (1 oz) or even 15 g (^{1}/$_2$ oz) for each pound.

Europe: British Isles

PICKLING SPICE WITH CHILLIES

"2 lb Jamaica ginger, 1^3/$_4$ lb yellow mustard seed, 1^1/$_2$ lb Zanzibar cloves, 2^1/$_4$ lb Indian black pepper, 1^1/$_2$ lb birdseye or Nyasa chillies, ^{3}/$_4$ lb mace, ^{3}/$_4$ lb coriander seed, 3^1/$_2$ lb pimento [allspice]."

PICKLING SPICE WITH CAYENNE

"2^1/$_2$ lb mustard seed, 2 lb cayenne pods, 2^1/$_2$ lb common black peppercorns, 1^1/$_2$ lb white peppercorns, 1 lb small cloves, 3 lb pimento [allspice], 1^1/$_2$ lb Jamaica ginger. Total 14 lb. "

PICKLING SPICE WITH CHILLIES

Yellow mustard seeds

Cloves

Coriander seeds

Allspice

Mace

Dried ginger

Dried birdseye chillies

PUDDING SPICE

Also known as mixed spice, this English blend of sweet spices is used in cakes, biscuits and puddings. The selection of spices and the proportions used vary according to individual taste, but here is one version:

| a small piece of cinnamon |
| 1 tbsp cloves |
| 1 tbsp mace |
| 1 tbsp grated nutmeg |
| 1 tbsp coriander seeds |
| 1 tbsp allspice berries |

METHOD

Grind all the spices to a fine powder. In an airtight jar, the mixture will keep for 3-4 months.

PUDDING SPICE

Black peppercorns

Coriander seeds

Cinnamon

Allspice

Cloves

Mace

Nutmeg

Pickling spice with chillies

American spice mixtures

United States

The United States is the land of commercial spice blends, invariably prepared to "secret formulae" protected by trade marks. Recipes call for apple-pie spice, barbecue blend, chicken seasoning and crab boil, all available at the local supermarket. Few cooks seem to blend their own. I have included a few versions of my own to help readers who may want to use American recipes. Make up as required.

CAJUN SEASONING

Cajun and creole cooking from Louisiana have spread throughout the States and abroad in recent years. Chillies, aromatic herbs, mustard and cumin are the main flavourings. Commercial blends tend to include onion and garlic powder, which I find have a decidedly chemical taste, so it is best to use fresh onion and garlic. This mixture is rubbed into meat or fish to be roasted or grilled, or is used to season *gumbos* (the local stews) and *jambalayas* (rice dishes). As variations, dried sage, basil or fennel can be used instead of the thyme and oregano. Other recipes from Louisiana appear on p.385.

1 fat clove garlic
¹/₂ small onion
1 tsp paprika
¹/₂ tsp ground black pepper
¹/₂ tsp ground cumin
¹/₂ tsp mustard powder
¹/₂ tsp cayenne
1 tsp dried thyme
1 tsp dried oregano
1 tsp salt

METHOD
Crush the garlic and onion in a mortar, and mix all the ingredients together.

Onion

Ground black pepper   *Cayenne*   *Salt*

Cajun seasoning

Garlic

Dried thyme   **Paprika**   **Ground cumin**   **Mustard powder**   **Dried oregano**

Barbecue spice mixtures

BASIC SPICE *Illustrated below*

A medium-hot blend; rub on meat before grilling.

1 tsp black peppercorns
1 tsp celery seeds
$^1/_2$ tsp cayenne
$^1/_2$ tsp dried thyme
$^1/_2$ tsp dried marjoram
2 tsp paprika
1 tbsp mustard powder
$^1/_2$ tsp salt
1 tbsp soft brown sugar

METHOD
Crush the peppercorns and celery seeds in a mortar and mix all the ingredients together.

PAPRIKA SPICE *Illustrated right*

A pungent blend, which goes well with chicken and gives it a light red colour.

a small piece of fresh ginger
1 clove garlic
1 tbsp paprika
2 tsp ground cumin

METHOD
Pound the ginger and garlic in a mortar and mix with the paprika and cumin.

JUNIPER SPICE

An aromatic blend, which is good with dense-textured fish such as monkfish, fresh tuna and swordfish, and with steaks and lamb.

2 tbsp juniper berries
1 tsp black peppercorns
6 allspice berries
3 cloves
3 dried bay leaves
$^1/_2$ tsp salt

METHOD
Grind the spices, finely crumble the bay leaves, and combine everything.

FENNEL SPICE

Fennel and lemon peel add a clean, fresh taste to this blend, which is excellent with fish.

1 clove garlic
1 tsp black peppercorns
2 tsp fennel seeds
$^1/_2$ tsp coriander seeds
1 tsp grated lemon peel
1 tsp dried thyme

METHOD
Crush the garlic in a mortar, grind the spices, and mix everything together.

BASIC SPICE

Mustard powder

Dried thyme

Cayenne

Dried marjoram

Paprika

PAPRIKA SPICE

Paprika

Ground cumin

Fresh ginger

Garlic

Paprika spice

Brown sugar

Celery seeds

Black peppercorns

Salt

Basic spice

Other spice blends

These spice mixtures, arranged by region, are either variations on the blends in the rest of this section or alternative recipes. They range from pastes and powders to a mixture of whole spices. Some are hot or medium-hot; others are mild and fragrant.

Far Eastern

SAMBAL TRASSI

a small piece of trassi (pp.430–31)

4–5 fresh red chillies

1 green chilli

1 tsp salt

1 tsp soft brown sugar

15 ml (1 tbsp) lemon or lime juice

METHOD
Wrap the trassi in foil and grill until it darkens, or bake in a preheated oven at 180°C, 350°F, gas 4 for a few minutes. Remove the seeds from the chillies and chop finely. Pound or process the trassi and chillies with the other ingredients until you have a smooth paste. Store in a jar in the refrigerator for a few days.

VARIATIONS
◆ For SAMBAL ASEM, add an extra teaspoon **sugar** and 5-10 ml (1-2 tsp) **tamarind concentrate.**

◆ For SAMBAL KEMIRI, add **10 candlenuts** that have been dry roasted and ground.

NAM PRIK for cooked vegetables

125 g (4 oz) unripe fruit, such as green mango, gooseberries, tart plums or grapes

6 dried red chillies

a small piece of trassi (pp.430–31)

3 cloves garlic

1 onion

15 ml (1 tbsp) fish sauce (see *Simple Thai Fish Soup*, p.388)

1 tbsp soft brown sugar

lime juice

METHOD
Chop the unripe fruit. Remove the seeds from the chillies and chop. Wrap the trassi in foil and grill until it darkens, or cook in a preheated oven at 180°C, 350°F, gas 4 for a few minutes. Then, either crumble and pound, or process it with the other ingredients, adding lime juice to dilute and to taste. Store in a jar in the refrigerator for a few days.

Indian

MADRAS CURRY POWDER

A fragrant, fairly hot curry powder, which is used to flavour lamb and pork dishes.

2 dried red chillies

25 g (1 oz) coriander seeds

1·5 g (¹/₂ oz) cumin seeds

1 tsp mustard seeds

15 g (¹/₂ oz) black peppercorns

2 fresh curry leaves

¹/₂ tsp ground ginger

1 tsp ground turmeric

METHOD
Remove the seeds from the chillies. Dry roast the whole spices until they darken. Leave to cool, then grind to a powder. Dry roast the curry leaves in the pan for a few minutes, then grind and add them to the mixture with the ginger and turmeric, blending well. In an airtight jar, the powder will keep for 3-4 months.

Indian influenced

CHAR MASALA

Neighbouring Afghanistan uses this simpler blend of spices than India for flavouring rice dishes.

1 tbsp cinnamon

1 tbsp cloves

1 tbsp cumin seeds

1 tbsp black cardamom seeds

METHOD
Mix all the spices together. Stored in an airtight jar, the blend will keep for 3-4 months.

WEST INDIAN CURRY POWDER

Hindus who migrated to the West Indies in the 19th century introduced their spice blends to the islands, and curries are now found throughout the region.

25g (1oz) coriander seeds
1 tbsp of each of the following whole spices: aniseed, cumin, black mustard, fenugreek, black pepper
a piece of cinnamon
2 tbsp ground ginger
2 tbsp ground turmeric

METHOD
Dry roast all the whole spices for about 5 minutes. Cool, then grind and blend with the ginger and turmeric. In an airtight jar, the powder will keep for 3-4 months.

African & Middle Eastern

WAT SPICES

A wat is a traditional Ethiopian stew, spiced either with Berbere (pp.368–69) or this simpler blend of spices. The recipe below is taken from A *Safari of African Cooking* by Bill Odarty.

> **"6 long peppers**
> **3 tablespoons black pepper**
> **3 tablespoons whole cloves**
> **1 long nutmeg**
> **a pinch of turmeric**

Roast spices over a low flame. Pound them in order to break up big pieces. Place a pinch of turmeric on the grinding stone and grind until a yellow coating of turmeric is spread over the working surface. Grind all the other spices together on the yellow grinding stone. These spices are added to the wat towards the end of cooking.**"**

TUNISIAN FIVE SPICES

Called *qâlat daqqa* in Arabic, this blend is used in vegetable dishes and with lamb.

2 tsp black peppercorns
2 tsp cloves
1 tsp grains of paradise
4 tsp grated nutmeg
1 tsp ground cinnamon

METHOD
Grind the peppercorns, cloves and grains of paradise together, then mix in the nutmeg and cinnamon. In an airtight jar, the blend will keep for 3-4 months.

DUKKA

This blend of spices with ground hazelnuts or roasted chick peas (available from Middle Eastern shops) comes from Egypt. Serve with bread: dip this in olive oil and then into the dukka.

125 g (4 oz) sesame seeds
75 g (3 oz) hazelnuts or roasted chick peas
50 g (2 oz) coriander seeds
25 g (1 oz) cumin seeds
1 tsp salt
1/2 tsp black peppercorns
1 tsp dried wild thyme or mint

METHOD
Dry roast the sesame seeds until lightly browned. Remove from the pan. Roast the hazelnuts for about 5 minutes and remove their skins (chick peas do not need roasting further), then roast the coriander and cumin seeds until they darken. When everything has cooled, combine all the ingredients and pound or process to a coarse powder. The mixture will keep for 3 months stored in an airtight jar in a cool place.

American

CRAB BOIL & FISH SEASONING

Crab boil is popular along the southeast coast of the United States, particularly in Louisiana. A similar blend, where the spices are ground, is used to spice fish.

1 tsp black peppercorns
1 tsp mustard seeds
1 tsp dill seeds
1 tsp coriander seeds
1 tsp cloves
1 tsp allspice berries
a small piece of dried ginger
3 dried bay leaves

METHOD
Tie the spices in a muslin bag and add to the water for boiling the crab.

4

Cooking with spices

Indispensable ingredients in all types of dish – from soups, salads and casseroles to cakes, pickles and drinks – spices add and enhance flavours while also aiding digestion. The following pages provide more than 100 recipes based on different spices and spice mixtures from around the globe. All the spices used are described in the Spice Index (pp.294–343); information about their preparation and storage is given on pp.430–31. The amount of spicing in each recipe is a guide; adjust according to your own taste and preference.

Soups & starters

Pumpkin Soup

SERVES 4

This soup is cooked in the pumpkin, which makes a handsome presentation, although you can make it in a pan if you prefer. Salted dried shrimps, much used in Southeast Asian cooking, can be bought from Chinese shops. They give the soup a more robust flavour.

1 small pumpkin, about 20 cm (8 in) in diameter
salt
2 medium onions, chopped
3 tbsp long grain rice
½ tsp ground mace
½ tsp ground cinnamon
¼ tsp ground cumin
about 750 ml (1¼ pints) chicken stock
25 g (1 oz) salted dried shrimps (optional)
10 ml (2 tsp) lemon juice (optional)

1 Cut a lid from the top of the pumpkin and reserve. Discard the seeds and stringy tissue, then scoop out most of the pumpkin flesh, leaving a fairly thick coating round the sides and bottom. Chop the flesh.
2 Rub the inside of the pumpkin with a little salt and put it into a close-fitting ovenproof dish. Put in the pumpkin flesh, onions, rice and spices. Pour enough boiling chicken stock into the pumpkin to fill it by three-quarters, then close with its own lid. Cook at 160°C, 325°F, gas 3 for 2 hours.
3 If using dried shrimps, soak them in a little water to soften for 5–10 minutes. Pound the shrimps to a paste with the soaking water and lemon juice. Stir the paste into the soup for the last 20 minutes or so of the cooking time.
4 To serve, lift the pumpkin out into a warmed serving bowl. If it is too tricky to do this, bring the pumpkin to the table in the oven dish.

Mussel Soup with Saffron

SERVES 6

1 kg (2 lb) mussels
40 g (1½ oz) butter
1 onion, chopped
2 leeks, thinly sliced
1 carrot, diced
1 slice celeriac, about 125 g (4 oz), diced
900 ml (1½ pints) water
a few saffron threads, crushed
salt and pepper

1 Scrub the mussels, remove the beards and discard any that are broken or open. Just cover the bottom of a large pan with water, add the mussels, cover with a lid and cook over high heat, shaking the pan occasionally, until they open. Remove the mussels from their shells and set them aside. Discard any that have not opened. Strain the cooking liquid through muslin and reserve.
2 Melt the butter and sauté the onion, leeks and carrot for 5 minutes. Add the celeriac and cook gently for 10 minutes. Stir in the mussel liquor and water and simmer for 15 minutes.
3 Dissolve the saffron in a little hot water and stir into the soup. Season with salt and pepper.
4 Put the mussels into the soup just long enough to heat through, then serve.

Simple Thai Fish Soup

SERVES 4

Fish sauce, called *nam pla* in Thailand and *nuoc mam* in Vietnam, is the brown liquid drained off fish that has been fermented in brine. Its aroma is like that of ripe cheese, but the taste is more subdued. It is available from Oriental stores.

500 g (1 lb) firm white fish fillets
1.25 litres (2 pints) light fish stock
2 tsp ground galangal
2 stalks lemon grass, sliced and pounded
3 kaffir lime leaves
45 ml (3 tbsp) lime juice
1 tsp sambal oelek (pp.350–51) or ground chilli
10 ml (2 tsp) fish sauce

Garnish
3–4 spring onions, chopped
1 tbsp chopped fresh coriander leaves
thin slices of lime

1 Cut the fish into small pieces. Bring the stock to the boil in a pan with the galangal, lemon grass and lime leaves. Simmer for 15 minutes, then strain.
2 Return the stock to the pan, add the fish, lime juice, sambal and fish sauce. Simmer gently for 4–5 minutes until the fish is cooked.
3 Remove the pan from the heat. Garnish with spring onion, coriander and lime slices, and serve.

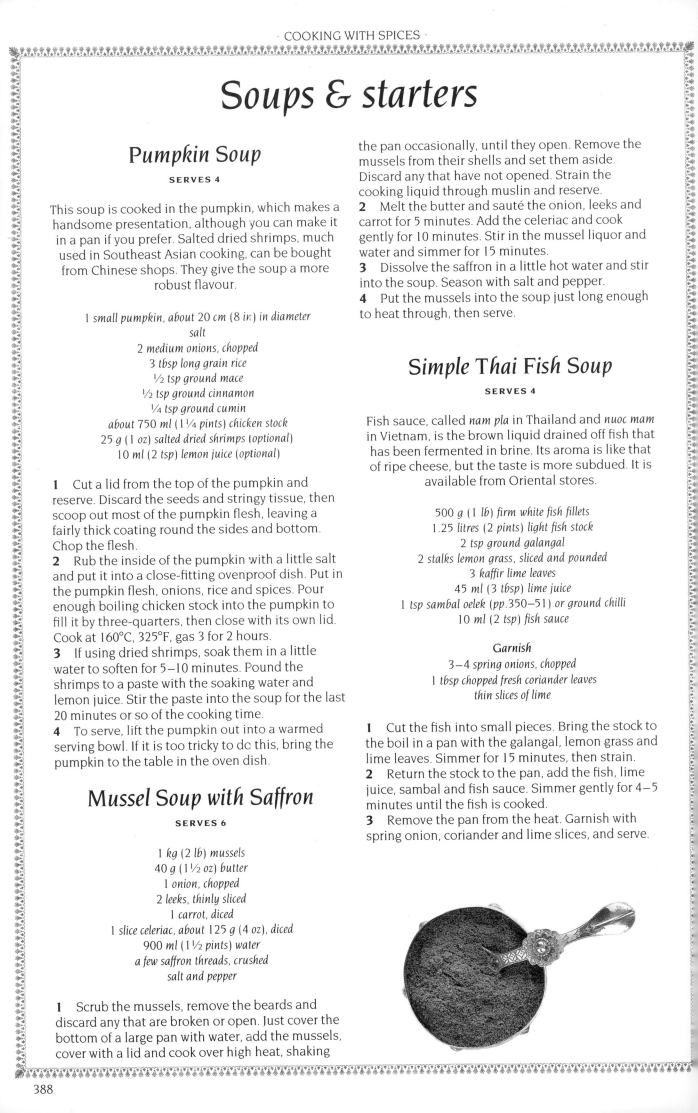

Chicken and Coconut Soup

SERVES 4

½ a small chicken
200 g (7 oz) creamed coconut dissolved in 1.25 litres (2 pints)
hot water
1 tbsp ground galangal
3 stalks lemon grass, bruised and sliced
3 green chillies, seeded and sliced
3 spring onions, sliced
45 ml (3 tbsp) lime or lemon juice
30 ml (2 tbsp) fish sauce (see Simple Thai Fish Soup)
2 tbsp chopped fresh coriander leaves

1   Remove the skin from the chicken, and the bones if preferred. Cut the flesh into small chunks.
2   Bring the coconut milk to the boil in a large pan. Put in the chicken, galangal and lemon grass, and simmer for 15–20 minutes until the chicken is cooked. (Leave the pan open; if it is covered the steam in the pan will curdle the coconut milk.)
3   Stir in the remaining ingredients, and serve.

Spiced Lentil Soup

SERVES 6–8

½ tsp ground ginger
½ tsp ground black pepper
½ tsp ground turmeric
½ tsp ground fenugreek
¼ tsp ground cloves
2 tsp ground cumin
1 tsp ground cassia or cinnamon
grated rind of 1 lemon
60 ml (4 tbsp) olive oil
1 large onion, chopped
3 cloves garlic, crushed
175 g (6 oz) brown lentils
2 stalks celery, chopped
350 g (12 oz) tomatoes, chopped
1.5 litres (2½ pints) stock or water
salt
30–45 ml (2–3 tbsp) lemon juice
large bunch of fresh parsley or coriander, chopped
¼ tsp ground chilli (optional)

1   Mix all the spices, except the chilli, with the lemon rind.
2   Heat the oil in a large pan and gently cook the onion until soft. Add the spices and cook, stirring, for 2–3 minutes. Add the garlic and lentils and stir to coat the lentils with the oil and spices.
3   Add the celery and tomatoes and cook for a few minutes, then pour in the stock. Simmer steadily, covered, for about 1 hour until the lentils are soft. Add salt to taste and cook for a few minutes more.
4   Purée the soup, adding more stock or water if needed to achieve the required consistency. Stir in the lemon juice, the parsley or coriander and a sprinkling of ground chilli if liked.

Ceviche

SERVES 4

In this Mexican hors d'oeuvre, the fish is tenderized by marinating in lemon juice for several hours.

175 g (6 oz) salmon
175 g (6 oz) brill or turbot
175 g (6 oz) cod fillet
juice of 2–3 lemons
1–2 fresh green chillies, seeded and finely chopped
1 small mild onion, chopped
½ avocado, peeled, stoned and cubed
2 tomatoes, skinned, seeded and chopped
125 ml (4 fl oz) olive oil
handful of coriander leaves, chopped
salt and pepper

1   Remove any skin or bones from the fish and cut the flesh into small cubes. Put the cubes into a dish with the lemon juice, turn to coat all the fish and leave to marinate in the refrigerator for a minimum of 5 hours.
2   Drain the lemon juice from the fish and combine with the chopped vegetables, olive oil and coriander. Season with salt and pepper to taste and pour over the fish in a serving dish. Leave in the refrigerator until ready to serve.

Spiced Fish Mousse

SERVES 4–6

1 tsp ground anise
2 tsp ajowan
½ tsp chilli powder
2 cloves garlic, crushed with a little salt
500 g (1 lb) white fish fillets, cut in small pieces
175 g (6 oz) large cooked prawns, shelled weight
15 ml (1 tbsp) oil
1 onion, chopped
3 egg whites
handful of coriander leaves, chopped
salt
150 ml (¼ pint) double cream, whipped

1   Mix the anise, ajowan, chilli powder and garlic to a paste. Rub the fish with the paste and leave to marinate for 30 minutes.
2   Cut the prawns into two or three pieces. Heat the oil and sauté the onion until soft but not coloured. Remove from the heat and leave to cool.
3   Put the fish and onion in a food processor and chop finely.
4   Beat the egg whites until frothy and fold into the fish and onion mixture. Add the prawns and coriander, and a little salt. Fold in the cream.
5   Butter a 1 litre (1¾ pint) soufflé dish and pour in the mixture. Cook in a bain-marie (water bath) in a preheated oven at 140°C, 275°F, gas 1 for 45–50 minutes. Cool, then refrigerate for several hours before serving.

Indian Fruit Chat

SERVES 6

The fruit for this dish can vary according
to availability, but try to make sure that some of
it is tropical.

3 potatoes, boiled and diced
½ cucumber, peeled, seeded and cubed
2 ripe bananas, sliced
1 ripe papaya, cubed
1 ripe mango, cubed
1 apple, cubed
2 slices fresh pineapple, cubed
1 orange, in segments
2 tbsp chat masala (pp.362–63)
juice of 1 lemon
lettuce leaves

1   Put all the vegetables and fruit into a bowl.
Sprinkle over the chat masala and lemon juice.
2   Arrange lettuce leaves on individual plates and
spoon over the fruit mixture.

Potted Shrimps or Prawns

SERVES 4

Small shrimps or prawns are best for potting, but
larger ones can be used, cut into pieces.

300 g (10 oz) cooked and peeled shrimps or prawns
175 g (6 oz) unsalted butter
large pinch of cayenne
½ tsp ground mace
black pepper
lemon juice

1   Divide the prepared shrimps or prawns among
four small ramekins.
2   Melt 125 g (4 oz) butter gently, remove from the
heat and pour off the clear liquid, leaving behind
the sediment. Stir in the cayenne and mace, some
freshly ground black pepper and a squeeze of
lemon juice.
3   Pour the spiced butter over the prawns and chill
the ramekins until the butter is firm. Then melt the
remaining butter and pour the clear liquid over the
prawns and butter to seal the pots. Chill again and
serve with toast and lemon wedges.

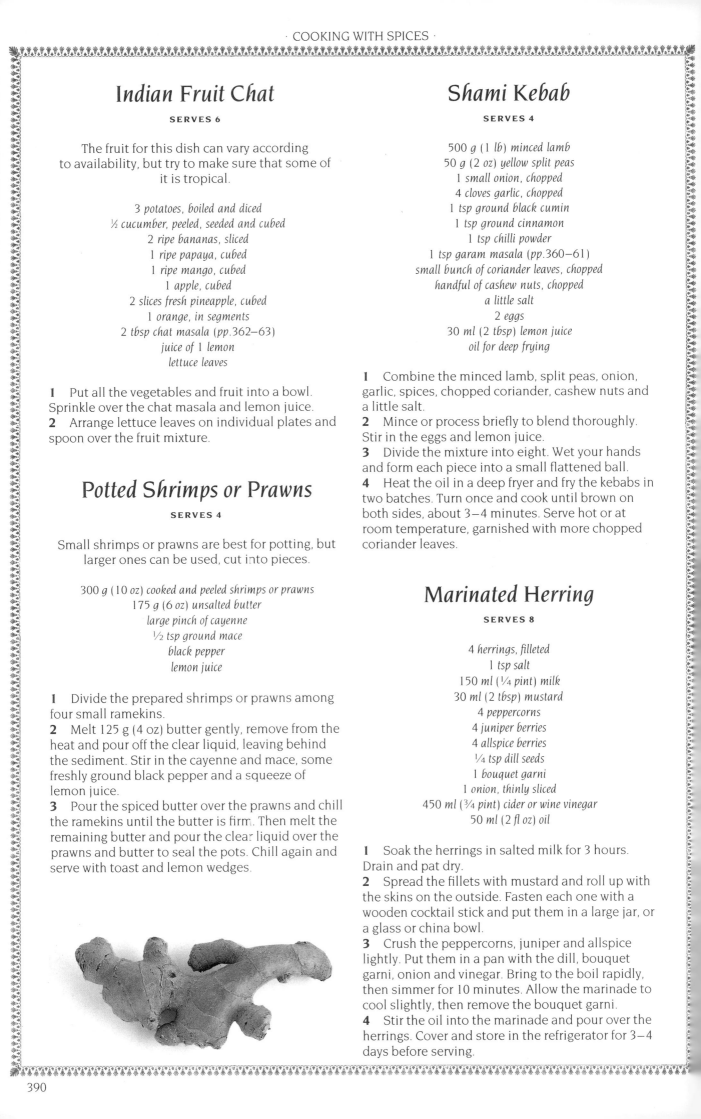

Shami Kebab

SERVES 4

500 g (1 lb) minced lamb
50 g (2 oz) yellow split peas
1 small onion, chopped
4 cloves garlic, chopped
1 tsp ground black cumin
1 tsp ground cinnamon
1 tsp chilli powder
1 tsp garam masala (pp.360–61)
small bunch of coriander leaves, chopped
handful of cashew nuts, chopped
a little salt
2 eggs
30 ml (2 tbsp) lemon juice
oil for deep frying

1   Combine the minced lamb, split peas, onion,
garlic, spices, chopped coriander, cashew nuts and
a little salt.
2   Mince or process briefly to blend thoroughly.
Stir in the eggs and lemon juice.
3   Divide the mixture into eight. Wet your hands
and form each piece into a small flattened ball.
4   Heat the oil in a deep fryer and fry the kebabs in
two batches. Turn once and cook until brown on
both sides, about 3–4 minutes. Serve hot or at
room temperature, garnished with more chopped
coriander leaves.

Marinated Herring

SERVES 8

4 herrings, filleted
1 tsp salt
150 ml (¼ pint) milk
30 ml (2 tbsp) mustard
4 peppercorns
4 juniper berries
4 allspice berries
¼ tsp dill seeds
1 bouquet garni
1 onion, thinly sliced
450 ml (¾ pint) cider or wine vinegar
50 ml (2 fl oz) oil

1   Soak the herrings in salted milk for 3 hours.
Drain and pat dry.
2   Spread the fillets with mustard and roll up with
the skins on the outside. Fasten each one with a
wooden cocktail stick and put them in a large jar, or
a glass or china bowl.
3   Crush the peppercorns, juniper and allspice
lightly. Put them in a pan with the dill, bouquet
garni, onion and vinegar. Bring to the boil rapidly,
then simmer for 10 minutes. Allow the marinade to
cool slightly, then remove the bouquet garni.
4   Stir the oil into the marinade and pour over the
herrings. Cover and store in the refrigerator for 3–4
days before serving.

Fish dishes

Sea Bass Stuffed with Star Anise

SERVES 4

1 sea bass weighing 1.5 kg (3 lb)
1 tbsp chopped fresh ginger
30 ml (2 tbsp) Chinese rice wine or sherry
2 tbsp Chinese five-spice powder (pp.348–49)
4 star anise
4 spring onions, finely chopped
15 ml (1 tbsp) soy sauce
10 ml (2 tsp) Oriental sesame oil
salt

1 Cut two diagonal slits in each side of the bass.
2 Mix together the ginger, rice wine and five-spice powder, then rub the fish with the mixture. Leave to marinate for 1 hour.
3 Combine the star anise, spring onions, soy sauce and sesame oil with a little salt and use to stuff into the cavity of the fish. Wrap the fish in a large piece of oiled foil.
4 Bake in a preheated oven at 200°C, 400°F, gas 6 for 20–25 minutes.

Salmon with Ginger and Lime

SERVES 4

I keep a small jar of chopped fresh ginger "pickled" in sherry in the refrigerator. It is excellent for this dish, but chopped fresh ginger works well, too.

15 ml (1 tbsp) sesame oil
15 ml (1 tbsp) soy sauce
1 tbsp finely chopped fresh ginger
30 ml (2 tbsp) dry sherry
4 salmon steaks
salt
zest of 1 lime
2–3 spring onions or a few chives, chopped
1 lime, cut into wedges

1 Mix together the sesame oil, soy sauce, ginger and sherry, then rub the salmon steaks with the mixture. Leave to marinate for 30 minutes.
2 Heat a little water in a steamer, sprinkle the fish with salt and put it on a plate that fits in the steamer basket. Cover with foil. If you cannot fit a plate in the steamer, wrap the fish in foil.
3 Steam for about 12 minutes until the salmon is firm to the touch. Serve with its juices, sprinkled with the lime zest and chopped spring onion, and wedges of lime.

Fish Couscous

SERVES 6

Couscous with fish is popular along the Tunisian coast. Saffron, cumin and coriander are the usual spices; if you wish, use tabil (pp.370–71) instead of the cumin and coriander. Grey mullet or bream would probably be used in Tunisia, but you could use any firm-fleshed fish. Reserve all the fish and vegetable trimmings so you can make a well-flavoured stock.

1.5 kg (3 lb) fish, cut into large slices
2 large onions, chopped
2 stalks celery, cut in chunks
3 carrots, cut in chunks
3 small turnips, quartered
3 courgettes, cut in chunks
125 g (4 oz) cabbage, shredded
125 g (4 oz) shelled peas
3 tomatoes, skinned and quartered
salt
pinch of cayenne
1.8 litres (3 pints) water
500 g (1 lb) couscous
45 ml (3 tbsp) oil
½ tsp saffron threads
1½ tsp tabil (pp.370–71) or ground cumin and coriander
harissa (pp.370–71) or paprika and cayenne, to taste

1 To make a fish stock, put the fish heads and vegetable trimmings, salt, cayenne and 1.2 litres (2 pints) water in a pan. Simmer for 20 minutes, then strain and reserve.
2 While the stock is cooking, prepare the couscous. Put the grain in a large bowl with 600 ml (1 pint) water. Stir well and leave for 10 minutes. Fluff up the grains between your fingers to get rid of any lumps. Sprinkle with 30 ml (2 tbsp) of the oil. The couscous is now ready to be steamed.
3 Heat the remaining oil in a large heavy pan and sauté the onions until golden. Add the celery, carrots, turnips and the stock made up to 1.8 litres (3 pints) with water. Stir in the saffron, tabil and salt to taste. Cover and simmer for 15 minutes. Add the remaining vegetables.
4 Put the couscous into a steamer, or in a colander lined with muslin that will fit on top of the pan, and simmer for 10 minutes. Check the liquid level and add more water if necessary, but keep it simmering steadily so that the steam penetrates the couscous. Add the fish to the stock and simmer until cooked, about 10–12 minutes.
5 Turn the couscous out into a large bowl, breaking up any lumps with a wooden fork. To make a hot-tasting sauce, take out a ladleful of stock and stir in harissa or paprika and cayenne to taste. Serve the stew on top of the couscous or separately.

Monkfish Parcels with Saffron

SERVES 4

750 g (1½ lb) monkfish, boned
salt and pepper
½–¾ tsp saffron threads
150 ml (¼ pint) dry white wine
150 ml (¼ pint) water
500 g (1 lb) large spinach leaves
butter

1 Cut the monkfish into cubes and season with salt and pepper.
2 Crush the saffron threads and soak in a little hot water for a few minutes. Heat the wine and water in a wide pan, add the saffron liquid and stir.
3 Put in the monkfish and simmer for 5–6 minutes. Drain carefully and reserve the liquid.
4 Select enough large spinach leaves to make three or four parcels per person. Wash the leaves, remove the stalks and blanch in boiling water for 2–3 minutes.
5 Arrange the leaves vein side up and put some pieces of monkfish at the stalk end. Wrap the parcels firmly, making sure the sides are tucked in. Put them into a buttered gratin dish with the end of the leaf underneath.
6 Strain the reserved cooking liquor over the parcels. Cover with foil and bake in a preheated oven at 180°C, 350°F, gas 4 for 15 minutes.

Monkfish Baked in Coconut Milk

SERVES 4

A very simple dish using the spicing of Southeast Asia.

1 kg (2 lb) monkfish
2 shallots, sliced
2 cloves garlic, sliced
piece of fresh ginger, peeled and sliced
¼ tsp ground chilli
½ tsp ground cumin
1 tsp ground coriander
¼ tsp ground galangal or piece of pounded root
salt
1 stalk lemon grass, crushed
25 g (1 oz) creamed coconut dissolved in 150 ml (¼ pint)
hot water

1 Bone the fish and cut the flesh in four.
2 Combine the shallots, garlic and ginger and put half in the bottom of an ovenproof dish that is just large enough to take the fish in one layer.
3 Mix together the ground spices with salt to taste and rub on both sides of the fish. Place the fish in the dish, arrange the lemon grass between the pieces and put the rest of the vegetables on top. Pour over the coconut milk.
4 Cover and bake in a preheated oven at 180°C, 350°F, gas 4 for 30–40 minutes.

Grilled Tuna Steaks

SERVES 4

I keep a few small pots of Seville orange juice in the freezer to use in the summer; but if you do not have any, use half lemon and half orange juice. If you have a wire holder, the fish can be barbecued.

1 tsp ajowan
1 tsp green peppercorns
1 tsp chopped fresh tarragon
salt
2 large or 4 small tuna steaks
juice of 2 Seville oranges
olive oil

1 Crush the ajowan and peppercorns and mix with the tarragon and a little salt.
2 Rub the fish on both sides with the mixture and pour over the orange juice. Leave to marinate for at least 30 minutes.
3 Heat the grill, sprinkle a little oil over the fish and grill for about 10 minutes, turning once. Baste from time to time.

Prawn and Mango Curry

SERVES 4

500 g (1 lb) large prawns, shelled
salt
4 onions
3 cloves garlic, crushed
piece of fresh ginger, crushed
45 ml (3 tbsp) oil
6 green chillies, seeded and sliced
2 tbsp ground coriander
½ tsp ground turmeric or zedoary
1 tsp ground anise
1 tsp ground fenugreek
½ tsp mango powder
½ tsp mustard seeds
250 g (8 oz) creamed coconut dissolved in 450 ml (¾ pint)
hot water
2 ripe mangoes, peeled and sliced

1 Rub the prawns with salt and set aside.
2 Slice two of the onions finely and chop the other two. Blend the crushed garlic and ginger to a paste with the chopped onion.
3 Heat the oil in a pan and fry the paste for 2–3 minutes, then add the sliced onion and the chillies and fry for a few minutes more. Stir in all the spices, then the coconut milk. Simmer for 8–10 minutes, uncovered, stirring to make sure it does not stick.
4 Put in the prawns and mango and simmer, covered, for 6–7 minutes until the prawns are cooked through. Do not overcook or they will become tough. Serve with rice.

Prawn and mango curry with ginger, fenugreek, anise, mango powder, turmeric, mustard seeds and coriander.

Spiced Crab with Green Beans

SERVES 4

250 g (8 oz) small green beans
90 ml (6 tbsp) dry sherry
30 ml (2 tbsp) sesame oil
15 ml (1 tbsp) soy sauce
2.5 ml (½ tsp) chilli sauce
½ tsp ground fagara
15 ml (1 tbsp) oil
zest of ½ a lemon
2 cloves garlic, chopped
350 g (12 oz) white crab meat, shredded
4 spring onions, finely sliced

1   Cook the green beans in a pan of boiling water until just tender.
2   Mix together the sherry, sesame oil, soy sauce, chilli sauce and fagara, then set aside.
3   Heat the oil in a pan and sauté the lemon rind and garlic briefly. Stir in the crab meat and cook for 1–2 minutes.
4   Pour over the sauce, toss to coat the crab and heat through. Turn out into the centre of a warmed serving dish, sprinkle the spring onion over the top and surround with the beans.

Scallops and Leeks with Star Anise

SERVES 4

8 scallops
25 g (1 oz) butter
2 shallots, finely chopped
350 g (12 oz) small leeks, finely chopped
½ glass dry white wine
2 star anise
15 ml (1 tbsp) lemon juice
salt and white pepper
30 ml (2 tbsp) double cream

1   Detach the coral from the scallops and cut the white flesh in half horizontally.
2   Heat the butter in a heavy pan and stew the shallots gently for a few minutes. Add the leeks, half of the wine and the star anise. Season with salt and pepper, cover and simmer slowly for 15 minutes. Remove from the heat.
3   Put the remaining wine in a small pan with the lemon juice. Add the scallops, bring to the boil and simmer for about one minute – until the scallops are opaque. Lift them out carefully.
4   Strain the leeks and add any cooking liquor and the star anise to the scallop pan. Arrange the leeks on four individual plates, top with the scallops and keep warm.
5   Reduce the juices to 45–60 ml (3–4 tbsp), then stir in the cream. Check the seasoning and spoon over the scallops and leeks.

Baked Cod with Mustard

SERVES 4

4 cod steaks
salt and white pepper
30 ml (2 tbsp) Dijon mustard
40 g (1½ oz) butter
350 g (12 oz) leeks, finely sliced
2 heads chicory, finely sliced
30–45 ml (2–3 tbsp) white wine or water

1   Season the fish with salt and pepper. Spread the mustard on both sides of the fish.
2   Melt the butter in a pan and cook the leeks and chicory until just wilted. Drain and transfer half to a buttered ovenproof dish.
3   Lay the cod steaks on the bed of vegetables and top each one with some of the remaining leeks and chicory. Spoon over the wine.
4   Cover and bake in a preheated oven at 200°C, 400°F, gas 6 for 20–30 minutes.

Oriental Seafood Salad

SERVES 6–8

The combination of seafood here is just a suggestion; quantities and types may be varied according to what is available.

350 g (12 oz) baby squid
500 g (1 lb) baby octopus
450 ml (¾ pint) fish stock
500 g (1 lb) uncooked medium prawns
500g (1 lb) spinach, shredded
1 cucumber
½ small melon
2 red peppers
2 papayas
handful of pine nuts

Dressing
juice of 1½ lemons
2 tbsp soft brown sugar
10 ml (2 tsp) chilli sauce
5–6 spring onions, finely chopped
piece of fresh ginger, peeled and finely chopped
30 ml (2 tbsp) fish sauce (see Simple Thai Fish Soup, p.388)
small bunch of coriander leaves, chopped
90 ml (6 tbsp) sunflower oil
salt

1   Clean the squid and cut into rings; the octopus can be cooked whole. Poach them in fish stock until tender – about 12 minutes for the squid and 20 minutes for the octopus. Drain and put aside.
2   Cook the prawns in a large pan of boiling salted water for 2–3 minutes until pink on the outside and white inside. Drain and plunge into iced water to cool them quickly. Drain and shell them.
3   Blanch the spinach for 1 minute, then drain and squeeze out all the moisture.

4 Cut the cucumber and melon into small cubes; cut the peppers and papaya to the same size. Toast the pine nuts in a dry frying pan until golden.
5 Combine the remaining ingredients to make a dressing, but taste before adding salt.
6 Spread the spinach on a large platter. Arrange the seafood, vegetables, fruit and nuts over it, then spoon over the dressing and serve.

Crab with Avocado and Ginger

SERVES 2

A light salad for two, or serve as a first course for four.

250 g (8 oz) white crab meat, shredded
2 tbsp Japanese pickled ginger, drained
zest of ½ a lemon
juice of ½–1 lemon
1 avocado, peeled, halved and stoned
a few rocket leaves
olive oil
sansho (p.337), to serve

1 Marinate the crab with the pickled ginger, the zest and most of the lemon juice for 30 minutes.
2 Slice the avocado and brush with the remaining lemon juice to prevent it discolouring.
3 Place a few rocket leaves on four plates. Arrange avocado slices on one side of each plate and some of the crab and ginger on the other. Pour a little olive oil over everything and serve with sansho.

Warm Mussel Salad

SERVES 4 – 6

1.5 kg (3 lb) mussels, cleaned (p.388)
150 ml (¼ pint) dry white wine
500 g (1 lb) Pink Fir or waxy yellow potatoes
1 cucumber, cubed
salt
30 ml (2 tbsp) olive oil
4 shallots, chopped
1 tsp ground aniseed
5 stalks celery, sliced
90 ml (6 tbsp) cream

1 Place the mussels in a large pan with the white wine. Cover and cook, shaking the pan from time to time, until the mussels have opened. Drain, reserve the liquor and discard the mussel shells and any mussels that have not opened.
2 Boil the potatoes until tender and drain. Slice them thickly.
3 Sprinkle the cucumber with salt and leave to drain for 30 minutes.
4 Heat the oil and sauté the shallots for a few minutes, then add the aniseed and stir for 2–3 minutes. Add the celery, potatoes and cucumber to the pan.
5 Strain the mussel liquor through muslin, add about 150 ml (¼ pint) to the pan and simmer for 5 minutes. Taste for seasoning.
6 Add the mussels and cream, stir carefully to blend, and serve.

Meat dishes

Lamb with Pomegranate Juice

SERVES 4 – 6

45 ml (3 tbsp) sunflower oil
3 cardamoms, crushed
3 cloves
1 tsp fenugreek seeds
1 kg (2 lb) lean lamb, cubed
1 large onion, sliced
2 cloves garlic, finely chopped
small piece of fresh ginger, peeled and finely chopped
juice of 2 pomegranates, about 300 ml (½ pint),
or 45 ml (3 tbsp) pomegranate syrup diluted with water
½ tsp ground black cumin
½ tsp ground cinnamon
½ tsp ground mace
salt
75 ml (5 tbsp) natural yogurt
chopped mint leaves

1 Heat the oil in a heavy pan and fry the whole spices briefly to bring out their flavour, shaking and stirring them so they do not burn.

2 Discard the spices, add the meat, tossing and stirring to brown it on all sides. Continue cooking until the meat re-absorbs its juices.
3 Add the onion, garlic and ginger and cook until the onion colours. Stir in the pomegranate juice, a little at a time, waiting until each addition is absorbed by the meat before adding more. There should be very little liquid left, except the oil.
4 Stir in the ground spices and salt to taste, then fry briefly. Add the yogurt.
5 Cover the pan tightly, put it on a heat diffuser and cook very slowly for 30–40 minutes until the lamb is tender. Check once or twice that the meat is not sticking, and add a little more yogurt or water if necessary. Garnish with chopped mint leaves and serve with rice.

Lamb Kofta

SERVES 4

These spicy minced meat kebabs are popular throughout the Middle East.

500 g (1 lb) lean lamb, minced twice
1 medium onion, finely chopped
handful of chopped fresh parsley
1 tsp ground allspice
¼ tsp ground fenugreek
pinch of ground red pepper
salt
oil for brushing
lemon wedges
ground sumac

1   Put the meat, onion, parsley, allspice, fenugreek, pepper and salt to taste into a large bowl and mix thoroughly.
2   Divide into four and, wetting your hands if necessary, form each piece into a sausage shape around a broad, flat skewer.
3   Brush each one lightly with oil and grill, preferably over charcoal, for 10–15 minutes, turning the skewers from time to time.
4   Serve the kofta with lemon wedges and a bowl of ground sumac to be sprinkled on them, if liked.

Lamb with Chick Peas and Lentils

SERVES 4

A version of a Turkish stew that makes an excellent winter dish.

4 large lamb chops
125 g (4 oz) chick peas, soaked overnight
125 g (4 oz) brown lentils, washed
1.8 litres (3 pints) water
50 g (2 oz) butter
2 large onions, chopped
30 ml (2 tbsp) tomato purée
1 tsp Turkish red pepper, or ½ tsp paprika and ½ tsp cayenne
1 tbsp coriander seeds, ground
salt and pepper
2 large potatoes, thickly sliced

1   Trim any excess fat from the meat and put the chops into a large pan with the chick peas, lentils and water. Bring slowly to the boil, then skim.
2   Meanwhile, melt the butter in a pan and sauté the onions until softened. Stir in the tomato purée, spices and seasoning. Remove from the heat and add to the meat, together with the potatoes.
3   Cover and simmer over low heat for 1½–2 hours until the chick peas are cooked and the stew is thick and rich. Check that there is enough liquid towards the end of the cooking time – if not, add a little more hot water before serving.

Lamb Mrouziya

SERVES 6

In the past, this Moroccan tagine served as a way of preserving the meat in a culture where freezing and refrigeration were not common.

a few saffron stamens
2 tsp ras el hanout (pp.372–73)
1 tsp ground black pepper
1 tsp ground cinnamon
salt
1.5 kg (3 lb) middle neck of lamb, with bone
250 g (8 oz) raisins
175 g (6 oz) blanched almonds
3 onions, finely chopped
125 g (4 oz) butter
150 ml (¼ pint) water
175 g (6 oz) thick honey

1   Powder the saffron and mix with the other spices and salt to taste. Rub the meat with most of the mixture and sprinkle the rest on the raisins.
2   Put the meat into a heavy pan with the almonds, onions, and butter. Add the water, bring to the boil, then simmer for 1–1½ hours until the meat is almost tender, adding more water as necessary to prevent the meat from burning.
3   Stir in the raisins and honey and simmer gently for a further 30 minutes, uncovered, until most of the liquid has evaporated and a thick, rich sauce has formed. Lift the lamb on to a warmed serving dish and cover with the sauce.

Thai Beef Curry

SERVES 6

45 ml (3 tbsp) oil
750 g (1½ lb) braising or stewing beef, cubed
4 onions, quartered
500 g (1 lb) potatoes, cubed same size as meat
30 ml (2 tbsp) red curry paste (pp.354–55)
30 ml (2 tbsp) fish sauce (see Simple Thai Fish Soup p.388)
1 ball tamarind soaked in 45 ml (3 tbsp) hot water
1 tbsp sugar
350 g (12 oz) creamed coconut dissolved in 900 ml (1½ pints) hot water
3 curry leaves
6 cardamoms, crushed

1   Heat the oil and brown the beef on all sides. Remove the beef and cook the onions and potatoes in the oil for a few minutes, then remove them.
2   Fry the curry paste, add the fish sauce, tamarind water, sugar and coconut milk, and bring to the boil.
3   Reduce the heat, return the meat and vegetables to the pan with the curry leaves and cardamom. Cover and simmer for about 2 hours. Check from time to time to make sure that it is not sticking and add a little water if necessary.

Sichuan Noodles with Beef

SERVES 6

350 g (12 oz) lean sirloin steak
60 ml (4 tbsp) soy sauce
45 ml (3 tbsp) rice vinegar
1 tsp finely chopped garlic
1 tsp finely chopped fresh ginger
1 tsp sugar
2–3 chillies, seeded and sliced
4 spring onions, finely chopped
small handful of coriander leaves, finely chopped
60 ml (4 tbsp) groundnut oil
350 g (12 oz) dried egg noodles
1 tbsp toasted sesame seeds
6 whole spring onions

1   Cut the steak across the grain into thin strips.
2   Make a marinade with the soy sauce, rice vinegar, garlic, ginger, sugar, chillies, chopped spring onions, coriander and 30 ml (2 tbsp) of the oil. Marinate the beef for 30 minutes.
3   Heat the remaining oil in a wok or heavy frying pan. Drain the meat from the marinade and sauté for 2 minutes.
4   Meanwhile, cook the noodles in a pan of boiling salted water for 5–7 minutes until *al dente*. Drain and place in a large, warmed serving dish. Pour over the remaining beef marinade.
5   Make a slight indentation in the centre of the noodles and spoon in the beef. Sprinkle with the sesame seeds and garnish the dish with the whole spring onions.

Hungarian Veal Paprikash

SERVES 4

25 g (1 oz) lard or butter
1 large onion, chopped
1 kg (2 lb) lean veal, cubed
1 large tomato, skinned and chopped
1–1½ tsp paprika
salt
1 green pepper, sliced
300 ml (½ pint) sour cream
1 tbsp flour

1   Melt the lard in a heavy pan and fry the onion until transparent. Turn the heat as low as possible and add the veal, tomato, paprika and salt to taste.
2   Cover and simmer very gently, stirring occasionally and adding a few tablespoons of water to prevent the meat sticking, if necessary.
3   After 20 minutes or so, add the green pepper. Continue to cook for a further 20 minutes until the veal is almost done. Cook until any remaining liquid evaporates.
4   Blend the sour cream with the flour, then stir into the pan. Cover again and simmer very slowly until the meat is tender. Serve with little egg dumplings or noodles.

Spiced Veal Boulangère

SERVES 6—8

4 cloves garlic
salt and pepper
½ tsp ground mace
¼ tsp ground cardamom
¾ tsp ground cinnamon
2 kg (4 lb) loin of veal, boned and rolled
olive oil
1 kg (2 lb) potatoes, sliced
300 ml (½ pint) water

1   Crush 2 cloves of garlic with a little salt and mix with half of the spices and a few grindings of pepper.
2   Pierce the meat here and there with the point of a sharp knife and insert the garlic and spice mixture. Rub the surface of the meat with oil and the rest of the spices. Finely slice the remaining 2 cloves of garlic.
3   Place the meat in a roasting tin. Brown in a preheated oven at 230°C, 450°F, gas 8 for 10 minutes. Take the tin from the oven and distribute the potatoes under and around the meat, seasoning layers with salt, pepper and slivers of garlic. Add the water.
4   Cover the tin with foil, return to the oven and cook at 160°C, 325°F, gas 3 for 1½ hours. Remove the foil and cook for a further 15 minutes. Rest the meat for 10 minutes in a warm place before carving.

Pork with Fennel

SERVES 6

¾ tsp fennel seeds, ground
½ tsp black peppercorns, crushed
salt
1 kg (2 lb) loin of pork, bones and skin removed, and rolled
1 onion, sliced
1 carrot, sliced
150 ml (¼ pint) water
1 tsp cornflour
150 ml (¼ pint) sour cream

1   Mix together the fennel and pepper with salt to taste. Rub the meat all over with the seasoning.
2   Put the onion and carrot in a small roasting tin. Lay the meat on the vegetables and pour the water around the pork.
3   Roast in a preheated oven at 200°C, 400°F, gas 6 for about 1 hour 20 minutes, basting the meat every 10 minutes or so. Add a little more water to the meat if necessary.
4   When the pork is cooked, remove it and leave to stand in a warm place for 10 minutes or so before starting to carve it.
5   To make the sauce, scrape the vegetables and other sediment loose in the pan. Stir the cornflour into the sour cream and whisk into the pan juices. Heat through, taste for seasoning and strain into a sauce boat.

Pork Satay

SERVES 6—8

A popular dish with the Chinese of Southeast Asia.

1 onion, finely chopped
2 cloves garlic, crushed
1 tbsp Chinese five-spice powder (pp.348–49)
small piece of fresh ginger, crushed
60 ml (4 tbsp) light soy sauce
15 ml (1 tbsp) honey
75–90 ml (5–6 tbsp) sunflower oil
1 kg (2 lb) loin of pork, cubed
2 stalks lemon grass, finely sliced

1 Blend together all the ingredients, except the pork and lemon grass, to make a smooth marinade.
2 Put the pork cubes and lemon grass in a bowl, coat thoroughly with the marinade and leave for at least 2 hours.
3 Thread the meat on to skewers and grill for 15–20 minutes until cooked. Serve with peanut sauce (p.418) or Indonesian soy relish (p.418).

Chicken Satay

SERVES 6—8

Serve this popular dish with peanut sauce (p.418).

1 kg (2 lb) chicken breast
small piece of fresh ginger, crushed
3 cloves garlic, crushed
1 tbsp ground coriander
½ tsp ground galangal
15 ml (1 tbsp) oil
50 g (2 oz) creamed coconut dissolved in 150 ml (¼ pint) hot water

1 Remove the skin from the chicken and cut the flesh into strips.
2 Combine the remaining ingredients in a blender or food processor to make a smooth marinade. Use to coat the chicken thoroughly. Leave to marinate for at least 2 hours.
3 Thread the pieces of meat on to small wooden skewers and grill for 5–6 minutes, turning as necessary to cook all sides.

Afelia

SERVES 4

750 g (1½ lb) pork fillet
50 g (2 oz) olive oil
salt and pepper
150 ml (¼ pint) red wine
1 tbsp coriander seeds, crushed

1 Remove any fat from the pork and cut the flesh into cubes. Heat the oil in a heavy pan and brown the meat on all sides. Season with salt and pepper.
2 Pour over the wine, bring to the boil, then cover and simmer gently for 20 minutes.
3 Stir in the coriander, cover, and simmer for another 20–25 minutes until the meat is tender and most of the liquid absorbed. Check the pan from time to time and add more wine, if necessary.

Cold Spiced Chicken

SERVES 6

45 ml (3 tbsp) natural yogurt
½ tsp garam masala (pp.360–61)
½ tsp ground turmeric
salt
6 chicken breasts, skinned
600 ml (1 pint) chicken stock
4 green cardamoms
1 curry leaf or bay leaf

Sauce
25 g (1 oz) butter
1 tbsp gram flour
½ tbsp plain flour
½ tsp garam masala
½ tsp ground turmeric
about 450 ml (¾ pint) reserved chicken stock
½ tsp ground mace
¼ tsp ground cardamom
60 ml (4 tbsp) double cream or thick yogurt

1 Blend together the yogurt, garam masala, turmeric and salt to taste. Rub the chicken breasts with the mixture and marinate for 1 hour.
2 Heat the stock with the cardamoms and curry leaf. Put in the chicken breasts and simmer for 15–20 minutes or until tender.
3 Lift out the chicken and transfer to a serving dish. Strain and reserve the stock. Leave to cool while making the sauce.
4 Melt the butter in a pan and stir in the flours until smooth. Add the garam masala, turmeric and a little salt, then whisk in the reserved stock. Bring to the boil and simmer for 15 minutes, stirring occasionally. Stir in the mace, cardamom and cream or yogurt. Spoon over the chicken and chill before serving.

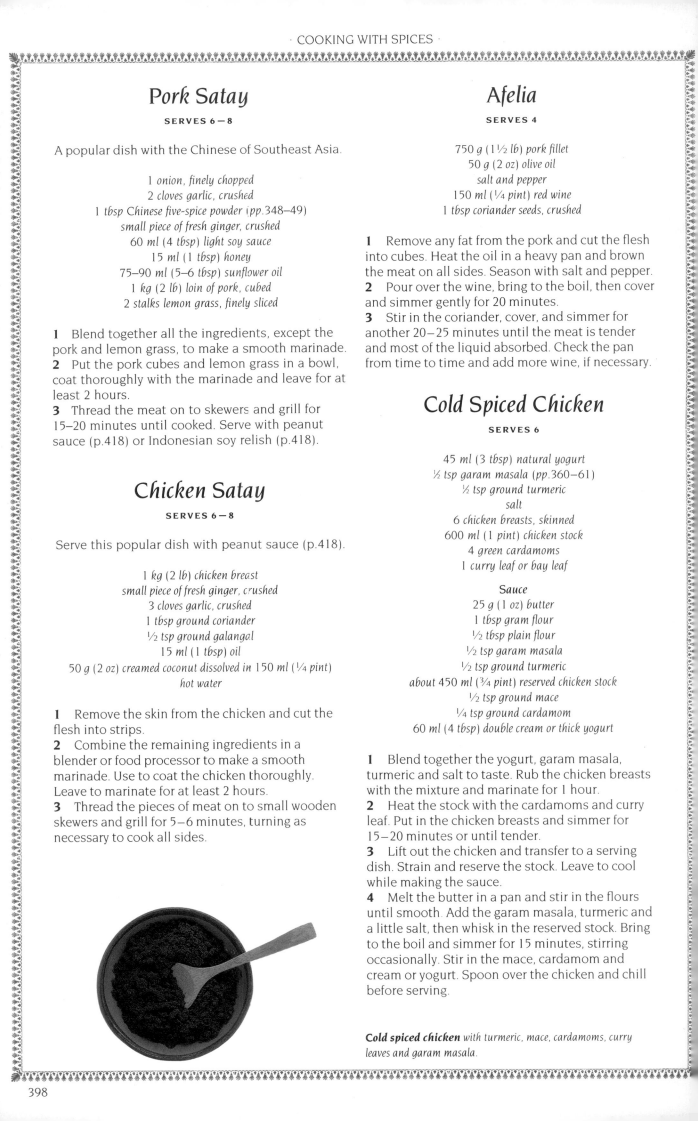

Cold spiced chicken *with turmeric, mace, cardamoms, curry leaves and garam masala.*

Chicken with Noodles

SERVES 4

A simple and comforting Japanese dish. Dashi granules or powder, requiring only the addition of water to make the stock, can be bought from Japanese shops. A good chicken stock can be used as a substitute. Mirin – very sweet rice wine used only for cooking – can, at a pinch, be replaced by sweet sherry and a spoonful of sugar.

350 g (12 oz) *udon or other wheat noodles*
350 g (12 oz) *chicken, skinned and boned*
6 *spring onions*
750 ml (1¼ *pints*) *dashi*
60 ml (4 *tbsp*) *soy sauce*
30 ml (2 *tbsp*) *mirin*
shichimi (pp.346–47), to serve

1 Boil the noodles in a pan until tender. Drain and rinse under cold running water.
2 Cut the chicken into small pieces. Cut the spring onions, including the green part, into 1.5 cm (½ in) lengths.
3 Combine the dashi, soy sauce and mirin in a pan and bring to the boil. Add the chicken and simmer for 5–6 minutes or until tender. Stir in the spring onions and simmer for 1 minute.
4 ' Reheat the noodles by pouring boiling water over them. Divide between four large warmed bowls. Ladle over the stock and arrange the chicken and onions on top. Serve with shichimi.

Chicken Braised with Coriander

SERVES 4

1 *large onion, roughly chopped*
4 *cloves garlic*
6 *candlenuts*
1 *tbsp ground coriander*
5 ml (1 *tsp*) *tamarind concentrate*
½ *tsp ground turmeric*
¼ *tsp ground galangal*
3–4 *hot chillies, seeded if preferred*
1 *tsp sugar*
salt
1 *medium chicken, cut into pieces*
250 g (8 oz) *creamed coconut dissolved in* 450 ml (¾ *pint*)
hot water
2 *kaffir lime leaves or* 1 *bay leaf*
piece of lemon grass or ¼ *tsp ground*

1 Pound together or process the onion, garlic, candlenuts, coriander, tamarind, turmeric, galangal, chillies and sugar with salt to taste.
2 Rub the chicken with the paste and leave for about 1 hour.
3 Transfer the chicken to a pan. Add the coconut milk, lime leaves and lemon grass. Braise gently in an open pan for about 45 minutes until the sauce thickens and the oil starts to glisten on the surface.

4 The chicken can be served straight away or it can be lifted from the pan and grilled, basting occasionally with oil, until lightly browned. Serve the sauce separately.

VARIATIONS

◆ In Indonesia, the pieces of chicken are often deep fried before serving.
◆ Use yogurt, stabilized with 1 tbsp cornflour blended with a little milk, instead of coconut milk.

Chicken and Groundnut Stew

SERVES 4—6

Stews and soups based on groundnuts (peanuts) are common throughout West Africa. This is a simple version using peanut butter, though you could grind plain peanuts instead. The vegetables can be varied according to what is available, but for an authentic taste keep the okra, aubergine and cabbage. Sweet potato is a good alternative to ordinary potato.

60 ml (4 *tbsp*) *groundnut oil*
1 *chicken, cut in pieces*
1 *large onion, chopped*
2 *tomatoes, peeled and chopped*
15 ml (1 *tbsp*) *tomato purée*
600 ml (1 *pint*) *boiling water*
175 g (6 oz) *peanut butter*
salt
1 *tsp grains of paradise or black peppercorns, crushed*
2 *carrots, sliced*
1 *small aubergine, cubed*
2 *potatoes, peeled and cubed*
½ *small cabbage, sliced*
175 g (6 oz) *okra*

1 Heat the oil in a large pan and brown the chicken. Remove and set aside. Add the onion and cook for a few minutes, then stir in the tomatoes and tomato purée. Return the chicken to the pan.
2 Pour on a little of the water and use the rest to thin the peanut butter. Add this to the pan and season with salt and grains of paradise. Stir well, cover, reduce the heat and simmer gently for 20 minutes, checking occasionally to see that the sauce is not sticking – it should be thick, but if necessary add a little more water.
3 Add the carrots and aubergine and continue cooking for 10 minutes. Stir in the potatoes and cabbage gently and cook for a further 15 minutes, or until the chicken and vegetables are tender. Put in the okra, simmer for 5 minutes more, then serve.

Venison with Sour Cherry Sauce

SERVES 6

90 ml (6 tbsp) olive oil
30 ml (2 tbsp) lemon juice
1 tbsp juniper berries, crushed
1 tsp salt
1 bay leaf, crumbled
2 kg (4 lb) saddle of venison
pork fat, to cover
1 onion, sliced
125 ml (4 fl oz) red wine
250 g (8 oz) morello cherries, stoned
30–45 ml (2–3 tbsp) redcurrant jelly
¼ tsp ground allspice
pinch of ground cinnamon
stock or water, if necessary

1　Combine 45 ml (3 tbsp) of the oil with the lemon juice, juniper, salt and bay leaf and rub over the venison. Leave to marinate for 2–3 hours.
2　Spread the pork fat over the meat. Put the sliced onion in a roasting tin and arrange the meat on top. Add the remaining oil and the wine.
3　Roast in a preheated oven at 180°C, 350°F, gas 4 for about 1¼ hours, basting frequently. Check to see if the meat is done – it should still be slightly rare and pink inside. Remove and leave to stand in a warm place while preparing the sauce.
4　Scrape loose any sediment stuck to the bottom of the roasting tin, stir briskly over medium heat and remove any excess fat. Strain the juices into a pan; there should be at least 150 ml (¼ pint) – if necessary add a little stock or water. Put in the cherries, jelly and spices and heat gently. Carve the venison, spoon over the sauce and serve.

Noisettes of Venison with Green Peppercorns

SERVES 4

50 g (2 oz) butter
8 noisettes of venison
4 shallots, finely chopped
30 ml (2 tbsp) brandy or armagnac
15 ml (1 tbsp) French mustard
250 ml (8 fl oz) stock
1 tbsp green peppercorns
150 ml (¼ pint) crème fraîche or double cream
salt

1　Melt the butter in a frying pan and sauté the venison 3–4 minutes on each side until lightly browned. Remove to a serving dish and keep warm.
2　Add the shallots to the pan and cook for 3–4 minutes. Heat the brandy in a small pan or ladle, then ignite and pour over the shallots.
3　Stir in the mustard, add the stock and bring to the boil. Boil rapidly to reduce by half, then add the peppercorns, cream and salt to taste. Heat through, spoon over the noisettes and serve.

Pheasant Chilindrón

SERVES 4

This dish from the province of Aragon in Spain can also be made with chicken or pork or lamb chops. The name chilindrón refers to the red peppers used in the dish. Use Spanish serrano ham if possible.

2 small pheasants, cut in half
salt
60 ml (4 tbsp) olive oil
1 clove garlic, chopped
1 onion, chopped
75 g (3 oz) smoked ham, diced
a few saffron threads, toasted briefly
2 tsp paprika
2 red peppers, cut in strips
2 large tomatoes, skinned and chopped
1 red chilli (optional)

1　Season the pheasants with salt. Heat the oil in a pan and sauté the pheasants until browned. Lift out and sauté the garlic and onion until the onion is softened.
2　Add the ham, saffron, paprika, red peppers and tomatoes. Cover and cook for 10 minutes, then return the pheasant halves to the pan. Add more salt, if necessary, and the chilli if using. Cover and simmer for 40 minutes.
3　Uncover and cook for another 20 minutes until the pheasant is tender and the sauce quite thick.

Rabbit with Mustard Sauce

SERVES 6

75 g (3 oz) butter
15 ml (1 tbsp) oil
2 rabbits, cut into pieces
sprig of fresh thyme or 1 tsp dried thyme
1 bay leaf
salt and pepper
4 shallots, finely chopped
150 ml (¼ pint) dry white wine
30 ml (2 tbsp) Dijon mustard
juice of ½ a lemon
125 ml (4 fl oz) double cream
chopped fresh parsley, to garnish

1　Heat 25 g (1 oz) of the butter and the oil in a flameproof casserole and sauté the rabbit until well browned. Season with the thyme, bay leaf and salt and pepper. Cover tightly.
2　Cook in a preheated oven at 160°C, 325°F, gas 3 for 50 minutes.
3　Heat the remaining butter in a pan and sauté the shallots. Moisten with the wine and reduce by half. Stir in the mustard, lemon juice and cream, then heat through.
4　Put the rabbit pieces on a warmed serving dish, pour over the sauce, and sprinkle with parsley.

Rabbit in Sour Cream with Caraway

SERVES 4

1 rabbit, jointed
65 g (2½ oz) butter
2 onions, chopped
2 carrots, diced
1 parsnip, diced
2 tbsp flour
150 ml (¼ pint) stock or water
300 ml (½ pint) sour cream
½ tsp ground caraway
salt and pepper

Marinade
1 onion, chopped
1 carrot, chopped
1 stalk celery, chopped
3 cloves garlic, crushed
2 bay leaves
sprig of thyme
1 tsp allspice berries, crushed
1 tsp black peppercorns, crushed
150 ml (¼ pint) cider vinegar
300 ml (½ pint) water

1   For the marinade, put the onion, carrot, celery, garlic, bay leaves, thyme, allspice, peppercorns, vinegar and water in a pan and bring to the boil. Allow to cool.
2   Pour the marinade over the rabbit. Leave to marinate for up to 24 hours.
3   Melt 40 g (1½ oz) of the butter in a heavy flameproof casserole and sauté the onions, carrots and parsnip for 5 minutes. Add the drained rabbit and brown gently.
4   Melt the remaining butter in a pan and stir in the flour until smooth. Add the stock gradually, stirring until well blended and bring to the boil. Stir in the sour cream, caraway and seasonings.
5   Pour the sauce over the rabbit, stirring well to amalgamate the pan juices. Cover and simmer for 40–50 minutes. Serve with noodles or potatoes.

Rabbit with Fennel and Garlic

SERVES 4

1 rabbit, cut into serving pieces
300 ml (½ pint) white wine
45 ml (3 tbsp) olive oil
2 tsp fennel seeds
salt
1 small onion, finely chopped
salt and pepper
175 g (6 oz) young runner beans, cut into pieces
175 g (6 oz) broad beans
1 head garlic
150 ml (¼ pint) cream and water, mixed

1   Marinate the rabbit in the wine with 30 ml (2 tbsp) of the oil, the fennel seeds and a little salt for 2–3 hours. Drain the meat and pat dry, reserving the marinade.
2   Heat the remaining oil and brown the rabbit. Add the onion, and sauté until transparent.
3   Stir in the marinade, bring to the boil and season with salt and pepper. Simmer gently for about 20 minutes.
4   Cook the runner beans and broad beans briefly in boiling water. Drain and add to the rabbit and cook for another 20 minutes.
5   Separate the garlic into cloves and blanch in boiling water for 3–4 minutes. Drain, cool and peel. Simmer the garlic in the cream and water for 15 minutes, then crush to a purée.
6   Check that the rabbit is tender, then stir in the purée. Serve with new potatoes.

Baked Liver

SERVES 4

A rich and delicate dish that can also be made with lamb's liver.

500 g (1 lb) calf's liver
1 tsp trassi (pp.430–31)
25 g (1 oz) creamed coconut dissolved in 60 ml (4 tbsp) hot water
2 tsp ground coriander
15 ml (1 tbsp) lemon juice
a few kaffir lime leaves, crushed, or ¼ tsp ground lemon grass

1   Dice the liver or cut it into thin strips.
2   Wrap the trassi in a piece of foil and heat through in a dry pan or medium oven (180°C, 350°F, gas 4) for a few minutes, then crumble it.
3   Combine the coconut milk, coriander, lemon juice, trassi and lime leaves to make a thick marinade. Coat the liver in the marinade in an ovenproof dish and leave for at least 1 hour.
4   Cook in a preheated oven at 180°C, 350°F, gas 4 for 20 minutes for thin strips of liver, and 25–30 minutes for larger pieces. The liver will have a very good texture and be pale pink in the middle.

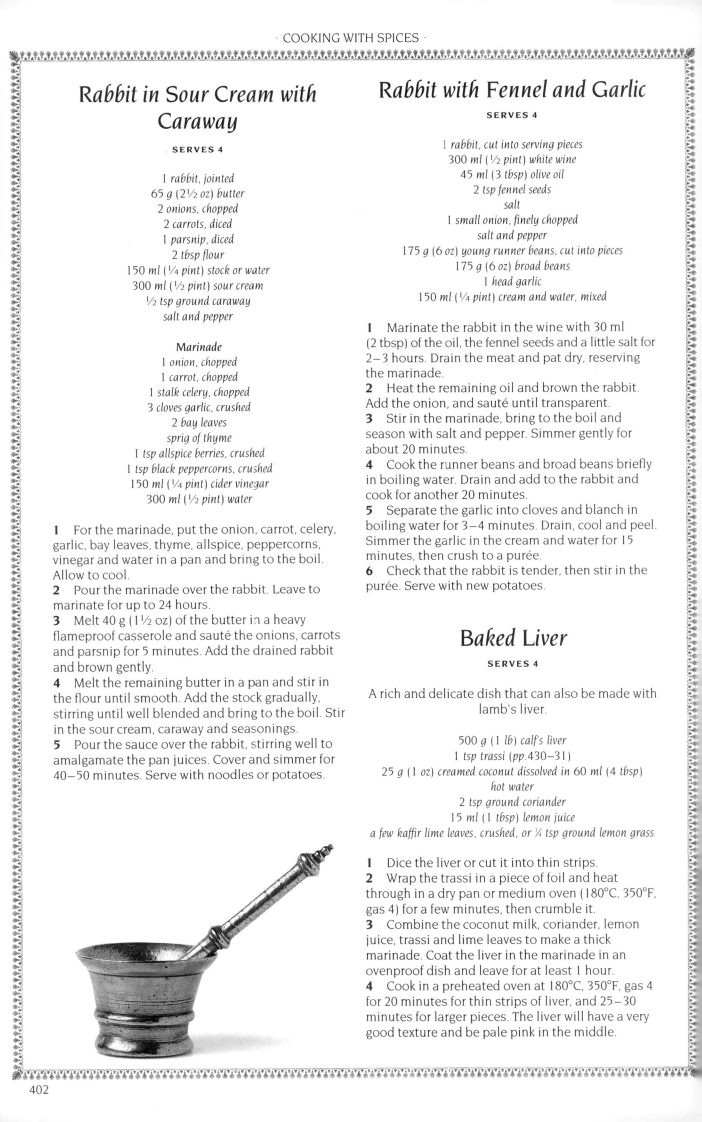

Vegetable & grain dishes

Stir-fried Noodles with Mange-touts and Prawns

SERVES 6

500 g (1 lb) Chinese flat noodles
salt
2–3 cloves garlic
2 stalks lemon grass
30 ml (2 tbsp) groundnut oil
small piece of fresh ginger, peeled and finely chopped
350 g (12 oz) mangetouts, trimmed
175 g (6 oz) fresh shiitake mushrooms, sliced, or 6 dried, soaked
for 20 minutes, drained and sliced (see p.406)
salt
soy sauce
3 spring onions, chopped
250 g (8 oz) peeled prawns

1 Cook the noodles in a pan of boiling salted water until *al dente*.
2 Meanwhile, pound together the garlic and the base of the lemon grass stalks. Heat the oil in a wok over high heat. Add the ginger, garlic and lemon grass and stir-fry for 1 minute.
3 Stir in the mange-touts and mushrooms and season lightly with salt and soy sauce. Continue to stir-fry for another 2–3 minutes, then add the spring onions and prawns.
4 Add the drained noodles to the wok. Toss and stir-fry until some of the noodles are browning and the other ingredients are well distributed. Turn into a warmed bowl and serve.

Stuffed Onions

SERVES 6

6 Spanish onions, unpeeled
45 ml (3 tbsp) olive oil

Stuffing
150 g (5 oz) long grain rice, cooked
125 g (4 oz) blanched almonds, coarsely chopped
1 tsp ground allspice
½ tsp ground mace
4 tbsp chopped fresh parsley
salt and pepper

Cooking liquid
2 tbsp ground sumac
450 ml (¾ pint) boiling water
2 cloves garlic, crushed
juice of 1 lemon

1 Blanch the whole onions in a pan of boiling water for 45 minutes, then remove carefully and leave to cool. When you can handle them easily, take off the outer skin, cut off the root and a larger slice from the stem end. Leave the prepared onions upside down to drain.
2 Use a small sharp knife to detach the centre of the onion, lifting it out with a small spoon. The surrounding layers can then be removed quite easily. Work carefully or the onions may collapse, although they can be reformed round the stuffing.
3 Chop the flesh from the onions and combine with the other stuffing ingredients. Fill the onions, mounding up the stuffing. Put the oil into a baking tin in which the onions fit snugly, cover them with the "lids".
4 Stir the sumac into the boiling water, add the garlic and lemon juice. Pour the liquid around the onions. Bake in a preheated oven at 180°C, 350°F, gas 4 for 20 minutes, basting the onions from time to time. Lift them out carefully because they are quite fragile.

Stuffed Peppers

SERVES 6

6 large green peppers
30 ml (2 tbsp) olive oil
1 onion, chopped
250 g (8 oz) minced pork or beef
1 tomato, skinned and chopped
salt and pepper
¼ tsp grated nutmeg
¼ tsp nigella
50 g (2 oz) long grain rice
50 g (2 oz) yellow split peas, soaked for 1 hour
3 tbsp chopped fresh parsley
a few mint leaves, chopped
2 small pieces cassia or cinnamon
300 ml (½ pint) passata (puréed tomatoes)
150 ml (¼ pint) water
30 ml (2 tbsp) lemon juice
2 tsp sugar

1 Cut "lids" from the stem ends of the peppers, clean out the seeds and white membranes. Blanch the peppers in a pan of boiling water for 3 minutes. Put upside down to drain.
2 Heat the oil and sauté the onion for 3–4 minutes. Add the meat, tomato, salt, pepper, nutmeg and nigella and cook for 5 minutes. Add the rice, and the same volume of water, the drained split peas and herbs. Simmer for 10 minutes.
3 Stuff the peppers with this mixture. Stand them upright in a casserole in which they just fit, put on their lids, and set the pieces of cassia or cinnamon between them.
4 Dilute the passata with the water, stir in the lemon juice and sugar and pour over the peppers. Cover and bake in a preheated oven at 180°C, 350°F, gas 4 for 45 minutes. Serve hot.

Mediterranean Spiced Lentils

SERVES 4

250 g (8 oz) brown lentils, soaked for 1 hour
450 ml (¾ pint) water
¼ tsp mustard seeds
½ tsp crushed black peppercorns
½ tsp ground coriander
1 bay leaf
1 tsp salt
1 clove garlic, crushed
60 ml (4 tbsp) olive oil
1 small onion, sliced

1 Place the lentils in a pan with the water. Bring to the boil and then leave to simmer, partly covered, for 20 minutes.
2 Add the spices, bay leaf, salt and garlic and continue cooking until the lentils are soft and virtually reduced to a purée. There should be little water left. Beat with a wooden spoon to achieve a smoother purée if wished.
3 Heat the oil in a pan and sauté the onion until golden. Pour over the lentils and serve.

Dal

SERVES 4—6

Moong dal, the yellow split mung bean, is widely used in Indian cookery. It is easy to digest and absorbs other flavours well. The tadka is a traditional and effective way of flavouring foods.

300 g (10 oz) moong dal (split mung beans), washed
1 onion, chopped
3 cloves
1 small piece cinnamon stick
3 cardamoms, crushed
1 tsp ground turmeric
1 tsp ground cumin
1 litre (1¾ pints) water
salt

Tadka (aromatized butter)
60 ml (4 tbsp) clarified butter or oil
3 cloves garlic, finely sliced
½ tsp cayenne (optional)
2 tbsp chopped fresh coriander, to garnish

1 Put the beans in a pan with the onion, cloves, cinnamon, cardamom, turmeric, cumin and water. Bring to the boil, cover and simmer for 20 minutes.
2 Add salt to taste and continue to cook until the beans are soft, about 35 minutes, topping up with more hot water if necessary. Virtually all the liquid should have been absorbed. Discard the whole spices and transfer the beans to a warmed dish.
3 For the tadka, heat the butter in a pan over high heat. Stir in the garlic and cayenne and fry until the garlic starts to colour. Pour at once over the lentils. Garnish with coriander and serve.

Pilaf with Peas

SERVES 6

5 saffron threads
15 ml (1 tbsp) rose water
150 ml (¼ pint) single cream
½ tsp ground cinnamon
¼ tsp black pepper
¼ tsp ground cloves
salt
60 ml (4 tbsp) oil or clarified butter
½ tsp ground cumin
2 curry leaves
small piece of fresh ginger, peeled and finely chopped
350 g (12 oz) shelled peas
350 g (12 oz) basmati rice
600 ml (1 pint) water

1 Crush the saffron and blend with the rose water. Stir the rose water into the cream together with the cinnamon, pepper, cloves and a little salt.
2 Heat the oil in a large pan, stir in the cumin, curry leaves and ginger.
3 Add the peas and rice. Cook, stirring, until the rice starts to turn brown. Add the water, bring to the boil, then simmer uncovered, until virtually all the water is absorbed.
4 Pour over the spiced cream. Cover with a piece of foil and the lid, then put over the lowest possible heat and leave for 20 minutes.

Malabar Rice

SERVES 6—8

Pilafs flavoured with whole spices are found in many parts of India; this one comes from Malabar, home of cardamom and pepper, and makes the perfect accompaniment to braised chicken or lamb. Except for the cumin seeds the spices are not eaten, but you won't come to harm if you accidentally chew on any of the others.

500 g (1 lb) long grain rice
900 ml (1½ pints) water
30 ml (2 tbsp) vegetable oil or clarified butter
1 large onion, chopped
8 green cardamoms
12 cm (5 in) cinnamon stick
8 cloves
1 tsp cumin seeds
12 black peppercorns
2 tsp salt

1 Wash the rice and leave to soak for 30 minutes in the water.
2 Heat the oil in a heavy pan and fry the onion until golden. Bruise the cardamoms lightly and break the cinnamon into three. Add them to the onion with the cloves, cumin and peppercorns. Fry gently for about 30 seconds until the spices are slightly puffed and browned.

3   Drain the rice, reserve the water and put the rice into the pan. Fry for about 3 minutes until the rice becomes translucent, then add the water and salt. Stir frequently and bring to the boil.

4   Reduce the heat to very low. Cover the pan and simmer for 20 minutes or until all the water is absorbed. The surface of the rice will be covered with tiny holes.

5   Turn off the heat, replace the lid and leave the rice to steam for another 10 minutes. (It will in fact stay warm for about 20 minutes if left covered.)

6   When ready to serve, turn out the rice on to a warmed platter with a wooden fork (a spoon might break the grains), fluffing it as you do so.

Steamed Aubergine with Sesame Sauce

SERVES 4–6

This dish tastes best if the sauce is made a day in advance so that the flavours have time to blend. Try at least to make it several hours ahead, and keep covered at room temperature. The aubergine can be served hot, but I prefer it at room temperature.

handful of coriander leaves
3 cloves garlic, crushed with salt
30 ml (2 tbsp) Chinese sesame paste
30 ml (2 tbsp) sesame oil
45 ml (3 tbsp) light soy sauce
30 ml (2 tbsp) rice vinegar
30 ml (2 tbsp) dry sherry
5 ml (1 tsp) chilli sauce
¼ tsp ground fagara
salt
4 long aubergines

1   For the sauce, chop the coriander coarsely in a food processor. Add the remaining ingredients, except the aubergines, to the coriander. Process to a thick smooth sauce. If the sauce thickens too much while standing, thin it with a little water.

2   Peel alternate strips from the aubergines, sprinkle with salt and leave to drain for 45 minutes.

3   Rinse, then steam the aubergines for about 35 minutes until soft. Cut the aubergines into strips and pour the sauce over them just before serving.

Hungarian Paprika Potatoes

SERVES 6

These potatoes are good with chops and sausages.

25 g (1 oz) butter
3 shallots, sliced
1½ tsp paprika
2 large tomatoes, skinned and chopped
salt
1 kg (2 lb) potatoes, thickly sliced
300 ml (½ pint) stock
150 ml (¼ pint) sour cream

1   Melt the butter in a flameproof casserole and stew the shallots until soft. Stir in the paprika and cook for a few minutes.

2   Add the tomatoes, salt to taste, and potatoes. Cover with the stock and sour cream.

3   Cover and cook in a preheated oven at 200°C, 400°F, gas 6 for about 1 hour, until the liquid is almost absorbed.

Spinach and Walnut Pasty with Tahina Sauce

SERVES 4

1.5 kg (3 lb) spinach, washed
40 g (1½ oz) butter
3 onions, sliced
75 g (3 oz) walnuts, finely chopped
½ tsp ground allspice
½ tsp ground cinnamon
salt and pepper
250 g (8 oz) frozen puff pastry, thawed
1 egg yolk

Sauce
90 ml (6 tbsp) tahina
30 ml (2 tbsp) sunflower oil
90–120 ml (6–8 tbsp) thick natural yogurt
lemon juice to taste

1   Cook the spinach in a pan with only the water clinging to the leaves for 4–5 minutes. Squeeze out all moisture and chop.

2   Melt the butter in a pan and stew the onions until soft. Mix together the onions, spinach, nuts, spices and seasoning.

3   Roll out the pastry to a large square, 25–30 cm (10–12 in). Put the filling in the centre, fold up the corners to meet in the middle and then pinch the seams closed.

4   Place on a baking sheet and brush with the egg yolk beaten with 15 ml (1 tbsp) water. Bake in a preheated oven at 220°C, 425°F, gas 7 for about 30 minutes or until golden.

5   Meanwhile, prepare the sauce. Blend all the ingredients to a smooth, quite liquid consistency and serve separately.

Barley with Mushrooms

SERVES 4

75 g (3 oz) butter
2 onions, sliced
250 g (8 oz) pearl barley
½ tsp dill seeds or ¼ tsp celery seeds
600 ml (1 pint) stock
salt and pepper
250 g (8 oz) mushrooms
150 ml (¼ pint) natural yogurt
paprika

1 Melt half the butter in an earthenware or cast-iron casserole and stew the onions until soft.
2 Stir in the barley and cook for a few minutes to coat well with the butter. Stir in the dill seeds and pour over the stock. Taste for seasoning.
3 Cover tightly and bake in a preheated oven at 180°C, 350°F, gas 4 for about 1 hour until the barley is soft and the stock absorbed.
4 Meanwhile, quarter or thickly slice the mushrooms. Melt the remaining butter in a pan and sauté the mushrooms briefly.
5 Stir the mushrooms carefully into the barley. Add the yogurt, sprinkle with paprika and serve.

Potatoes with Bacon and Juniper

SERVES 4

A satisfying potato stew which can be varied by using different spices.

15 g (½ oz) butter
4 shallots, chopped
175 g (6 oz) smoked bacon, diced
500 g (1 lb) potatoes, peeled and sliced
salt and pepper
½ tsp juniper berries, crushed
150 ml (¼ pint) water

1 Melt the butter in a pan and cook the shallots slowly until soft. Add the bacon and cook a few minutes more.
2 Put a layer of shallots and bacon in the bottom of an earthenware casserole, followed by a layer of potatoes. Season well with salt and pepper and put in some of the juniper. Add more layers, finishing with potatoes. Pour over the water.
3 Cover tightly with foil and then the lid. Cook in a preheated oven at 160°C, 325°F, gas 3 for 1½–2 hours – the potatoes will not come to any harm if left for the longer time.

VARIATIONS

◆ Use ground allspice instead of juniper and add a layer or two of sliced tomatoes if wished.
◆ Use ¼ tsp ground celery seeds or ½ tsp ground fenugreek in place of the juniper and add some sliced parsnip to the potatoes.

Falafel

SERVES 4

Falafel are perhaps the most popular street food of the Middle East. They are tricky to make without a food processor because the paste must be smooth enough not to disintegrate when fried. If you have trouble making the falafel adhere, add a tablespoon or two of flour to the mixture.

250 g (8 oz) chick peas, soaked for 36 hours
1 large onion, chopped
3 cloves garlic, crushed
handful of fresh parsley or coriander, chopped
1 tsp ground coriander
1 tsp ground cumin
¼ tsp cayenne (optional)
salt
¼ tsp baking powder
oil for deep frying

1 Drain, rinse the chick peas and grind to a purée in a food processor. As they crumble, add the onion, garlic and parsley, and continue processing to a fine purée. (You will need to stop and start the processor several times and scrape around the sides of the bowl.)
2 Blend in the spices, salt and baking powder. Leave the mixture to rest in a cool place for at least 1 hour.
3 Form the mixture into small balls, each the size of a walnut. Flatten them slightly and leave to rest again for 15 minutes.
4 Deep fry the falafel for 3–4 minutes, turning once. Drain on kitchen paper towels and serve with tahina sauce (p.332), a tomato salad and slices of pita bread.

Shiitake Mushrooms with Ginger, Fagara and Garlic

SERVES 4

These Japanese mushrooms have a delicious flavour and are available from Oriental stores and some supermarkets.

350 g (12 oz) fresh shiitake mushrooms
60 ml (4 tbsp) oil
small piece of fresh ginger, peeled and finely chopped
3 cloves garlic, crushed
1 tsp fagara, crushed
Chinese or ordinary chives, chopped, to garnish

1 Wipe the mushrooms and cut them in pieces.
2 Heat the oil in a frying pan and fry the ginger, garlic and fagara for 1–2 minutes.
3 Add the mushrooms and sauté for 4–5 minutes. Serve garnished with Chinese or ordinary chives.

Mushrooms in Sour Cream

SERVES 6

40 g (1½ oz) butter
1 small onion, sliced
500 g (1 lb) mushrooms, sliced
½ tsp caraway seeds
salt and pepper
150 ml (¼ pint) sour cream
paprika

1   Melt the butter in a pan and stew the onion until soft.
2   Add the mushrooms and caraway seeds and season to taste. Simmer for 10–12 minutes.
3   Stir in the sour cream, heat through and serve sprinkled with paprika.

Courgette Fritters

SERVES 6

15 g (½ oz) butter
1 large onion, grated
500 g (1 lb) courgettes, peeled and grated
125 g (4 oz) curd cheese
4 eggs
½ tsp ground cumin
¼ tsp nigella
salt and pepper
oil for frying

1   Melt the butter in a pan and sauté the onion briefly. Add the courgettes and cook for 2–3 minutes. Drain well.
2   Mix the vegetables with the cheese, eggs, spices and season to taste.
3   Heat enough oil to cover the frying pan to a depth of 5 mm (¼ in). Spoon in the mixture, 1 tbsp at a time, keeping the fritters well apart. Cook until golden brown, 3–4 minutes, turning once. Drain on kitchen paper towels and serve.

Onion Purée

SERVES 4

125 g (4 oz) butter
750 g (1½ lb) onions, finely sliced
1 tsp salt
2 tsp ras el hanout (pp.372–73)
45 ml (3 tbsp) honey
30 ml (2 tbsp) sherry vinegar

1   Heat the butter in a pan until a deep golden colour. Put in the onions, salt and ras el hanout and stir to mix.
2   Cover and cook slowly over a heat diffuser for 30 minutes, stirring from time to time.
3   Add the honey and sherry vinegar and cook, uncovered, for another 30 minutes, stirring the mixture frequently.

Aubergine and Sesame Purée

SERVES 4—6

A natural combination; the vegetable and the spice complement each other perfectly. In the Middle East, tahina paste and garlic are blended with aubergine purée to make *Baba Ghanoush*. I have made a simple Oriental version using Chinese sesame paste.

2 large aubergines
2 cloves garlic, crushed with salt
22–30 ml (1½–2 tbsp) Chinese sesame paste
15–30 ml (1–2 tbsp) Oriental sesame oil
¾ tsp Chinese five-spice powder (pp.348–49)
juice of 2 lemons
safflower or paprika, to garnish

1   Wipe the aubergines and prick a few times with a fork. Place in a baking dish and cook in a preheated oven at 180 °C, 350°F, gas 4 for 20–30 minutes until soft.
2   Cut off the stalks, then peel when cool enough to handle. Squeeze out any excess liquid and chop the flesh roughly.
3   Purée the aubergine, garlic, sesame paste, sesame oil and Chinese five-spice powder in a food processor, or pound well in a mortar. Add lemon juice to obtain a smooth purée and to your taste – the juice of two lemons should be about right.
4   Serve at room temperature, sprinkled with a little safflower or paprika.

Spinach with Ginger

SERVES 2

500 g (1 lb) spinach
15 ml (1 tbsp) sunflower oil
¼ tsp ground cumin
2 mild green chillies, seeded and sliced
1 tsp Japanese pickled ginger, shredded
salt

1   Cut the spinach leaves into broad ribbons. Wash, then blanch them in a large pan of boiling water for 1 minute.
2   Drain and run cold water over the spinach until cool. Press thoroughly to extract excess water; it must be dry before frying.
3   Heat a wok or large frying pan to a high temperature. Add the oil and, when smoking, stir in the cumin and chillies and toss for a few seconds.
4   Add the spinach, tossing rapidly to separate the pieces and to coat with the oil. Sprinkle on the ginger and a little salt. Stir to blend and serve immediately. The whole frying operation should take only about 1 minute – if the spinach cooks too slowly it becomes watery.

Chakchouka

SERVES 4

This is a Tunisian dish, now popular throughout the Middle East. It is usually made with eggs broken into hollows in the vegetables, then cooked until set. I prefer to use merguez sausages instead.

30 ml (2 tbsp) olive oil
2 green, red or yellow peppers, seeded and sliced
2 onions, sliced
4 merguez sausages, sliced
4 large tomatoes, peeled and quartered
salt and pepper
5 ml (1 tsp) harissa (pp.370–71)

1   Heat the oil in a pan and sauté the peppers and onions until nearly soft.
2   Add the sausages, cook for a few minutes, then stir in the tomatoes. Season with salt, pepper and harissa to taste.
3   Cook slowly for a further 8–10 minutes until the vegetables have blended.

Braised Leeks

SERVES 3 — 4

500 g (1 lb) leeks
25 g (1 oz) butter
½ tsp Chinese five-spice powder (pp.348–49)
¼ tsp ground galangal
30 ml (2 tbsp) vegetable stock

1   Slice the leeks, but not too finely.
2   Melt the butter in a heavy pan just large enough to take the leeks, stir in the spices and fry for a few minutes. Add the leeks, turn and stir to coat them in the spiced butter. Put in the stock.
3   Cover tightly, turn the heat to low and cook for 20 minutes.

Spiced Cabbage with Beans

SERVES 6

250 g (8 oz) haricot beans, soaked overnight
30 ml (2 tbsp) oil
2 cloves garlic, chopped
4 shallots, chopped
1 tsp mustard seeds
1 tsp dill seeds
1 small cabbage, red or green, shredded
30 ml (2 tbsp) wine vinegar
30 ml (2 tbsp) sherry
salt and pepper

1   Cook the beans in a pan of unsalted water for about 1 hour until tender. Drain and reserve the cooking liquid.
2   Heat the oil in a pan and sauté the garlic and shallots for 5 minutes. Add the mustard and dill seeds, and cover because the mustard seeds will jump and splutter as they heat.
3   When this has subsided, put in the cabbage and stir to coat with the spices. Add the beans, vinegar and sherry, salt and pepper. Mix all together well.
4   Pour over 75 ml (3 fl oz) of the bean liquid, cover and cook for 20 minutes, stirring occasionally. There should be almost no liquid left when the vegetables are ready.

Braised Cucumber

SERVES 4

2 cucumbers
1 tbsp sugar
½ tsp salt
60 ml (4 tbsp) vinegar
30 ml (2 tbsp) water
25 g (1 oz) butter
4 shallots, chopped
1 tbsp flour
½ tsp fennel seeds
450 ml (¾ pint) chicken stock
chopped fresh dill, to garnish

1   Peel the cucumbers, cut in half lengthways, remove the seeds and cut into chunks. Put the cucumber in a bowl.
2   Dissolve the sugar and salt in the vinegar and water. Add to the cucumber and leave to stand for 1 hour, then drain.
3   Melt the butter in a pan and sauté the shallots until soft. Sprinkle over the flour and fennel seeds and cook until the flour turns golden. Whisk in the stock and bring to the boil. Reduce the heat and simmer for a few minutes until the liquid has thickened slightly.
4   Put in the cucumber and simmer, uncovered, for 10–15 minutes; the cucumber should be tender but not soggy. Garnish with chopped dill and serve.

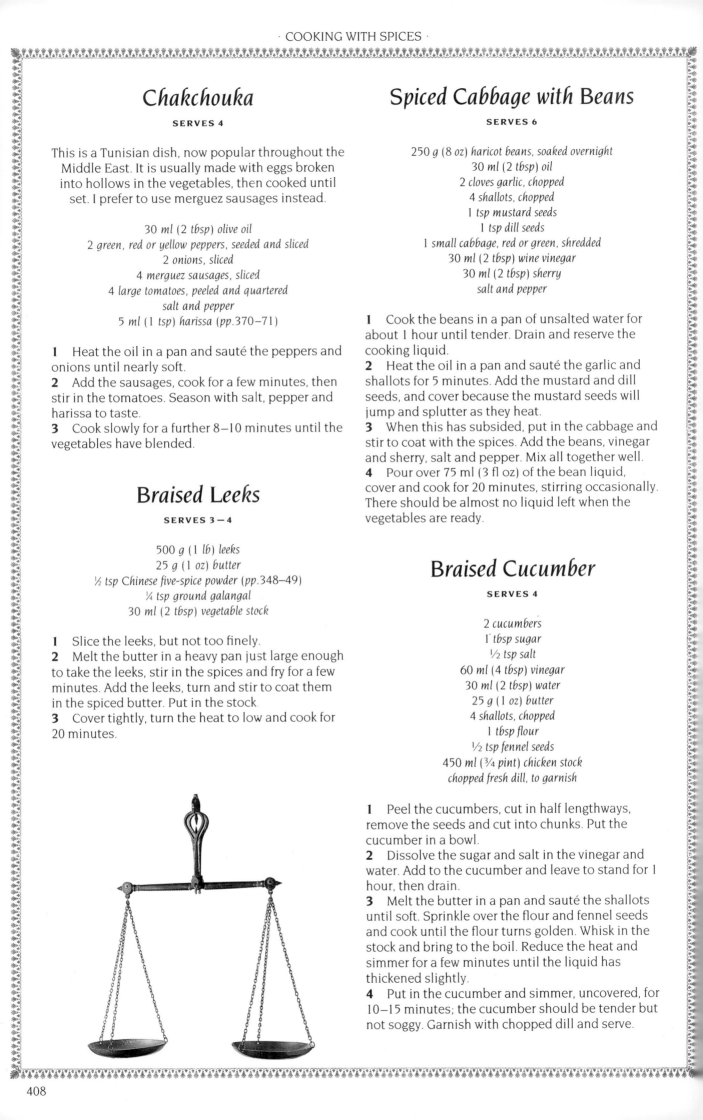

Salads

Olive, Pomegranate and Walnut Salad

SERVES 4

This is a version of a salad served at lunch to a group of visiting food enthusiasts by the women's council of Gaziantep in Southeastern Turkey. It is a town surrounded by olive and pistachio groves and noted for the variety of its kebabs and the excellence of its baklava. The lunch, a buffet of some 30 dishes, was remarkable for its refinement and richness.

2 large pomegranates
125 g (4 oz) green olives, stoned and chopped
bunch of coriander leaves, chopped
6–8 spring onions, chopped
125 g (4 oz) walnuts, coarsely chopped

Dressing
22 ml (1½ tbsp) lemon juice
45 ml (3 tbsp) olive oil
pinch of red pepper
salt

1 Cut open the pomegranates and extract the seeds. Combine with the olives, coriander, spring onions and walnuts.
2 Make a piquant dressing with the remaining ingredients. Pour over the salad, toss and serve.

VARIATION
◆ A few shredded young sorrel leaves make a pleasant addition.

Savoy Cabbage Salad

SERVES 4

1 small Savoy cabbage
50 g (2 oz) pine nuts, toasted

Dressing
60 ml (4 tbsp) olive oil
30 ml (2 tbsp) wine vinegar
¼ tsp poppy seeds
pinch of celery seeds
¼ tsp paprika
2 tsp soft brown sugar
salt

1 Remove the large central stalks from the cabbage leaves, then shred finely.
2 Blanch the cabbage for 1 minute in boiling water, drain and refresh under cold water. Drain thoroughly and cool. Put the cabbage and pine nuts in a bowl.
3 For the dressing, whisk together all the other ingredients. Pour over the salad, toss and serve.

Indian Carrot Salad

SERVES 4–6

This salad is based on a recipe in Julie Sahni's *Classic Indian Vegetarian Cooking*.

500 g (1 lb) carrots
15 ml (1 tbsp) mustard oil
1 tsp mustard seeds
2 green chillies, seeded and chopped
good pinch of ground asafoetida
2 tsp sugar
1 tsp curry powder (pp.356–57)
squeeze of lemon juice
pinch of ground cloves
salt
60 ml (4 tbsp) thick natural yogurt
2 tbsp roasted cashew nuts, chopped
fresh mint leaves, to garnish

1 Slice the carrots very thinly.
2 Heat the oil in a large frying pan and add the mustard seeds. Cover with a lid when they start to jump about. As the spattering subsides, add the chillies, asafoetida, sugar and curry powder. Shake the pan and stir for a few seconds.
3 When the sugar dissolves, add the carrots and toss well to separate the slices and coat them with the oil and spices. Cook for 3–4 minutes, then transfer to a bowl and leave to cool.
4 Stir the lemon juice, cloves and salt into the yogurt and toss the carrots in the dressing. Sprinkle the nuts and a few mint leaves over the salad. Serve at room temperature.

Beetroot Salad

SERVES 4

350 g (12 oz) beetroot

Dressing
45 ml (3 tbsp) wine vinegar
90 ml (6 tbsp) olive oil
2 tsp sugar
½ tsp fennel seeds or ¼ tsp celery seeds
pinch of ground ginger
4 spring onions, chopped
salt

1 Cook the unpeeled beetroot in a pan of boiling salted water until tender. Drain, skin and cut in julienne strips.
2 For the dressing, whisk together all the other ingredients. Pour the dressing over the beetroot and leave to stand for 1 hour for the flavours to blend before serving.

Bean and Pasta Salad

SERVES 8–10

125 g (4 oz) dried haricot beans
125 g (4 oz) dried red kidney beans
125 g (4 oz) flageolets
350 g (12 oz) pasta shells or bows
125 g (4 oz) French beans
1 large clove garlic, finely chopped
large handful of assorted chopped fresh herbs, such as parsley,
chives, tarragon, basil, chervil, sweet cicely
about 120 ml (8 tbsp) olive oil
30–45 ml (2–3 tbsp) wine vinegar
salt and black pepper
10 g (2 tsp) mustard

1 Soak the dried beans separately for 2–3 hours.
Cook the beans separately in boiling water until
just tender, fast boiling the red beans for the first
ten minutes. Do not allow them to become too soft.
Drain and leave to cool.
2 Cook the pasta shells in a pan of boiling salted
water until *al dente*; again it is important not to
overcook them, because soft pasta does not take
well to being dressed and served cold. When ready,
drain and cool under cold running water.
3 Briefly cook the French beans in boiling salted
water. Drain, cool and cut in two.
4 Combine the pasta and cooked dried beans in a
large serving bowl with the garlic and herbs.
5 For the dressing, whisk together the oil, vinegar,
salt, pepper and mustard. Pour the dressing over
the salad.
6 Add the French beans and toss carefully. Chill
the salad for 1–2 hours before serving.

Cucumber Salad

SERVES 4–6

An Oriental salad influenced by one I enjoyed in a
Korean restaurant. Use sansho if you want a hot
chilli flavour; fagara for a milder taste.

1 tbsp sugar
1 tsp salt
60 ml (4 tbsp) wine or rice vinegar
½ tsp sansho or crushed fagara
30 ml (2 tbsp) sesame oil
1 cucumber, finely sliced
1 tbsp black sesame seeds, toasted

1 Whisk the sugar and salt into the vinegar until
dissolved. Add the sansho or fagara and oil.
2 Pour over the cucumber, sprinkle with sesame
seeds and serve at room temperature.

VARIATIONS

◆ Toasted white sesame seeds can be used
instead, but the black look more dramatic.
◆ About 5–10 ml (1–2 tsp) light soy sauce can be
added to the dressing; finely sliced onion can be
added to the cucumber.

Gado Gado

SERVES 4

An inexpensive Indonesian salad that is excellent
on its own or as an accompaniment to a main
course. The selection of vegetables can be varied to
suit your taste, but do keep the bean sprouts for an
authentic dish.

250 g (8 oz) bean sprouts, washed
250 g (8 oz) cabbage, shredded
250 g (8 oz) leek, cut in julienne strips
250 g (8 oz) carrots, cut in julienne strips
250 g (8 oz) celery, cut in julienne strips
1 hard-boiled egg, finely chopped, to garnish

Sauce
1 clove garlic
1 small onion
1 tsp trassi (pp.430–31)
1 tsp dark brown sugar
1 small ball tamarind
30 ml (2 tbsp) coconut cream
30 ml (2 tbsp) milk
60 ml (4 tbsp) crunchy peanut butter
½ tsp ground cumin
½ tsp chilli powder (optional)
½ tsp ground lemon grass
5 ml (1 tsp) dark soy sauce

1 Put the bean sprouts in a large serving dish.
2 Steam the other vegetables until just tender.
Arrange them on top of the bean sprouts.
3 For the sauce, crush the garlic and onion to a
paste with a pestle and mortar.
4 Wrap the trassi in foil and heat it in a dry pan or
moderate oven (180°C, 350°F, gas 4) for a few
minutes, then crumble and mix it with the sugar.
Dissolve the tamarind in 15–30 ml (1–2 tbsp)
water. Stir the coconut cream into the milk to make
a thick coconut milk.
5 Blend the sauce ingredients together to make a
sauce thick enough to coat the vegetables and not
run to the bottom of the dish. Pour over the
vegetables and garnish with the chopped egg.

Onion Salad with Sumac

SERVES 4

A simple side dish that is encountered all through
the Middle East.

2 onions, thinly sliced
½ tsp ground sumac
salt

1 Put the onions in a bowl and sprinkle with
sumac and a little salt.
2 Leave to stand for 30 minutes before serving.

Gado Gado with tamarind, cumin, chilli powder and lemon
grass, and **Onion Salad with Sumac** in the foreground.

Desserts

Spiced Cream Cheese

SERVES 4

250 g (8 oz) cream cheese
150 g (5 oz) thick natural yogurt
125 g (4 oz) caster sugar
¼ tsp saffron threads
30 ml (2 tbsp) hot milk
¼ tsp grated nutmeg
seeds of 6 cardamom pods, crushed

1   Combine the cream cheese, yogurt and caster sugar in a bowl.
2   Crush the saffron and infuse in the hot milk for 10 minutes, then strain.
3   Stir the saffron milk and nutmeg into the cream cheese. Sprinkle the crushed cardamom seeds on top and serve cold.

Kheer (Indian Rice Pudding)

SERVES 4–6

Do not think of this as a Western rice pudding; the two dishes are utterly different. Kheer is cooked for several hours so that the rice breaks down and the pudding has the consistency of a thick cream.

1.2 litres (2 pints) milk
75 g (3 oz) long grain rice, washed
125 g (4 oz) sugar
75 g (3 oz) raisins
40 g (1½ oz) dried apricots, cut into small pieces
seeds of 6 cardamoms, bruised
2 cm (¾ in) cinnamon stick
40 g (1½ oz) blanched, slivered almonds or pistachios
10 ml (2 tsp) rose water

1   Boil the milk and add the rice. Stir over a high heat for 1 minute, then turn the heat as low as possible and continue to cook for 10 minutes, stirring all the time. Leave to cook for a further 1½ hours, stirring occasionally.
2   Add the sugar, raisins, apricots, cardamom and cinnamon. Cook for about 1 hour, stirring from time to time. The dried fruit will plump up and the pudding will thicken. Stir in most of the almonds and cook for another 30 minutes.
3   Leave until cold, then mix in the rose water. The kheer will now have a thick pouring consistency.
4   Put the kheer into a shallow glass bowl or individual bowls, sprinkle the top with the remaining almonds and chill. Kheer may also be decorated with edible gold or silver leaf, bought from Indian grocers.

Orange and Cardamom Salad

SERVES 6

10 oranges
30 ml (2 tbsp) orange flower water
½ tsp ground cardamom
generous pinch of grated nutmeg
50 g (2 oz) sugar
125 ml (4 fl oz) water
icing sugar

1   Peel the oranges, removing all pith and reserving the peel from one or two. Divide into segments. Put them into a serving bowl and sprinkle with the orange flower water and spices.
2   Take the reserved peel, make sure no pith is adhering to it, and cut into julienne strips. Blanch in boiling water for 3 minutes.
3   Melt the sugar in the water in a pan. Add the blanched strips of orange peel and poach slowly for 4–5 minutes. Drain the strips on a wire rack.
4   To serve, scatter the peel over the oranges and sift over a dusting of icing sugar.

Bananas with Cinnamon and Rum

SERVES 4

4 ripe bananas
25 g (1 oz) butter
1 tsp ground cinnamon
75 ml (5 tbsp) rum or whisky
45 ml (3 tbsp) clear honey
50 g (2 oz) walnuts, coarsely chopped

1   Cut the bananas into thick slices. Melt the butter in a pan and fry the banana slices until soft. Lift the bananas out and keep them warm on a serving dish.
2   Add the cinnamon to the butter, then the rum and honey and cook until the sauce thickens slightly. Stir in the walnuts.
3   Pour the sauce over the warm banana slices and serve with cream.

Clementines in Brandy

MAKES 1 KG (2 LB)

This recipe is based on "Clementines in Armagnac" from Jane Grigson's *Fruit Book*. They make an excellent dessert or sweetmeat.

1 kg (2 lb) small clementines
625 g (1¼ lb) sugar
1 vanilla pod
1 litre (1¾ pints) water
brandy or armagnac

1 Prick the fruit a few times with a needle.
2 To make a syrup, heat the sugar, vanilla pod and water in a pan. When the sugar has dissolved, bring to the boil and boil for 3–4 minutes.
3 Put in the clementines, bring back to the boil, then simmer very gently for about 30 minutes. The time depends on the size of the fruit – large fruit may need a little longer. If the skins start to split they are certainly ready.
4 Lift out the fruit and put into warmed preserving jars. Add brandy or armagnac almost to cover the fruit.
5 Boil down the syrup by half and use to top up the jars. Divide the vanilla pod between them.
6 Put a clean stone or a crumpled piece of foil on top of the fruits so that they are totally immersed in the liquid. Seal the jars and keep for 2–3 weeks before eating.

VARIATIONS

◆ Use 5–6 bruised cardamom pods instead of the vanilla, but do not put them into the syrup until the fruit is added. Whisky is a good alternative to brandy with cardamom.
◆ Clear spirit such as vodka, or continental preserving spirit such as plain *alcool blanc*, can be used instead of brandy.

Spiced Fruit Salad

SERVES 4

3 oranges, peeled and cut in segments
2 bananas, peeled and sliced
½ small melon, cut in cubes
4 apricots, quartered
4 greengage plums, quartered
2 peaches, sliced
2 tbsp vanilla sugar (p.336)
juice of 2 oranges
juice of 1 lemon
15 ml (1 tbsp) orange flower water
½ tsp ground cinnamon
¼ tsp ground coriander

1 Put the fruit in a serving bowl.
2 Dissolve the sugar in the fruit juices. Stir in the orange flower water and spices.
3 Pour the spiced fruit juice over the fruit and mix carefully. Chill for 2–3 hours before serving.

Poppy Seed Ice Cream

SERVES 4

300 ml (½ pint) milk
1 vanilla pod
3 egg yolks
50 g (2 oz) sugar
75 g (3 oz) poppy seeds
125 g (4 oz) honey
150 ml (¼ pint) double cream

1 Put the milk and vanilla pod in a pan and bring to the boil. Remove from the heat and leave to infuse for 10 minutes.
2 Whisk the egg yolks and sugar together until thick and cream coloured in a bowl set over a pan of simmering water.
3 Remove the vanilla pod from the milk and pour the milk on to the egg and sugar. Stir constantly until the mixture thickens enough to coat the back of a spoon, but do not let it boil or it may curdle.
4 When the custard is thick enough to leave a clear trail from a wooden spoon on the bottom of the bowl, remove the bowl to a cool surface.
5 Toast the poppy seeds in a dry pan. Stir the seeds and honey into the custard and leave to cool.
6 Whip the cream to soft peaks and fold into the custard. Freeze in an ice cream machine or a shallow container, beating the ice cream after 1–2 hours, then freeze until firm.

Vanilla and Cardamom Ice Cream

SERVES 4

300 ml (½ pint) milk
1 vanilla pod
150 ml (¼ pint) double cream
6 green cardamoms, crushed
4 egg yolks
125 g (4 oz) sugar

1 Put the milk and vanilla pod in a pan and bring to the boil. Remove from the heat and leave to infuse for 10 minutes. Remove the vanilla pod.
2 Heat the cream with the cardamom pods and leave to infuse.
3 Whisk the egg yolks and sugar in a double boiler or in a bowl set over a pan of boiling water until thick and pale coloured. Add the warm milk and stir briskly to blend. Keep stirring until the mixture thickens.
4 Remove the cardamom pods from the cream, it doesn't matter about the seeds, and add the cream to the custard. Cook and stir for a further 10 minutes until the mixture thickens again.
5 Freeze in an ice cream machine or a shallow container, beating the ice cream after 1–2 hours, then freeze until firm.

Breads, cakes & biscuits

Onion and Juniper Bread

A very quick and easy loaf that is best eaten soon after it is made. Fennel, caraway, celery seeds, anise and cumin all combine well with the onion in this recipe if you want to try a different flavour.

175 ml (6 fl oz) milk
1 tsp salt
15 g (½ oz) butter
½ packet easy-blend dried yeast or 7 g (¼ oz) dried yeast
350 g (12 oz) strong white flour
175 ml (6 fl oz) warm water
2 tbsp finely chopped onion
2 tbsp finely chopped juniper berries

1 Heat the milk in a pan and stir in the salt and butter until dissolved.
2 Sprinkle the easy-blend yeast over the flour. Prove ordinary dried yeast in the warm water. Stir the water into the flour, then the milk.
3 Scatter over the onion and juniper and stir to mix well. The dough should be quite soft and batter-like; it is easily mixed with a wooden spoon.
4 Cover and leave in a warm place to rise until it has doubled in bulk – about 1 hour. Beat thoroughly for 1–2 minutes, then pour the dough into a greased 20 cm (8 in) loaf tin.
5 Bake in a preheated oven at 180°C, 350°F, gas 4 for about 1 hour. The loaf should sound hollow when tapped on the bottom.

Churek

This bread comes from the republics of the Caucasus, but a similar anise-flavoured bread is popular throughout Morocco.

½ packet easy-blend yeast or 7 g (¼ oz) dried yeast
500 g (1 lb) strong white flour
1 tsp salt
1 tbsp ground anise
50 g (2 oz) butter, melted
300 ml (½ pint) warm milk
1 egg, beaten
sesame seeds

1 If using easy-blend yeast, stir it into the flour with the salt and anise. Prove ordinary dried yeast in a little warm water, then stir into the flour.
2 Add the melted butter and enough of the warm milk to make a soft dough. If it is too firm, add a little more milk or warm water.
3 Knead the dough on a floured surface for about 5 minutes or until smooth. (This can also be done in a food processor or a food mixer with a dough attachment.)

4 Put the dough in a lightly oiled bowl, and cover with clingfilm or a cloth. Leave to rise until it has doubled in bulk – about 2 hours.
5 Knock back and divide the dough in two. Form each one into a round. Alternatively, divide each piece of dough in three, form each third into a rope and plait them, pinching the ends together.
6 Put the loaves on greased baking sheets, cover and leave to rise for about 45 minutes. Brush the top of the bread with beaten egg and sprinkle thickly with sesame seeds.
7 Bake in a preheated oven at 180°C, 350°F, gas 4 for 35–40 minutes until the bread sounds hollow when tapped on the bottom.

VARIATIONS

◆ Substitute the seeds scraped from a vanilla pod for the anise and sprinkle the top of the bread with flaked almonds.
◆ Use 1 tbsp mahlab instead of the anise.

Arab Bread

½ packet easy-blend yeast or 7 g (¼ oz) dried yeast
500 g (1 lb) strong white flour
1 tsp salt
about 450 ml (¾ pint) warm water
olive oil and zahtar (pp.372–73) or 1 beaten egg with nigella,
poppy seeds or sesame

1 Sprinkle the easy-blend yeast over the flour with the salt. Prove ordinary dried yeast in a little of the warm water, then stir into the flour. Add enough water to mix to a fairly stiff dough.
2 Knead the dough on a floured surface until elastic. Put the dough in a lightly oiled bowl and cover with clingfilm or a cloth. Leave to rise until it has doubled in bulk – about 1½ hours.
3 Knock back and divide the dough into two. Form the two pieces into round loaves and put them on a greased baking sheet. Cover and leave to rise for 30 minutes.
4 Either spread the tops thickly with a paste of olive oil and zahtar or brush with beaten egg and sprinkle with one of the spices.
5 Bake in a preheated oven at 200°C, 400°F, gas 6 for 8–10 minutes, then reduce the temperature to 160°C, 325°F, gas 3 for a further 15–20 minutes.

Spice Bread

Breads such as this are common throughout Europe. The spicing may vary according to the country, but the general principles are the same. Spices, dried fruit and nuts may be changed to suit your own preference.

175 g (6 oz) butter
75 g (3 oz) vanilla sugar (p.336)
2 eggs
300 g (10 oz) strong white flour
2 tsp baking powder
50 g (2 oz) raisins
50 g (2 oz) almonds, chopped
50 g (2 oz) candied orange peel, chopped
50 g (2 oz) candied citron or lemon peel, chopped
1 tsp anise seeds
1 tsp ground cinnamon
½ tsp ground cloves

1 Cream the butter and sugar together in a bowl until pale. Beat in the eggs, one at a time.
2 Sift the flour and baking powder and stir in all the dried fruits and spices. Stir half the flour mixture into the bowl and mix well. Add the remaining flour gradually, and a little milk if the dough is too dry.
3 Knead the dough briefly on a floured surface until it can hold its shape. Cut it in two and place in two small 500 g (1 lb) buttered loaf tins.
4 Bake in a preheated oven at 180°C, 350°F, gas 4 for about 40 minutes – a skewer inserted in the centre should come out clean.

Swedish Limpa Bread

300 ml (½ pint) water
1 tbsp caraway seeds
1 tbsp fennel seeds
1½ tbsp grated orange rind
75 g (3 oz) soft brown sugar
1 packet easy-blend yeast or 15 g (½ oz) dried yeast
500 g (1 lb) strong plain white flour
2 tsp salt
300 ml (½ pint) milk
250 g (8 oz) rye flour

1 Bring the water to the boil and pour it over the caraway, fennel, orange rind and sugar.
2 When it has cooled to tepid, stir in the ordinary dried yeast, if using, and leave to prove. Mix the easy-blend yeast into the white flour with the salt.
3 Add the white flour to the water with the milk and mix. Add as much rye flour as necessary to make a fairly stiff dough.
4 Knead the dough well on a floured surface for about 10 minutes until quite elastic.
5 Put the dough in a lightly oiled bowl, and cover with clingfilm or a cloth. Leave to rise until it has doubled in bulk – about 2 hours.

6 Knock back and form the dough into two round loaves. Put them on greased baking sheets, cover and leave to rise for about 1 hour.
7 Bake in a preheated oven at 180°C, 350°F, gas 4 for 35–40 minutes.

Saffron Bread

½ tsp saffron threads
30 ml (2 tbsp) hot water
300 ml (½ pint) milk
1 packet easy-blend yeast or 15 g (½ oz) dried yeast
50 g (2 oz) butter, melted
4 tbsp sugar
½ tsp salt
about 625 g (1¼ lb) plain flour

1 Steep the saffron in the hot water for 5 minutes.
2 Heat the milk, pour off a little to cool to lukewarm and prove the dried yeast in it, if using.
3 Add the butter, sugar and salt to the rest of the milk. Stir in the saffron and proved yeast. Mix the easy-blend yeast into the flour.
4 Add half the flour to the milk and beat well with a wooden spoon. Add the remainder gradually to make a shiny, cohesive dough.
5 Knead the dough for 10 minutes, until smooth and elastic. Put the dough in a lightly oiled bowl, cover with clingfilm or a cloth. Leave to rise until it has doubled in bulk – about 1½–2 hours.
6 Knock back, and form the dough into a loaf. Put the dough into a 1 kg (2 lb) buttered loaf tin, and leave to rise until it almost reaches the top.
7 Bake in a preheated oven at 220°C, 425°F, gas 7 for the first 10 minutes, then lower the temperature to 180°C, 350°F, gas 4 and bake for a further 15–20 minutes. The loaf should sound hollow when tapped on the bottom.

Banana Bread

75 g (3 oz) butter
125 g (4 oz) sugar
1 egg, beaten
250 g (8 oz) plain flour
2 tsp baking powder
7.5 cm (3 in) vanilla pod
pinch of salt
2 bananas, mashed
75 g (3 oz) raisins

1 Cream the butter and sugar together in a bowl, then add the egg.
2 Sift together the flour and baking powder. Scrape the seeds from the vanilla pod and add to the flour with the salt.
3 Add the flour mixture to the butter and sugar alternately with the bananas. Mix in the raisins. Grease a 500 g (1 lb) tin and pour in the mixture.
4 Bake in a preheated oven at 190°C, 375°F, gas 5 for about 30 minutes until the top is golden and a skewer inserted into the loaf comes out clean.

Gingerbread Biscuits

These gingerbread biscuits are very easy to make and popular with children.

150 g (5 oz) honey
75 g (3 oz) soft brown sugar
25 g (1 oz) butter
2 tsp ground ginger
pinch of ground cinnamon
pinch of ground cloves
pinch of ground black pepper
½ tsp ground cardamom
375 g (13 oz) plain flour
1 egg yolk
1 tsp bicarbonate of soda
50 g (2 oz) icing sugar, sifted
5 ml (1 tsp) lemon juice

1 Heat the honey, sugar and butter in a heavy-based pan, stirring until the mixture is smooth and the sugar has dissolved. Stir in the spices and then leave to cool.
2 Sift two-thirds of the flour into a bowl and add the egg yolk and honey mixture. Mix well. Dissolve the bicarbonate of soda in a spoonful of warm water and add to the mixture. Knead in enough of the remaining flour to make a firm mixture that comes away from the sides of the bowl.
3 Roll out the gingerbread dough on a floured surface until about 1 cm (½ in) thick. Cut out shapes with biscuit cutters or animal or gingerbread figures. Place on a greased floured baking sheet.
4 Bake in a preheated oven at 160°C, 325°F, gas 3 for 10–12 minutes. Mix the icing sugar and lemon juice together with 5 ml (1 tsp) warm water. Use to ice the cooled biscuits.

Chocolate Macaroons

75 g (3 oz) plain chocolate
125 g (4 oz) sugar
150 g (5 oz) ground almonds
Seeds from ½ vanilla pod
¾ tsp ground cinnamon
2 egg whites

1 Melt the chocolate in a bowl over a pan of hot water. Remove from the heat and stir in the remaining ingredients to make a soft paste. A food processor will achieve a good texture quickly.
2 Line a baking sheet with edible rice paper or baking parchment. Roll the mixture into small balls and place them on the sheet. Flatten the tops with a knife.
3 Bake in a preheated oven at 180°C, 350°F, gas 4 for 12–15 minutes until almost firm to the touch. Leave to cool on the paper, then break off the excess rice paper or peel off the baking parchment (if the macaroons stick, wipe the underside with a wet cloth).

Anise Shortbread

125 g (4 oz) butter
40 g (1½ oz) granulated sugar
25 g (1 oz) icing sugar, sifted
250 g (8 oz) plain flour
1 tsp ground anise
¼ tsp salt
10 ml (2 tsp) orange flower water
pine nuts (optional)

1 Cream the butter in a bowl, then add the granulated sugar and icing sugar and beat again.
2 Sift the flour with the anise and salt. Work the flour into the butter mixture, a little at a time, alternating with the orange flower water until a smooth dough is formed.
3 Divide the dough into four or five pieces, then shape into bars or rounds about 8 mm (⅓ in) thick. Put pine nuts on the top if wished, pressing them in slightly with your finger. Place the shortbread on ungreased baking sheets.
4 Bake in a preheated oven at 150°C, 300°F, gas 2 for 15–20 minutes until pale golden, not brown. Leave to cool on the sheets, then transfer to a rack.

VARIATIONS
◆ Other spices can be used instead of anise. Cinnamon, vanilla, cardamom, saffron and safflower all make excellent shortbread.

Cinnamon Biscuits

300 g (10 oz) plain flour
2 tsp ground cinnamon
1 tsp baking powder
150 g (5 oz) soft brown sugar
75 g (3 oz) butter
1 egg
50 g (2 oz) golden syrup
blanched almonds or sesame seeds (optional)

1 Sift the flour, cinnamon and baking powder into a bowl and stir in the sugar.
2 Cut the butter into small cubes and rub it into the flour with your fingertips until the mixture looks like breadcrumbs.
3 Beat the egg, add the golden syrup and beat until smooth. Make a well in the centre of the flour mixture and pour in the egg and syrup.
4 Mix the dough to a smooth ball. Wrap in clingfilm and chill for 30 minutes.
5 Roll out the dough on a lightly floured surface to 5 mm (¼ in) thick. Cut into rounds or shapes. If you wish, decorate the biscuits with blanched almonds or sesame seeds, or leave plain and ice them after baking.
6 Bake in a preheated oven, 160°C, 325°F, gas 3 for 8–10 minutes until golden brown. Cool on a rack.

Chocolate macaroons with vanilla and cinnamon.

Sauces & preserves

Indonesian Soy Relish

An easy relish to accompany satay or even just a bowl of rice.

45 ml (3 tbsp) oil
1 small onion, chopped finely
2 cloves garlic, crushed
½ tsp sambal oelek (pp.350–51) or chilli powder
salt
90 ml (6 tbsp) dark soy sauce
45 ml (3 tbsp) vinegar
2 tsp sugar
2 kaffir lime leaves or ¼ tsp ground lemon grass
30–45 ml (2–3 tbsp) water

1   Heat the oil in a pan and fry the onion until golden brown. Add the garlic, then all the remaining ingredients and cook for 3–4 minutes, stirring well.
2   Taste and adjust the seasoning if necessary. Remove the lime leaves and serve.

Peanut Sauce

An excellent Indonesian sauce that accompanies satay, rice or vegetables. The recipe may seem to make a large amount, but it usually disappears fast, and leftovers keep well. Thinned with coconut milk or with water, it can be used as a sauce for Gado Gado (p.410).

30 ml (2 tbsp) sunflower or groundnut oil
½ tsp ground coriander
2 tsp ground cumin
1 tsp ground ginger
a few curry leaves
1 tsp trassi, crumbled (optional, pp.430–31)
1 kg (2 lb) large onions, finely chopped
350 g (12 oz) peanut butter
60 ml (4 tbsp) coconut cream
1 tbsp sambal oelek (pp.350–51, or available from Oriental stores)

1   Heat the oil, add the dry spices, curry leaves, trassi and onions. Stir well, put a heat diffuser under the pan and turn the heat as low as possible. Add the peanut butter and coconut cream.
2   Cover and cook for several hours, stirring occasionally to ensure that the mixture does not stick. It should make enough liquid of its own to prevent this, but if necessary add 15–30 ml (1–2 tbsp) water.
3   Eventually the sauce will become thick and smooth when stirred vigorously – you can speed this up by using a food processor, but the sauce will be inferior to one produced by long, slow cooking.

4   Remove the curry leaves and add the sambal, but do not cook for more than another hour or so because the taste of sambal gets hotter and hotter as it cooks.

Romesco Sauce

This versatile sauce comes from the province of Tarragona in Spain. The name derives from the romesco pepper, an aromatic, mildly hot *capsicum annuum*, that is almost impossible to find outside Spain. Alternatively, use a fresh red pepper and a pinch of cayenne. The sauce is usually served with fish or shellfish, but also goes well with boiled vegetables and vegetable salads. It makes a good spread for bread too.

1 dried romesco pepper or 1 fresh red pepper and a pinch of cayenne
4 cloves garlic, unpeeled
175 g (6 oz) tomatoes
10 hazelnuts
10 almonds
sprig of parsley, chopped
30 ml (2 tbsp) wine vinegar
75 ml (3 fl oz) olive oil
salt and pepper

1   Remove the seeds from the romesco pepper and soak the pepper in water for 30 minutes.
2   Put the fresh pepper, garlic, tomatoes and nuts on a baking sheet. Place in a preheated oven at 200°C, 400°F, gas 6. Remove the nuts after a few minutes when they are lightly toasted, the garlic and tomatoes when soft and the pepper when the skin has blistered and looks withered – it will take about 25 minutes.
3   Peel all the vegetables. Drain the romesco pepper, if used.
4   Pound or process the garlic and pepper with the nuts. Add the tomatoes and parsley and blend well. Beat in the vinegar and oil as if making mayonnaise. Season with salt and pepper to taste.
5   Leave to stand at room temperature for at least 2 hours before serving.

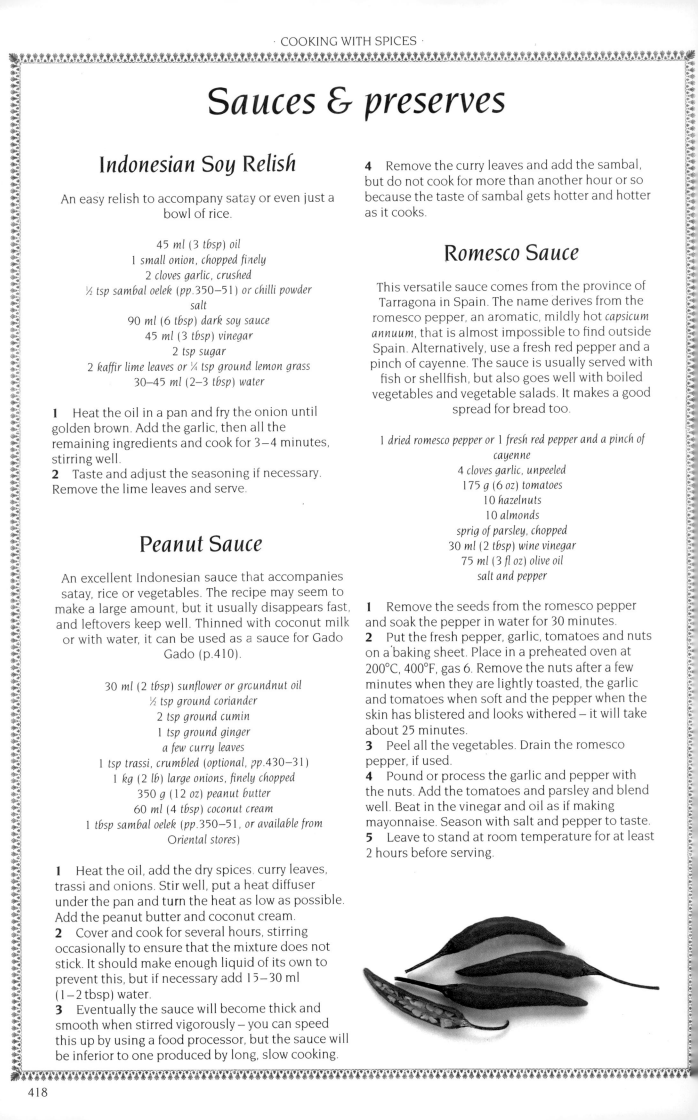

American Cucumber Pickles

MAKES ABOUT 2 KG (4 LB)

1.5 kg (3 lb) cucumbers thickly sliced (ridge cucumbers if
possible)
4 large onions, thickly sliced
75 g (3 oz) coarse salt
crushed ice
900 ml (1½ pints) cider vinegar
1 tsp ground turmeric
1 tbsp mustard seeds
1 tsp celery seeds
½ tsp black peppercorns
6 cloves
750 g (1½ lb) sugar

1   Put the cucumbers and onions in a large bowl
with the salt and ice. Put a plate and weight on top
to press them and leave for 3–4 hours.
2   Bring the vinegar, spices and sugar to the boil,
stirring to dissolve the sugar. Take off the heat.
3   Drain the cucumber and onion thoroughly.
Bring the spiced vinegar syrup to the boil again and
add the vegetables. When the pan comes to the
boil again, turn off the heat.
4   Put the pickles into warmed preserving jars.
Cover and keep for 2 weeks before using.

Black Olives with Fennel and Allspice

MAKES ABOUT 500 G (1 LB)

500 g (1 lb) black olives in brine
1 tbsp fennel seeds
1 tbsp allspice, crushed
3 bay leaves
olive oil

1   Drain and rinse the olives. Put them into a large
jar, sprinkling the layers with the spices.
2   Tuck in the bay leaves, then pour over enough
olive oil to cover the olives completely. Store in a
cool place for 3–4 weeks before using.

Green Olives with Coriander

MAKES ABOUT 500 G (1 LB)

500 g (1 lb) green olives in brine
4 large cloves garlic
1 tbsp coriander seeds, crushed
½ lemon, sliced
olive oil

1   Drain and rinse the olives. Crack them by hitting
with a mallet or rolling pin. Transfer the olives to a
large jar, interspersed with the garlic, coriander and
lemon slices.
2   Cover with olive oil. Store for at least 3 weeks
before using.

Garlic Pickle

MAKES ABOUT 250 G (8 OZ)

The flavour of the garlic mellows pleasantly over
time and, after 3–4 months, if there is any left, it
can be crushed to add to vegetable and meat
dishes.

250 g (8 oz) garlic
1 tbsp salt
3 tbsp fennel seeds
1 tbsp black peppercorns or long pepper
1 tbsp garam masala (pp.360–61)
1 tbsp nigella
1 tsp chilli powder
¼ tsp ground asafoetida
900 ml–1.2 litres (1½–2 pints) sunflower oil

1   Peel the garlic and check that it is free from
blemishes.
2   Put the whole cloves together with the salt and
spices into a preserving jar. Cover with oil and put
on the lid.
3   Place the jar in a warm place – on the boiler or
in the sun if it is hot enough. Stir a few times a day
for 5 days. Leave for at least a week, still in a warm
place, before using.

Lime Pickle

MAKES ABOUT 300 ML (½ PINT)

6 limes
50 g (2 oz) salt
1 tbsp mustard seeds
1 tsp fenugreek seeds
seeds from 2 star anise
4 small green chillies
125 g (4 oz) brown sugar
1 tbsp ground ginger
45–60 ml (3–4 tbsp) water

1   Cut the limes into quarters. Put them in a wide,
flat bowl and sprinkle the salt over them. Leave
until next morning.
2   Heat the mustard seeds, fenugreek, star anise
and chillies in a dry frying pan. Cover with a lid
because the seeds will sputter. When the sputtering
subsides, remove from the heat and put aside.
3   Strain the liquid from the limes into a pan. Add
the sugar, ginger and the water and boil until the
sugar dissolves. Leave to cool.
4   Put the limes and the roasted spices into a
preserving jar, mixing them well. Pour the cooled
sugar mixture over the limes. Cover and keep for 4
weeks before using.

Tomato Chutney

MAKES ABOUT 1.25 KG (2½ LB)

1.5 kg (3 lb) ripe tomatoes, peeled and chopped
2 large onions, chopped
4 cloves garlic, sliced
175 ml (6 fl oz) white vinegar
1 tsp salt
¼ tsp paprika
¼ tsp ground cloves
¼ tsp ground mace
¼ tsp ground cardamom
250 g (8 oz) sugar

1 Cook the tomatoes, onions and garlic in a heavy pan until reduced to a thick pulp.
2 Stir in half the vinegar, the salt and spices. Bring to the boil and cook to a jam-like consistency.
3 Dissolve the sugar in the remaining vinegar and add to the pan. Cook steadily, stirring frequently for about 15 minutes. The chutney should be very thick. Pour into preserving jars while hot.

Apricot and Apple Chutney

MAKES ABOUT 1.5 KG (3 LB)

500 g (1 lb) dried apricots, chopped
2 green apples, peeled and chopped
3 large onions, sliced
125 g (4 oz) raisins
450 ml (¾ pint) white vinegar
250 g (8 oz) brown sugar
½ tsp mustard seeds
¼ tsp ground ginger
½ tsp ground allspice
1½ tsp salt

1 If they are very dry, soak the apricots for a few hours in a bowl of water, then drain and proceed with the recipe.
2 Put all the ingredients into a preserving pan and cook gently to a thick pulp – it will take about 45 minutes. Stir frequently to prevent sticking. Pour into jars while hot.

Spiced Blackberry Jelly

MAKES ABOUT 1 KG (2 LB)

1.5 kg (3 lb) blackberries
300 ml (½ pint) water
¼ tsp grated nutmeg
¼ tsp ground cinnamon
pinch of ground cloves
sugar
juice of 2 lemons

1 Put the blackberries into a preserving pan with the water and spices. Bring to the boil and cook steadily for 30 minutes until all the juice is extracted. Stir and press the fruit occasionally.

2 Strain through a jelly bag. Measure the juice and for each 600 ml (1 pint), add 500 g (1 lb) sugar.
3 Put the blackberry juice, sugar and lemon juice into the preserving pan and cook gently until setting point is reached. Pour into jars while hot.

Green Walnut Preserve

MAKES ABOUT 750 G (1½ LB)

This unusual preserve comes from Greece. It is rather time-consuming but well worth making if you have a supply of green walnuts.

1 kg (2 lb) green walnuts
1 kg (2 lb) sugar
1 litre (1¾ pints) water
juice of 3 lemons
12 cloves

1 Wear rubber gloves while preparing the walnuts or your hands will be badly stained. Peel off the outer skin – a potato peeler works well – and soak the nuts in cold water for 6–7 days, changing the water twice a day. This will draw off any bitterness.
2 In a stainless steel or enamelled pan, boil the sugar, water and lemon juice to make a thick syrup.
3 Drain the nuts and add to the syrup with the cloves. Simmer for 40 minutes, then remove the pan from the heat and leave to cool.
4 Make sure the nuts are submerged in the syrup, put a plate on top if necessary. Leave for 48 hours.
5 Remove the walnuts and bring the syrup to the boil again, then simmer for a further 40 minutes.
6 Pour the walnuts and syrup into warmed preserving jars, cool and close.

Preserved Plums

MAKES ABOUT 1 KG (2 LB)

1 kg (2 lb) small firm plums
175 g (6 oz) sugar
300 ml (½ pint) wine vinegar
2 pieces cassia bark
½ tsp cloves
3–4 blades of mace

1 Soak the fruit in cold water for 10 minutes. Drain and prick each one a few times with a needle. Put the plums into preserving jars.
2 Put the sugar, vinegar and spices into a pan and bring to the boil. When the sugar has dissolved, continue to simmer for 4–5 minutes, then cool.
3 Pour the spiced mixture over the plums, distributing the spices evenly. Make sure that all the plums are covered by the liquid.
4 Cover and keep for 10 days before using.

VARIATIONS

◆ Apricots may be prepared in the same way, so may larger fruits such as peaches or pears, but they should be quartered and pears should be peeled.

Drinks

Spiced Tea

SERVES 4—6

1 litre (1¾ pints) water
1 cinnamon stick
3 cloves
3 allspice berries
3 cardamoms, crushed
15 ml (1 tbsp) black tea

1 Simmer the water and spices for 5 minutes.
2 Bring to the boil and pour on to the tea in a warmed tea pot. Infuse for 5 minutes.

Mexican Coffee

SERVES 4—6

In Mexico, the coffee is made in the earthenware mugs in which it is served, but it can be made in a saucepan or coffee pot.

½ cinnamon stick
4 tsp dark brown sugar
900 ml (1½ pints) water
60 ml (4 tbsp) coarsely ground dark roasted coffee

1 Heat the cinnamon, sugar and water slowly until the sugar has dissolved.
2 Stir in the coffee, bring to the boil and remove from the heat. Bring to the boil again, remove from the heat and leave to infuse for 1–2 minutes. Strain and serve.

Spiced Ayran

SERVES 4

A refreshing drink that is widely served in Turkey.

450 ml (¾ pint) natural yogurt
450 ml (¾ pint) cold water
seeds from 8 cardamom pods
ice cubes (optional)

1 Whisk the yogurt until creamy, then whisk in the water, a little at a time.
2 When the drink is well blended, stir in the cardamom seeds. Serve at room temperature or over ice cubes.

Chilli Vodka

Infuse 2 *red chillies* in a *bottle of vodka* for 24 hours. Strain and keep the vodka in the freezer. It is very good for head colds.

Caribbean Ginger Beer

MAKES ABOUT 4.8 LITRES (8 PINTS)

250 g (8 oz) fresh ginger, peeled
2 limes, thinly sliced
15 g (½ oz) cream of tartar
1 kg (2 lb) sugar
4.8 litres (8 pints) water
1 tbsp dried yeast

1 Grate the ginger into a large bowl or jar, then add the lime slices, cream of tartar and sugar.
2 Warm a cupful of the water, sprinkle over the yeast and leave to prove.
3 Boil the rest of the water and pour over the ginger and sugar mixture. When this has cooled to lukewarm, whisk the yeast to a paste and stir it in.
4 Cover and leave to stand for 2 days. Strain and bottle. The ginger beer will keep for up to a week in the refrigerator, otherwise for 2–3 days.

Mulled Wine

MAKES ABOUT 750 ML (1¼ PINTS)

150 ml (¼ pint) water
1 small piece of cinnamon stick
1 small piece of dried ginger, bruised
8 cloves
a few pieces of orange zest (optional)
75 g (3 oz) sugar
1 bottle red wine

1 Bring the water to the boil in a pan with the spices, orange zest and sugar to make a thick syrup.
2 Pour in the wine and heat almost to boiling point, then serve.

Clove Cordial

"Take of bruised cloves and cassia buds a quarter of an ounce each, and a dozen Jamaica peppercorns [allspice]. Infuse the spices in hot water and keep the bottle by the fire, close stopped, for a night or two. Strain this to three pints of proof spirit, and add syrup to taste. Filter, and colour with burnt sugar, or a bit of cochineal. Mace or nutmeg, bruised, may be added to clove cordial. It is grateful and tonic."

Extract from *The Cook And Housewife's Manual*, Mistress Margaret Dods, 1833 edition.
NOTE: The spirit may be clear eau-de-vie or (as befits a Scottish recipe) whisky. It is not necessary to colour it, in my opinion.

5

Spices in the home

In the past, spices played a much wider role in the home than the limited culinary one we assign to them today. As well as flavouring and preserving foods, they freshened the air, warded off unwelcome insects and helped to prevent and cure a wide range of ills. The following pages provide some traditional ideas for using spices as room fresheners. Their medical applications are examined, and detailed instructions are provided for the best ways of preparing and storing spices in the home.

Spiced delights

" I'll choose a small orange as round as the moon is,
That ripened its cheek in the sunniest grove,
And when it is dry as a midsummer hayfield
I'll stick it all round with the head of a clove."

Eleanor Farjeon, *The Clove Orange*

T HESE DAYS we associate spices primarily with cooking, but their fragrance has long been important to sweeten the air, and they were even thought to ward off the plague and other diseases with their alleged antiseptic properties. Sweet-smelling herbs were strewn on the floor, spice balls carried in the hand or hung from a belt, lavender bags and bundles of herbs put into cupboards and drawers, bowls of pot-pourri used to freshen and scent the air.

By Elizabethan times soaps and disinfectants, lotions and ointments, tinctures and cordials, mouthwashes and medicines were made in the home from flowers and herbs from the garden and drugs and spices from the apothecary or grocer. Early receipt books usually had as many instructions for these still-room preparations as for food. The following recipe for *Aqua composita* is a typical example.

Aqua composita

" Take a gallon of Gascoign wine, of ginger, galingale, cinnamon, nutmegs and graines [of paradise], annis seeds, fennell seeds, and carroway seeds, of each a dram; of sage, mints, red roses, thyme, pellitory, rosemary, wild thyme, camomile, lavender, of each a handful, bray [crush] the spices small, and bruise the herbs, letting them macerate 12 houres, stirring it now & then, then distil by limbecke of pewter [in a pewter still] keeping the first cleare water that commeth, by it selfe, and so likewise the second. You shall draw much about a pinte of the better sort from everie gallon of wine."

From *Delights for Ladies*, Sir Hugh Plat, 1602

Aqua composita and similar waters such as *aqua mirabilis*, cinnamon water, and aniseed water were taken for all sorts of ailments - heartburn, melancholy, loss of memory, to aid digestion and "to comfort the heart". At least they probably had a tonic effect on the sufferer.

Distilling spiced waters and making soaps and mouthwashes may no longer be practical domestic activities, but it is agreeable and easy to make pot-pourri, clove oranges and other spice and herb bags to scent your rooms and cupboards, and to keep out moths and other insects.

Essential oils, distilled from plants, provide an easy way to impart aroma, but because they are volatile and rapidly lose their fragrance, a fixing agent is needed to absorb and hold the oil. In the past animal fixatives such as musk were common, but now vegetable fixatives, usually orris root and gum benzoin, are the norm. Vanilla pods, cinnamon sticks and cloves are also effective fixatives.

A *sweet rose bag*

" Cut the white part from some scented rose petals. Let them dry thoroughly, then mix with a few drops of rose oil and ground cloves. Fill small bags to put in your drawers."

From *The Compleat Confectioner*, Hannah Glasse, 1760

Rosemary and verbena bags

a handful of dried rosemary flowers
a handful of dried lemon verbena leaves
25 g (1 oz) ground orris root
grated dried rind of 1 orange
½ nutmeg, grated

Mix all the ingredients together and use to fill small cotton or muslin bags.

Sweet bag to perfume linens

" ½ cup dried rosebuds
⅓ cup ground orris root
1 cup coriander seeds, bruised in mortar
1 tsp ground cinnamon
10 slightly bruised whole cloves
½ cup dried orange flowers
½ tsp common salt

Mix well and fill small cotton bags."

From *Potpourris and other Fragrant Delights*, Jacqueline Hériteau, 1975

Moth bags

Moths were a bane in many households and a variety of scented mixtures was developed to deter the insects from laying their eggs amongst fabrics and clothes. Here is a recipe based on one in *The Practical Housewife*, 1860.

1 Mix together equal amounts of *ground caraway, cloves, nutmeg, mace, cinnamon* and *tonka beans*.
2 Add as much *ground orris root* as the total amount of spices, mix well and put into little bags.

A clove orange

Choose a thin-skinned orange, score it in quarters and tie a ribbon around it, leaving a length to hang it by. Make holes with a darning needle or bodkin before proceeding to stick the fruit full of cloves or you will end up with several broken stalks and get sore fingers. Arrange the cloves so that the heads are touching. Mix together equal quantities of orris root powder and ground allspice or cinnamon and roll the orange in it so that it is coated with the powder. Wrap it in tissue paper and leave it for two weeks. With time the pomander will dry out completely and get smaller, but it will keep its fragrance for a year or two.

Traditional pot-pourri

1 litre (1¾ pints) *dried fragrant leaves and flowers*
200 g (7 oz) *coarse salt*
50 g (2 oz) *ground cloves*
50 g (2 oz) *ground allspice*
75 g (3 oz) *ground benzoin*
75 g (3 oz) *ground orris root*
50 g (2 oz) *brown sugar*
a few small pieces of cinnamon
45 ml (3 tbsp) *brandy*

1 Choose an assortment of sweet-smelling sprigs and flowers from the following selection: *rose petals, lavender, scented geranium, rosemary, lemon balm, marjoram, bay leaves*, and make sure they are thoroughly dry. Put them in a bowl and mix with 150 g (5 oz) of the salt. Leave for 3-4 days.
2 Mix the remaining salt with the dry ground ingredients and sugar, and add to the pot-pourri with the bits of cinnamon. Transfer the mixture to a jar with a lid and sprinkle over the brandy. Mix well and keep tightly covered when not in use. Stir it occasionally, and if the pot-pourri dries out add a little more brandy.

Eleanour Sinclair Rohde's pot-pourri

" 1 litre (1¾ pints) *rose petals*
175 g (6 oz) *coarse salt*
3 tbsp *allspice, bruised*
3 sticks *cinnamon, bruised*
1½ tbsp *cloves, bruised*
3 nutmegs, *crushed coarsely*
1 tbsp *anise*
50 g (2 oz) *lavender flowers*
25 g (1 oz) *ground orris root*
5 ml (1 tsp) *oil of jasmine*
3 drops each *oil of rose geranium, lavender, lemon*
2 drops *oil of neroli*
1 drop *oil of patchouli*
1 drop *oil of rosemary*

Gather rose petals in dry weather, and dry in shade by spreading out well on paper. Damask roses are best. When quite dry make in a covered crock, one handful of salt to three of rose leaves. Let it remain five days, turning twice a day. Then add allspice and cinnamon. Let it remain a week, turning from bottom to top. Then add everything else, including oils. You can add fresh dried leaves of marjoram, sweet balm, verbena, tuber rose, orange blossom, gardenia, clove carnation, violets, etc. Stir with a wooden spoon at intervals."

From *Gardens of Delight*, Eleanour Sinclair Rohde, 1934

Floral pot-pourri

The word "leaves" here means petals as well as sweet-scented leaves. For bay salt use sea salt.

" Take a large quantity of *rose-leaves* and dry them in the house, not out of doors because the air is inclined to take the scent away. Add sweet-scented *geranium, verbena, honeysuckle,* and *lavender*. Sprinkle the leaves with *powdered cloves*, a large tablespoonful of *bay salt, musk, oil of lavender, oil of cinnamon, oil of cloves*, and mix these ingredients well together."

From *A Book of Scents and Dishes* by Dorothy Allhusen, 1926

Pomanders & pot-pourris

Most pot-pourri blends contain a number of aromatics among their ingredients. Spices such as cloves and vanilla impart their own sweet, warming fragrance as well as helping to retain the scents of aromatic oils. Secured in a fabric bag, a blend of spices is an effective way of scenting clothes in storage and protecting them from insects. Another traditional air-freshener is the clove orange.

SWEET BAGS

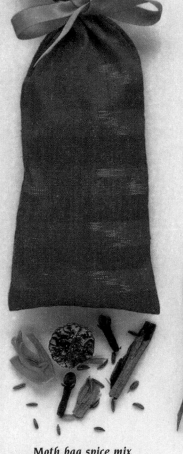

Rosemary and lemon verbena (recipe, p.424).

Moth bag spice mix (recipe, p.425).

Sweet bag to perfume linens (recipe, p.424).

CLOVE ORANGE

An orange stuck with cloves keeps its fragrance for a year or two (p.425).

POT-POURRI BLENDS

Eleanour Sinclair Rohde's pot-pourri (recipe, p.425).

Traditional pot-pourri (recipe, p.425).

Floral pot-pourri (recipe, p.425).

POT-POURRI BOX

An attractive way of displaying pot-pourri.

Spices as medicines

ALTHOUGH SPICES are little used in Western medicine today, they are still widely prescribed in China and in Indian Ayurvedic medicine, much as they were thousands of years ago. Cassia, ginger, cardamom, pepper, sesame and poppy have perhaps the oldest history of medicinal use in the East; in the ancient civilizations of Mesopotamia, the seed spices - dill, anise, caraway, fennel - were more common. The Egyptians, Greeks and Romans all used large numbers of medicinal plants, both local and Oriental. Seven of the 37 volumes of Pliny's *Natural History*, written in the first century AD, were devoted to medicinal plants. The Arabs, for centuries at the centre of the spice trade, drew on much of the knowledge left by the Greeks as well as the wealth of medical learning that came from the East. This was brought to the West by the writings of Avicenna, a leading physician in 11th-century Arabia.

The demand for spices in Europe was as much for their medicinal applications as for their culinary appeal. The pepperers and spicers who sold them later became the apothecaries who dispensed medicines. For centuries, the population of Europe suffered from plagues and epidemics. Many believed that these were spread by foul air, and spices became popular as air purifiers. People took to carrying balls of aromatic spice blends, or pomanders, as protection against pestilence and unpleasant odours.

The range of conditions for which spices have been used is extensive and includes treating snakebites, bed-wetting, menstrual problems, poor eyesight, piles, jaundice, indigestion, diabetes, migraines, insomnia and lack of sexual energy. The warming quality of spices such as mustard and cayenne led to their use in the treatment of colds, circulatory problems, and muscular aches and pains. In ancient Greece, mustard was mixed into a plaster form to alleviate lung congestion. The mustard plaster was thought to warm the skin and open the lungs, making breathing easier, although if applied for too long or made too strong, it caused skin blisters. Powdered mustard was added to baths to soothe tired aching feet and to help cure colds by raising the body temperature.

Chillies contain capsaicin, a chemical that increases blood circulation upon contact. The increased flow of blood brings relief to strained muscles, and chillies are common ingredients in muscle liniments. Unbroken chilblains, neuralgia and lumbago are also sometimes treated with ointments containing cayenne.

Another warming spice, ginger, was considered so beneficial by the Chinese that at one time it was planted in pots and carried on long sea voyages so it could be eaten by the crew to prevent scurvy. In contemporary China it is a traditional remedy for colds and coughs, kidney problems and even hangovers. Once introduced to Europe ginger was taken freely for its wide-ranging medical effects and recent research has proved that it stimulates blood circulation, helps in the digestion of fatty foods and prevents travel sickness.

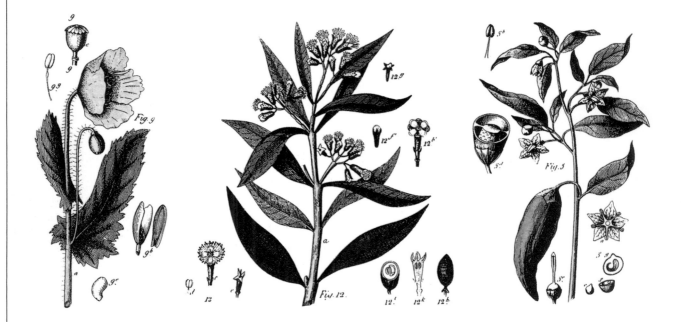

Opium poppy *The plant yields seeds for spicing and a sticky sap - the source of the painkillers opium, morphine and codeine.*

Cloves *Antiseptic and an effective painkiller, cloves are a traditional cure for toothache and nausea.*

Chillies *A source of capsaicin, which improves circulation, chillies also have powerful antibacterial properties.*

The value of spices in aiding digestion has been recognized since ancient times. The Romans used to serve spice cakes at the end of a banquet to help the body digest rich foods, and today a dish including anise, fennel seeds, caraway and dill is often presented at the end of an Indian meal. Other spices known to help digestion include ajowan, cassia, celery seeds, chillies, cumin, fenugreek, ginger, mustard and pepper. Dill water is a traditional cure for hiccups and colic in babies.

Recent research has shown that cinnamon, used in ancient Egypt in embalming mixtures, is effective against bacterial and fungal infection. Anise is another spice with antibacterial properties, although its main use today is as a flavouring in cough medicines and as a carminative. Cloves, long recognized as a toothache cure, are antiseptic and have a mild anaesthetic effect if chewed whole or rubbed on the gums. Clove tea is a traditional remedy for nausea and indigestion.

Spices as essential oils

Ancient cultures valued aromatic plant oils not only for their healing properties, but also as perfumes, anointing oils and preservatives. In the days of the Muslim Empire (7th to 11th centuries), Arab scientists perfected the art of distillation, developing techniques to extract the essential oils from aromatic plants. Cinnamon and cloves were two of the earliest spices from which they distilled the essential oil, although the most renowned was the costly attar of roses. The Crusaders and their followers brought the knowledge of distillation to Europe and by the 14th century the apothecaries' guilds were established, their members supplying oils, ointments and infusions to the public.

Today many essential spice oils are distilled in producing, as well as importing, countries. It is a time-consuming, expensive operation requiring very large quantities of the best raw materials in order to extract a minute amount of oil. Pure essential oils are therefore costly. Some oils have been copied synthetically, but only the aroma is reproduced, not the therapeutic properties. Synthetic oils can be used in the cosmetic and food industries, but not for any healing process.

An important use of essential oils today is in the science of aromatherapy, a modern, holistic version of an old healing art, intended to strengthen the body's self-defence mechanisms against disease. The oils are applied through massage, baths and inhalations; some have a calming effect, others stimulate the body. Of the spice oils, cinnamon, juniper and clove are the most important for aromatherapy.

Inside an apothecary's shop *Spices and herbs were ground together in different combinations and prescribed to treat a wide range of ills.*

Preparing & storing spices

Selecting spices

Spices come in many forms, from seeds and powders to fresh roots and aromatic leaves. When buying dried berries, fruits and seeds, always choose whole spices as these keep their flavour and aroma much longer than powdered forms, and can be ground easily as required. Ready-ground spices may be adulterated; if you grind your own you can be sure about their content. When selecting dried spices check that they are a good colour, not faded, and that they do not smell musty. Avoid fruits and pods that look cracked, shrivelled or hollow, and bags of seeds that contain a lot of powder and dust. Fresh galangal, ginger and lemon grass have a cleaner taste than the dried versions, and are better for some dishes.

How to store spices

Fresh spices: Lemon grass, screwpine, curry leaves and kaffir lime leaves will keep for a week or so when fresh if stored in the salad drawer of the refrigerator. Try putting the leaves in a sealed plastic bag with a little moisture and air to prevent them wilting. Galangal, ginger and chillies will keep for 2-3 weeks in the refrigerator. Ginger and galangal may benefit from being wrapped in kitchen paper to absorb any moisture that can cause rot. Lemon grass, chillies and leaves can also be frozen for up to six months. An alternative method for keeping fresh ginger for several months is to peel, slice and bottle it in sherry.

Dried spices: Store in airtight containers in a cool, dry cupboard as direct light, heat and moisture impair their quality. Whole spices will keep for several months, even up to a year, if stored in this way. However, most ground spices fade in colour and taste within a few months. When unsure how long your spices have been stored for, check if they smell musty, or if their aroma is faint, in which case they should be replaced.

Other spices: Mustard can be stored both ready-made and in powdered form for up to a year. Some spices such as dried tamarind and vanilla pods can be stored for several years.

Preparing spices

Detailed information about the best ways of preparing each spice is provided in the Spice Index (pp.294–343). Here are some general instructions on basic techniques referred to throughout the book.

Grinding: Spices are crushed or ground to release their flavour and aroma. With a few exceptions such as dried ginger, mace, turmeric, cassia and cinnamon, whole spices are easy to grind. Grind them as you need them rather than in advance, so that the full flavour is preserved. The traditional Indian method is to pound them with a large pestle against a block of stone with a recess in it. Japanese mortars, which have ridged bowls, are good for pulverizing chillies and garlic when making pastes. Some spices, such as allspice, coriander and fenugreek, will grind down successfully in a pepper mill. A quicker method is to use a coffee grinder, either electric or hand-operated. I keep a separate grinder for this purpose. A food processor also comes into its own for making pastes and purées, although you need to grind a relatively large quantity for the blades to work effectively.

Bruising: Rather than being ground to a powder, some spices such as dried ginger, juniper berries, and cardamom pods are just slightly crushed to release their flavour. Either press lightly with a pestle in a mortar or place the spices in a bag or envelope and tap them with a rolling pin.

Dry roasting: This process heightens the flavour and aroma of such spices as coriander, cumin, fagara, fenugreek, mustard seeds, nigella, poppy seeds and sesame seeds, and is considered essential in Indian cookery. Heat a heavy frying pan and after 2-3 minutes, put in the whole spices. Dry roast over a medium heat for several minutes, stirring or shaking the pan frequently to prevent the spices burning. Continue roasting until the spices turn dark brown and give off a heady, fragrant aroma - this should take about 5 minutes. Remove the spices from the heat and allow to cool in a dry bowl before grinding them to a powder.

Some special points & ingredients

A few spices require special handling, which is described on the relevant pages in the Spice Index (pp.294–343). Here is additional advice for preparing specific spices and some unusual ingredients commonly used in spice recipes from Asia.

Black salt: An aromatic, rather unsalty condiment that is sold in Indian grocery shops. A smaller quantity of ordinary salt may be used as a substitute when required in spice mixtures.

Chillies: Be careful when handling chillies. It can help to wear a pair of rubber household gloves, especially if there is a lot of preparation involved. If you need to remove the seeds from a chilli before using it in a recipe, it is easier to do so before chopping it. For a fresh chilli, cut it in half and scrape out the seeds using the point of a knife. With a dried chilli, cut off the stalk end with a knife or a pair of scissors and shake out the seeds.

Coconut milk: An essential ingredient in Indonesian cuisine which can be made from fresh, desiccated or creamed coconut. It is easiest to use creamed coconut, which is sold in firm white blocks. To make 175 ml (6 fl oz) thick coconut milk, dissolve 75 g (3 oz) chopped creamed coconut in 175 ml (6 fl oz) hot water; for thin milk, use only 25 g (1 oz) coconut. The milk can be kept for 24 hours in the refrigerator; if it separates, stir well before use.

Garlic: Crushed garlic is a common ingredient in a lot of spice mixtures. A quick and effective way of crushing garlic is to place an unpeeled clove on a work surface and press down on it with the heel of your hand on the flat blade of a large knife. The garlic skin will work loose. To crush further, pound the clove in a mortar with a few grains of salt.

Ginger: To use fresh ginger, first remove the skin with a sharp knife and then either slice, chop or grate it with a fine grater. Ginger is easier to chop if it is first crushed with the flat side of a knife to separate the fibres.

Trassi: A firm paste made of rotted shrimps that is used widely in Southeast Asian cookery. It has an extremely pungent smell similar to a meat extract and can be bought in packets in Oriental grocers, sometimes under the Malay name *blachan*. To heat trassi, wrap it in foil and grill it until it darkens, or put it in a preheated oven at 180°C, 350°F, gas 4 for a few minutes.

Alternative names for spices

Some of the more unusual spices can only be bought in Indian, Chinese or Southeast Asian shops. The spices are often not labelled with their English name; this list should help identify them.

Names are given according to the type of shop in which they can be useful. The Southeast Asian names are indicated by country: Indonesia (I); Malaysia (M) and Thailand (T).

SPICE	INDIAN	CHINESE	SOUTHEAST ASIAN
ajowan	ajwain, carom, lovage		
anise	saunf	yan kok	jintan manis (M)
asafoetida	hing		
caraway	kala jeera, shia jeera		
cardamom	elaichi	wok lok wuat	kapulaga (I); buah pelaga (M); (luk) kravan (T)
cassia buds	nagkesar		
cayenne / chilli powder	lal mirch		pisi hui (T)
coriander	dhania		ketumbar (I,M); pak chi met (T)
cubeb			tjabé djawa (I)
cumin	jeera		jinten (I); jinten putih (M); yee raa (T)
cumin, black	kala jeera		
curry leaves	kari patta		daun kari (I); daun kai pla (M); bai karee (T)
dill	sowa		adas cina (I)
fennel	saunf	wooi heung	adas (I,M)
fenugreek	methi		
galangal, greater			laos (I); lengkuas (M); khaa (T)
galangal, lesser		sa leung geung	kencur (I)
kaffir lime leaves			daun jeruk purut (I); bai makrut (T)
lemon grass			sereh (I,M); ta krai (T)
mace			bunga pala (M); dawk chand (T)
mango powder	amchoor		
mustard seeds	rai		biji sawi (M)
nigella	kala jeera, kalonji		
pomegranate	anardana		
poppy seeds	khas khas		kas kas (M)
saffron	kesar		kunyit kering (M)
screwpine	rampe		daun pandan (I); bai toey hom (T)
sesame	til	chee ma	bijan (M); dee la (T)
star anise		pak kok	bunga lawang (I,M); poy kak bua (T)
tamarind	imli		asam (I); asam java (M); mak kam (T)
turmeric	haldi	wong geung	kunjit (I,M); kamin (T)
zedoary	amb halad, gandhmul, kachur		kentjur (I)

Index

Page numbers in **bold** refer
to entries in either the Herb
Index or Spice Index.

Useful addresses for herb suppliers

When writing to any of the addresses listed below, we suggest you enclose a self-addressed stamped envelope to ensure a reply.

GENERAL SOCIETIES

The Herb Society
134 Buckingham Palace Road
London, SW1W 9SA
Provides members with information about all aspects of herbs, cultivation and new developments. Publishes a quarterly journal.

Royal Horticultural Society
80 Vincent Square
London, SW1P 2PE

The National Trust
36 Queen Anne's Gate
London, SW1H 9AS

Henry Doubleday Research Association
Ryton Gardens
Ryton-on-Dunsmore
Coventry, CV8 3LG
Provides information on organic gardening and supplies seeds for Inca marigold and comfreys.

The National Institute of Medical Herbalists
56 Longbrook Street
Exeter, EX4 6AH
Provides a register of qualified herbal practitioners.

School of Phytotherapy
Bucksteep Manor
Bodle Street Green
Hailsham
E. Sussex, BN27 4RJ

HERB SUPPLIERS

The following supply plants, seeds and accessories. Many also have herb gardens worth visiting. A longer list is produced by The Herb Society.

East West Herbs Limited
Langston Priory Mews
Kingham
Oxon, OX7 6UP

G Baldwin & Co
171-174 Walworth Road
London, SE17 1RW

Hambleden Herbs
Court Farm
Milverton
Somerset, TA4 1NF

Hartwood Aromatics
Enterprise House
Courtauld's Way
Coventry
West Midlands, CV6 5NX
The above are mail order herb suppliers.

Herbs in Stock
Whites Hill
Stock
Essex, CM4 9QB

Herbs of Grace
5 Turnpike Road
Red Lodge
Bury St Edmunds
Suffolk, IP28 8JZ

Hollington Nurseries Limited
Woolton Hill
Newbury
Berkshire, RG20 9XT

Iden Croft Herb Garden
Frittenden Road
Staplehurst
Kent, TN12 0DH

Lathbury Park Herbs
Newport Pagnell
Buckinghamshire, MK16 8LD

Neal's Yard Remedies
31 King Street
Manchester, M2 6AA
For mail order herb supplies.

Norfolk Lavender Limited
Caley Mill
Heacham
King's Lynn
Norfolk, PE31 7JE

Suffolk Herbs Limited
Monk's Farm
Pankings Lane
Kelverdon
Essex, CO5 9PG

PRODUCT SUPPLIERS

The following supply dried herbs and herbal products unless otherwise stated.

Baldwins
173 Walworth Road
London, SE17

Bodytreats International Limited
15 Approach Road
Raynes Park
London, SW20 8BA
For essential oils.

The Cotswold Perfumery Limited
Bourton-on-the-Water
Gloucestershire, GL54 2BU
Supplies ethyl alcohol.

Culpeper Limited (Headquarters)
Hadstock Road
Linton
Cambridgeshire, CB1 6NJ

Fibrecrafts
Style Cottage
Lower Eashing
Godalming
Surrey, GU7 2QD
For natural dyestuffs.

Neal's Yard Apothecary
15 Neal's Yard
London, WC2H 9DP

Potters (Herbal Supplies) Limited
Leyland Mill Lane
Wigan
Lancashire, WN1 2SB

Shirley Price Aromatherapy
Essentia House
Upper Bond Street
Hinckley
Leicestershire, LE10 1RS
For essential oils.

NATIONAL TRUST HERB GARDENS

The following gardens include herbs in beds and borders.

Acorn Bank
Temple Sowerby
Penrith
Cumbria, CA10 1SP

Bateman's
Burwash
Etchingham
E. Sussex, TN19 7DS

Castle Drogo
Drewsteignton
Devon, EX6 6PB

Clumber Park
Worksop
Nottinghamshire, S80 3AZ

East Riddlesden Hall
Keighley
West Yorkshire, BD20 5EL

Felbrigg Hall
Boughton
Norwich
Norfolk, NR11 8PR

Gunby Hall
Burgh-le-Marsh
nr Spilsby
Lincolnshire, PE23 5SS

Hardwick Hall
Chesterfield
Derbyshire, S44 5QJ

Little Moreton Hall
Congleton
Cheshire, CW12 4SD

Melford Hall
Long Melford
Sudbury
Suffolk

Moseley Old Hall
Wolverhampton
Staffordshire, WV10 7HY

Scotney Castle
Lamberhurst
Kent, TN3 8JN

Sissinghurst Castle
nr Cranbrook
Kent, TN17 2AB

Snowshill Manor
Snowshill
Broadway
Gloucestershire, WR12 7LU

Springhill
Moneymore
Magherfelt
Co. Londonderry
Northern Ireland

Bibliography

Allhusen, D: A Book of Scents and Dishes London, 1926

Anderson, Dr Anne: Herbs of Long Ago – Canadian Indians University of Alberta, Canada, 1982

Apicius: De Re Coquinaria trans Flower and Rosenbaum as The Roman Cookery Book London, 1958

Arctander, S: Perfume and Flavoring Materials of Natural Origin New Jersey, 1960

Bacon, Francis: Collected Essays Rowman & Littlefield, New York, 1976

de Bairacli Levy, Julietta: Herbal Handbook for Farm and Stable Faber & Faber, London, 1975

Beckett, Kenneth and Gillian: Planting Native Trees and Shrubs Jarrold, London, 1979

Beckmann, J: A History of Inventions, Discoveries and Origins London, 1846

Binding, G J: About Garlic: The Supreme Herbal Remedy Thorsons, New York, 1976

Black, P: The Book of Potpourri London, 1989

Bohm, David: Wholeness and the Implicate Order Methuen Inc, New York, 1980

Boxer, Arabella and Back, Philippa: The Herb Book Octopus, London, 1980

Boxer, C R: The Dutch Seaborne Empire London, 1965

Braudel, F: The Mediterranean and the Mediterranean World in the Age of Philip II trans Reynolds, London, 1972

Braudel, F: Structures of Everyday Life trans Reynolds, 1981

Braudel, F: The Wheels of Commerce trans Reynolds, London, 1983

Bremness, Lesley: The Herb Garden: Growing and Using Herbs Netherfield Herbs, England, 1984

Brennan, J: Thai Cooking London, 1981

Brissenden, R: South East Asian Food London, 1969

Browne, P: The Civil and Natural History of Jamaica London, 1755

Buchman, Dian Dincin: Feed Your Face Duckworth, London, 1973

Burkill, I H: Dictionary of the Economic Products of the Malay Peninsula Kuala Lumpur, 1966

Ceres: Herbs to Help You Sleep Thorsons, New York, 1981

Chancellor, Philip: Handbook of the Bach Flower Remedies Keats, New Canaan, Conn., 1980

Clair, C: Of Herbs and Spices London, 1951

Clarkson, Rosetta E: The Golden Age of Herbs and Herbals Dover, New York, 1972

Clarkson, Rosetta E: Herbs and Savory Seeds Dover, New York, 1972

Clifton, Claire: Edible Flowers McGraw, New York, 1984

Cobbett, A: The English Housekeeper London, n.d.

Cost, B: Asian Ingredients London, 1990

Culpeper's Complete Herbal Sterling, New York, 1959

Dalby, Gill: Natural Dyes, Fast or Fugitive Ashill Publications, England, 1985

David, E: A Book of Mediterranean Food London, 1950

David, E: Spices, Salt and Aromatics in the English Kitchen London, 1970

Delaveau, P: Les Epices Paris, 1987

Diaz, B: The Conquest of New Spain trans Cohen, London, 1963

Duff, Gail: A Book of Pot-Pourri Beaufort Books, New York, 1985

Dyer, T F Thiselton: The Folk-Lore of Plants Appleton, New York, 1889

Dye Plants and Dyeing Brooklyn Botanic Garden, New York, 1964

Evelyn, John: Acetaria: A Discourse of Sallet (1699) Prospect Books, London, 1982

Fu Weikang: Traditional Chinese Medicine and Pharmacology Foreign Languages Press, Beijing, China, 1985

Garland, Sarah: The Herb and Spice Book Francis Lincoln, London, 1979

Genders, Roy: Scented Flora of the World St. Martin's, New York, 1977

Gerard, J: The Herball London, 1633 edition

Glasse, H: The Art of Cookery made Plain and Easy London, 1747

Glasse, H: The Compleat Confectioner London, 1760

Goldstein, D: A Taste of Russia London, 1985

Goodwin, J: A Dyer's Manual Pelham Books, London, 1982

Gosling, Nalda: Herbs for Colds and 'Flu Thorsons, New York, 1976

Grae, Ida: Nature's Colors Collier Books, New York, 1979

Graham, Dorothy: Chinese Gardens George Harrap, New York, 1938

Graves, Robert: The White Goddess Hippcrene Books, New York, 1972

Greenberg, S and Ortiz, E L: The Spice of Life London, 1983

Grieve, M: A Modern Herbal London, 1931

Griggs, Barbara: The Home Herbal Jill Norman & Robert Hale, London, 1986

Grigson, Geoffrey: The Englishman's Flora Phoenix House, London, 1959

Grigson, Geoffrey: A Herbal Of All Sorts Phoenix House, London, 1959

Grigson, J: Jane Grigson's Fruit Book London, 1982

Guinaudeau, Z: Fez Vu Par Sa Cuisine Rabat, 1966

Halici, N: Nevin Halici's Turkish Cookbook London, 1989

Hall, Dorothy: The Book of Herbs Charles Scribner's, New York, 1974

Harrison, Masefield, Wallis: The Oxford Book of Food Plants Oxford, 1969

Hemphill, R: The Penguin Book of Herbs and Spices London, 1968

Hériteau, J: Potpourris and Other Fragrant Delights London, 1975

Hills, Lawrence: Fertility without Fertilisers Henry Doubleday Assoc., 1975

Hoffmann, David: The Holistic Herbal The Findhorn Press, Scotland, 1986

Hortus Third: A Concise Dictionary of Plants Cultivated in USA and Canada Macmillan, New York, 1976

Hunan Province, China Health Committee: A Barefoot Doctor's Manual Cloudburst Press, Seattle 1977

Huxley, Anthony: An Illustrated History of Gardening Paddington Press, New York, 1978

Inglis, Brian: Natural Medicine Collins, London, 1979

Jaffrey, M: An Invitation to Indian Cooking London, 1976

Jump, M: Cooking with Chillies London, 1989

Kaptchuk, Ted J: The Web That Has No Weaver: Understanding Chinese Medicine Congdon & Weed, New York, 1983

Kennedy, D: The Art of Mexican Cooking New York, 1989

Kerik, Joan: Living with the Land: Use of Plants by the Native People of Alberta Provincial Museum of Alberta, Canada, 1978

Khawam, R: La Cuisine Arabe Paris, 1970

Kitchiner, W: The Cook's Oracle London, 1817

Lamb, Kelley and Bowbrick: Nursery Stock Manual Grower Books, London, 1975

Landry, R: Les Soleils de la Cuisine Paris, 1967

Larkcom, Joy: *The Salad Garden* Viking, New York, 1984

La Varenne: *Le Cuisinier François* Paris, 1651

Law's Grocer's Manual: London, 1950 edition

Leipoldt, C L: *Leipoldt's Cape Cookery* Cape Town, 1975

Leyel, C F: *Herbal Delights* Faber & Faber, London, 1987

Little, Kitty: *Kitty Little's Book of Herbal Beauty* Penguin, London, 1981

Lovelock, J E: *Gaia, A New Look at Life on Earth* Oxford University Press, 1979

Loewenfeld, C and Back, P: *The Complete Book of Herbs and Spices* Newton Abbot, 1974

Luke, H: *The Tenth Muse* London, 1962

Lust, John: *The Herb Book* Bantam, New York, 1974

Mabey, Richard: *Food for Free* Fontana, London, 1975

Mabey, Richard: *Plants with a Purpose* Collins, London, 1977

Macleod, Dawn: *A Book of Herbs* Duckworth, London, 1968

Marcin, Marietta Marshall: *The Complete Book of Herbal Teas* Congdon & Weed, New York, 1983

Masselman, G: *The Cradle of Colonialism* London, 1963

Maxwell-Hudson, Clare: *The Natural Beauty Book* Macdonald, London, 1983

McCormick: *Spices of the World Cookbook* New York, 1964

Meilink-Roelofsz, M A P: *Asian Trade and European Influence* The Hague, 1962

Le Ménagier de Paris, 1393, trans Power as *The Goodman of Paris* London, 1928

Monardes, N: *Joyfull Newes out of the New-found Worlde* trans Frampton, London, 1596

Morrison, S E: *Journals and Other Documents on the Life and Voyages of Christopher Columbus* New York, 1963

de Nola, R: *El Libro de Guisados, Manjares y Potajes* Logroño, 1529

Nott, J: *The Cook's and Confectioner's Dictionary* London, 1726

Odarty, B: *A Safari of African Cooking* Detroit, 1976

Origo, I: *The Merchant of Prato* London, 1963

da Orta, G: *Colloquies on the Simples and Drugs of India* trans Markham, London, 1913

Ortiz, E L: *The Best of Caribbean Cooking* London, 1975

Owen, S: *Indonesian Food and Cooking* London, 1986

Palaiseul, Jean: *Grandmother's Secrets* G P Putnam's Sons, New York, 1974

Palmer, Catherine: *Beauty for Free* Jonathan Cape, London, 1981

Parkinson, J: *Paradisi in Sole* London, 1656 edition

Parkinson, J: *Theatrum Botanicum* London, 1640

Parry, J H: *The Spanish Seaborne Empire* London, 1974

Parry, J W: *The Spice Handbook* New York, 1945

Parvati, Jeannine: *Hygieia: A Woman's Herbal* Freestone, New York, 1979

Petulengro, Leon: *Herbs and Astrology* Keats, New Canaan, Conn., 1977

Philbrick, Helen and Gregg, Richard: *Companion Plants and How to Use Them* Stuart & Watkins, London, 1967

Pigafeta, A: *Magellan's Voyage around the World* trans Robertson, Ohio, 1906

Pires, T: *Suma Oriental* 2 vols, trans Cortesão, London, 1944

Plat, H: *Delights for Ladies* London, 1602

Polo, M: *The Travels* trans Latham, London, 1958

Price, Shirley: *Practical Aromatherapy* Thorsons, New York, 1983

Pruthi, J S: *Spices and Condiments* New Delhi, 1976

Purseglove, J W; Brown, E G; Green, C L; Robbins, S R J: *Spices* 2 vols, London, 1981

Quelch, Mary Thorne: *Herbs and How to Know Them* Faber & Faber, London, 1946

Redgrove, H S: *Spices and Condiments* London, 1933

Richardson, Maureen: *Plant Papers* The Herb Society, London, 1981

Robertson, S: *Dyes from Plants* Van Nostrand Reinhold, New York, 1977

Roden, C: *A New Book of Middle Eastern Food* London, 1985

Rohde, E S: *Gardens of Delight* London, 1934

Rohde, Eleanour Sinclair: *Rose Recipes from Olden Times* Dover, New York, 1973

Rohde, Eleanour Sinclair: *Shakespeare's Wild Flowers, Fairy Lore, Gardens, Herbs, Gatherers of Simples and Bee Lore* Medici, London, 1935

Rohde, Eleanour Sinclair: *The Scented Garden* Gale New York, 1974

Rosengarten, F: *The Book of Spices* Pennsylvania, 1969

Sahni, J: *Classic Indian Cooking* London, 1986

Sahni, J: *Classic Indian Vegetarian Cooking* London, 1987

Scappi, B: *Opera dell'Arte del Cucinare* Venice, 1570

Schafer, E H: *The Golden Peaches of Samarkand* Berkeley, 1963

Sfikas, George: *Medicinal Plants of Greece* Efstathiadis Group, Athens, 1981

da Silva Gameiro, E: *A Viagem de Vasco da Gama* Lisbon, 1972

Simmons, Adelma G: *Herb Gardens of Delight* Clinton Press, USA, 1974

Singleton, Esther: *The Shakespeare Garden* Methuen, London, 1923

Smires, L B: *La Cuisine Marocaine* Paris, 1971

Smith, William: *Herbs to Ease Bronchitis* Thorsons, New York, 1973

Stead, Christine: *The Power of Holistic Aromatherapy* Javelin, England, 1986

Stevens, John: *The National Trust Book of Wild Flower Gardening* Dorling Kindersley, London, 1987

Stobart, T: *Herbs, Spices and Flavourings* London, 1970

Stodola, Jiri and Volak, Jan: *The Illustrated Book of Herbs* Octopus, London, 1984

Stuart, Malcom: *The Encyclopedia of Herbs and Herbalism* Grosset & Dunlap, New York, 1979

Tannahill, R: *Food in History* London, 1973

Taw Kritikara, M L and Pimsai Amranand, M R: *Modern Thai Cooking* Bangkok, 1977

Thomson, William: *Herbs that Heal* A & C Black, London, 1976

Tisserand, Maggie: *Aromatherapy for Women* Thorsons, New York, 1984

Tompkins, Peter and Bird, Christopher: *The Secret Life of Plants* Avon Books, New York, 1973

Tropp, B: *The Modern Art of Chinese Cooking* New York, 1982

Tsuji, S: *Japanese Cooking* Tokyo, 1980

Universidad Melendez y Pelayo: *Conferencias Culinarias* Barcelona, 1981

Uyldert, Mellie: *The Psychic Garden* Thorsons, New York, 1980

Valnet, Dr Jean: *The Practice of Aromatherapy* C W Daniel, Saffron Walden, 1982

Vuyk, B: *Eet een Beetje Heet* Amsterdam, 1966

Weiner, Michael A: *Earth Medicine – Earth Foods* Collier Macmillan, New York, 1972

Wickens, H: *Natural Dyes for Spinners and Weavers* Batsford, London, 1983

Wilson, C A: *Food and Drink in Britain* London, 1973

van Winter, J M: *Van Soeter Cokene* Bussum, 1976

Zukav, Gary: *The Dancing Wu Li Masters* Bantam Books, New York, 1980

Authors' acknowledgments

Lesley Bremness
Jill Norman for introducing me to Dorling Kindersley; Daphne Razazan at Dorling Kindersley for her committed vision of the book and Carolyn Ryden for her kind and patient editing. Tina Vaughan for her imaginative art direction; Jill Dow for the accuracy of her garden drawings and Dave King and his assistant Jonathan Buckley who took care to photograph each herb at its best.

Jan Butcher of Beanfeast and Ruth Bolton of The Chalice Restaurant, Bury St Edmunds for contributing original recipes, and Eileen Clarke for her inspiring recipes and ideas.

Ann Mulley for her meticulous dye experiments and Sonia Berrisford-Hobbs for her wonderful decorations. Vivienne Boulton for her herbal handicraft experiments; Joy Larkcom for supplying unusual salad herbs; Chao Hen of Hangzhou, my guide to gardens and herbs in China; John Stephen of the Cotswold Perfumery Ltd.; Mary Chipper for her advice on aromatherapy and also for keeping Netherfield Herbs going while I was busy researching and writing. Finally, special thanks to my eldest son, Toby Lowe and my husband, J. Roger Lowe, and to all my family for their patience, help and support.

Jill Norman
The Tropical Products Institute, Kent, The Commonwealth Secretariat and The American Spice Trade Association have been very helpful in answering questions, supplying trade figures and other information.

The Saffron Walden museum and Maria Jose Sevilla of Foods from Spain gave help on saffron production; Jane Grigson on the Rotterdam Museum of Ethnology's exhibition of spices and the spice trade. Alicia Rios, Suzanne Hodgart, Nevin Halici, Darra Goldstein and other friends brought spices and information back from their travels. Paul Breman provided recipes and notes on Indonesian food. Marion Burdenuik, Sasha Breman and Elinor Breman tested recipes.

My curiosity and enthusiasm for spices grew from many years of publishing cookery books, and I am grateful to all my authors – and most notably to Elizabeth David – who are indirectly responsible for this book. Those whose work I have drawn on directly are acknowledged in the text.

Carolyn Ryden and Tanya Hines at Dorling Kindersley have been thorough and helpful in their editing, and Sarah Scrutton has been imaginative and painstaking in her design for the book.

Dorling Kindersley would like to thank Nicola Nieburg, Claire Benson, Annabel Martin, Lindy Newton, Clare Mitchison, Jill Somerscales, Laura Harper, Heather Dewhurst and Barbara Croxford for editorial work; Tracey Ward for helping with the design; Richard Bird and Hilary Bird for the index; Audrey Bamber and Ruth Carim for help with proofreading; Anne Warren-Davis MNIMH for her constructive comments on the chapter on herbal medicine; Val Baxter for use of her kitchen and garden; Margaret and Geoffrey Ellis and Joy Larkcom for permitting photography in their gardens; Phil Ladd for supplying herbs; Maureen Richardson for supplying herbal papers; Lyn Rutherford for preparing food for photography; Kew library; the National Spice Bureau; the Indian Spice Information Bureau. Sue Brown; Linda Fraser; Steve Wilson; Henrietta Winthrop; SPAN for their speedy and accurate typesetting.

The following people and companies have provided props and helped to track down and supply spices for photography: Elizabeth David, 46 Bourne St, London SW1; Philip Poole 'His Nibs,' 182 Drury Lane, London WC2; David Mellor, 4 Sloane St, London SW1 (and branches at 26 James St, London WC2; 66 King St, Manchester); Naturally British, 13 New Row, London WC2; Tables Laid, Novello St, London SW6; Josiah Wedgwood & Sons, 32 Wigmore St, London W1; Kirit Patak at Patak (Spices) Ltd, Wigan, Lancs; Judith and Robert Dahan; L.B. Scrutton; Erol Acarturk.

ILLUSTRATORS
Julia Cobbold: pp. 288tl, 289r, 292bl, 296, 297, 302, 305, 308, 309, 312, 313, 314, 318, 319, 322, 324, 325, 326, 327, 332, 333, 336, 337, 338, 346, 348, 350, 352, 356, 360, 366, 368, 370, 372, 374, 376, 378, 380
Jill Dow: pp. 19, 20–1, 22, 24, 27, 28, 30–1, 32, 33
Nick Hall: pp. 232–3, 234
Lorraine Harrison: pp. 17, 19, 20, 26, 31, 150, 163, 194, 212, 228, 238, 251, 252–68, 270
Antonia Enthoven: pp. 298, 299, 306, 307, 310, 311, 316, 317, 320, 321, 328, 330, 331, 334, 335

PICTURE CREDITS
All photography by Dave King (pp.1–279) and Martin Norris (pp.280–431) except for:

A-Z Botanical Collection Ltd: p.141tr
Heather Angel (Biofotos): pp.18, 25tr
Anthony Blake: pp.293t, 294b
Clive Boursnell: pp.2–3, 6–7, 14–15, 23bl
Lesley Bremness: p.13, 29, 105tr
Pat Brindley: p.47tr
The British Library: p.290t
Linda Burgess (Botanical Pictures): pp.1, 10, 23tr, 36–7
Peter Chadwick: pp.294-5, 360-1
Eric Crichton: pp.34, 75tr, 76tr, 89tr, 90tr, 112tr, 119tr
Philip Dowell: pp.46, 47, 118–19, 208-9
E.T.Archive: pp.287t, 289t, 429
Julie Fisher: pp.217, 221
Chao Hen: p.25b
Hulton Picture Library: pp.288, 291b
Mansell Collection: p.286
Tania Midgley: p.11
Monique le Luhandre (Monstyle): pp.215, 223
National Spice Bureau: pp.290r, 291r, 293b
The National Trust: pp.6, 257
Peter Smith: pp.169, 171, 175, 179, 181, 184, 187, 189, 192–3
Jessica Strang: pp.23br, 35
Michael Warren (Photos Horticultural): pp.9, 147tr

Key: t = top; b = bottom; l = left; r = right